Patients, Physicians and Illness

Patients, Physicians and Illness

SOURCEBOOK IN BEHAVIORAL SCIENCE AND MEDICINE

EDITED BY

E. GARTLY JACO

ASSOCIATE PROFESSOR OF MEDICAL SOCIOLOGY
UNIVERSITY OF TEXAS MEDICAL BRANCH

THE FREE PRESS OF GLENCOE

To My Wife Adele

whose healing powers far surpass

the greatest physician

Contents

[v]

III. SOCIO-CULTURAL ASPECTS OF MEDICAL CARE AND TREATMENT

IV. THE PATIENT: A PERSON WITH AN ILLNESS

VII. THE MEDICAL SETTING: HOSPITAL, CLINIC, AND OFFICE

Patients, Physicians and Illness

1   INTRODUCTORY: MEDICINE AND
BEHAVIORAL SCIENCE

By E. Gartly Jaco

To the individual who has ever been a patient, or to the physician, nurse, medical scientist, or health technician, the contents and orientation of this volume may seem novel, if not unique. As an effort to bring together the writings, research and ideas of representatives of the behavioral sciences on varied aspects of medicine within a single cover, this sourcebook presents a view of medicine not well-known nor often recognized. Because medicine has traditionally had a biological orientation and basis, the entry of the sociologist, cultural anthropologist and social psychologist may seem a strange, if not bold, venture. Indeed, such a view may also feasibly be held by many social scientists. The patient, the physician, and illness itself, however, may be given newer significance and understanding when examined from the perspective of these disciplines becoming known as "the behavioral sciences."

The introduction of the behavioral sciences to medicine is a relatively recent development. At present, the relationship between the two fields is like a courtship, with the marriage and acceptance into both families not yet fully established. A number of developments in both medicine and the behavioral sciences have helped to bring many aspects of both realms closer together. We shall attempt to explore some of these developments in the past several decades, beginning with some changes in the institution of medicine, that have led to a bridging of the gap between the two divergent disciplines and the introduction of behavioral science into medicine.

The changing concepts of disease have had a direct impact upon the changes occurring in the practice or art of medicine. The earliest theories of disease, which still prevail to a varied extent in all societies today, were of a supernatural, religious, or mystical origin. These early conceptions regarded the etiology of disease as essentially due to the invasion of the body by evil, or other types of, supernatural spirits, forces, or agents of all descriptions. Under such conditions, it was feasible that the persons best qualified to treat such diseases were those also qualified in the religious aspects of that particular society, such as the medicine-man or witch-doctor. Their major task was the removal of the offending agents through various religious rites, ceremonies, and incantations, often augmented by herbs and other medications designed to relieve or otherwise remove discomfort from the patient. Supernatural medicine might, thus, be regarded as a type of environmental medicine. However, as disease came to be increasingly regarded as of a biological nature and as the disease process itself took on more secular than sacred or supernatural elements, the treatment of disease began to fall into the hands of secular healers having more training in the biological sciences than in theology.

A number of other developments in Western culture took place more or less paralleling the increase in knowledge emanating from the laboratory sciences. The wide-spread development of Christianity and the Protestant Reformation, the Industrial Revolution and the growth of cities, and the increase in the value of the individual life along with the "age of enlightment" and the growing belief in the powers of man to control forces in his environment, all contributed to an increasing faith in applied science as a means of improving the general lot of mankind.

As the biological sciences expanded, the development of medicine as an applied science correspondingly grew. The status of the physician became increasingly more professional. As laboratory research in biology and its branches began to increase and significant scientific discoveries occurred, the physician began increasingly to concern himself with more minute aspects of the human body, such as organs, tissues, and cells. He developed greater specificity in his ministrations. His theorizing and orientation began to resemble more and more that of the laboratory scientists upon whom he increasingly depended for his basic knowledge. As a result, the art and science of medicine began to move away from the total patient (or whole person with a disease) and to concentrate on the pathology or the disease process itself. This increasing knowledge in medical science and its subsequent fragmentation of the patient into laboratory artifacts and research objects in turn was paralleled by increasing specialization of the practice of medicine itself. This led to an increasing complexity in the role and status relationships in medicine, not only between the doctor and the patient, but also between the physicians themselves in terms of their specialty or sub-specialty.

Specialization of medical practice, in turn, has contributed to a further fragmentation of the patient and segmentation of the doctor-patient relationship. The decline in the number of "family doctors" or general practitioners as contrasted to the increasing percentage of medical specialists is a significant indication of this trend. Consequently, it is not by accident today that specialists in psychiatry, pediatrics, and internal medicine often proclaim to be the "only" physicians who treat the "whole person" or who are the "new family doctors." It is not also mere coincidence that the decline in the percentage of general practitioners has been correlated to an increase in the number of, and demand for, psychiatrists and their services as well as for the internist who also treats psychophysiologic disorders and "functional illness" in general.

Another development in medicine that has contributed to a fragmentation in the physician-patient relationship, not too widely recognized, has been the shift in the treatment-setting. The setting in which most medical treatment is conducted has changed following a pattern generally of movement from the home, to the physician's office, to the hospital. The early practice of medicine was conducted almost entirely in the home of the patient and "house calls" constituted the bulk of the professional activity of the typical physician. The use of facilities in the home of the patient along with the physician's rather meager array of medical instruments carried in his "little black bag" composed the essential elements of the treatment-setting of the early era of medicine. The physician's office at that time assumed a secondary part of his practice insofar as actual treatment took place. As the technology of medicine began to increase and the need for concentrating medical equipment in a more suitable and centralized location developed, along with public acceptance of medicine as a profession in its own right, the treatment-setting began to shift to the doctor's office primarily, and the home diminished to secondary importance as a place for medical treatment. With the growing acceptance of the hospital as a recognized medical institution and the continuing increase in the techniques and technology of medicine which brought about the expansion of its technical staff, the treatment-setting shifted again; and this time to the hospital. The doctor's office began to take on a more secondary position as a site for treatment, while the home became an even more rare setting for actual medical treatment. One index that dramatically reveals this change is the fact that today a child *not* born in a *hospital* is exceedingly rare, while, not too many decades ago, a child *not* born in the *home* was a rare individual. Furthermore, hospitalization for purely diagnostic purposes, which is daily becoming more acceptable was extremely rare in the not-too-distant past.

The specialization of medicine has been enhanced if not made entirely possible by the expansion of hospital facilities. Unusual, indeed, is the medical specialist who practices without benefit of hospital facilities and an allotment of beds for his patients, for it would be doubtful that the typical specialist could practice his specialty without a close working relationship with modern hospital facilities and technical assistance.

As the pattern of the treatment-setting changed from the home to the office to the hospital, it is understandable that the physician-patient relationship likewise changed. In the patient's home, the physician was able to appraise the patient in an entirely personalized and significant social situation. When the patients began to relate to the physician in his office, an increased degree of formality entered into the relationship. The fragmentation of the relationship between the patient and his physician reached its peak upon entry into the hospital. The patient finds that others, such as nurses, technicians, residents and interns, as well as other medical specialists occasionally enter into the treatment process in addition to his own physician. The treatment-setting in the hospital now often includes total strangers who take his pulse, temperature, blood, urine, x-rays, bring meals, ask him personal questions, make his bed and clean his room, administer sedatives, and attend to his many needs.

The more fragmented the patient becomes to the physician the more segmentalized and fragmented the physician becomes to him. When the physician visited the home on a "house call," there were often no limits to the admiration and esteem given him by the patient and his family. After several house calls, the so-called "family doctor" often became an honorary member or "Dutch-Uncle" of that family, which accepted him as a complete person as well as a welcome healer. When the patient went to the physician's office for treatment or diagnosis of an ailment, the physician took on a more formal professional and technical identity and became less of a personal friend. When in the hospital, the patient sees the physician as one among many members of the total treatment team which includes administrative, nursing, and technical staff in addition to the medical staff. Under such institutionalized conditions, it is understandable that in the hospital especially, the patient finds it necessary to segmentalize increasingly his relationships to his physician and the others with whom he is in contact during the typical 24-hour period in the hospital.

With the increasing specialization of medicine, and the consequent increase in the cost of medical education, medical practice, and medical care, and the increasing technical component of medical diagnosis and treatment, the status of medicine is showing signs of change. Criticism of rising medical costs and the overall practice of medicine is increasing in the Western world, with one outstanding index being the rising number of successful malpractice lawsuits, and the increasing number of published articles in the press and other mass media of communication that are critical of the medical profession and many of its practices. Such conditions have contributed to a reappraisal of current trends in medical practice and education, and a redirection of efforts toward a return to the "total patient." This has led many medical educators and practitioners to turn to the behavioral sciences for help in obtaining more useful knowledge about human personality and the impact of social and cultural factors upon human life beyond the scope of the biological sciences.

Another major development that has aided in bringing behavioral science into medicine has been the increasing recognition and treatment of "functional illness," those ailments without apparent physical etiology. Although the father of medicine, Hippocrates, recognized the emotional and environmental aspects of illness, the orientation of medicine has traditionally been biological or "physical." The typical physician then and now feels more at home in his role of healer when he treats the organic components of the individual than when he tries to cope with the emotional and "mental" complaints and ailments of his patients. One partial explanation for this is that the physical and biological sciences have far exceeded the social and psychological sciences in both their development and maturity as scientific fields; in turn their own contributions to the education and training of the physician were accepted earlier. However, functional disorders often strikingly reveal the limitations of the biological sciences in comprehending them. Consequently, lacking training in the behavioral sciences, the physician is less secure in handling patient-problems that may be regarded as falling within the domain of psychology and the social sciences.

Functional illness is still today an area of frequent controversy both in medical and non-medical circles. The etiology of the entire gamut of psychiatric disorders, such as the psychoneuroses and psychoses, and the psychophysiologic illnesses is still essentially unsettled. Some take the view that such disorders are caused by the biogenetic constitution of the patient, others proclaim unconscious psychological explanations, others look to the social environment, while still others take a somewhat eclectic view of multiple causation involving all three. Regardless of what explanation is offered for functional illnesses, their pathology and symptomatology are generally regarded as being different to some degree from physical diseases. Those who were dissatisfied with organic explanations for functional illnesses began to look first into the psychological makeup and later to the social situation of their patients in an effort to comprehend the significance and possibly etiology of such disorders. The concept of "psychosomatic" illness emerged as a recognition of the significance of both the life situation and the psychological reaction to stressful living conditions confronting the individual as factors contributing to many disease processes, including some previously regarded as solely of organic etiology. In turn, social stress began to emerge as a significant area for research in an attempt to understand many of the life conditions of the individual that may contribute to the onset of certain of his illnesses. The patient began, therefore, to be studied again in his totality. And now that the human being is being studied in larger terms than his organic aspects, a great number of disciplines other than the biological sciences are necessarily becoming involved, particularly the group of related disciplines broadly labeled the "behavioral sciences," comprising the fields of sociology, cultural anthropology, and social psychology.

Recognition of the value of behavioral science to medicine was consequently slow to develop, and still today is not completely established. The introduction of behavioral scientists into medical schools, hospital staffs, and health institutes is only recent, although increasing rapidly. Considerations to revise the long-standing medical school curriculum to include courses on human behavior and other contributions of the behavioral sciences are developing. Particularly in the medical specialty of psychiatry the belief is emerging that the behavioral sciences comprise the "basic science" of their specialty in addition to the biological sciences already well established in the medical school curriculum. By the same token, it is possible that the behavioral sciences eventually will constitute a "basic science" for all other branches of medicine also.

Because so many diversified and multitudinous efforts in behavioral science and medicine have been going on during the past few years, an effort to bring together some of the representative efforts by behavioral scientists as well as physicians under one cover now seems appropriate. This is the primary purpose of this volume. In these pages, the reader will become acquainted with some of the social and personal components of illness that have been discovered by studies in the social epidemiology and etiology of many forms of illness. He will find studies that relate social attitudes and values to the health of the community and affect their use or non-use of available medical sciences, illustrating the impact of the social community upon the health of its members. The socio-cultural aspects of medical care and treatment are also represented by studies indicating that healing ways may vary with the subcultural composition of a population and also that medical men themselves have their own subcultural norms of behavior that effect the treatment process itself. Studies of the patient and how he reacts to pain and the disease process itself are included. Sociological studies of the process of medical education and its impact upon the medical student comprise a section of this book. The physician and his practice, the doctor-patient relationship, along with non-medical healers and their function in human society are also examined. Finally, the medical setting has been an important subject of research by behavioral scientists, including such studies as those concerning the hospital social structure and its lines of communication and authority, the nursing profession, and the ancillary and technical staffs which also comprise the medical milieu of the modern treatment setting.

These contents are offered as a sourcebook of representations of the type and extent of the efforts and thoughts of behavioral scientists and medical men attempting to expand the horizons of medicine. Because so many articles exist in a tremendous array of various publications, not every excellent work, unfortunately, could be included. Articles dealing with social psychiatry, an area which has accumulated a voluminous literature in a wide variety of studies by behavioral scientists, were omitted both for lack of space and because several compilations already exist. Methodological studies were also omitted in order to devote more space to content.

The reader may observe that, although most of the 63 contributors are behavioral scientists, sixteen per cent are physicians. Of the 55 total chapters, 36 per cent are original and heretofore unpublished. The editor wishes to express his gratitude and appreciation to the authors and publishers for their contributions to this sourcebook.

This volume consequently offers a new approach and orientation to medicine, augmenting rather than supplanting pre-existing medical fields. It is hoped to present a different, though important, slant on patients, physicians, and illness. The contributions of behavioral science to medicine are only beginning. The categories and efforts presented herein may feasibly become altered and expanded in the future as sociologists, cultural anthropologists and social psychologists join forces with biological scientists and physicians to contribute further to a better understanding of the health and welfare of Mankind.

I

Social and Personal

Components of Illness

THIS SECTION has been divided into two major parts. The first section deals with social epidemiology, while the latter is concerned with social etiology, or the connection between conditions of social stress and the onset of illness.

Epidemiology involves the study of the incidence and prevalence of various forms of illnesses among a particular population or group of individuals. In the behavioral sciences, the orientation and methodology of demography and human ecology are especially useful in these types of studies. Perhaps the most typical variables to be used in social epidemiologic research have been social class, socio-economic status, ethnic or subcultural groups, occupation, education, marital status and other family factors, and such ecological and demographic factors as differential migration, areas, zones, regions, to mention a few.

Infant mortality has long been regarded as a reliable index of the economic and health level of a population and one readily affected by shifts in socio-economic circumstances. The original article by Odin Anderson traces some of the historical trends and contemporary patterns of infant mortality as they relate to a variety of socio-environmental conditions, and points ahead to some future trends in research on this problem.

One of the last publications of a pioneering medical sociologist is the late Bernhard J. Stern's analysis of some socio-economic correlates to the incidence of heart disease. Professor Stern analyzes the impact of economic factors, urban-rural differentials, sex and race differentials, and occupation, upon heart disorders.

The articles by John Ellis and P. S. Lawrence take divergent approaches to the study of socio-economic status and chronic illness. Ellis presents data to support the hypothesis that mortality from chronic diseases shows an inverse relationship to socio-economic status. On the other hand, Lawrence presents data indicating that chronic illness is more significant as a factor reducing socio-economic status than status itself as a factor affecting the rate of chronic diseases. Until further standardization of research techniques and definitions are made, it is likely that contradictory findings on the problem of chronic illness and socio-economic status will continue.

Some significant contributions of the ecological approach to epidemiological research are presented in the original paper by John Mabry which completes this sub-section.

While knowledge of the factors of the etiology of illness may be considerably advanced by epidemiological findings, these data alone are inadequate to establish conclusively the sufficient conditions of a disease in either an individual or groups of persons. Inquiry into social etiology is a relatively recent effort on the part of behavioral scientists. Perhaps the term most frequently used by behavioral scientists in their etiologic theories and explanations is "social stress." Harold Wolff, M.D., delineates many social patterns of human behavior and assesses their impact upon a variety of bodily diseases. Stanley King surveys the extensive literature on rheumatoid arthritis in offering evidence associating certain psychosocial factors with this illness.

A new approach to determine some of the social and personal resources used by a group of businessmen in coping with environmental stresses is reported in the original article by John and Ruth Useem. Their orientation opens a little-explored avenue to investigation that attempts to determine conditions that may minimize the disease-process itself rather than factors that cause the onset of disease.

One of the first experimental studies to indicate a significant relationship between church attendance and stress-reactions affecting the cardiovascular system is reported by Stanley King and Daniel Funkenstein, M.D.

The overall social and personal components of health and illness are analyzed and given a theoretical conceptualization by John Maclachlan in concluding this section. He proposes the concept of "sociosomatic" illness as an extension of the psychosomatic concept now currently used in medicine.

This section represents a wide variety of the contributions of behavioral scientists to medicine. It is possibly in the area of social epidemiology that the feasible existence of social and personal correlates to diseases of many varieties was made plausible. On the other hand, behavioral science has yet to make its mark in the medical and health fields in the area of etiology. Any inadequacies or shortcomings in the behavioral science disciplines are more likely to be pointed up in those efforts to determine the necessary connection between various social conditions and the onset of illness. Considerable behavioral science effort, therefore, can be expected to be devoted to this latter subject in the future.

2   INFANT MORTALITY AND SOCIAL AND CULTURAL FACTORS: HISTORICAL TRENDS AND CURRENT PATTERNS*

By Odin W. Anderson

I. Statement of the Problem. It is readily apparent that infant mortality, the number of deaths under one year of age per 1,000 live births in a year, has improved tremendously in Western countries since the turn of the century. Before 1900, infant mortality rates of 100 to 150 were common in countries like Sweden, England and Wales, Germany and New Zealand and a rate over

50 is now regarded as excessive. In other words, an infant mortality rate under 50 is now a "normal" standard in terms of present-day knowledge and its application.

It is also readily apparent that there are great variations in infant mortality rates over the world between countries, between areas within countries, and even between residential areas within cities. An examination of data for recent years reveals an infant mortality rate in 1949 of 169 in Chile and 23 in Sweden.[1] In 1947, Scotland reported an infant mortality rate of 27 in Social Class I and 89 in Social Class V, Class I presumably experiencing the best environmental conditions and Class V the worst.[2] Thus one can easily find infant mortality differentials by income, occupation, class, country, race, and so on. The factual data abound in the extensive literature on infant mortality which has appeared in the last 50 years.

The time may now be appropriate to attempt a synthesis of these profuse data in order to point up patterns that reappear from place to place and from time to time, and to indicate the general social factors which have been associated with the changing infant mortality picture during the past 100 years, and in greater detail the past 50 years. We know that high infant mortality rate is associated with poverty; we know that mortality began to drop perceptibly in many countries at a certain stage of their technical development; we know that infant mortality before the turn of the century was higher in cities than in rural areas until after roughly 1920 or so, at which time the rates in the cities were lower. These facts are known, but what do they mean?

Infant mortality is regarded as a sensitive index of the health level of an area and one readily responsive to environmental conditions. As an example, Berlin in 1943 had an infant mortality rate of 66; two years later as a result of extreme disruption caused by bombing the rate had shot up to 359! A year later, 1946, the rate had dropped to 123 and in 1949 it was 75.[3] Similarly, but to a lesser degree, the French rate increased from 73 in 1941 to 109 in 1945. The catastrophe of the French, however, was considerably less than the normal course of events in Chile, because Chile's rate has always hovered around 186 or more.[4]

Obviously, it is difficult if not impossible to isolate the specific factors influencing a given infant mortality rate. A reasonable goal, however, is to break the factors into fairly general ones and show how they may operate at any given time and place. For the purpose of analysis it may be useful to divide the factors with which we are concerned into *biological, social,* and *cultural* and indicate to what extent certain social and cultural factors appear to influence the biological ones.

A. *Biological Factors.* There are biological factors which are immutable and independent of time and place, and there are other such factors which are inherently biological but responsive to certain environmental influences which can be classified as physical and social. The immutable biological factors are age, sex, and inherited predisposition toward certain diseases. Age and sex are biological facts independent of time and place and for the purpose of mortality analysis are basic independent variables. From a representative sample of the population, there can be found a given number of individuals who may be predisposed to certain diseases because of inherited constitutional factors, and such conditions can be regarded as biological facts which cannot be changed in the short run.

There are other factors which are basically biological, but are to some degree responsive to environmental influences as to magnitude and distribution in time and space. Death itself is a biological fact, but age at death differs markedly between various populations. In some contemporary populations, for example, most of the deaths occur after age 65, in others most occur under 50. Similar differences are found even within the first year of life. This is evident in the observations: The higher the infant mortality rate, the lower is the proportion of deaths occurring in the first month of life during the first year, and, the lower the infant mortality rate, the higher is the proportion of deaths occurring in the first month of life during the first year.

Another biological factor responsive to environmental influences is birth itself since the number of births in a population, size of family, and order of birth vary considerably according to circumstance. These in turn have real but undetermined influences on infant mortality. For example, a high birth rate is associated with a high infant mortality rate. A low birth rate could conceivably be associated with a high neonatal mortality rate (deaths during the first month of life) because a low birth rate suggests a high proportion of first births which in turn is associated with a relatively high mortality rate during the first month of life.

A final biological factor responsive to environmental influence is morbidity or sickness. Sickness is, of course, basically biological, but its magnitude and distribution in time and space vary considerably.

B. *Social Factors.* There are commonly accepted social indices influencing magnitude and distribution of the biological factors mentioned above. These social indices are occupation, income, class in the social hierarchy, level of education, marital status, and residence, e.g., rural, urban, slums, or high-income residential areas. It should be immediately apparent that these indices are not mutually exclusive but overlap considerably. They provide some rough indication of the environment in which people of different occupations, incomes, and levels of education, live. They yield little knowledge of the quality of the basic human material itself unless one automatically assumes that the higher the income or class the more "fit" are the people in that income group or class. Except for a residue of so-called "problem families" and apparent social misfits, this assumption is at the moment scientifically untenable, because there are so many other factors than "ability," however defined, which are responsible for the particular social niche a person or family may occupy.

C. *Cultural Factors.* The foregoing is permeated by prevailing life values found in a general population and by sub-groups like occupational groups and ethnic groups. Under prevailing life values can be placed religion, customs, attitudes toward human life, concepts of standards of living, hygienic habits, in short, what social anthropologists mean by the term *culture.*

II. **Factual Evidence—Biological.** Long-term trends and contemporary patterns of infant mortality should provide the points of departure to indicate associations of certain infant mortality rates and social and cultural factors.

Countries of Northwest Europe including England and Wales, Scotland and Iceland, revealed great annual oscillations in infant mortality rates until the latter part of the Nineteenth Century. At the turn of the Twentieth Century these oscillations diminished, indicating that the periodic epidemics of childhood communicable diseases were becoming less common and virulent. There are many factors other than direct controls which have operated in reduction of infant mortality, but they cannot be isolated.

Sweden's recorded infant mortality rates go back further than any other country. For the country as a whole during the decades from 1751 to 1949, the oscillations in infant mortality narrowed from 164–286, decreasing each decade until the 1940's when the rate had dropped to an all-time modern low with an oscillation of 23-27.[5]

Another area reporting annual rates for infant mortality during the last 100 years is Scotland. During the period from 1855 to 1900 the infant mortality rate ranged annually between 108 and 138. In subsequent decades both the absolute rates and the oscillations of high and low dropped to 54-83 during the period 1941-1947.[6]

Similar patterns are found in Iceland, England and Wales, Denmark and Norway.[7] There is also evidence that a similar change in the trends of the infant mortality rates has taken place in areas like India, Cyprus, Jamaica and Spain, suggesting that the annual oscillations are narrowing, eventually resulting in relatively steady although declining infant mortality rates.[8]

An analysis of the periods during which the infant mortality rates broke perceptibly in various countries revealed interesting patterns suggesting that similar forces influencing the decline of infant mortality were operating simultaneously over wide areas. Table 1 shows the breakpoints in the infant mortality rates.

It will be noted that an extremely important decade in the history of infant mortality in Europe is 1890–1900, because so many countries experienced a clearly perceptible improvement in mortality in that decade. A similar pattern was found in certain large cities in the United States by Winslow and Holland.[9] Other areas reveal later decades during which their infant mortality rates showed distinct improvements and it should take little investigation to demonstrate that the periods during which the infant mortality rates began to decline are associated with certain levels of sanitary and hygienic development. Note areas like Quebec, India, Spain and Cyprus.

A final set of facts in the long-term trends in infant mortality indicates that during the first year of the infant's life the greatest improvement has taken place during the period from the first to the 12th month. There have also been improvements during the first month of life, but hardly to the same degree as during the ensuing 11-month period.

The commonly accepted reason for this consistent pattern lies in the causes of death and their relative potential control. In all studies of causes of infant mortality so far it has been found that prematurity and congenital malformations account for the largest proportions of deaths during the first year of life and the majority of these deaths usually occur before the end of the first month. The greatest proportion of deaths from respiratory and gastro-intestinal conditions usually occur after the first month. Analysis of improvements in infant mortality by cause reveals that respiratory and gastro-intestinal causes have declined markedly, prematurity to a lesser degree, and congenital malformations hardly at all. The following studies support these generalizations.

In the long-term study of infant mortality in Cleveland, Green found that from 1919 to 1937 the mortality among white infants in the age-group from one to twelve months improved 73 percent while neonatal mortality improved only 23 percent.[10]

Table 1—Onset of Fall in Infant Mortality Rates by Areas and Decades

1880-	1890-	1900-	1910-	1920	1930-
	Denmark	Luxembourg	Quebec	Jamaica	Cyprus
	England				
	& Wales		India	Spain	
	Iceland				
	Scotland				
	New Zealand				
	Sweden				
	Switzerland				
	Norway				
	France				

Sources of basic data: Danmark. Statistiske Department: Statistisk Årbog, 1950. Köbehavn, Bianco Lugo, 1950. p. 33; Great Britain. General Register Office: Statistical Review of England and Wales for the Year 1945. (New Annual Series, No. 25) Tables. Part I. Medical. London, H.M. Stationery Office, 1947. p. 2; Vilmundur Jonsson: Skipun Heilbringdismala a Islandi. Reykjavik, Gutenberg, 1942. p. 150, approximated from a graph on opposite page; Scotland. General Register Office: Ninety-Third Annual Report, 1947. Edinburgh, H.M. Stationery Office, 1950. p. 68; New Zealand. Census and Statistics Department: New Zealand Official Year-Book, 1947-1949, Fifty-fifth Issue. Wellington, N.Z., Government Printer, 1950. p. 72; Sverige. Statistika Centralbyrån: Statistisk Arsbok för Sverige. Trettiosjunde Årgången, 1950. Stockholm, Statistika Centralbyrån, 1950. pp. 63–67; Schweiz. Eidgenössischen Statistischen Amt: Statistisches Jahrbuch der Schweiz, 1949. Basel, Birkhäuser, 1950. p. 79; Norge. Statistisk Sentralbyrå: Statistiske Oversikter, Oslo, Aschehoug, 1949. p. 40; Luxembourg, Ministere des Affaires Economiques: Statistiques Economiques Luxembourgeoises, Aout, 1949. Luxembourg, Bour-Bourger, 1949. p. 7; Jean Bourgeois-Pichat: Evolution Generale de la Population Francaise depuis le XVIII Siecle. Population, October–December, 1951, 6, pp. 635–672; Quebec. Bureau of Statistics: Statistical Yearbook, 1921. Quebec City, Proulx, 1922. p. 2; and Canada. Dominion Bureau of Statistics: Vital Statistics, 1946, 26th. Annual Report. Ottawa, The Bureau, 1948. p. 24; Kingsley Davis: The Population of India and Pakistan. Princeton, N.J., Princeton University Press, 1951. p. 34; Jamaica. Registrar-General's Department: Annual Report for the Year Ended 31st, December, 1949, Kingston, Government Printers, 1950. p. 38; Espana. Instituto Nacional de Estadistica: Anuario Estadistico de Espana, 1950. Madrid, Instituto Nacional de Estadistica, 1950. p. 108; Cyprus. Colonial Administrative Service: Census of Population and Agriculture, 1946, Report, London, Crown Agents for Colonies, 1949, p. 18.

A study of infant mortality in the United States revealed a similar pattern. From 1915 to 1949 the mortality among infants, in the age-group from one to twelve months, improved 83 percent and in the age group: one month and under, 52 percent.[11]

In another area, Ontario, infant mortality rates from 1921–25 to 1941–45 improved 55 per cent, while the neonatal rate improved 39 per cent, indicating that the greater improvements had occurred in the age-group: from one to twelve months.[12]

The foregoing is an analysis of improvements in infant and neonatal mortality in a few areas over a period of time. A similar pattern is apparent if different areas over the world are compared at the same time.

Table 2 illustrates the relationships of infant and neonatal mortality indicated above. Three countries with very low infant mortality rates and three with very high rates were selected and arranged in order of magnitude of their infant mortality rates. The percent of infants dying during the first month as of the total deaths during the first year for each country was calculated. A close correlation will be noted.

Table 2—Infant Mortality Rates in Order of Magnitude and Percent of Deaths Occurring During First Month of Life, Selected Countries and Years, 1945–1947.

Country	Infant Mortality Rates	Percent Dying During First Month
New Zealand	26	73
Sweden	30	64
United States	34	71
Guatemala	110	36
Mexico	111	33
Egypt	153	14

Source of basic data: United Nations: Demographic Yearbook, 1948. Lake Success, New York, United Nations, 1949, p. 408–455.

Long term studies of the changing causes of mortality by age are few in number, but an excellent and authoritative one has recently been published using data from England and Wales for the past one hundred years. Table 3, abstracting pertinent data for the age-group one and under will show the relative improvements in mortality by broad causes between 1901–10 and 1947.

Table 3—Changing Relative Importance of Selected Groups of Causes of Infant Mortality, England and Wales, Between 1901–10 & 1947

Disease Group	Rate per 1,000		Percent Improvement
	1901–10	1947 (m a l e)	
Total Rate	167	48	71
Communicable Diseases*	19.3	2.3	89
Diahorrea and Enteritis	26.4	5.8	74
Developmental and Wasting†	56.4	21.5	62
		(F e m a l e)	
Total Rate	133	37	74
Communicable Diseases*	17.4	2.1	88
Diahorrea and Enteritis	21.7	4.3	82
Developmental and Wasting†	44.1	17.0	61

* The original article uses the term infections
† Prematurity, congenital conditions, etc.

Source: W. P. D. Logan: Mortality in England and Wales from 1848 to 1947; A Survey of the Changing Causes of Death during the Past Hundred Years. Population Studies, September, 1950, 4, pp. 132–178.

The greatest relative improvements occurred among diseases that are more likely to occur after the first month of life, communicable diseases and diahorrea and enteritis, than those which occur in the first month of life, the developmental and wasting diseases. Also, the developmental and wasting causes of death accounted for a higher proportion of deaths in 1947 than in 1901–10. Among the males the developmental and wasting causes of death accounted for 34 per cent of all deaths in 1901–10 and 45 per cent in 1947; among females the percentages were 33 and 46 respectively. Even accounting for a reasonable margin of error in recording and judgment in classifying the causes it would seem that the table presents a clear pattern which is generally true.

A summary study in the United States of changing causes of mortality again documents the familiar pattern of precipitous decreases in the communicable diseases, diahorrea and enteritis, and relatively little improvement in deaths from premature births and other conditions involving hereditary, congenital and physiological problems.[13]

So, in summary, the following facts will provide a framework to which are related the known associations of social factors of one kind or another as gleaned from published studies:

A. The infant mortality rates first broke in Western European countries during the 1890–1900 period. Other areas with less well-developed health controls and healthful environments broke later as conditions improved.

B. The neonatal mortality rate has shown much less improvement than the post-natal period.

C. In a cross-section of countries of the world today the higher the infant mortality rate, the lower is the proportion of deaths that occur during the first month of life, and vice versa.

D. The causes of mortality that have experienced the greatest declines are communicable, respiratory diseases and diahorrea and enteritis. The conditions relating to prematurity, congenital malformations, and so on, have decreased least.

III. Factual Evidence—Social and Cultural. Obviously, class, occupation and income are very closely related and in turn are associated with given infant mortality rates. The higher the class and income, and the more well-paid the occupation, the lower is the infant mortality rate. There are interesting and significant exceptions, as will be discussed later.

A study of infant mortality among the ruling families of Europe since 1500 reveals a fascinating long-term trend among a wealthy segment of the population. Over 8,460 children of ruling families were born to parents who married between 1500 and 1930 (Table 4).

Table 4—Infant Mortality Rates in Ruling Families by Time of Parents' Marriage 1500–1930

Time of Parents' Marriage	Under One Month	Whole of First Year
1500–1599	98	193
1600–1699	96	246
1700–1799	60	153
1800–1849	50	96
1850–1899	17	41
1900–1930	5	8

Source: Sigismund Peller: Studies on Mortality Since the Renaissance. Bulletin of the History of Medicine, 1943, 13, pp. 427–461.

It can be stated that the improvements in neonatal and infant mortality rates among ruling families preceded those of the general population by 50 or more years. Infant mortality rates of 96 and 41 did not begin to appear among Western countries in the general population until the turn of the century and the decade of 1940, respectively. An infant mortality rate of 8 has never been recorded for the general population, nor a neonatal mortality rate of 5. These rates seem to be almost impossible in terms of present medical knowledge, but they may be a function of the small number of infants involved. One of the lowest neonatal mortality rates recently is 18, recorded in Norway. It will be noted that the ruling classes reported such a rate during the period 1850–1899.

A crude and early, but still significant study of age-specific mortality by social class was done by Chapin in Providence, Rhode Island, in 1865. He separated the population into taxpayers and non-taxpayers and found that the non-taxpayers' infants suffered twice the infant mortality rate of the infants of taxpayers, 190 and 93, respectively.[14] Since the study was restricted to income-taxpayers, it is reasonable to assume that those who paid an income tax in 1865 were in the very high income brackets.

At the turn of the century, Rowntree completed his famous study of poverty in York, England, repeated in 1936, in which, among other things he investigated the infant mortality by class. As was to be expected he found a class differential in the infant mortality rates, but also a clear differential among three levels of the working class (Table 5).

Table 5—Infant Mortality Rates by Class, City of York 1899 and 1936

Residential Areas	Infant 1899	Mortality	Rates 1936	
Area 1:				
Poorest working class	247		78	
Area 2:				
Middle working class	184		75	65
Area 3:				
Highest working class	173		41	
Servant keeping class	94		..	
City of York as a whole	176		56	

Source: B. Seebohm Rowntree: Poverty and Progress: A Second Social Survey of York. London, Longmans, Green, 1941. pp. 297, 298.

Around 1920, a study of infant mortality by income was conducted in Stockholm, Sweden, which revealed probably the lowest reported infant mortality rates ever recorded for a relatively large population. It is particularly revealing that this was possible 30 years ago (Table 6).

Table 6—Infant Mortality Rates by Four Income Groups, Stockholm 1918–1922

Income Groups	Infant Mortality Rates	Neonatal Mortality Rates
I. (Highest)	14	11
II.	32	20
III.	38	15
IV. (Lowest)	49	24
All Groups	37	18

Source: E. Rietz: Sterblichkeit und Todesursachen in den Kinderjahren. Stockholm, 1930. Quoted in: Richard M. Titmuss: Birth, Poverty and Wealth: A Study of Infant Mortality. London, Hamish Hamilton Medical Books, 1943, p. 97.

At irregular intervals for the past forty years the General Register Office for England and Wales has published infant mortality rates by social classes divided into a five-class scale.[15] (Table 7).

Table 7—Infant Mortality Rates by Social Class of Father, England and Wales, 1911, 1930–32 and 1939

Class	Infant Mortality Rates 1911a	Infant Mortality Rates 1930–32a	Percent Decline 1911 to 1930–32	Percent Mortality Rates 1939b	Percent Decline 1930–32 to 1939
I.	76	33	57	27	18
II.	106	45	58	34	24
III.	113	58	49	44	24
IV.	122	67	45	51	24
V.	153	77	43	60	22

Sources: a. Richard M. Titmuss: *Birth, Poverty and Wealth: A Study of Infant Mortality.* London, Hamish Hamilton Medical Books, 1943, p. 26.
b. Great Britain. Royal Commission on Population. *Reports of the Biological and Medical Committee.* London, H.M. Stationery Office, 1950, p. 14.

It will be noted that the infant mortality rate for Class V in 1939 was lower than the rate for Class I in 1911. During the period from 1911 to 1930–1932 the higher the class the greater was the relative improvement, but from 1930–1932 to 1939 the classes under I experienced an improvement greater than Class I and almost equal to each other. This may indicate that the upper class is reaching a diminishing of returns because of its relatively low rate of 27 and the other classes are beginning to take up the slack in their own rates. Similar data are available for neonatal mortality (Table 8).

Table 8—Neonatal Mortality Rates by Social Class of Father, England and Wales,— 1911 and 1939

Class	Neonatal Mortality Rates: 1911a	1939b	Percent Decline
I.	30.2	18.9	37
II.	36.5	23.4	36
III.	36.8	25.4	31
IV.	38.6	27.7	28
V.	42.5	30.1	29

Sources: a. Richard M. Titmuss: *Birth, Poverty and Wealth: A Study of Infant Mortality.* London, Hamish Hamilton Medical Books, 1943, p. 37.
b. Great Britain. Royal Commission on Population. *Reports of the Biological and Medical Committee.* London, H.M. Stationery Office, 1950, p. 17.

In both 1911 and 1939 the differences in the infant mortality rates between Classes I and V are far greater than the differences in the neonatal mortality rates, indicating the relatively less variability of the neonatal mortality rates both in terms of class and in terms of time. It is apparent that the infant mortality rates declined much more than the neonatal rates among all classes. A similar breakdown by social class was reported for Scotland in 1947.[16]

A recent study of infant mortality by social class in Great Britain attempted to refine the overlapping categories used by the General Register Offices of England and Wales and Scotland and to re-classify each occupation individually into four classes. The re-defined social classes are: I. Professional and salaried; II. Black-coated (clerical); III. Manual workers; and IV. Agricultural workers. (Table 9).

Table 9—Monthly Infant and Neonatal Mortality Rates by Social Class, England and Wales Among Births Occurring During One Week in March, 1946

Class	Infant Mortality Rate	Neonatal Mortality Rate
I.	23.7	16.9
II.	30.5	23.3
III.	44.9	25.8
IV.	41.6	27.3

Source: J. W. B. Douglas: Social Class Differences in Health and Survival during the First Two Years of Life; the Results of a National Survey. Population Studies, July, 1951, 5, p. 41.

One exception to the familiar gradient is the lower infant mortality rate found in Class IV, agricultural workers, than in Class III, manual workers. This is not an unreasonable differential judging by rural-urban differences in the past.

In 1946 extremely low rates were experienced by all classes because an infant mortality rate under 45 is, according to present standards, regarded as favorable. Again, note that there is a greater spread between the highest and lowest infant mortality rates than among the highest and lowest neonatal mortality rates.

Further, historical data of a fragmentary nature have been recorded in Holland for the period 1877–1881. The infant mortality rates by economic status and rural and urban residence were calculated (Table 10).

Table 10—Infant Mortality Rates by Economic Status and Residence, Holland 1877–1881

Economic Status	Infant Mortality Rates: Urban	Rural
Rich	93	110
Well-to-do	139	91
Less-well-to-do	157	107
Poor	166	112

Sources: Selwyn D. Collins: Economic Status and Health: A Review and Study of the Relevant Morbidity and Mortality Data. Washington, Government Printing Office, 1927, p. 45. (U.S. Public Health Service. Public Health Bulletin No. 165). Taken from: Friedrich Prinzing. Handbuch der Medizinischen Statistik. Jena, Fischer, 1906, especially the sections on "Kindersterblichkeit nach Stand, Beruf und Wohlhabenheit der Eltern," pp. 300–304, and "Sterblichkeit und Wohlhabenheit," pp. 432–442.

As is to be expected, differential mortality rates by income follow the same pattern as those by class. In an early study of infant and neonatal mortality in seven cities in the United States by the Children's Bureau from 1911 to 1916 the following relationship of income and infant mortality was found (Table 11).

Table 11—Infant and Neonatal Mortality Rates by Earnings of Father in Seven American Cities, 1911–1916

Annual Income	Infant Mortality Rates	Neonatal Mortality Rates
Less than $450	166.9	55.8
$450–549	125.6	46.0
$550–649	116.6	43.3
$650–849	107.5	46.5
$850–1049	82.8	38.0
$1050–1249	64.0	33.1
$1250– and over	59.1	38.2
No earnings	210.9	60.7
Not reported	139.7	41.1
Total	110.0	44.4

Sources: Robert M. Woodbury: Causal Factors in Infant Mortality: A Statistical Study Based on Investigations in Eight Cities. Washington, Government Printing Office, 1925. p. 148. (U.S. Children's Bureau. Publication No. 142).

A familiar pattern is repeated in this table: there is much less variation of the neonatal mortality rate by income groups than the infant mortality rate.

A study of economic status and infant mortality in Cleveland repeats the pattern even when income groups are subdivided into economic tenths.[17] The same relationship of infant mortality to income is found in a study of 973 cities in the United States for the period 1939–1940.[18]

There are other variants of income and class such as residence, race or color, ethnic groups, foreign-born or native-born, and, perhaps, others. Suffice it to say that there are great variations in the infant mortality rates by residential areas within cities,[19] rural rates are higher than urban rates,[20] non-whites are higher than whites,[20] certain ethnic groups are higher than other ethnic groups,[21] foreign-born are higher than native-born, and so on.[21]

In summary, when the gross relationships of infant mortality and various social factors are examined, it is obvious that there are positive correlations between high income, high social status, well-paying occupations, and all the other variables involved and low infant mortality rates. An allegedly obvious inference flowing from this conclusive fact is that if all families could enjoy the general standard of living, i.e., food, clothing, shelter, medical care and public health services, attained by the level of society experiencing the lowest infant mortality rate, all families would then approximate this rate. In short, there is assumed to be a direct and undiminished correlation between income and infant mortality.

IV. Critique. It might reasonably be suggested that where infant mortality rates exceed 30 or more, a broadside approach to this problem in terms of a standard of living will have a long-run effect as was apparent in the downward trends of infant mortality since 1890 by countries. It would seem that once the rate drops down to 30, the broad economic and social factors operate with lessening effect and personal behavior factors of the families in the high infant mortality groups involved, particularly the mothers, begin to exercise an increasingly dominant influence. Perhaps the dividing line of 30 is too high or too low, but it is submitted that a theoretical line exists at one point or another.

It is suggested that there are fairly specific practices in infant care that can be followed, if these practices are known, which are relatively independent of economics, once basic essentials of living are accessible.[21a] The attainment of an infant mortality rate of 15 to 20 would require the most painstaking and rigid observance of rules of infant care, which, if followed, could be achieved by families in Canada and the United States earning considerably less than those in the upper 10 per cent of the present income scale.

Among the 45 or so studies on infant mortality and social and cultural factors, there are three studies which suggest the plausible fact that there is a point of diminishing returns between infant mortality and income, occupation and class, once the basic minimum standard of living has been attained.

The series of studies of infant mortality in eight cities in the United States during the period from 1911 to 1916 by the U. S. Children's Bureau was summarized in 1925 by Woodbury. He revealed the usual relationships between infant mortality and income, color, foreign-born, native-born, and so on. These studies were excellent pioneer ventures and they provided a conclusive factual underpinning for the now known relationships between infant mortality and social and cultural factors. During the period, the infant mortality rate in eight cities was 111, indicating a tremendous area of potential improvement by means of broadside attacks on poverty, housing, and ignorance with demonstrable effects in a short time. Since Woodbury was analyzing the gross relationships between infant mortality and income, occupations, and so on, it may be understandable that he completely overlooked one startling and significant exception to the usual correlations that he found. One of the breakdowns was by color and nationality of mother as follows:

Colored
Native-born white
Foreign-born white
    Italian
    Jewish
    French-Canadian
    German
    Polish
    Portuguese

Even though the Jewish-group was foreign-born, lived in as crowded conditions as other foreign-born, bore just as many children fifth and later in order, and enjoyed an income which was much lower than that of the native born whites, this group experienced the lowest infant mortality rate of all groups (Table 12).

Table 12—Infant Mortality Rates by Nationality of Mothers; Eight Cities in the
United States, 1911–1916

Nationality	Infant Mortality Rates
White	108
Native born white	94
Foreign-born white	127
Foreign-born Jewish	54
Colored	154
Total	111

Source: Robert M. Woodbury: Causal Factors in Infant Mortality: A Statistical Study Based on Investigations in Eight Cities. Washington, Government Printing Office, 1925, p. 104. (United States Children's
Bureau. Publication No. 142).

Likewise, the foreign-born Jewish group experienced the lowest neonatal
mortality rate (Table 13).

Table 13—Neonatal Mortality Rates by Nationality of Mother; Eight Cities in the
United States, 1911–1916

Nationality	Neonatal Mortality Rates
White	43
Native-born white	42
Foreign-born white	46
Foreign-born Jewish	28
Colored	65
Total	45

Source: Robert M. Woodbury: Causal Factors in Infant Mortality: A Statistical Study Based on Investigations in Eight Cities. Washington, Government Printing Office, 1925, p. 106. (U.S. Children's Bureau. Pub.
No. 142).

An examination of the causes of infant mortality reveals that the foreign-
born Jewish group had less than half of the mortality from gastric and intestinal conditions experienced by the native-white group and only 69 per
cent of the respiratory conditions (Table 14).

Table 14—Infant Mortality Rates from Specified Causes by Nationality of Mothers;
Eight Cities in the United States, 1911–1916

Nationality	Causes	
	Gastric and Intestinal	Respiratory
White	33	18
Native-born white	25	13
Foreign-born white	42	24
Foreign-born Jewish	11	9
Colored	28	45
Total	32	20

Source: Robert M. Woodbury: Causal Factors in Infant Mortality: A Statistical Study Based on Investigations in Eight Cities. Washington, Government Printing Office, 1925, p. 104. (U.S. Children's Bureau,
Pub. No. 142).

There are obviously factors other than general economic ones which account for the low infant mortality among the foreign-born Jewish groups. A closer examination would probably reveal a pattern of infant care of a high order embedded in the Jewish culture, since even bottle-fed Jewish infants experienced a lower mortality rate than infants of native-born whites.

Another very detailed study in the Newcastle-upon-Tyne area in England for the period 1930 to 1937 revealed the usual gross correlations between infant mortality and income. A significant finding, however, was that for the same size family the middle class mortality rate for the age group from birth to five showed no advantage over the mortality rate experienced by the black-coated workers, or clerical workers.[22]

Finally, a third study in British Columbia for the period 1945 to 1946 revealed infant mortality rates by occupation of father. The range was from 16 to 56 with an average of 31. The clerical workers were the lowest and personal service occupations the highest.[23] The professional and owners-managers groups had a rate appreciably higher, of 27 and 28 respectively. Anything under 30 is a very low rate today, and the fact that the clerical group attained a rate of 16 indicates painstaking diligence in the care of their infants independent of their income level.

It would seem that during the past 50 years, so-called "problem families" have become more visible because of the increasing standard of living which is being enjoyed by all classes. The "lower third" 50 years ago conceivably contained a large proportion of families which, given better economic opportunities could improve themselves. Rowntree, in his studies of social conditions in York in 1899 and 1936, previously mentioned, showed that in 1899 approximately 16 per cent of the working-class population was living in primary poverty, i.e., absolutely bare subsistence. In 1936, this percentage had been reduced to 7. Thus, the proportion of the working-class population living in abject poverty had been reduced by more than a half in the course of 37 years, despite the fact that in 1899 trade in York was booming, and unemployment accounted for only 2.31 per cent of the primary poverty in contrast to 44.5 per cent in 1936.[24]

From the foregoing it would seem that the nearer the infant mortality rate approaches a virtually irreducible minimum in terms of our present knowledge, the less operative are the social and environmental factors and the more operative are so-called "maternal efficiency," "copability," and other personal factors. Also, since the infant mortality rates are declining to very low levels in many areas, a high standard of social and medical services often obscures the significance of those rates for the mapping out of pertinent public health problems.[25]

V. Next Steps In Research. It is then suggested that any further research revealing relationships between infant mortality and income level, class, occupation, and so on, would be a waste of time, money and effort, because the gross relationships have been established conclusively enough. The next steps in research in infant mortality which may yield useful information for public health activities should be directed toward relationships between infant mortality and morbidity and mothercraft, specific infant-care customs and practices, intelligence, and others.

It is a pleasure to report that just at the time this sentence was completed the author received in the mail a new and valuable study by Dr. Grundy & Dr. Lewis-Faning, the former mentioned earlier. In addition to the usual class variables he introduced variables of mothercraft, housing and birth-weight. He found the expected differences, but more, he was able to show differences within classes as well, thereby really refining and pin-pointing the problem. With their usual modesty, Drs. Grundy & Lewis-Faning conclude: "We conclude by reiterating that in some respects the present enquiry has failed to fulfil expectations. We believe however that it has furnished a fair and reliable estimate of the volume and nature of infant sickness in general, that it has indicated some of the technical difficulties involved in defining illness in infancy and that it has illustrated the limitations of local surveys in the field. If it has done these things and helped to identify the fields in which executive action might be taken and fresh enquiries might be pursued, then it can be viewed as a modest contribution towards the elucidation of problems which like so many of the problems in medicine, are to some extent solving themselves with the passage of time, without our knowing precisely how."[26]

3   SOCIO-ECONOMIC ASPECTS OF HEART DISEASE

By Bernhard J. Stern

The noted physician, William Osler, once said "Tuberculosis is a social disease with medical aspects." When this thought became a working principle of tuberculosis societies, they began their most satisfying work. Similarly, the range and importance of the field of nutrition widened decisively when Goldberger and his collaborators showed the relation of pellagra and other deficiency diseases to socio-economic conditions. I believe that the time is ripe for a comparable underscoring of the importance of the socio-economic factors in the field of degenerative diseases, particularly cardiovascular disease.

Medical educators are recognizing increasingly that medicine is a social science as well as a biological science. Yet, it cannot be said that this idea has percolated more than faintly into the curriculum of the schools and into medical practice. The successes of medical science in the control of external agents in communicable disease have tended to detract attention from the study of the patient as a whole and, at the same time, from the prodigious social changes which have been taking place that have affected the living and working conditions and consequently the health of the populace.

The development of clinical medicine and pathology with its emphasis on checking symptoms against lesions focused attention on specific organs and militated against an approach to patients as members of families and of society. The importance of taking cognizance of the patient as a human being

From *The Journal of Educational Sociology*, 24, (April, 1951), 450–462.

in a specific cultural setting has also been in danger of being neglected because of the formality in physician-patient relationships arising out of urbanization and medical specialization. The treatment of patients under hospital conditions tends to negate the importance of the effect of home and working conditions on the health of the patient who becomes an organism abstracted from his social environment. It is thus one of the incongruities of modern medicine that while developments in the field of deficiency and degenerative disease and particularly in psychiatry and psychosomatic medicine have impelled consideration of patients in the context of their life histories and socio-economic and cultural environments, many specialists persist in ignoring as irrelevant anything but the particular matter under scrutiny and treatment.

In dealing with cardiovascular diseases, it is especially important to bear in mind that human development takes place in the course of human activity and so is dependent upon the concrete historical conditions of human life, i.e., the material and social relations in which human beings mature. This is more than saying that an individual with certain hereditary characteristics is affected by conditions of his environment. The person and his social environment are in fact indivisible. The individual does not end with his skin, but his existence and his development are part of a process of continuous, active relationship with his social and cultural situation. In this sense persons, sick or well, are not merely organisms fulfilling their life cycles. They are also socially defined by the role given them by the society in which they are participants, by the work they do, by the sanctions and restraints by which each society regulates their conduct. Sex, for example, is something more than differences in anatomy and hormones; it is socially defined by cultural dictates of anticipated and enforced behavior along sex lines, by sex division of labor and differential sex etiquette which vary widely in different communities. Likewise differences in skin pigmentation, head form, facial features, and stature become important when, because of such differences, persons and groups are discriminated against or privileged in job and cultural opportunities, and their full physical and emotional development are thwarted or take place under special conditions. Thus sociological factors must be taken into consideration in the interpretation of differences in rates of cardiovascular diseases by sex, and race. These differences cannot be considered exclusively, or perhaps even primarily in organic terms.

Mortality and Morbidity Statistics. Mortality and morbidity statistics substantiate the importance of socio-economic environment in cardiovascular diseases. There are variations in accuracy of diagnosis and reporting; difficulties in isolating statistically the many factors involved in the etiology of cardiovascular diseases; and hazards in collating data originally collected and compiled for different purposes. Moreover changes in terminology over time complicate the analysis of the findings. Yet, in spite of these difficulties substantial statistical evidence is available which is sufficient to corroborate the thesis that socio-economic factors play a significant role in cardiovascular diseases.

Let us first consider general mortality and morbidity studies, a large number of which directly or indirectly demonstrate the relationship between the socio-economic environments and diseases designated statistically as chronic, degenerative, cardiovascular-renal and circulatory. They reveal differential rates by income levels, by social status, by extent of urbanization, by degrees of industrialization and by racial groups.

Role of Economic Factors. The role of economic factors, as measured by differences in income, is shown in a nation-wide study of the relationship between per capita income and mortality in ninety-two cities of 100,000 or more population.[1] The cities were arranged into three approximately equal groups on the basis of per capita buying power. It was found that in the case of the chronic diseases, which included intra-cranial lesions of vascular origin, all forms of heart disease, diseases of the coronary arteries and nephritis, the age-adjusted death rate per 100,000 population in 1939 and 1940 for the lowest income group was 514.9, for the middle group, 487.0 and the highest income group 479.7. The mortality rates of these diseases thus decrease consistently from the lowest to the highest income groups with an especially significant difference between the mortality rates of the lowest and middle income groups.

These findings are substantiated by morbidity data derived from the Health Survey,[1a] which was conducted by the U.S. Public Health Service in 1935–36 and based upon a house-to-house canvass of some 800,000 families including 2,800,000 persons in eighty-four cities and twenty-three rural areas in nineteen states. When the data are classified under the category of degenerative diseases the generalization that income affects disability emerges clearly. The annual per capita days of disability per person per year is, for the age group under twenty-five years, almost three times as high in families on relief, and twice as high for families with incomes under $1000 as for families with incomes $5,000, or over, and for the ages twenty-six to sixty-four years, it is over three and one-half times as high for families on relief, and over twice as high for families with incomes under $1,000 as for families over $5,000.

Local mortality studies in New Haven,[2] Chicago,[3] New York,[4] and Boston,[5] corroborate the conclusions of the national studies. In England and Wales, the statistics of the Registrar-General show a steep rise in mortality for valvular heart disease and chronic endocarditis with a decline in social status associated with occupational differences not only for men[6] but for their wives.[7]

Urban-Rural Differences in the United States. Recorded mortality for diseases of the heart in the United States in 1940 declined as the size of city decreases, with clearly marked urban-rural differences. The extent of industrialization and related factors such as income and availability of medical facilities and services are correlated with heart disease when the size of the city is held constant.[8] In the case of the major component, disease of the myocardium, the rural rate was only about two-thirds that of urban parts of the United States.[9] Deaths from diseases of the coronary arteries and from acute endocarditis showed similar differences between urban and rural rates. Both urban and rural mortality recorded for all diseases of the heart in 1940 was slightly higher in the North than in the South and Eastern than Central sections of the United States. The broad regional distribution of industrialization, as measured by the percentage employed in manufacture, generally corresponds to that of mortality from heart disease.[10]

Mott and Roemer, who also compared the crude and age-adjusted death rate of rural communities with those of towns and cities concluded: "While the problem of heart disease is complex, and must be considered in relation to its different causes it seems fair to assume that this differential is due mainly to the oft-described stresses and strains of urban life and occupations. Wherever may be the actual pathogenesis of arteriosclerotic or hypertensive heart disease, the most common types found, there is much evidence to point to a relationship with the nervous strains more typically a part of urban than of rural life."[11]

Sex Differentials. Sex differentials in mortality from heart disease in 1940 strongly suggest socio-economic determinants. Seven of the eight specific forms of heart disease showed a higher mortality for men of all ages than for women, the exception being acute rheumatic fever where the rate was almost the same.[12] The greatest sex differential was the case of syphilitic heart disease with the male rate nearly four times that for females. Death rate from diseases of the coronary arteries among males exceeded those of the females by 141 per cent. In urban areas the excess of male over female heart disease mortality was markedly higher than in rural with the exception of valvular heart disease and congenital heart disease.

Race Differences. The Census Bureau publication on "Vital Statistics Rates in the United States, 1900–1940" aptly declares, "An observed difference in mortality between races may in actuality be no more than a difference in mortality of different economic classes." This offers the clue to the understanding of the differential mortality rate for cardiovascular-renal diseases among non-whites and whites. A comparison of the crude and age-adjusted death rates per 100,000 for non-whites and whites for 1919–21, 1929–31, and 1939–41 for diseases of the heart, intracranial lesions of vascular origin and nephritis, shows that adjusted rates are consistently to the disadvantage of the non-white.[13]

Similar results are brought out by a comparative analysis of the mortality rates among industrial policyholders of the Metropolitan Life Insurance Company[14] for the years 1911–15 and 1940–44 which showed that the death rates for cardiovascular-renal diseases were consistently higher for all ages and at both periods for the colored males and the females as compared to whites. The death rate for colored males in the 45–54 age category, was in 1940–44, 747.9 per 100,000 as compared to 573.8 for the white, higher than the white rate was in 1911–15 (713.8). Similarly in the 55–64 age group the rate was 1801.5 per 100,000 for the colored males as compared to 1449.3 for the white males, also higher than the rate of the white group in 1911–15 (1782.14).

Further evidence of differential rates for Negroes and whites is shown by the fact that the incidence of defects from cardiovascular diseases among the first two million selectees in World War II, ranging in age from 21–36 years was found to be 46 per 1000 for Negroes and 27 per 1000 for whites.[15]

The high incidence of hypertension in the Negro at an earlier age, may be ascribed to the tensions involved in their adjustment to an unfavorable environment.[16] The high rate of syphilitic heart disease among Negroes, a sequel to the very high rate of syphilis, has been demonstrated statistically as being associated with the poverty of the Negro and with inadequate medical care.[17] Information on the comparative rates for coronary diseases among national groups in the United States is fragmentary and inconclusive.

Relation to Occupation. There has long been considerable interest in the relation of coronary diseases to occupation. Physicians have generally followed the early judgment of Osler that coronary artery disease occurs more frequently among persons in the business and professional groups than among persons in other occupations. This observation, which has been based largely on clinical impressions, may perhaps be derived in part from the fact that cardiologists engaged in consultation practice, deal for the most part with patients among the well-to-do classes. Careful statistical studies are necessary before this judgment or the contrary judgment that the incidence is practically the same for all walks of life,[19] can be fully validated. Space does not permit a review of the conflicting conclusions of the published studies.

Answers to questions of the relation of occupation, social status or social class to coronary occlusion are closely associated with judgments on the role of effort, trauma and work in the onset and subsequent course of coronary artery occlusion. Whether or not coronary occlusion can be precipitated by physical exertion has been a matter of considerable medical debate.

The trend in medical judgment on this issue may be ascertained by the fact that in New York and New Jersey, persons who experience cardiac infection while undergoing some unusual strain while at work are now allowed workmen's compensation benefits.

Rheumatic Fever and Rheumatic Heart Disease. In the case of rheumatic fever and rheumatic heart disease the evidence clearly confirms the importance of socioeconomic factors. Long before rheumatic fever was associated with streptococcal infections, it was observed that the prevalence of the disease was greater among poor people living within poverty-stricken sections of communities. Findings made in Kiel and Leipzig as early as 1885 have been frequently quoted, but for a long period especially between 1910 and 1925, there was a marked lack of interest in the socio-economic aspects of the disease. As in the case of other public health programs, attention was then focused narrowly on the processes of infection to the exclusion of the broader sociological factors.

In the 1920's, however, studies began to consider again the relationship between rheumatic fever and living conditions, particularly poverty in cities. These researches first undertaken in Great Britain sustained the general impression rheumatic fever and rheumatic heart disease were relatively rare among the well-to-do but frequent in working class populations. Their initial conclusion, however, that these diseases were more prevalent among the artisan class than among very poor workers, immediately provoked considerable controversy, and has since proved invalid. Whatever may have been the special circumstances which led to this judgment supported in the United States by Wilson[20] on the basis of a limited study of a clinic population, recent statistical studies of Morris and Titmuss[21] in England do not confirm it.

In the United States the findings of Collins[22] based on the National Health Survey and the supplementary Communicable Disease Survey of 1936, also invalidate the artisan theory of the disease. They found that the incidence and prevalence of rheumatic fever for ages five to nineteen among the white canvassed population rose consistently as the economic status decreased, and with the exception of one income group, the same was true for heart disease. The rates were generally twice as high for persons on relief and, in the case of heart disease, were sometimes three and four times as high. The relative increase in the rates as income decreased, aside from the high relief rate, was slightly greater in new cases than in total prevalence.

Local studies in Cincinnati,[23] New Haven,[24] Denver,[25] and Philadelphia,[26] bear out the association of poverty and rheumatic fever. The much quoted studies by Wilson, Schweitzer and Lubschez,[27] dealing with the familial epidemiology of rheuumatic fever do not contravene the evidence of the importance of environmental factors. Their data are limited to only 109 families in a clinic population excluding the well-to-do, and the range between the best and worst environments was too narrow for a difference to be demonstrable.

Many studies have been made associating rheumatic fever and rheumatic heart disease with urbanization, over-crowded housing and nutritional deficiency. More detailed studies have shown, however, that these are important not as specific factors but primarily because they are associated with poverty. The general effects of poverty upon rheumatic fever, for example, is shown by the fluctuations in the mortality rate of the British working classes as they moved from unemployment to employment after 1930. Full employment and higher wages favorably affected the course of mortality in spite of the deterioration in the housing situation.[28]

The fact that throughout the United States in almost all geographic divisions and individual states and in all age groups, whenever the death rates are based on large enough population numbers, the non-white children show a higher mortality for rheumatic heart diseases than do the white children, gives further evidence that rheumatic fever and heart diseases are influenced by adverse conditions of the social environment. Unfavorable social-environment conditions arising from poverty, especially bad housing, lack of hospitalization, lack of public health education and hygiene abetted by the factor of discriminatory practices against Negroes, all contribute to spread the acute disease, to increase rheumatic complications and consequently to increase the death rates.

A comparison[29] of mortality rates from rheumatic fever and chronic rheumatic heart disease during 1939—1940 for persons under twenty-five years of age in cities of 100,000 or over where diagnostic facilities are better, shows that in the North mortality from rheumatic fever among colored persons is about twice that among the white, (4.6 per 100,000 compared to 2.4 per 100,000), while in the South where mortality is lower, the death rate for colored persons is three times that among the white, (3.8 per 100,000 compared to 1.3 per 100,000). In the case of chronic rheumatic heart disease, in the North the death rate for the colored was 16.2 per 100,000 compared to 10.8 per 100,000 for the whites, while in the South the rates were 7.6 per 100,000 and 2.8 per 100,000 respectively.

Socioeconomic influences also account for the extremely high death rates for white children from rheumatic fever and rheumatic heart afflictions in the Mountain States where the relative high proportion of the population is persons of Mexican origin for whom socioeconomic conditions are less favorable than for the remainder of the population classified as white.[30] The high rate among new immigrant groups, such as the Puerto Ricans may be ascribed in large part to their under-privileged social and economic status. Comparative data on other national groups is very fragmentary and inconclusive.[31]

In summary, authorities have come to conclude that the basic factor to be considered in the genesis of rheumatic fever and rheumatic heart disease is poverty itself and only secondarily its many specific manifestations, psychological as well as physical. This position is cogently stated by Morris and Titmuss;[32] "The upshot seems to be that the whole life of the underprivileged child is involved. 'The destruction of the poor is their poverty.' In social medicine such multiple non-specific causation is not unexpected." These data all point to one basic conclusion. Since cardio-vascular diseases are, to a large extent, community products, they are a community responsibility. It will require the resources of all community agencies to conquer them.

4   SOCIO-ECONOMIC DIFFERENTIALS IN MORTALITY FROM CHRONIC DISEASES

By John M. Ellis

Demographic research dealing with mortality differentials between socio-economic groups has been oriented to the patterns of a period when death rates were high and largely the result of the high incidence of contagious diseases which frequently reached epidemic proportions. Economic differences and the resultant marked differences in the physical conditions of life were reflected in a quite pronounced tendency for upper income groups to have a most favorable mortality experience in comparison with persons of low income. High death rates for the infectious diseases are closely related to poor conditions of the physical environment such as deteriorated and crowded housing, poor diet, and inadequate medical care. In the past, most studies of socio-economic differences dealt with this relationship. The high mortality from such diseases as tuberculosis, pneumonia, influenza, and typhoid fever among the lower economic groups attracted much study which doubtlessly helped stimulate measures directed toward reducing the toll of these diseases through education, free medical treatment, and improvement in sanitary conditions. The decline in the importance of the infectious diseases has been striking. In 1900 in the United States tuberculosis, pneumonia, influenza, diphtheria, and typhoid fever accounted for more than one-fourth of all the deaths. In 1950 the percentage of deaths caused by the infectious diseases mentioned above had fallen to less than six percent, while the cardiovascular-renal diseases alone accounted for more than half the deaths and malignant neoplasms for an additional fourteen and one-half per cent.[1]

In spite of the obvious success of public health measures in reducing deaths from infectious diseases, such measures operate in a situation of diminishing returns. At the beginning, reductions in mortality are huge. In time, as the death rates for the infectious diseases fall to low levels and in some in-

stances virtually disappear, greatly increased effort and expenditure are required to make only small reductions in the number of deaths. At this point,
which has been reached by the United States and the other urban-industrial
countries, the causes of death most responsive to public health measures such
as sanitation and immunization cease to play an appreciable part in the mortality experience of the society. The death rate is low and is largely the result
of deaths from the chronic diseases. Socio-economic differences in mortality,
were they assumed to be entirely the result of the effect of differences in the
physical environment upon deaths from infectious diseases would disappear.
Slight differentials would in fact remain, however, due to a tendency for the
lower economic groups to have higher death rates for certain other causes of
death such as accidents and homicides. But the virtual disappearance of
socio-economic differentials may be assumed, an assumption that is implied
in studies which have shown declines in mortality differentials which are associated with economic status.[2] Also, several studies of socio-economic differentials by cause of death have found no significant differentials for the chronic
diseases. Allen, in studies of Cincinnati,[3] reported that the chronic disease
rates did not differ very greatly between economic groups. Coombs had a
similar finding for data from Chicago.[4] In contrast, a recently published study
of Buffalo, New York, indicated an inverse relationship between socio-economic status and deaths from chronic diseases, although the relationship was
less pronounced than it was for infectious diseases.[5]

When death rates are low, if a differential in mortality between socio-
economic groups still appears, its explanation can hardly lie in the former
assumptions concerning differences in the physical environment. The chronic
diseases which at present account for a majority of the deaths in the United
States are not related to differences in economic status in the same manner
as are the infectious diseases. They are not apparently aggravated by poor
sanitation, crowded and inadequate housing, and similar environmental conditions that figure so prominently in mortality from the infectious diseases.
If, therefore, such diseases as malignant neoplasms, heart disease, diabetes
mellitus, nephritis, and vascular lesions are inversely related to economic
status, the explanation must lie in factors other than those associated with
poor living conditions. Even without Yeracaris' finding,[6] it is reasonable to
assume that the chronic diseases should show higher death rates among
people of low economic status. These diseases respond to treatment in many
cases if they are diagnosed early and adequate treatment is secured. This
requires both access to information regarding the importance of early diagnosis and the financial ability to afford expensive and often prolonged treatment. It is logical to suppose the lower economic groups with neither adequate
information regarding the diseases nor financial ability to provide treatment
would have higher death rates from the chronic diseases.

The purpose of the research presented here is to offer evidence in support
of the hypothesis that deaths from chronic diseases show an inverse relationship to socio-economic status. If a differential is found, since it can hardly result from differences in physical living conditions, its explanation must be
sought in terms of other factors such as differences in sub-culture between
the groups or in terms of the characteristics of the social organization.

Sources of Data and Research Techniques. Mortality data were secured from the Bureau of Vital Statistics of the Health Department of the City of Houston, Texas, through the cooperation of Mr. W. H. Alban, Registrar and Statistician. Death rates were based upon the average number of deaths for the three years, 1949–1951.

These rates were calculated by use of population data from the bulletin of census tract statistics for Houston.[7] Population estimates for the entire population and for the tracts as of July 1, 1950 were made, so that the death rates were calculated for the customary mid-year population. These rates were standardized using the age-sex distribution of the white population of the United States in 1940 to construct a standard million.[8] The indirect method of calculation, which is presented in detail in Hagood,[9] was used for all death rates.

For the white population, the socio-economic ranking of census tracts used was made by Dodson in his study of differential fertility in Houston.[10] Dodson grouped the tracts by a modification of the index of social rank developed by Shevky and Williams. This index utilized measures of education, occupation, and rental value to form a composite index. For the Houston tracts in 1950, Dodson used median family income rather than rental value since this latter had originally been used as an approximation of income. Census data on income in 1950 made the use of rental data no longer necessary.[11] In constructing rank groups the data used were for the white population of Houston, which constituted almost 80 percent of the total population of the Central City. The whites were so widely dispersed throughout the city that Dodson excluded only four census tracts from his social rank groupings. The tracts were grouped into five socio-economic rank groups each containing either 12 or 13 tracts.[12] Group I represents the highest socio-economic rank and Group V the lowest. These groups in size of total estimated white population, July 1, 1950, ranged from 129,107 in Group II to 68,825 in Group V. The death rates used to compare white and nonwhite mortality were calculated for the total populations of these groups in Houston.

Differentials in Total Mortality for Social Rank Groups. The standardized death rates for whites for all causes are presented by sex and rank group in Table 1. These rates indicate that mortality in the lower rank groups is ap-

Table 1—White Death Rates, Houston, Texas, 1949–1951 by Social Rank Group
(Rates per 100,000 Population)

Sex	Group I	Group II	Group III	Group IV	Group V
Male	7.46	7.91	9.07	11.11	9.91
Female	5.39	5.29	5.59	7.11	7.49
Both Sexes	6.17	6.56	7.43	9.12	8.73

preciably higher than in the upper rank groups. Group IV is an exception in that it has a rate above that of Group V. This failure of the inverse relationship to hold for Group IV is difficult to explain. It may result from the mere fact that Groups IV and V are small relative to Groups I and II. The two lower rank groups had a combined population of 146,000, not very much higher than the 129,107 population of Group II alone. If the two lowest rank groups were combined into one group, the inverse relationship would be without exception, for the rate of Group V is little smaller than that for Group IV. Such a combination in order to satisfy preconceptions regarding the data would, however, be arbitrary and unwarranted. As is shown by the later tables, there is a real differential between groups IV and V for the causes of death most markedly associated with social rank, a fact that suggests validity for the rank group division.

Moreover, the failure of Group V to show the highest death rate could be attributed to a differential access to free medical care. Yeracaris suggested this as a possible explanation for a similar finding.[13] It may be that persons in the lowest economic group, having no means to provide for their medical needs, are eligible for free medical service, while persons in Group IV may have sufficient means to disqualify them for public aid and at the same time insufficient ability to secure adequate treatment.

The death rates by sex indicate that the high total mortality in Group IV is the result of an unusually high male mortality in the rank group, for Group IV females have a lower death rate than females in Group V. If, therefore, differential access to free medical care is a factor in the high mortality of Group IV, it is a factor in male rather than female mortality. It is also significant that the magnitude of male differentials is greater than that of females. The difference between the lowest and highest male rates is 3.65 (Groups I and IV), while the difference for females is 2.20 (Groups II and V). The data indicate a higher male mortality for those causes of death more differentially associated with socio-economic status. It should be pointed out that the male and female death rates in Table 1 are not exactly comparable. They are each standardized to the age distribution of the sex in the standard million; hence they are not standardized to the same age distribution. In calculating standardized rates by the indirect method, one may easily derive such rates by sex. Since the concern in the study is with rank group differentials, it was not thought worthwhile to standardize the female and male rates to the same age distribution. The female rates for the rank groups are comparable to each other, as are the male rates and the total rates. This is sufficient for making the comparisons desired. Actually, the age distributions of males and females in the standard million did not vary enough to change the standardized rates by sex materially had they been reduced to a single distribution. Consequently, the male and female rates are roughly comparable, although not absolutely so. The rates in all of the tables have been treated in this manner.

Mortality Differentials for the Leading Diseases for Social Rank Groups. Standardized death rates for the seven leading diseases in Houston mortality (Table 2.) show an inverse relationship between mortality and economic status for both the infectious and the chronic diseases. The two infectious diseases, tuberculosis and pneumonia, show a more pronounced relationship to social rank, but the relationship for such diseases as malignant neoplasms and heart disease is quite clear if not so marked. In every instance the rates for the chronic diseases in Group V are higher than in Group IV, with the single exception of nephritis. That this differential is not the result of the mortality pattern of only one of the sexes is indicated by the standardized death rates for males and females. The male death rates in Table 3 show an

Table 2—White Death Rates By Social Rank Group for Selected Causes of Death, Houston, Texas, 1949–1951

(Rates per 100,000 Population)

Cause	Group I	Group II	Group III	Group IV	Group V
Tuberculosis	8.54	12.70	23.65	37.14	49.07
Pneumonia	7.02	9.23	13.78	13.39	15.09
Malignant neoplasms	98.08	116.00	123.31	130.64	133.78
Diseases of the heart	210.03	191.02	212.58	247.23	270.00
Diabetes mellitus	10.63	8.60	11.94	10.24	15.71
Nephritis	10.22	5.53	4.85	18.10	12.27
Vascular Lesions	90.80	85.17	76.64	95.59	115.17

inverse relationship between socio-economic status and mortality for both the infectious and the chronic diseases. But the rates for tuberculosis, pneumonia, and malignant neoplasms are higher in Group IV than in Group V, and the rates for diseases of the heart, diabetes mellitus, and nephritis are higher in Group I than in Group II. Vascular lesions have their lowest incidence in Group III. In spite of these exceptions to the inverse relationship, comparison of the highest and lowest economic groups shows the death rates for each

Table 3—Death Rates of White Males by Social Rank Group for Selected Causes of Death, Houston, Texas, 1949–1951

(Rates per 100,000 Population)

Cause	Group I	Group II	Group III	Group IV	Group V
Tuberculosis	11.72	20.48	41.79	56.31	51.05
Pneumonia	4.94	10.17	16.48	17.27	7.85
Malignant neoplasms	101.89	109.10	125.41	133.13	125.27
Diseases of the heart	292.90	282.18	293.73	336.07	343.69
Diabetes mellitus	13.33	7.63	13.13	10.97	16.47
Nephritis	12.72	5.96	6.02	18.98	19.43
Vascular lesions	84.76	99.34	81.09	96.69	107.45

disease in Group V much higher than in Group I. The lower economic groups have an unfavorable mortality experience for both infectious and chronic diseases.

The death rates for women in Table 4 show a mortality pattern not greatly

Table 4—Death Rates of White Females by Social Rank Group for Selected Causes of Death, Houston, Texas, 1949–1951

(Rates per 100,000 Population)

Cause	Group I	Group II	Group III	Group IV	Group V
Tuberculosis	5.51	5.80	8.15	15.75	46.77
Pneumonia	8.74	8.27	11.09	9.44	22.52
Malignant neoplasms	95.96	122.36	121.68	127.45	142.26
Diseases of the heart	136.29	110.85	131.81	157.31	194.39
Diabetes mellitus	8.91	9.89	10.58	9.42	14.78
Nephritis	8.03	5.12	3.71	17.21	4.77
Vascular lesions	96.02	74.96	73.08	95.47	124.04

different from that of males. In comparison of the two extreme economic groups, Group V has higher death rates than Group I for all diseases except nephritis, for which the rates are low for all groups. The female death rates for nephritis and vascular lesions are lowest in Group III, while for diseases of the heart Group II has the lowest rate. The tendency indicated in the total death rates (See Table 2) for Groups II and III to have favorable mortality experience for the chronic diseases, except for malignant neoplasms, is not the result of a pattern of mortality peculiar to either sex.

Mortality Differentials Between Whites and Nonwhites. The nonwhites in Houston may be considered representative of a lower socio-economic status than the whites. Comparison of the white and nonwhite death rates shows an inverse relationship to economic status for both the infectious and chronic diseases. This further supports the findings for the white social rank groups. The total death rates contained in Table 5 show higher nonwhite rates for all

Table 5—Death Rates for Whites and Nonwhites by Sex for Selected Causes of Death, Houston, Texas, 1949–1951

(Rates per 100,000 Population)

	White			Nonwhite		
Cause	Male	Female	Total	Male	Female	Total
Tuberculosis	27.64	7.84	17.59	55.82	30.19	42.33
Pneumonia	10.96	9.44	10.22	43.09	43.44	43.39
Malignant neoplasms	114.59	113.98	113.51	162.95	175.51	168.91
Diseases of the heart	296.74	131.30	211.73	290.09	243.23	267.11
Diabetes mellitus	11.37	10.09	10.56	6.23	29.42	17.80
Nephritis	10.56	6.69	8.54	37.99	31.17	34.54
Vascular lesions	87.68	84.94	86.18	188.26	180.59	183.81

seven causes of death. Nonwhite females, furthermore, have higher rates than white females for all causes. White males, however, have slightly higher rates than nonwhite males for diseases of the heart and for nephritis, but the differences are small. In contrast, the nonwhite male death rate for vascular lesions is more than double that of white males. In general, therefore, the comparison of white and nonwhite mortality supports the hypothesis that the death rates of chronic diseases, and well as those of infectious diseases, are higher in the lower economic group.

Summary and Conclusions. In summary, mortality data for the seven leading diseases in Houston reveal the existence of an inverse relationship between mortality and socio-economic status for both the infectious and chronic diseases, with that of the infectious diseases most pronounced. The higher death rates of the lowest economic group, therefore, are not solely the result of higher rates for the infectious diseases and causes such as accidents and homicides, which have a high incidence in the lower economic groups. In part the higher mortality in the lower groups results from a differential in the chronic disease rates. This finding is contrary to the frequently held assumption that these diseases bear no relationship to socio-economic status. For the white rank groups the inverse relationship does not hold, however, in comparing Group I with Groups II and III, for the lowest rates for all of the chronic diseases except malignant neoplasms is found in one or the other of the latter groups. This fact would suggest a defect in the social rank categorization were it not that the infectious diseases, which are assumed more reflective of economic differences, actually do have their lowest rates in Group I, as would be expected.

Several conclusions may be drawn that have implications for both demography and public health policy. In recent years there has been a great deal of publicity given the chronic diseases by public health and charitable organizations, with emphasis upon the importance of early diagnosis and treatment in the control of the diseases. Many of these diseases can be controlled, and life-expectancy thereby increased. The Houston data indicate a possible differential in either access to or receptivity to the information disseminated regarding the chronic diseases. The low rates for these diseases in Groups II and III suggest that possibly the people in these groups have greater contact with the agencies which publicize information about the diseases or with the communications media through which the information is conveyed. Organizations working for a reduction of deaths from chronic diseases should attempt to direct their programs toward reaching more people in the lower economic groups.

There is the further possibility that differences in the sub-cultures of the groups may have a bearing on socio-economic differentials in mortality when death rates are low. The striking tendency for Group I to rank higher for all but one of the chronic disease rates (See Table 2.) than one or the other of the next two groups can hardly be explained by a lesser ability to afford treatment. The higher rates for heart disease and vascular lesions could result from greater tensions associated with the group's superior social status. This possibility needs investigation.

The fact that Groups IV and V have much higher chronic disease rates may well result from the organization of medical assistance in society together with an inability to afford treatment. The treatment of chronic diseases is not only expensive but is frequently of long duration. The lower economic groups can afford neither the cost of treatment nor the loss of wages during the periods of prolonged treatment. Those in the lower economic strata need not only free medical assistance but also some compensation to offset income losses. The latter is seldom available at all and the former only to the lowest income group. The data suggest the effect of this situation. The lowest economic group, which is presumed to have greater eligibility for free medical assistance, actually does have a lower death rate. (See Table 1.) But this is the result of the male rather than the female mortality experience. It is the high male mortality for both infectious and chronic diseases, in Group IV which explains the high death rates of the group. (See Table 3.) Apparently this group devotes its inadequate financial resources largely to supplying treatment for the females, who are also more likely to be able to undergo treatment of long duration, since this will result in less income loss, if any, through loss of wages.

Finally, the data reported here suggest the possibility that socio-economic differentials in mortality are increasing so far as the chronic diseases are concerned. The findings, together with those of Yeracaris,[14] are in contrast to the earlier reports of no association between economic status and deaths from the chronic diseases. This could reflect merely the improvement in the accuracy of mortality data and the availability of more detailed information upon which socio-economic categories may be constructed. But it is reasonable to assume that the publicity giving information regarding the chronir diseases, together with the development of more effective treatment which often requires large financial outlay, may be producing a significant differential for these diseases. Data for Houston were not available for a study of trends in the differentials to test whether they are actually becoming larger. Further research on this aspect of the problem may well indicate the need for the agencies concerned with the control of the diseases to direct their efforts toward reducing the differential.

5   CHRONIC ILLNESS AND SOCIO-ECONOMIC STATUS

By P. S. Lawrence

An illness survey was conducted in Hagerstown, Md., in 1943 on white families that had been subjects of a comprehensive study during a three-year period from 1921 to 1924. The resurvey was undertaken to furnish information on the relationship between health status, familial and socio-economic characteristics recorded in 1921–24, and the subsequent record of sickness and mortality. This report represents data on chronic diseases in families and in individuals, in relation to economic status at the time of each survey, and change in status during the twenty-year span.

Material. The basic material used in this paper has been described by Ciocco (1). Of 1,822 families which participated in the original survey, contact was made with one or more members of 1,628 families in 1943. The present data do not include families which were untraced in 1943. The following are also excluded from this report: (a) Families in which ages were unknown or unrecorded; (b) families which were "broken" in 1923 through death or separation of husband or wife, or which were not true families, but only groups of persons with no definite household head; (c) families which were observed for less than 12 months in the original survey.

Excluding these groups leaves 1,310 families that were under observation for 12–36 months in 1921–24 and consisted of husband, wife, and children, all of known ages.

The 1943 survey revealed that 228 of these 1,310 families were no longer intact—either both parents were dead or information on a surviving parent could not be obtained. These families are necessarily excluded from the tabulations which are based on knowledge of socio-economic status of the family in 1943. Among the remaining 1,082 families, there were 72 in which one of the parents had died of a nonchronic disease during the 20-year period. Since any conclusions regarding interrelationships between chronic illness and socio-economic status might be biased by the inclusion of persons who died from nonchronic causes, the 72 families in which such deaths had occurred are excluded from the tables which are based upon the resurvey data.[1] In substance, in 1943 there were 1,010 families of known socio-economic status which were unaffected by death from nonchronic causes and in which at least one of the parents was alive.

From *Public Health Reports,* 63, (November 19, 1948), 1507–1521.

Evaluation of socio-economic status—When the preliminary canvass was made in Hagerstown in the autumn of 1921, each household was classified according to economic status. The classification was discussed and checked by members of the statistical staff, who personally visited the households.

As stated by Sydenstricker, the families were roughly classified into five categories, "well-to-do," "comfortable," "moderate," "poor," and "very poor." Since the range of income included the richest as well as the poorest families in town, the classification was deemed accurate enough for broad distinctions (2). At the same time, other observations were made which further defined and described the categories used. These findings included data on persons per room, sanitary conditions, type of excreta disposal, and general type and amount of milk supply.

The following tabulation shows the percentage of households in each economic group in the total 1923-survey populations reported upon by Sydenstricker. The corresponding figures for the 1,310 families included in this study reveal that selection of complete families has not affected the distribution of families by economic status.

Socio-economic status	Total 1923 survey population	1,310 selected families, 1923	1,010 families, 1943
Well-to-do	2.0	2.1	4.7
Comfortable	10.1	8.9	12.2
Moderate	47.3	47.5	62.9
Poor	38.0	37.7	19.1
Very poor	2.7	3.9	1.2

In evaluating economic status in 1943 the families were classified according to the same categories used in the earlier survey. Elements in the evaluation were location, conditions, and taxable value of the dwelling and place and type of employment. Actual family income was not obtained. It appears from the above tabulation that, with due regard for differences in judgment in assigning socio-economic ratings during the two surveys, these families were in better socio-economic circumstances in 1943 than they were in 1923. This change is probably a reflection not only for a general improvement in economic circumstances throughout the community, but also of an improvement in this specific sample due to the aging of the group and employment of children still residing in the household.

Change in economic status from 1923 to 1943 was recorded only in three categories, "improved," "same," and "reduced." These changes are not solely dependent upon the differences between economic ratings of 1923 and 1943, but were recorded independently when the family was visited in the second survey. The interviewer had the original data at hand and based the conclusion upon a comparison between the conditions previously recorded and those observed. Fine distinctions were of course impossible, hence an improved or reduced classification represents a gross change, and a considerable range of changes is actually embodied within the classification "same." Out of 1,010 families, 14.5 percent were recorded as having an improved status, 80.9 the same, and 4.6 reduced.

Chronic illness—During the 1923 survey interviews visited each household at intervals of 6 weeks to 2 months, obtaining records of illness during the interval. To assure complete reporting of cases of chronic disease, this paper includes only families observed for 12 months or longer. If no one in the family was recorded as having had an attack of chronic illness during the entire period of observation, that family or person is considered in this paper as having been free of chronic illness in 1923.

Illnesses in the 1943 canvass were recorded by cause of illness according to the knowledge of the respondent and were classified as chronic on the basis of the nature of the disease in the same manner as in the 1921–24 survey. The terms "ill" or "well" are used in the text and tables of this paper to mean with or without *chronic* disease. Causes of chronic illness are listed by broad groupings in the second report based on these data (3). For persons who died or were interred in Washington County, information as to date and cause of death was verified by death certificates.

Chronic Illness and Socio-Economic Status in Families. *Prevalence of chronic illness*—Table 1 shows, according to economic class in the 1921–24 survey, the number and percentage of families in which one or more persons had an attack of chronic illness while under observation. The crude rates show

Table 1—Prevalence of chronic illness in families, according to socio-economic status, 1923

Socio-economic status	Total	Number Well	Ill	Observed	Percent ill Expected[1]	Adjusted[2]
Total	1,310	590	720	55.0	55.0	55.0
Well-to-do	27	18	9	33.3	56.6	27.7
Comfortable	116	63	53	45.7	56.8	47.3
Moderate	622	280	342	55.0	54.7	55.0
Poor	494	212	282	57.1	54.7	57.7
Very poor	51	17	34	66.7	56.3	61.3

[1] Rates that would prevail if chronic illness and socio-economic status were unassociated.
[2] Rates that would prevail if there were no age or family-size differences in the groups considered.

an increase in prevalence from 33.3 percent for the highest economic class to 66.7 percent for the lowest. This table also shows the expected percentage ill and the rates adjusted for age and family size. In this and subsequent tables concerning families (except table 5), the "expected" percentages ill are obtained by applying the age and family-size specific rates for the total population of the sample to the age and family-size distribution within each socio-economic class. The "expected" numbers of families with chronic illness thus obtained are summed within each class and divided by the appropriate total. The resulting "expected" rates of this paper are, therefore, the percentage ill that would be expected if chronic illness and the socio-economic characteristic were unrelated. In computing the adjusted rates shown in the final columns, the age of father- and family-size distribution of the total population of the sample is used as the standard.[2] The adjusted rates, or percentages, are the figures that would prevail if there were no age or family-size differences among the socio-economic groups considered.

In table 1, the observed increase in prevalence of chronic disease with successively poorer economic status is statistically significant. When the differences between the observed rates and the expected rates are examined by means of a chi-square test, it is found that differences as great as these could have arisen by chance alone less than one time in 100 population samples of the same size as the one in this table. Since a probability of chance occurrence of less than 0.01 is very small, it is assumed that the differences between the observed and expected figures are true differences resulting from variations in socio-economic status.

The relationship observed for 1923 also holds true in 1943, as may be seen in table 2. In the higher socio-economic categories the observed prevalence rates are less than the expected, while in the poorer categories the rates are higher than expected. These differences yield a probability of chance occurrence of 0.06. Although a probability of 0.05 or less is a usual criterion for statistical significance, supporting data from other studies indicate that the relationship observed in this table is real. It should be noted that the family prevalence rates of table 2 are useful for comparisons among socio-economic classes in this sample, but are not representative of the rates that would be obtained for the population in general. This sample is composed of families in which, by 1943, there had been a considerable reduction in family size, a large proportion had only one surviving parent, and all persons were over 20 years of age.

Table 2—Prevalence of chronic illness in families, according to socio-economic status, 1943

Socio-economic status	Total	Number Well	Ill	Observed	Percent ill Expected[1]	Adjusted[2]
Total	1,010	585	425	42.1	42.1	42.1
Well-to-do	47	32	15	31.9	44.2	29.3
Comfortable	123	74	49	39.8	44.6	39.8
Moderate	635	374	261	41.1	41.8	41.1
Poor	193	99	94	48.7	41.0	50.6
Very poor	12	6	6	50.0	41.9	44.0

[1] Rates that would prevail if chronic illness and socio-economic status were unassociated.
[2] Rates that would prevail if there were no age or family-size differences in the groups considered.

The relationship between chronic illness and economic status has been previously shown. Bigelow and Lombard demonstrated this association in their Massachusetts study (5). In a 1931 survey of persons over 40 years of age, those in "comfortable" circumstances had a chronic illness rate of 255 per 1,000; in "high moderate," 270; in "low moderate," 305; and among "poor," 412. For persons on relief the rate was 514 per 1,000. There was chronic illness in 62.3 percent of the *families* on relief. Figures based upon the National Health Survey, 1935–36, revealed that the percentage of disability from chronic disease on the day of visit was 4.8 for persons on relief, 2.7 for persons not on relief but with family incomes of less than $1,000 and 1.8 for persons with family incomes of $1,000 to $1,500 (6). Another National Health Survey report showed that the frequency of chronic disease disability lasting a week or longer during a 12-month period was almost twice as high for members of relief families as among those in better economic circumstances; for other persons with family incomes of less than $1,000 the frequency was one and one-half times as high as among those in better economic circumstances (7).

Although there is little doubt as to the inverse relationship between socio-economic status and the prevalence of chronic illness, the static nature of data from a single survey precludes estimation of the extent to which low socio-economic circumstances may cause, or result from, chronic disease. It is hoped that by a new approach, introduction of the time element, information may be furnished concerning the dynamics of the observed association.

Table 3 reveals that one or more persons had chronic illness in 1943, or had died from chronic disease between 1923 and 1943, in 91.5 percent of the families that had a reduction in socio-economic status between the two

Table 3—Proportions of families in which one or more persons were ill or dead from chronic disease in 1943, according to change in socio-economic status, 1923–43

Change in socio-economic status, 1923–43	Number, 1943			Percent ill or dead, 1943		
	Total	Well	Ill or dead	Observed	Expected[1]	Adjusted[2]
Total	1,010	377	633	62.7	62.7	62.7
Reduced	47	4	43	91.5	64.0	87.2
Same	817	293	524	64.1	63.2	63.6
Improved	146	80	66	45.2	59.5	44.2

[1] Rates that would prevail if chronic illness and socio-economic status were unassociated.
[2] Rates that would prevail if there were no age or family-size differences in the groups considered.

surveys. The rate was 64.1 percent for families whose status remained the same and 45.2 for those with improved status. Adjustment for age and family size does not alter substantially the crude figures. When compared with the expected figures, the observed percentages are found to differ by a statistically significant amount, the value of P being less than .01. The marked difference between the reduced and improved categories demonstrates the dynamic nature of the chronic disease problem.

Socio-economic status as a factor affecting chronic illness—In order to clarify the relationship between socio-economic status and the subsequent record of chronic illness, table 4 presents data on families which were free of chronic disease during the 1921–24 survey and had the same socio-economic status in 1943 as in 1923. The attempt is thus made to reduce the possibility that modification of chronic disease incidence may have resulted primarily from an improved or reduced economic status subsequent to the 1923 observations. Even so, this factor may not be entirely eliminated. As previously stated, the category "same" includes all except gross changes in socio-economic status. Furthermore, a family may, for example, have had a change in status shortly after the 1923 survey and reverted to approximately the same status shortly before the 1943 canvass. The data do not give a record of changes during the twenty-year period.

This lack of interim data is true also of chronic illnesses. It is quite possible that a person who was well in 1923 could have developed a chronic ailment during the interval, and yet by 1943 have recovered, become accustomed to the disability, or otherwise felt so well that he did not report any ailment. Such conditions may have occurred to approximately the same degree within the several socio-economic groups of 1923, and hence should result in an over-all error, rather than a bias in favor of any particular economic class. However, it is well to keep in mind these limitations of the data. Table 4 includes families in which one or both parents, though well in 1923, had died of chronic disease by 1943. The dead must be included if the effect of socio-economic status on the occurrence of chronic illness is to be evaluated properly.

Although possibly containing some error due to lack of interim data, by and large table 4 presents the incidence or rate of appearance of new cases of chronic illness from 1923 to 1943 according to socio-economic status of the family. With due consideration for differences in age, family size, and

Table 4—Proportion of families in which one or more persons were ill or dead from chronic disease in 1943 among families which were free of chronic disease in 1923, according to socio-economic status in 1923

Socio-economic status, 1923	Number, 1943			Percent ill or dead, 1943		
	Total	Well	Ill or dead	Observed	Expected[1]	Adjusted[2]
Total	431	159	272	63.1	63.1	63.1
Well-to-do	13	4	9	69.2	69.9	56.4
Comfortable	55	19	36	65.5	68.1	59.5
Moderate	224	88	136	60.7	63.1	62.4
Poor	132	45	87	65.9	60.1	68.6
Very poor	7	3	4	57.1	70.3	30.2

[1] Rates that would prevail if chronic illness and socio-economic status were unassociated.
[2] Rates that would prevail if there were no age or family-size differences in the groups considered.

the size of the sample, differences in the proportions of families which developed chronic illness should be indicative of the effects of differences in socio-economic status.

Rates in table 4 adjusted for age and family size show an upward trend from an incidence of 56.4 percent for the well-to-do to 68.6 percent for the poor. This association may also be seen in the differences between the observed and expected figures. However, these differences are not large and are of an order which yields a probability of chance occurrence of about 0.55. Because of the small number of cases in the "very poor" category, no significance can be attached to the figures in this group. Combining very poor with poor yields the same probability of chance occurrence. It is apparent that the association found in this table is not of as high an order as is found in the preceding tables, and that, judging from this sample, socio-economic status in itself does not seem to play an important part in the chances of developing chronic disease.

Chronic illness in the family as a factor in changed socio-economic status —The percentage of families which had a reduced, unchanged, or improved status is shown in table 5 according to history of chronic illness in 1923 and 1943. Families in which there was a death from chronic disease during the interval are included. None of the families which were unaffected by chronic illness in 1923 and remained unaffected had a reduced socio-economic status. Of the 215 families in this group, 21.6 percent (adjusted for age and family size) had an improved status and the balance remained the same. These percentages are undoubtedly influenced by the generally high economic level of the war years, but this factor applies to all groups. This point will be discussed further in a subsequent section. The proportions in section A may, for comparative purposes, be considered as representative of the expected changes in socio-economic status of families free of the impact of chronic disease. For this reason, expected percentages of sections B, C, and D of table 5 are based upon the observed figures of section A, and therefore differ from the observed percentages of A only because of variations in the age and family-size structure of the groups.

Section B of this table is composed of families which were well in 1923 but which were reported as having illness or death from chronic disease at the 1943 survey. Over 9 percent of these families had a reduction in economic status, while the percentage with an improved status was less than half of that which would be expected of families which suffered no chronic illness. Some of the families in section B may have had a reduction in status between 1923 and the time of occurrence of illness or death. Thus the differences between observed and expected figures in this section may not be solely a result of chronic disease.

However, this would not be true of the families included in section D, for among these families there was chronic illness prior to the change in economic status. The differences between observed and expected percentages in section D may actually be an underevaluation of the effect of chronic illness on economic status. Some of these families, in which there was illness in 1923, may have suffered a reduction in status prior to the initial survey and, having already financially accommodated themselves, had no further gross change in status between 1923 and 1943.

From these considerations it appears that the percentage of families in which there was reduction in economic status following chronic illness or death lies between 5.5 and 9.2, the limits indicated by the adjusted figures of sections D and B, respectively. Similarly, between 9.5 and 11.5 percent of the families with illness or death improved their economic status as compared with 21.6 percent of families which remained well. The observed percentages of sections B and D are both significantly different from the expected figures based on section A. In testing significance, "reduced" was combined with "same" because the zero percentage would yield no expected cases in the reduced catagory.

The observed percentages in section C also differ significantly from the expected, although the differences are not as great as for families in which illness or death was reported in the 1943 survey. The figures in this section indicate that families in which the ill members had recovered, had become accustomed to, or at least no longer complained of chronic illness, showed more improvement in economic status during the 20-year span, than families in which illness developed or continued. However, they showed less improvement than those which remained entirely free of disease.

Chronic Illness and Socio-Economic Status of Individuals. The families traced in 1943 originally contained 7,239 persons. There were 5,622 members of the 1,310 families that were unbroken, of known ages, and observed for more than 12 months in 1923. During the 20-year period ended in 1943 many children left the original households. Consequently their economic status in 1943,

Table 5—Proportion of families in each category of change in socio-economic status, according to history of chronic illness in 1923 and 1943

Change in socio-economic status	A. Well in 1923; well in 1943 Percent			B. Well in 1923; illness or death 1943 Percent				C. Ill in 1923; well in 1943 Percent				D. Ill in 1923; illness or death 1943 Percent			
	Number	Observed	Adjusted[2]	Number	Observed	Expected[1]	Adjusted[2]	Number	Observed	Expected[1]	Adjusted[2]	Number	Observed	Expected[1]	Adjusted[2]
Total	215	100.0	100.0	262	100.1	100.0	100.0	162	100.0	100.0	100.0	371	100.0	100.0	100.0
Reduced	0	0.0	0.0	24	9.2	0.0	9.2	4	2.5	0.0	2.5	19	5.1	0.0	5.5
Same	160	74.4	78.4	214	81.7	79.2	81.3	133	82.1	75.8	80.6	310	83.6	81.3	83.0
Improved	55	25.6	21.6	24	9.2	20.8	9.5	25	15.4	24.2	16.9	42	11.3	18.7	11.5

[1] Percentages that would be expected if this group had had no chronic illnesses.
[2] Percentages that would prevail if there were no age or family-size differences in the groups considered.

even when known, referred to family units other than those of which they were members in 1923. Such information was therefore of doubtful value for the determination of the relationship of socio-economic status to chronic illness. At the time of the resurvey there were then 2,483 individuals still alive and still members of an original family group in which at least one of the parents remained alive in 1943. Figures concerning the economic status of individuals in 1943 include only these persons.

Table 6 shows the age and sex adjusted prevalence rates by socio-economic status of 5,622 persons in 1923 and 2,483 persons in 1943. In each survey the prevalence of chronic disease increases with poorer socio-economic status. There is, in general, increased prevalence in the 1943 data because the population is 20 years older. Chi-square tests reveal that both for 1923 and 1943, after adjustment for age and sex variations in the several socio-economic classes, the increase in prevalence with successively poorer status is statistically significant. These findings are in agreement with the figures presented where the family was used as the unit of observation. Individual and family results are compared in a later section.

Table 6—Prevalence of chronic illness among individuals, according to socio-economic status in 1923 and 1943

Socio-economic status	Adjusted percent ill[1] 1923	1943
Total	18.8	24.2
Well-to-do	4.7	15.3
Comfortable	14.8	20.2
Moderate	18.4	23.2
Poor	19.6	33.3
Very poor	23.0	32.8

[1] Rates that would prevail if there were no age or sex differences in the groups considered.

The percentages of persons ill or dead from chronic disease in 1943, according to change in socio-economic status from 1923 to 1943 are: among individuals with reduced status, 40.9; same status, 25.1; improved status, 13.9. This relationship is statistically significant. These age and sex adjusted figures are based upon a population of 2,483 persons.

Table 7 shows the observed, expected, and age-sex adjusted percentages of persons who were ill or dead from chronic disease in 1943, among persons who were well at the time of the first survey. All these persons, numbering

Table 7—Proportion of persons ill or dead from chronic disease in 1943 among persons who were free of chronic disease in 1923, according to socio-economic status in 1923.

Socio-economic status, 1923	Percent ill or dead, 1943 Observed	Expected[1]	Observed[2]
Total	36.8	36.8	36.8
Well-to-do	40.4	44.7	32.5
Comfortable	39.5	44.5	32.9
Moderate	36.4	38.3	35.0
Poor	36.6	32.2	41.8
Very poor	35.7	32.8	32.8

[1] Rates that would prevail if chronic illness and socio-economic status were unassociated.
[2] Rates that would prevail if there were no age or sex differences in the groups considered.

2,040, had the same socio-economic status in 1943 or presumably at the time of death as in 1923. Granting possibilities of error already discussed in connection with table 4, it is probable that whatever variations exist in the rates of occurrence of chronic illness and death are attributable to differences in socio-economic status. The crude rates of illness and death in table 7 show a slight decrease from 40.4 percent for the "well-to-do" to 35.7 percent for the "very poor." Other columns of this table reveal that this decrease is artificial, being caused by differences in the age and sex composition of the several groups. Actually, the percentage who died or became chronically ill in the three highest socio-economic categories is somewhat less than the expected; and in the two lowest categories it is somewhat greater than expected.

When tested for the probability that these differences may have arisen by chance, it is found that chi-square equals 10.22 and the value of P is approximately 0.04. If it be accepted that a probability of 5 in 100 is significant, then the deviations from the expected rates are probably not due to chance fluctuations. The differences between the observed and expected numbers in the "poor" group contribute to over half of the total value of chi-square given above. Comparisons among the other groups reveal no differences that could not have arisen by chance according to the usual methods of interpreting significance tests. Here, as in the figures based on families, it appears that socio-economic status is a factor of small importance in the development of chronic disease.

The observed and the age and sex adjusted percentages of persons whose socio-economic status changed is shown in table 8, according to presence or absence of chronic illness in 1923 and 1943. There are 1,596 persons included in section A, 425 in section B, 286 in C, and 176 in D. Almost the same pattern may be seen in this table as was observed for families in table 5. On the basis

Table 8—Percentage of persons in each category of change in socio-economic status according to history of chronic illness in 1923 & 1943

Change in socio-economic status	A Well in 1923; well in 1943		B Well in 1923; ill in 1943		C Ill in 1923; well in 1943		D Ill in 1923; ill in 1943	
	Observed	Adjusted[1]	Observed	Adjusted[1]	Observed	Adjusted[1]	Observed	Adjusted[1]
Total	100.0	100.0	100.0	100.0	100.0	100.0	100.0	100.0
Reduced	2.5	2.5	8.2	6.8	3.9	4.0	5.1	5.9
Same	76.9	78.0	81.7	79.6	74.8	73.9	87.5	83.5
Improved	20.6	19.5	10.1	13.6	21.3	22.1	7.4	10.6

[1] Rates that would prevail if there were no age or sex differences in the groups considered.

of the adjusted figures, 6.8 percent of the persons who became ill, and 5.9 percent of those who remained ill, had a reduction in economic status as compared to 2.5 percent among persons who remained free of chronic disease. When chi-squares were computed in the same manner as for the family data, it was found that the socio-economic changes of groups B and D differed significantly from the changes expected in a well population.

It will be noted that the adjusted percentages for persons who were ill in 1923 but who were reportedly well in 1943 are higher both in the "reduced" category and in the "improved" category than the corresponding percentages among persons who had no illness in either survey. This is true of the observed and expected figures computed for section C, but the differences are not statistically significant. There may be some suggestions from the high percentage in the "improved" category that cure or rehabilitation (possibly psychological) of the chronically ill led to the improvement of their socio-economic position.

Discussion. It is apparent that when chronic illness and socio-economic status are investigated from the standpoint of either the individual or the family one finds that an inverse relationship exists. Yet it is doubtful that one could obtain a true account of the economic aspects of the impact of chronic disease upon the population through a study based solely on individuals, for illness affects the status not only of the ill person, but also of every member of his family. Thus considering the 1923 figures, which contain persons of all ages, 18.8 percent of the individuals were affected by chronic disease, whereas 55.0 percent of the families were so affected. From these observations it may be concluded that a clearer view of the magnitude of public health or welfare problems is obtained when they are measured in terms of families rather than of individuals.

It is known that unfavorable economic circumstances make difficult the arrest of certain chronic illnesses, because of the need for constant medication, proper food or diet, favorable working conditions, or sufficient rest. But the number of chronic diseases for which it has been shown that poor economic and environmental circumstances play a part in causing the illness is limited, and these, with the exception of tuberculosis, are of low prevalence save in certain geographic sectors. Though tuberculosis is included among the diseases in this report, a study of these cases reveals that their exclusion from tables 4 and 7 would alter little the figures shown. These figures, for families and for individuals, indicate that socio-economic differences probably have an effect on the occurrence of chronic illnesses, but that the association is not of great magnitude and, in the case of families, is not statistically significant.

Information as to the extent to which lowered economic welfare is related to, and may cause, illness is given in a study by Perrott and Collins (8). This survey of 10 localities included all types of illnesses and accidents within 3 months of the interview, these ailments being classified as to whether they were disabling or nondisabling and further as to whether the onset was during the 3-month period or before that period. The latter group included diseases of a more or less chronic nature. Persons who dropped from a comfortable economic status in 1929 to a poor status in 1932 had a disabling illness rate of 174 per 1,000 for the three month survey period as compared with a rate of 120 per 1,000 for persons who remained in comfortable circumstances from 1929 through 1932. The rates for disabling diseases with onset prior to the survey period, were, respectively, 53 per 1,000 and 30 per 1,000. Since the sickness rates were higher among the families that suffered the greatest change in standard of living, and since the excess in illness existed among children as well as among adults it was concluded that the income loss had a part in causing these higher sickness rates in 1933.

The social and economic strains imposed by chronic illness in the family are well known and have been discussed by Boas (9). In addition to physicians' and nurses' bills, medicines, and special foods, the family often suffers loss or reduction of income, costs for household help, or costs for care of children. Such expenses place a severe burden not only on the poor but also on families in comfortable circumstances. Evidence of the extent to which chronic disease may impair socio-economic status is shown in tables 5 and 8. Again the value of employing the family, rather than the individual, as the unit of study may be seen. There were 40 individuals who, though well in 1923 and 1943, had a reduced economic status in the later period. But it is evident from the absence of families in the corresponding category of table 5 that all these 40 persons were members of families in which chronic illness occurred.

About 10 percent of the families with illness improved their status in spite of the chronic disease, as compared with approximately 20 percent showing improvement among families free of disease. It is difficult to assess the extent to which the high level of employment and economic conditions of this area in 1943 may have influenced these figures. However, it is known that persons previously "unemployable" because of chronic disease or impairment were full-time or part-time employees during the war years. Many of these persons were exempted from military service because of their disability. Further, large numbers of women whose husbands or fathers were dead or disabled, and who previously had little income, were fully employed at good wages in 1943. Hence it is quite possible that, although the economic status of the general population improved during the war, families in which there existed chronic illness had a relatively greater economic improvement. If this is true, the figures shown in this report present a modest picture of the influence that chronic illness would have on change in socio-economic status during "normal" times.

Summary. This report is based upon 1,310 families and 5,622 persons surveyed in 1923, and 1,010 families and 2,483 persons resurveyed in 1943. These families were classified into five socio-economic groups in each of the two surveys, and the gross change in socio-economic status between the two periods was recorded. Information concerning chronic illnesses in the family was recorded in 1923 and again in 1943, along with deaths from chronic diseases during the twenty-year span. Analysis of these data reveals:

1. For families and for persons the prevalence of chronic diseases progressively increased from the "well-to-do" to the "very poor" in 1923 and also in 1943.

2. Families which had a reduction in socio-economic status between 1923 and 1943 had an adjusted chronic disease rate in 1943 of 87.2 percent, almost twice as high as the rate for families with an "improved" status.

3. Among families which were free of chronic illness in 1923, those which were in favorable socio-economic circumstances in 1923 and remained in favorable circumstances developed chronic diseases at a rate which was only slightly lower than the computed expected rate. Families which were poor

in 1923, and remained poor, developed chronic illnesses at a rate slightly above the expected. For families, the differences between observed and expected figures are without statistical significance. When individuals are used as the unit of observation, the trend is the same as for family units, but the differences, though small, are probably outside the limits of chance variation. It is concluded that socio-economic status is a factor, but of only slight importance, in the chances of occurrence of chronic illness in this population.

4. Chronic disease is a more significant factor in causing reduced socio-economic status. Of the families in which there was no chronic illness in 1923 or in 1943, none had a reduction in status and 21.6 percent showed an improvement. Of those families which had no chronic illness in 1923 but which in 1943 reported illness or death from chronic disease, 9.2 percent suffered a gross reduction in status while 9.5 percent "improved." Among families in which chronic illness existed in 1923 and in which there was reported chronic illness or death in 1943, there were 5.5 percent with "reduced" status and 11.5 percent "improved." The same picture is presented when the material is studied for individuals, but the differences between the percentages for the well population and for the chronically ill populations are not as marked as in the case of families. This results from the fact that 2.4 percent of the well persons in this study had a reduction in status, but all these persons were member of families in which chronic illness occurred.

6 SOME ECOLOGICAL CONTRIBUTIONS TO EPIDEMIOLOGY*

By John Mabry

There has been rapidly increasing recognition that the social environment has a direct relevance to many medical problems. For years public health specialists have been aware that certain social pathologies (over-crowding, unsafe housing, dirt and filth, for example) contribute toward malnutrition and lowered resistance to the threats of disease.[1] On another level, Jacque May and his associates[2] have been describing some very gross correlations between biospheric conditions (temperature, barometric pressure, precipitation, land forms and uses) and the global occurrence of disease. There has been increased emphasis upon the social psychological factors underlying nutritional,[3] psychosomatic[4] and psychiatric disorders.[5] These studies and interests have furthered our knowledge of the etiology of disease, provided some recognition of predisposing factors, and have thus contributed toward our understanding of public health measures necessary for prevention and/or control.

A consideration of more specific family and community variables may result in increased prediction and control of disease, just as our knowledge

---

The writer wishes to express his appreciation to R. Straus and W. L. Cupp, who critically read the manuscript with helpful suggestions.

of etiology profits by the combination of the clinical and epidemiological approaches.[6] The concept of epidemiology as the "circumstances under which illness occurs" includes not only clinical analysis and preventive action. It also includes the environmental and social factors in illness occurrence.[7] The purpose of this paper is to discuss the relevance of two ecological variables to epidemiology: *first,* some correlations between community land occupation and use, exposure to disease, and antibody development; and *second,* the relationship between "interaction space" and communicable disease. This paper does not attempt to explore certain other worth-while epidemiological problems like nutrition and emotional disorders.

Community Ecology. The findings of Melnick and Ledinko[8] pose an intriguing problem in social serology and epidemiology. In studying antibody levels before, during, and after an epidemic of poliomyelitis they found that: *first,* there were significant social class differences in antibody levels in both the pre sera and post sera periods for the following antibodies—Lansing poliomyelitis neutralizing, antistreptolysin O, streptococcus agglutinin, and Gamma globulin. *Second,* that the direction of this difference was for higher antibody production in the lower income groups. *Third,* that there were *not* significant differences between social classes for the following antibodies— Coxsackie virus (high point) neutralizing, Coxsackie virus (high point) complement fixing. *Fourth,* that there is no consistent direction tendency in the differences that were observed. The frequently agreed upon interpretation is that the lower income groups live in more unhealthy surroundings with greater exposure to disease and more opportunity for developing a variety of antibodies. Although the death rate may be higher in a young population, it would appear that those who survive achieve higher immunity levels, statistically speaking, for certain diseases including poliomyelitis.[9]

It may be suggested that the processes of exposure risk, for both clinical and sub-clinical infections, and the production of antibodies has a direct relationship to the sociological processes of community change in patterns of land use and spatial arrangements. It is apparent to the perceptive observer that communities, large or small, have four basic kinds of land use: commercial, industrial, residential, and public. Zoning laws characteristically further sub-divide each of these land uses into wholesale and retail (commercial), light and heavy manufacturing (industrial), single-family and multiple-family dwellings (residential), and parks and buildings (public).[10] The following observations are based upon the substantial literature[11] which deals with the interrelations between land use and home living arrangements. *First,* seldom does any municipal zoning law preclude residential dwelling units in commercial and industrial areas; the common trend is to find residential uses inter-mixed with heavy industry, large warehouses, and retail stores. *Second,* there would appear to be a direct economic relationship between the rising value of land in expanding industrial and commercial areas and the declining desirability of living amidst heavy railroad or trucking traffic, noise, and unpleasant fumes or odors. Frequently, land values increase as rental housing values decline. Those without effective income, or different spending habits, tend to locate in areas characterized by over-crowding, sub-standard housing and, it would seem, greater exposure risks to malnutrition and disease.

If communities were static agglomerations of people, the problem would be fairly easy to define although difficult to remedy. Essentially, one could recommend slum-clearance and the provision of land to encourage new industry, the erection of public housing, or the building of new parking lots. The prohibitive effect of zoning laws is appreciated by the physician who may have wished to open a private practice in a restricted neighborhood or who wanted to enlarge a garage too close to the lot boundary. Perhaps, on the other hand, a neighbor proposed to convert a single-family home into a multiple-family dwelling unit with increased traffic, parking problems and congestion of living arrangements. In any growing and expanding community, and most cities are in this category,[12] there are processes of change at work, almost inevitably, which lead to differences in the structure of neighborhood areas. Although discussed elsewhere,[13] brief mention of these community processes may be made. First, similar land uses tend to cluster together in a process called *aggregation* not only because zoning laws say so but also because of certain transportation economies and the influence of custom and belief.[14] That is, new industries tend to locate near established transportation lines and new housing tends to locate adjacent to already established housing areas. *Second*, any expanding land use must, of necessity *invade* an area characterized by some other land use. Suburban housing invades farming areas, and expanding industry and commerce moves in to residential areas. *Third*, if the invasion is successful over a period of years then succession is said to have taken place.

The consequence of these processes for the character of an area are easily observed for one who cares to look. Once spacious-lawned homes may now be converted into apartment buildings with other houses "in between" and the attendant piling up of cars, parking problems, and greater concentrations of people. Or these large homes may now contain a tavern in the basement, pawn shop on the first floor, over-crowded apartments above that and two gasoline stations and a drive-in laundry on the corner. Most frequently, this commercial invasion of a neighborhood began down the street when someone began taking in roomers, or started an automotive repair shop in their garage, or converted their front two rooms into a grocery store. Over the years, the invasion has moved up the street with each succession serving as the basis for another further invasion. In general, those who can afford it move. They either invade the countryside and farming areas or, in very large cities, invade the atmosphere on the upper floors of apartment buildings. Those who cannot afford much else move into this changing area from one which has already been successfully invaded.

It is suggested that these ecological processes, as a sociologist would view them, has a direct and relevant connection with emergent, expanding conceptions of epidemiology. Previous medical studies[15] have emphasized the movement of mass populations and the results entailed when a group of susceptible hosts place themselves in an area where diseases and, their vectors, may be endemic. It may be wise to consider those less dramatic population (host and human vector) movements which more slowly, but none-the-less surely, occur in expanding metropolitan areas.

In terms of a comprehensive theory of disease, the "living zone of exchange"[16] between the internal organismic or cellular environment and the broad external environment may be said to include protective adaptive processes (leucocytes, agglutinins, neutralizing antibodies, antitoxins, complements and so forth), some of which would seem to have a direct relationship to continuous, everyday processes of community change. The finding of Melnick and Ledinko would seem to be quite conclusive for the antibodies considered in their particular normal young populations. For incorporation into a systematic theory of pathology, it would seem that a great deal more research into different populations, living in clearly defined ecological areas, would be appropriate. The present plea is for an extension of, and more precise conceptualization of, the pathological, analytical and clinical ranges of epidemiological research.

Interaction Space and Communicable Disease. Dwelling unit over-crowding has long been known to be an important factor in the spread of communicable diseases.[17] Although the amount of living space available for family pursuits is partly contingent upon the ecological characteristics discussed above, there is another dimension which may be added to the health and disease implications of how individuals live together in groups whether it be the family, school, factory or military organization. In traditional epidemiological research, the concept of over-crowding is construed to mean the proportion of dwelling units, in a given area, which have more than 1.0 persons per room. This criticism is most frequently used because the Bureau of the Census publishes tabulations in which this ratio is used.[18] There are two deficiencies in the use of this kind of index of over-crowding: *first*, it is not specific to individual families and their homes, but, rather it is characteristic of an area defined by the Bureau of the Census (census tract or block). Consequently, the average-number-of-persons-per-room index cannot be meaningfully applied to both sick and relatively healthy people within the same area. It is suggested that home visits would provide the opportunity for data more refined than that found in the census publications. *Second,* the use of this criterion is quite gross and vague in the light of the knowledge that rooms differ in size and arrangement as well as in the amount and frequency of human contact which takes place within them. If agents of infection are ingested and exchanged by air, contamination of the hands or other parts of the body, and/or bed linen or clothing it would seem that further precision in measuring the amount and kind of human contact would be of ascendant importance.

A concern with communication in small groups has led to the development of an "interaction space index."[19] In this context social interaction refers to the way in which individuals modify their behavior, and respond to the presence and behavior of others within prescribed space limitations. It is extremely unfortunate that no systematic and comprehensive inquiry has been made either of home living arrangements or institutional design from the point of view of space for optimum interaction and health comfort. While there is some literature which deals with economic and functional design in terms of life activities (sleeping, dressing, personal care, dining, and so forth) this has been largely concerned with architectural arrangements in a physical sense[20] and not with the "architecture of social interaction." It may well be that the minimum health standards set by housing specialists is quite accurate; our chief problem is that we do not know whether it is or not.

According to Bossard[21] the index of spatial interaction may be computed simply on the basis of two facts; *first*, the number of people in a room at any given time, and *second*, the dimensions of the room. The Index of Spatial Interaction is found by dividing the number of square feet by the square of the numbers minus the number of persons divided by two. Thus,

$$\text{I.S.I.} = \text{Sq. Ft.} \left/ \frac{y^2 - y}{2} \right.$$

where,

I.S.I. = index of spatial interaction,

and

y = number of persons

For example, a living room twelve by fourteen feet presents a total area of 168 square feet. According to housing planners, the space for "recreation and self-improvement" (that life activity which would require a living room) for a family of four should be 286 square feet.[22] If our family of four with a twelve by fourteen feet living room assembled in this room after the evening meal certainly "over-crowding" would result. Through use of the index of spatial interaction, however, we may get a more accurate measure of the degree of over-crowding as well as a specification of the area of interaction. In this case, the index of spatial interaction for a family of four in the above living room would be twenty-eight (28) square feet per personal contact. This is less than the recommended 47.7 square feet per personal contact in the living room.

This kind of calculation may be accomplished for each of the rooms in the dwelling unit including kitchen, dining room, bedrooms, and so forth. These measurements have a direct and immediate relevance to the rise and resolution of personal tensions and of family "togetherness" patterns. Even more important from the point of view of this paper, the spatial potentials and limits to personal contacts among family members may contribute toward our increased understandings of the familial and institutional incidence and transmission of communicable diseases. The concept of "over-crowding" means, essentially, that the density of dwelling unit population is too great for the maintenance of health and/or the treatment of ill-health. The "index of spatial interaction" proposed in this paper provides a more precise way of measuring the density of dwelling unit population.

Summary. The purpose of this paper is to suggest two possible ecological contributions to epidemiological theory and research. *First*, knowledge of community growth processes and areas was related to the acquisition of antibodies and their development. *Second*, a statistical procedure for more precisely measuring and describing the concept of "over-crowding" was proposed as a variable in the transmission of disease by human vectors.

There are other implications of the processes of community ecology and of measures of spatial interaction which have not been a part of the foci of this paper but which are, none-the-less, quite important. The individual perception of these spatial environmental events are interpreted with psychological over-lays so that they may be important from the point of view of emotion and/or psychosomatic pathologies. Spatial arrangements from the point of view of the chronically ill person at home, or in the nursing home and hospital, may either facilitate or hinder the management of the patient. These are important problems but they are beyond the scope of this discussion.

7   DISEASE AND THE PATTERNS OF BEHAVIOR

By Harold Wolff

It is my purpose to select, from a quarter century of bedside and laboratory experience, those "moments of discovery" which served to indicate a path, however, indistinct, rather than those that momentarily fiercely lighted my feet.

Like many others before me, I have rediscovered that the perception of an order in the universe is for man a moralizing experience. The more inclusive the arrangement, the more moving is the spectacle. Especially is this so if the order perceived concerns man directly. The exploration of man's relation to the universe, and especially of man's nature, is thus an endlessly life-giving pursuit. Whether one orients oneself to such order in theistic or humanistic terms, becomes, in the main, a matter of esthetic preference.

I would like to start with some studies on pain. We early discovered, much to our surprise, that all human beings have the same threshold; the point at which they first perceive pain is the same for all persons. Indeed, my colleague, Dr. Hardy, just back from regions near the North Pole, worked with Eskimos, and found their pain thresholds to be the same as ours. We found also, that there are a limited number of discriminable steps between the point at which pain is first perceived and the point beyond which discriminations are impossible.

However, what one does with such pain perception is extremely variable. It soon became apparent that it did not make much difference what the nature of the damaging influence was; whether much or little was made of this painful sensation seemed to depend more upon the individual and his background than upon the intensity of the stimulus.

It also became apparent that man, constituted as he is, was capable of responding in much the same way to tissue damage—which is, after all, the basis for the painful sensation—and to symbols or threats of danger. And, interestingly enough, the responses to pain, tissue damage, or to the symbols of tissue damage—to threats, in other words—were often more destructive than were the effects of the damaging agent.

The next step in our observations had to do with the fact that man, being a tribal animal and so much dependent upon the support and encouragement of his group, is jeopardized by their disapproval and much taken up with his fear of being incapable of carrying on as a man. Such environmental forces, representing the impact of man on man, being ubiquitous, constitute one of his greatest threats. This led us to extend our studies beyond those on pain as a sensation and the reactions to tissue damage. We began to analyze the brigade of human reaction to threats and symbols of danger—epitomized in what man does to man; we studied his attitudes, the conflicts his goals engender, and the price he pays for his achievements.

Let me illustrate by example. If someone strikes your forearm with a ferrule, the skin will become red, and after a while, if the blow has been forceful enough, a wheal, or a whitened, elevated area will appear. The latter represents the lack of capacity of the small blood vessels in the skin to hold on to their bloody contents, and some of them leak out into the tissue, and, in a sense, protect for the moment that area of skin against further injury.

If after such an experience, and as a sham blow, that ferrule is brought down to within an inch of the arm, the skin behaves very much as if it had been struck, although there has been no actual damage done. Reaction to the threat, therefore, is like that to the blow.

Let us now consider a person with hives—large swollen areas of the skin, with various technical names. Out of the medley of information gleaned from a survey of the subject's major interests, relations and past, pertinent topics were selected that were potentially traumatic. When that individual was then confronted by and contemplated such topics, he exhibited in his skin the same reaction as he did under circumstances when his skin was actually struck. The reaction to a variety of traumatic agents was found to be the same. Also, the reaction to a symbol or a threat of assault was repeatedly observed to be the same as that to the assault itself.

The individual, when asked what he feels under these circumstances, if articulate, may say, "I feel as though I were taking a beating and that I can do nothing about it."

We interested ourselves in the stomach because complaints from the abdomen and from the head constitute, in the physician's ears, the bulk of human complaining.

We were much helped by a man who came into our circle of friends and workers. He was at that time about sixty-five, and as a child of nine, had occluded his gullet by drinking scalding hot clam chowder. Thereafter, he had to be fed through a hole made in his abdomen. Becoming as he did, a part of our laboratory family, he allowed us to examine every day what was going on in this hole in his abdomen. He also allowed us to try to relate the overall circumstances of his life, the way he felt about them, with what we saw as regards blood flow, the amount of secretion, and the motility of the stomach. It was his custom to come to us each morning, having fasted after his evening meal. He would narrate, and we would observe and note.

A characteristic situation and reaction was one such as this: his income as a university employee was small, and in order to swell it, he took on the task of dusting the apartment of an associate. He was not a good housekeeper and was indifferent about dust. My associate wished to dismiss him and finally did so under laboratory circumstances. While he was being denounced by his employer and told of his ineffectiveness as a worker, the mucous membrane lining of the stomach became fiery red, large amounts of digestive juices were secreted, and his stomach began to churn. Subsequently, when my colleague left, the subject said, "I'd like to wring his neck."

Now, what did we see? We saw exactly what we would have seen had we placed some attractive, platable food into this man's stoma. Here was a man angered by another man, whose stomach acted under these circumstances as if he were preparing to eat! Why do we use an eating pattern when we are angry? To be sure, this is not universal, but under certain circumstances, feelings of anger are associated with a preparation for eating. If this preparation for eating goes on (as it can) for days, weeks, or months, the individual may digest his own digestive apparatus; he bores a hole, so to speak, in the lining of his stomach.

We have now considered two examples of the inappropriate use of protective or adaptive patterns. A city man cannot "eat" his enemy; he cannot minimize the effects of an unfriendly remark by any protective action within his skin. And yet, maintaining such patterns for days, weeks, or months at a high intensity may seriously damage organs and parts. Not because they were originally weak. Indeed, they may have been strong; but they are damaged because of prolonged and excessive use of structures not designed to meet such needs.

The digestive equipment exhibited an ejection pattern when a zealous young Jewess was confronted by an incident indicating to her that Zionists were being prosecuted. She reacted with feelings of disgust and her stomach took on the pattern which the word, "disgust," suggests, namely, faulty digestion. The contents of the stomach were ejected just as though she had taken in some poison.

The pattern of dealing with disgusting behavior on the part of man was the same as that evoked by putting ipecac or a "disgusting" tasting material into the mouth.

Later, we were fortunate in being able to study four individuals who, for surgical reasons, had to have parts of their large intestine exposed to the outer world. Again we could correlate from hour to hour, day to day, and month to month the life circumstances, the feelings aroused by threats and delights, and the change in the large bowel. Likewise, we found that if we put irritant substances into the bowel, say, croton oil, the mucous membrane got red, mucous poured out, the gut became hypermotile, and soon this irritant was pushed out of the gut.

One of these unfortunate men, following the death of his mother, became the nominal head of his household. A timid, shy person, he was unprepared for the position of family authority. He felt himself challenged when his brother's wife came into the household to live and because of her temperament, began to dominate him and the situation. Humiliated and angered, his discussion of this topic caused the lining of his gut to become fiery red, pour out secretions, and become hypermotile. Under these circumstances, the slightest injury, ordinarily sustained with indifference, caused hemorrhage. He repeatedly bled from his bowel and, as an end-picture, exhibited ulcerative colitis, following the inappropriate use of a pattern design to meet the special circumstances of a poisonous substance on its surface. He was using this pattern to get rid of a situation which could never be got rid of in that particular way.

The nose affords an easy opportunity for examination because it is always available and the contents of the airways are clearly in view. When one sits before a subject, holding an irritant substance such as smelling salts, and allows these fumes to ascend into his nostrils, the mucous membranes get red, become swollen, secretion pours out, the airways become obstructed and narrowed; the diaphragm goes into cramp and breathing becomes impossible for a moment. The individual presents the pattern of shutting out, washing away, and neutralizing a dangerous environmental gas.

There came to us a woman who had had endless nose difficulties, for which she had undergone many operations. Although unhappily married, she never fully expressed her dissatisfaction. Nor did she fully assume her responsibilities as a wife and mother. When confronted by the suggestion that her nose troubles might have been related to her attitudes and to the situation in which she found herself, the mucous membranes of the airways acted just as though she had inhaled a noxious gas. They became red, swollen, wet, and obstructed the passage of air. She attempted to shut out, neutralize, and wash away a set of circumstances that could never be so dealt with— another inappropriate use of a pattern.

Coming back to the theme, "moments of discovery," and the order that they reveal, I offer you these patterns: patterns integrated not by any one part of the nervous system, or any one structure or endocrine organ, but representing overall reactions of an individual to threats.

Seldom do substituted patterns effectively work for one, except incidentally. Thus, weeping under humiliating circumstances does not right a wrong, yet the fulfillment of the weeping pattern often makes us feel more comfortable.

All loads, or threats, dangerous though they be, do not evoke the same responses. Why does one person behave in one way, and another behave in a different way? Why does one man use his stomach, another his bowel, another his heart, another his head?

Perhaps that is not a fair question to ask of Nature, any more than to ask why the retriever dog more readily retrieves than the Boston bull, or why the beaver builds dams, whereas the squirrel collects nuts.

Patterns run in stocks, and a man may come of a "stomach family," of a "head family," or a "heart family."

I repeat, situations have no universal significance and evoke quite different responses in different people, and even in the same individual at different times.

Some penetrating observations in this regard were made by the professor of medicine, Dr. J. Groen, at the University of Amsterdam, who, being a Jew, was able to care for certain Jewish merchants in Amsterdam before and after the German occupation. These prosperous, successful citizens had in common the disorder known as ulcers of the stomach. They weathered the days of starvation with the Dutch without either strikingly good or bad effects on their digestive function. Ultimately, they were put into concentration camps and indeed their lives were then gravely threatened. No one knew when he awakened in the morning whether he would survive that day.

They were separated and deprived in many ways; they were filled with hatred—often enough for their own groups of different nationalities: the Dutch hated the Polish, the Polish hated the French, etc. They fought and snarled and sneered and snatched. They maintained no standards; fought for no banner of human ethic; they merely attempted to survive the day.

Yet during that time those men lost all signs of ulceration of their stomachs. Here were people who were exposed to great trouble and yet they lost the bodily disorder engendered by civil life. Ironically enough, they regained it when after the war they returned to "Main Street" and pursued their civilian goals.

In brief, man's mucous membranes, participating as they do in his bodily reactions to man's impact on man, may exhibit engorgement, ischemia, hemorrhage, edema, erosion, modification in secretion, ulceration, altered reaction to chemical agents, modification of cellular components and inflammation, with lowering of the pain threshold. Such alterations may become the basis of further and, in some cases, irreversible tissue damage with the well known manifestations of "organic" disease.

To continue then with the consideration of the meaning of a situation, let me cite as evidence a group of missionaries in Korea, ostensibly successful in their work, but who suffered frightfully with headache. During their incarceration in Japanese prison camps, deprived and threatened as regards their very lives, this group lost their headaches entirely. When at the end of the war they were able in many instances to return to this country and resume parish work or teaching, headaches returned.

In other words, threats are perceived differently and individually, and depending on what they mean, they evoke one or another adaptive or protective response.

Many headaches result from the improper use of the muscles of the head and neck, muscles that would ordinarily be used in preparing for action which, in these persons, is not perpetrated. Headaches also result from the engorgement of blood vessels on the outside and in the inside of the head; often such headaches occur in individuals who look at life in special terms. The man with headache, wishing "to get something done," drives himself "against time," is persistent, meticulous, order-loving, insistent on promptness, impatient of defects in himself and others, pushes himself to limits beyond his capacity, ultimately depletes himself and then starts a painful chain of events. In a comparable way, the person with hives feels as though he were "taking a beating"; the individual with the peptic ulcer is angered at mistreatment or the deprivation of his needs; the individual with the ulcerated bowel feels as though he would like to get rid of a menace; the individual with the obstructed nose wishes to avoid "taking part." A man vomiting at the side of a dead child run over by him in his automobile, may say, if articulate, "Oh, if only it had never happened"—a reaction to the situation as if he could deal with it by ejection, an act of riddance. These patterns so useful in themselves, are inappropriately used in each instance.

These orderly arrangements represent adaptive patterns involving portals of exit and entry. However, there are patterns that involve the circulation and general mobilization equipment. So may be viewed the response of the man with high blood pressure who is meeting an emergency by being alert and ready for any danger, a bodily response which is never actually put into proper use. Such an individual is poised, collected, ostensibly calm, but in reality, is alerted in readiness for an action which is never carried out. His response illustrates again the prolonged, inappropriate use of adaptive devices designed for short-time service.

Again, the end of such inappropriate use is "organic" disease: the heart overworks, the blood vessels to important organs constrict, parts run short of nourishment, the blood becomes sticky and coagulates too readily, the head aches severely, the muscles of the back "cramp." Let me then epitomize what I have tried to impart: man is capable of reacting to threats as though to assaults; that in so doing he inappropriately uses, over long periods, patterns designed for short-term and phasic actions, and to no end that they can meet; in so doing, he damages himself and threatens survival.

Along with these bodily changes, complaints of discomfort, of pain and suffering are uttered. Feelings and behavior are altered concomitantly. He may be frankly anxious and exhibit it; he may turn his fears into meticulous actions of perfectionism and excessive orderliness and promptness. He may blame others for those things that have gone wrong with his life. He may withdraw into himself and imply, "I am superior to all this and nothing can do me harm"—a resolution that may end in disaster. And, most conspicuous in our time, and for whatever reason, are feelings of guilt.

What then does this perception of an order represent? For review I have picked out from an apparent chaos of fortuitous responses, sequences which are destructive, but fit into patterns full of meaning. They challenge us to see man in his inner character and his place in nature. Also, in increasing understanding, we are encouraged to seek a way out of such perverse use of our endowments.

The important aspect of these experiences is not whether they "have registered" in the "conscious" or the "unconscious," but what threatening significance a given event has to an individual. Often significant events and relationships of a threatening nature, because of their ubiquity and the distress they create, are "pushed out of awareness," and evidences of their effects may be found in the "unconscious" if the search be made. But it is to be emphasized that often they may be found in the conscious, too, and be as destructive.

Again, it is of less concern whether the conflicting elements from an experience, or the unpleasant feeling state be "conscious" or "unconscious," but more the degree to which the individual at the time perceives his danger and can operate in terms of the threat. True, much of experience falls out of memory or consciousness and therefore is seemingly lost to us, and lost to us especially from the point of view of willful operation and correction. Yet, despite this incomplete awareness, we often "muddle through" (perhaps painfully); sometimes when these matters are brought to the surface, we are able to come to grips with them more effectively.

The human environment has much to do with this, and the stability of society is relevant. A most dangerous feature of man's experience is rapid and violent change.

Nearly twenty-five centuries ago Hippocrates reminded his contemporaries of the risks of change when he said, "Those things which one has been accustomed to for a long time, although worse than things which one is not accustomed to, usually give less disturbance. . . ."

A striking and relevant observation was made upon Hopi Indians. The young Hopi Indian, American schooled, may be contrasted with his father. His father believed that when he trod upon the track of a snake he would experience sore ankles unless he took himself to the medicine man, who, having the know-how, would rid him of the risk of sore ankles. This he unquestioningly believed, and acting so, his sore ankles were prevented. In contrast, his American schooled son, treading upon the track of a snake, no longer believing in the powers of the medicine man, considering him a "fake," a "phony," a "humbug," nonetheless experiences sore ankles.

The implication is clear. In a rapidly changing society, the anxiety inducing factors (society decrees it is dangerous to step on the track of the snake because the snake may be nearby) are carried along in the traditions of a society and outlive the anxiety-resolving factors, namely, in this instance, the capacity of the medicine man to free the individual of the consequences of his transgressions.

We live in a rapidly changing society, in an environment where anxiety-inducing features outlast the devices for resolving them. Few institutions survive under these circumstances, and those that do are strained. Among the latter are marriage and the patient-physician relationship. We well know that the marital relationship is showing evidence of the strain. The patient-physician relationship is also pressed because the physician is reluctant, and often unable, to assume the responsibilities formerly spread over many institutions.

What is the evidence that these factors are relevant to disease? It is no accident that ulceration of the stomach, predominantly a woman's disease in the middle of the nineteenth century, occurring then about three to one in favor of women, has now become, in the middle of the twentieth century, with many changes in the man-woman relationship, a man's disease to the extent in some areas of 12–16 to 1.

It is no accident that tuberculosis mortality reaches its peak within ten to twenty years of the industrialization of a society and thereafter rapidly falls off. It is no accident that when populations are moved, troubles ensue. When an Irish Population emigrated to a new environment in American seacoast cities, despite the fact that people were better fed, had more opportunities, were titillated, and had more promise for the future, the mortality from tuberculosis among the Irish in New York City, for instance, was one hundred percent greater than it was at the same time in Dublin.

It is no accident that the American Indians, moved from the plains to reservations, geographically not very far distant, exhibited a great increase of tuberculosis; or that the Bantu natives, removed from the country outside of Johannesburg into the environs of the city, died of tuberculosis in great numbers. Some, knowing they were about to die, asked to be brought to their kraals. Many died; a few recovered, but tuberculosis was widely spread in the native villages. Interestingly, mortality from tuberculosis did not vastly increase with such spread, suggesting that the natives in their proper environment could deal with the infection.

It is no accident that the incidence of Graves' disease, or hyperthyroidism, in Norway, increased one hundred percent during the first year of World War II when that country was invaded.

I am not discouraged by this sad story because we begin to learn what price we pay for our goals; that disease is indeed related to our attitudes, our individual and group actions, our goals, and the conflicts they engender.

There are values far more important than the avoidance of discomfort, pain, illness; and occasionally even individual survival is not important. There is strength in this knowledge. We begin to know the price we pay for a way of life. We need to accept personal limitations and be willing to deal with the consequences of our acts. But a man should appreciate what his actions and goals are costing him. Then if he chooses, he may pay for them in pain and disease. Often he will decide that his values are poor, that he has been confused, and thereon changes his direction and pace.

All of these elementary facts we have relearned. These "moments of discovery" touched upon so lightly here have reemphasized what has long been known: that the impact of man on man may be as catastrophic as earthquakes, volcanic eruptions, and micro-organisms. On the other hand, it is also clear that much of the mischief, being man-made, can be undone by men who, speaking with the voice of authority, can encourage, teach, and assuage guilt.

8   PSYCHOSOCIAL FACTORS ASSOCIATED WITH RHEUMATOID ARTHRITIS

By Stanley H. King

For many years some physicians have felt that psychologic factors are associated with the onset or exacerbation of rheumatoid arthritis. Beginning in the early twenties there were reports[25, 37, 38, 42, 43, 46] that it was necessary to consider the effect of the psyche in certain bony pathologies, that loosened emotions incompletely expressed in action had an effect on the body, that emotional trauma, or the mental state, was associated with the onset of rheumatoid arthritis and that the psycho-physio-chemical reaction of the arthritic might be due to years of emotional conflict.

In recent years there has been an increase in studies concerned with the personality characteristics of arthritis, including emotional conflicts and psy-

From *Journal of Chronic Diseases*, 2, (September 1955), 287–302. Copyright 1955 by the C. V. Mosby Co., St. Louis, Mo.

chologic defenses, and with environmental stress factors which are other than of a physical or biologic nature. Although thorough studies of this kind are still few in number, it may be important at this point to evaluate our knowledge about psychologic and social factors in rheumatoid arthritis so that future research may be more carefully planned. That is the aim of this review.

Material from the studies reviewed here has been grouped according to the following topics: personality characteristics and conflicts, social background factors, precipitating factors, mechanisms, and rheumatoid arthritis and schizophrenia. An evaluation section follows each topic. Suggestions as to necessary factors in experimental design for future research in rheumatoid arthritis and fruitful directions that this research might take conclude the review.

Personality Factors in Rheumatoid Arthritis.

1. *Personality Traits.*—Certain traits have been noted by various investigators as occurring frequently in people with rheumatoid arthritis. These people are described as leading quiet lives, being "home birds,"[21] as complaining of shyness and social inadequacy,[10] and as having marked feelings of inadequacy and inferiority.[32] The majority of some samples[22, 26] were noted to be self-sacrificing, overconscientious, and having a strong need to serve others. Also, two investigators[21, 26] have commented on the presence of obsessive and compulsive characteristics. Finally, there is some question about a tendency to depression. This has been noted in arthritic children and their mothers,[7] and in one study of adults[50] a depression preceded the arthritis in 9 of 31 cases.

2. *Personality Problems and Conflicts.*—Among the personality problems reported to be present in arthritis, the most prominent is in the area of *aggression.* Both children[7] and adults[32] have been described as having a strong reservoir of hostility below consciousness, primitive in nature, with sadistic and destructive fantasies. However, the arthritic is tremendously fearful of his angers and resentments,[10] fearful that expression of these feelings will have drastic consequences for him. This may be the reason for his marked emotional self-restriction, especially in the inability to show anger overtly.[7, 21, 26, 32, 36] This is especially true in the face of frustration.

It is not surprising in view of this emotional limitation that there should be a *difficulty in forming close relationships with other people.* In one study[8] half of the 43 patients studied stated that they had difficulty in making friends. Other investigators[1, 32, 36] also noted this difficulty in developing satisfactory relationships with others. The arthritics were described as extremely sensitive and highly perceptive of other's feelings, especially if these were of a hostile or unfriendly nature, allowing themselves to be imposed upon rather than to risk offending and so losing the regard of others. This problem also appeared in arthritic children[7] in that they could not transfer feelings for parents to hospital personnel and could not balance off the frightening aspects of hospitalization with positive feelings of trust and support from hospital personnel.

This difficulty in forming relationships may be related to another problem which could be characterized as *difficulty in achieving separateness from certain key people in the environment.* The arthritic typically has a fear of separation, and, when it does occur, especially from a key figure on whom he depends, there is an inadequate expression of grief, as if to deny that the separation had taken place.[32] It is suggested that this difficulty begins in childhood with an extreme mother-child interdependence and a good deal of conflict in the child about trying to move apart from the mother.[7]

A final personality conflict appears to be in the area of *sexual identification and adjustment.* A number of investigators[1, 8, 26, 50] have reported that the sexual adjustment of their patients was unsatisfactory. In one of these studies,[26] this was spelled out in more detail as far as the female is concerned. The investigators affirmed that there was a rejection of the female role with classical examples of masculine protest reaction in all 29 cases. This resulted in hostile masculine identification. In a few cases the masculine protest reaction was intensified as a defense against fear of sexual attack. Another study[36] showed that in twelve male patients the sexual identification was masculine in only one case, all showing partial impotence. Of ten female patients there was clear-cut masculine identification in nine cases.

Another factor in the problem of sexual adjustment is that two studies[10, 31] have reported a high incidence of voyeuristic and exhibitionistic fantasies among arthritics. This is undoubtedly related to difficulties in sexual identification.

3. *Defensive Techniques.*—The literature indicates that a prominent feature among people who later develop rheumatoid arthritis is a great deal of *muscular activity in sports or hard work.* It has been noted[1, 32] that these patients were frequently inclined to be overactive and tended to overwork, to take jobs requiring hard work rather than initiative or responsibility. Female patients[26] had a tendency toward bodily activity, especially outdoor and competitive sports. This was true also in male patients,[36] where 10 of 12 studied engaged in hard labor or vigorous sports. In one study[10] rheumatoid arthritis patients were compared with low-back-pain patients. The former reported a significantly higher interest in hunting and fishing, and participation in sports. They also had a higher interest in household duties and cooking. Finally, it has been suggested[8] that physical activity gives some form of libidinous satisfaction to these people, except that their drive to be active is in excess of their capacity to find useful channels for the release of their energy. This interest and participation in muscular activity can be thought of as a form of sublimation, or a means of relieving tension, perhaps tension due to unexpressed aggression, with the individual more susceptible to arthritis when the sublimation is no longer available or effective. This is discussed more fully under "Mechanisms."

Another defensive technique is to *stay out of situations that might bring them into disagreement with other people.* This seems to be indicated in male patients[1, 8, 36] by an absence of competitive employment, little drive to accomplishment, and a lack of wholehearted interest in work. The literature does not indicate ways in which this defense might be exemplified in women.

4. *Evaluation of Personality Factors.*—The material reported in this section is largely descriptive. This is most important in the understanding and treatment of any disorder; but description is crucial only insofar as it enables the investigator or therapist to distinguish the disorder from other disorders.

Adequate description, therefore, depends on the presence of control studies or groups. In most of the studies mentioned in this section controls were singularly lacking. A good example of the difficulty thus imposed can be seen in the factor of excessive interest in sports and muscular activity. Only one study here[10] had a control group, and this group was composed of patients with low-back pain. Certainly it is possible that such patients might represent a deviant group in the direction of little interest in muscular activity, leaving the rheumatoid arthritis group more near the general norm. There is no information about the interest and participation of normals in muscular activity and sports against which to judge that of the arthritics. In fact, knowledge of cultural pressures would suggest that there is considerable emphasis on sports for all young people, especially young men. Furthermore, the studies to date have not provided any information about the *meaning* of muscular activity to these people.

Much of the material in this section presents a difficult measurement problem. The conclusions about the presence of intense hostile aggressive feelings below the level of consciousness depend on clinical insights, usually as the result of many psychotherapeutic sessions. Evidence may come from many different places and have to be painstakingly pieced together. However, if indeed this is a common characteristic of rheumatoid arthritis patients, there should be further evidence in the presence of similar patterns on projective tests, like the Rorschach and Thematic Apperception Test. This again necessitates the use of control groups and as yet no studies of this kind have been reported.

The question of sexual identification appears to be an important one, although it is not clear whether difficulties in sexual identification are peculiar to the rheumatoid arthritis patient or are characteristic of a larger group composed of all individuals who are susceptible to stress. It is unfortunate that an adequate device does not exist for measuring objectively the direction and degree of sexual identification, as well as the amount of conscious acceptance of one's sexual role. The lack of such an instrument makes it difficult to evaluate the data obtained by different investigators in this area.

Psychosocial Background Factors In Rheumatoid Arthritis. It has been reported[1, 21] that arthritic patients frequently perceived one or both of their *parents as rather strict and uncompromising in discipline.* More specifically, this has been related in other studies to the role that the mother exemplified. A report based primarily on female cases[26] stated that in the family background there was usually a strong, domineering, demanding mother, and a gentle, compliant father. A different study, based on male patients,[10] said that the mother was perceived as a hard-working, efficient, "Christian" woman, exemplifying self-sacrifice to the point of martyrdom, but also acting as the main disciplinarian, and a strict one at that. Father was seen as inconsistent in his behavior, being both weak and strong, and somewhat unpredictable, as in outbursts of feeling to situations where he usually showed minimal feeling.

A fairly consistent finding has been that the histories of rheumatoid arthritis patients show *the loss of a parent or important relative by some means;* death, separation, or psychologic absence through illness. This loss usually occurred in childhood, or at least by the time of adolesence, and was true for about 50 percent of the cases.[1, 8, 31] This factor was also noted in three other investigations[7, 10, 32] although the percentage of cases in which this occurred was not given.

Two other reports are pertinent in this area. First, it was observed[32] that mothers of rheumatoid arthritis patients seem to have provided an *inadequate feeling of security in early life.* This was manifested by a rejection of the child, either openly, or by an extreme degree of overprotectiveness and overanxiety. The result was a hampering of the child's development toward a free, independent existence, and the fostering of attitudes of dependence and helplessness. Second, in the study of arthritic children[7] it was noted that there frequently was a history of *severe emotional or physical deprivation early in life.*

Evaluation of Psychosocial Background Factors.—Although the data in this section have not been highlighted in the literature, they are particularly intriguing to this author in view of previous research in which he has participated.[15, 28] In this previous work normal subjects were studied in laboratory stress situations. It was found that subjects who perceived their mothers as stern disciplinarians and their fathers as rather ineffectual in this area showed a more emergency type of reaction (physiologically and emotionally) than did subjects who perceived father as occupying the strong authority role. The interpretation made was that the material reported in the rheumatoid arthritis studies represents a general condition in people who are susceptible to stress rather than something peculiar to people with rheumatoid arthritis.

Essentially the same result occurred with the loss of a parent by some means. Subjects who had gone through this experience showed a more emergency kind of reaction (physiologically and emotionally) than those who had not lost a parent. Again this may be a factor which in some way makes a person more susceptible to stress.

The last two points in this section, the inadequate feeling of security early in life, and severe emotional or physical deprivation, may well be of the same order as the above.

Clearly, the emphasis here must be of two kinds, accurate and objective measurement and information from a wide source of subjects. Funkenstein and King[15] have suggested a way of measuring the first factor, perception of parental roles in authority, affection, and identification. The second, loss of a parent or significant person, must depend on the subjective report of the subject or others. The third, adequacy of security feelings, still depends on the subjective judgment of the psychiatrist or psychologist and there is at present no other way of obtaining information here. The fourth, early emotional or physical deprivation, must depend on subjective reports of parents or close relatives. The importance of these factors for stress illnesses and particularly for rheumatoid arthritis, however, depends on future information as to the distribution of these factors in the general population.

Precipitating Factors. Emotional reactions to disturbing environmental events have been considered by a number of different people to bear some relationship to the onset or exacerbation of rheumatoid arthritis. *Worry over financial matters* has been suggested[9, 12, 42, 43] as occurring frequently in association with onset or exacerbation. Another factor is anxiety over sick relatives or *family worry.*[3, 9, 12, 14, 42] *Grief* has often been noted,[3, 12, 43] which is a part of the general problem of *loss or separation*.[32] *Unrelieved anger* is also suggested as an emotional reaction[26, 43] especially if there is an unconscious resentment against men which for some reason is increased.[26]

Perhaps it is pertinent at this point to mention that one author[16] contended that the degree of emotional stability and the satisfactoriness of one's philosophy of life is related to recovery and freedom from relapse of the disease.

There is, however, some disagreement in this area of precipitating factors. One investigator who has seen many arthritic patients[3] has stated that in his experience emotional crises have seldom been related temporally to the onset of rheumatoid arthritis. In studying 100 soldiers he found an emotional upset to be a possible factor in only one case.

Other negative evidence is from a study for the Empire Rheumatism Council.[30] Here there was a relatively large number of cases, using controls matched with the rheumatoid arthritis patients on the basis of age, sex, and marital status. Both patients and controls were given an extensive questionnaire in which information was obtained about recent traumatic events. This section of the report concludes:

"The analysis suggests that such mental stresses as may be engendered by the circumstances studied are likely to occur as frequently among non-sufferers as sufferers. From this it follows that any difference between the reaction of sufferers and non-sufferers to these stresses resides in some feature of the sufferer himself rather than in any difference of stress experience. Whatever case-studies or other detailed investigations may show, no evidence was obtained from the present enquiry that traumata or other events likely to be associated with mental stress were precipitating factors in rheumatoid arthritis."

Evaluation of Precipitating Factors.—Only two of the papers considered in this section have utilized controls, Cobb, Bauer, and Whiting[12] and Lewis-Faning,[30] and only one, Lewis-Faning, had a large sample. The former study had certain definite advantages in design in that it involved a recording of chronological events, both illness and environmental events, over an extended period of years. The latter study was limited to time of onset, asking the respondents about events in the three months prior to onset. However, each patient was matched with a control and each pair was questioned about events over the same time span. Lewis-Faning concluded that the patients did not report a significantly greater number of traumatic events than the controls, whereas Cobb indicated that the rheumatoid arthritis patients experienced more stressful events than the varicose ulcer patients, although he did note that this was more frequent in the older age group.

It is difficult to compare these two studies and to evaluate their somewhat different results because the methodology is so different. Certainly it is obvious that although Lewis-Faning noted that the arthritics did not report a greater number of traumatic events than the controls, this does not say that the traumatic events were not associated with onset. Furthermore the design that was utilized by Cobb enables a number of observations on the same patient over a period of years, with the possibility of patterns of stress-response relationships arising. These might not be seen if observation was confined merely to a period prior to onset.

A further point might be raised about the Lewis-Faning study. About two thirds of his control group were hospital cases, admitted for the repair of hernia, or burns, wounds, or fractures. It is thus possible that a sizable number of "accident-prone" individuals were included.

In the other study sited[3] as a source of negative information, the author ruled out the possibility of emotional factors entirely. However, he seems to have overlooked a most important fact. All of the patients used as the source of data for his paper were soldiers in wartime. It seems quite possible that many of these men may have been in conflict about being soldiers, especially as many of them probably came into the Army via the draft rather than as volunteers. Such a conflict might well have had serious physiologic repercussions.

The relationship of stressful environmental events to onset or exacerbation of arthritic symptoms is far from clear, especially as so few well-designed studies have been carried out on the problem. Only continuing, controlled studies can provide the answer.

Mechanisms. One of the most important aspects of the relationship of psychologic and social factors with rheumatoid arthritis is that of the mechanisms by which emotions or interpretation of environmental events are related to the physiologic changes of the disease. This is also the aspect about which we have the least amount of information. The material presented in this section is perhaps still so general that it does not really constitute a contribution toward an understanding of mechanisms. However, it represents a tendency in this direction.

1. *Muscle Tension.*—It has been noted[16] how the autonomic nervous system can affect the tone of plain muscles, and how derangement of bodily function can be brought about by the modification of postural tone and activity of the skeletal musculature. The implication here is that in some cases emotional factors can end in bodily derangement and rheumatoid arthritis symptoms. The view has also been expressed[26] that muscle spasms and increased muscle tonus, these being due to emotional conflict, could under certain conditions precipitate an arthritic attack. This has been stated in another way:[27]

"Many persons with or without clinically obvious arthritic deformities exteriorize habitually their psychic tensions through sustained regional or generalized hypertonia of somatic muscle, which may in turn give rise to musculoskeletal symptoms. These psychogenically induced symptoms can be exceedingly severe. Some patients obtain relief from symptoms when they can be taught not to exteriorize mental tensions through sustained hypertonia of somatic muscle, or when their mental tensions are lessened through directed psychotherapy or through changes in the environment."

There is only one study that has sought to measure the relationship between muscle tension and emotional conflict in rheumatoid arthritis patients.[18] The authors reported that the rheumatoid arthritis group reflected psychologic tensions and conflicts through variations in the tensions of the somatic muscular system. They also found that a hypertensive group reacted in the same manner.

2. *Symbolic Manifestation.*—It has been suggested by a number of authors that the symptoms of rheumatoid arthritis may in some manner be a

symbolic manifestation of conflict. For example, the localization of the disease seemed to one investigator to be in the joint or joints in which the conflict was focused.[8] The joint might thus play an important part in an activity that was disliked, or be essential to the assumption of an attitude which expressed in a symbolic way the patient's general demeanor (being "stiff-necked" in attitude toward things), or the joint may have been subjected to a physical trauma which had marked psychologic significance.

This has been discussed further[20, 23] in showing how a symptom may be attached to a part of the body through symbolism. For example, we think of a proud, upright person as an individual who stands straight, and an individual with a bent back may be saying, "My pride has been hurt, I can't stand up straight." The same author feels that there is a basis in folklore and etymology for the left side in the collective unconscious to be associated with ideas relating to disaster or misfortune. This may be a factor in patients with peripheral involvement of only the left side.

At this point it is pertinent to refer to two papers[2, 45] dealing with rheumatoid arthritis in soldiers during the last war. The first one describes a number of cases in an Army hospital in this country and notes that in the cases with peripheral joint complaints, 70 per cent had symptoms confined to the lower extremities, in contrast to the percentage encountered in civilian life. The second is concerned with soldiers in the Mediterranean area, where only 19 percent of the cases with peripheral complaints had symptoms confined to the lower extremities.

The author of the first paper, Boland, is not able to explain the high percentage unless, as he says, "the preponderant use of the lower extremities in soldiers serves as a factor." It is worth raising the question whether or not these men may have had an intense conflict about becoming soldiers. If this were true, the logical place for the symbolic focus of such a conflict would be in the lower extremities. Those soldiers who had a serious conflict about being in the Army, so serious that they were incapacitated because of it, would likely be weeded out before going overseas. For the men in the Mediterranean theater the main conflict might then be one around the meaning of overseas service, that is, getting killed or not. Such a conflict would not necessarily find expression in the lower extremities, but all over the body, as indeed 75 per cent of the cases showed both lower and upper extremity involvement.

3. *Symbolic Control.*—It has been suggested by some investigators that the arthritic symptoms represent a means of controlling or preventing the expression of hostile aggressive impulses, that if the joints are stiff and rigid, motion is limited, the anger will be encapsulated, and danger to others and the patient will be averted. This was expressed some years ago in the following statement:[25]

"Clinical experience has seemed to indicate to the authors of this book how the fundamental affective trends finding symbolic expression, at the psychological level, in terms of the unconscious criminal endeavoring to escape from the reality of his desires, have tied up the joints of various individuals in incapacitating arthritic involvements."

The conclusion has also been drawn from projective tests on arthritic patients that the outer rigidity of the body represents a way of inhibiting something bad within, the bad being unacceptable hostile aggressive feelings.[10]

Closely related to this are some data from a study of the emotional reactions of rheumatoid arthritis patients to ACTH.[36] The authors asked their patients whether or not they remembered their dreams and found that this was associated significantly with improvement or nonimprovement on ACTH. Of twelve patients who reported that before treatment they remembered their dreams, ten had a remission or major improvement. Of nine patients who reported that they did not remember their dreams, none had a remission or major improvement.

Many psychologists feel that remembrance or nonremembrance of dreams is related to leniency or severity of emotional control by the ego, especially of unconscious material. Certainly if this is true there is a continuum here, and patients who did not remember their dreams had relatively more repression than did patients who remembered them. They also had more intractable rheumatoid arthritis in that it did not yield to ACTH therapy.

4. *Evaluation of Mechanisms.*—It is obvious that there are some large gaps between activity of the skeletal musculature and the symptoms of rheumatoid arthritis. Furthermore, there is no evidence in the literature that people predisposed to arthritis are any different from other groups in terms of muscle tension. The only study that attempted some measurements in this area[18] found that the arthritics were no different from hypertensives in reflecting psychologic conflict by muscle tension. Clearly it would seem that this is one of the weakest areas of our present knowledge about rheumatoid arthritis. Until adequate measurements of muscle tension of rheumatoid arthritis and other groups are made, and until we understand the physiologic effects of sustained muscle tension, this aspect of the problem is questionable.

Symbolic manifestation is close to the area of conversion symptoms, and conversion symptoms as they have traditionally been defined do not produce the drastic physiologic changes seen in rheumatoid arthritis. However, a number of writers have felt that certain arthritics have features which are suggestive of conversion symptoms. If there is to be clarification in this matter, a needed first step will be a careful study of the site of symptoms and the relation of this to relevant psychodynamic factors. The literature to date is only suggestive that such a relationship may exist.

In talking about symbolic control we see the biggest gap between the psyche and the somatic symptom. There are many intermediate steps here that we cannot yet formulate or even find a logical basis for speculation about. However, the empirical evidence presented in the McLaughlin study[36] is arresting. Seldom in the field of psychosomatic medicine does one find such a strong relationship between psyche and soma as these investigators found between dream remembrance and reaction to ACTH therapy. Furthermore, if one assumes a relationship between remembering dreams and strictness-leniency of ego control, these data fit with the conclusions of other investigators. The typical rheumatoid arthritis patient is said to be an individual who controls his emotions tightly and does not form close emotional relationships with other people. It may be that in some cases there is a positive relationship between amount of emotional control and susceptibility to rheumatoid arthritis and, further, between strict control and severity of rheumatoid arthritis. Certainly the empirical evidence in this one study merits further investigation. One necessary step will be to enlarge and scale the questions about dream remembrance in terms of frequency, duration, and vividness, also to search for other methods of obtaining objective measures of ego control. The long and exhaustive techniques of the clinical psychologist or the extensive interviews of the psychiatrist do not lend themselves to studies in which a large number of cases is under consideration. These scaled questions will then need to be administered to subjects in which there is a careful medical history in terms of diagnosis, severity, and course of disease. Associations can then be sought between frequency, duration, and vividness of dreams and the type and course of the disease process.

Rheumatoid Arthritis and Schizophrenia. The relationship between rheumatoid arthritis and schizophrenia appears from the literature to be one in which there are certain similarities in personality. Also there is some evidence indicating that it is unusual for the two diseases to be present simultaneously in the same individual.

The similarity was noted twenty years ago,[38] the only difference being the outlet thrust upon the individual. As Nissen wrote:

"In one, dysfunction of the personality predominates; in the other dysfunction of the bone and joint furnishes an unrecognized alibi for withdrawal from active life, or a means, through capitalizing disability, of gaining attention which had been previously unobtainable."

In a study of equal groups of atropic and hypertrophic arthritics,[14] the premorbid personality was classified as being predominantly schizoid, syntonic, or mixed. Twice as many of the atrophic cases showed predominately schizoid features as did the hypertrophic cases, whereas this situation was reversed when the syntonic features were considered.

Rorschach studies on male arthritics[10] showed many of the pathologic features usually seen in the psychotic personality, including contamination and confabulatory responses, color naming, and extensive poor form level. Thirteen of the 25 cases studied were this seriously disturbed.

The unlikelihood of the simultaneous occurrence of the two disorders was noted in a study of a mental hospital[39] where there was not one arthritic among 2,000 patients. Also in 500 arthritic cases, there were only 3 cases of mental disease, and in these 3 gonorrhea had been responsible for the arthritis.

In a study of hospitalized psychotics in Massachusetts in 1938,[19] it was found that only 20 of 15,196 cases were partially or completely bedridden with arthritis. This was 17 times less than the rate in the non-psychotic population. In addition, the results of 3,000 autopsies of psychotics showed no frank arthritic joints.

Further evidence here comes from a case presentation of a woman with rheumatoid arthritis who became psychotic.[21] During the four years she spent in a mental hospital the rheumatoid arthritis was quiescent, but upon recovery from the psychosis the arthritis returned to the extent that she became completely crippled. A somewhat similar case[34] showed evidence of a psychotic break, followed later by an exacerbation of arthritic symptoms.

1. *Evaluation of Relationship of Arthritis and Schizophrenia.*—In the two main studies reported in this section, that by Nissen and Spencer[39] and that by Gregg,[19] there are certain serious difficulties. In the study by Nissen and Spencer there is the difficulty of accurate determination of arthritic symptoms in a large psychotic population. This depends partly on the acuity of the physician in recognizing true arthritic conditions and partly on the screening process used for finding the group of patients that have some sort of rheumatic complaints. If one depends on disabling conditions, it must be on the assumption that both psychotics and non-psychotics react in the same manner to bodily conditions. This is a dangerous assumption. Furthermore, Nissen and Spencer do not state the factors they would consider in making a diagnosis of rheumatoid arthritis in psychotics.

The study by Gregg is confusing in comparing bedridden and disabled patients and in not distinguishing between rheumatoid arthritis and other forms of arthritis or chronic rheumatism. In this case the question of diagnosis is even more acute than in the other study. Also it must be noted that there are few good studies of the distribution of rheumatoid arthritis in the general population.

Although many workers in this field think that rheumatoid arthritis and schizophrenia have much in common, the evidence thus far must be considered mainly suggestive. The suggestiveness is sufficiently strong, however, for undertaking further careful, objective research.

Discussion. The evidence from the literature indicates that we still do not have a clear picture of the role that psychologic and social factors play in predisposition, onset, or exacerbation in rheumatoid arthritis. It does indicate, however, that these factors have a role in some cases of rheumatoid arthritis and that the importance of this role varies from one individual to another. It is clear that psychologic and social factors can be considered as only part of a series of factors, all of which contribute in some measure to the disease. An accurate determination of the relative importance of each of the factors in this series for a given individual must wait until we have better objective measuring devices and mathematical techniques for weighing the results of these. In the meantime, well-designed studies can contribute much toward the assessment of the importance of emotions, conflicts, family and group pressures, and other psychosocial variables in arthritis.

1. *General Factors in Research Design.*—As pointed out in the evaluation sections, one of the crucial problems in new research is that of control groups. Studies to date in this area have shown a paucity of controls. The crucial question is whether or not people with psychosomatic disorders have many psychosocial factors in common, or whether there is a higher incidence of these in certain diseases. A casual survey of the psychosomatic literature highlights the commonality rather than the specificity. The use of control groups, normals as well as other disease groups, will help decide what factors contribute to a general susceptibility to stress and what to the predisposition to a specific disorder.

Another crucial aspect of future studies lies in the necessity of correlating the results of a careful medical examination with the occurrence and strength of various psychological data. It is important to group the rheumatoid arthritis cases according to type (peripheral, spondylitic, etc.), severity, duration, frequency of exacerbations and remissions, age of onset, etc. This necessitates the use of larger samples, which is expensive and time consuming, but it would seem that previous studies have been weak because of neglect here.

A third point has already received attention, that being the necessity of using objective measuring instruments wherever possible. This is possible in many of the areas discussed in this paper. The behavioral sciences now have at their disposal a variety of ready techniques or knowledge about the construction of techniques for this. In particular this is true for scaling techniques in attitudes and practices. It is possible to devise questions that, when added together, give information that do not reveal to the subject the investigator's purpose. It must be recognized, however, that some material, especially that pertaining to individual psychodynamics, cannot be handled in this manner. In these cases it is important to present as far as possible the evidence for conclusions drawn.

A fourth general point is relative to longitudinal studies. Ideally such a study might begin with a group of subjects who have not yet developed rheumatoid arthritis. Such a group might be chosen from people who report that they have morning stiffness. Cobb[11] has suggested, for example, that morning stiffness may exist in all rheumatoid arthritics before definite symptoms of the disease appear, but that all people with morning stiffness do not develop rheumatoid arthritis. Therefore, some of these subjects would be expected to develop rheumatoid arthritis, others not, and psychosocial data obtained during the premorbid state could then be considered for each group. The temporal relationship between environmental events and the course of the disease would then come under scrutiny, especially as some of the subjects would not develop rheumatoid arthritis. Though there are difficulties of personnel commitment and financing, there is much merit in a research design which includes this feature.

2. *Specific Areas of Fruitful Study Based on Previous Work.*—A number of specific topics would seem to hold promise for advancing our knowledge about rheumatoid arthritis. First, there is the variable of the importance of losses or separations in the lives of arthritics, beginning in early childhood. Which parent was lost? What happened in the family when the mother was lost? What were the reasons for losing father? Were there any common factors in terms of type of death or loss? What kinds of loss were there besides death? In later life it would be fruitful to ask what kinds of situations are felt to be losses or separations and, thus, perhaps, activators of a basic separation anxiety.

Second, is the factor of activity patterns. This involves a determination of pressures toward activity in different subcultural groups, types and amount of activity patterns in these groups. With this background, the relative degree of activity, holding class or subcultural factors constant, in arthritics and nonarthritics can be determined. Inasmuch as heightened bodily activity "makes sense" in terms of a psychologic defense against strong aggressive drives, it is important to answer this question for rheumatoid arthritis.

Third, is the question of remembrance or nonremembrance of dreams. As suggested previously, this may have some relevance for the amount of ego control. The frequency, duration, and vividness of recall need to be studied and scaled and information obtained from other disease groups as well as from subjects free from disease.

Fourth, is the variable of direction and acceptance of sexual identification. Evidence from the literature is sufficiently strong here to hypothesize that sexual identification will be reversed. There is no evidence about the acceptance or rejection of such identification. Important here will be the presentation of material that forms the basis of the investigator's judgment as to sexual identification.

Fifth, is the problem of the perception of parental roles in authority. Again there seems sufficient evidence in the literature to hypothesize that the mother will be perceived as dominant here. In addition, it is important to obtain information about the perception of parental roles in affection and identification. Considering three factors here makes possible a number of combinations, thus providing more specific information than could be obtained from asking about authority alone. Also it is important, wherever possible, to get some judgment by the investigator, and the parents themselves, as to the manner in which they fulfill these roles, or think they fulfill them.

Finally, the symbolization of symptoms merits further attention. Supporting evidence here is not so strong and unfortunately we do not yet have the tools for a conclusive experiment in this area. Furthermore, this may be a factor in only a small number of cases. However, this factor should be considered wherever possible in a research design.

3. *New Areas of Study.*—Certain aspects of the concept of self may prove to be fruitful in new research. A consideration of the personality characteristics and problems of the arthritic indicates that the way he sees himself in relation to the rest of the world may be important to his disease. Two aspects of the concept of self would seem to be important. First there is the way he sees his body in fantasy, or his body image. If there is truth to the assertion that arthritic symptoms represent a control of disturbing aggressive impulses, one would expect the body image of these people to be different from non-arthritics. In fact, this would seem to be one way to test the hypothesis of symbolization. Second, there is the way the individual sees himself in terms of personality characteristics. The study by Funkenstein and King, mentioned earlier, indicated an association between ability or inability to master continued acute stress and this aspect of self concept. Subjects who showed a discrepancy between self rating and the way they thought others would rate them on a series of traits did not handle continued acute stress as well as subjects where there was little or no discrepancy. This relationship was strong enough to indicate its possible importance in studying stress diseases.

Second, social scientists now posit that social mobility factors are important sources of threats to and tensions within the individual. This is especially true if this mobility is not encouraged by the individual's family, or if it precipitates conflicts over values. Important variables here are the distance the individual moves in the class scale, the changes he makes in class identification through marriage, organizations, attitudes, etc., and the support from wife and other class members for his new values. Also of great importance are class pressures toward the control of emotional expression and legitimate avenues for such expression, especially if these are at variance with outlets in his previous class position.

Finally, there are indications that religiosity bears a relationship to susceptibility to stress. Swaim[49] made a frank appeal for the use of spiritual exercises as an adjunct to medical treatment in this disease, believing this would have a beneficial effect on the underlying anxiety and resentment. Funkenstein and King (see Chapter 10 herein) found a significant relationship between religious practice and cardiovascular reaction during laboratory stress, in that those who indicated frequent religious practice had a more homeostatic pattern, while those who indicated weak or infrequent religious practice had an emergency type of pattern. Though this area has tended in general to be ignored in psychologic and medical research, it may well prove to be a fruitful area.

Summary. The literature on psychologic and social factors associated with rheumatoid arthritis has been reviewed according to personality characteristics and conflicts, social background factors, precipitating factors, mechanisms, and the relationship between rheumatoid arthritis and schizophrenia.

After an evaluation of this material, it is suggested that general factors in research design include control groups, careful medical history and examination, objective measuring devices in the psychologic and social area, and longitudinal studies wherever possible. It is suggested that fruitful areas for further research are the importance of losses and separations in childhood, activity patterns, remembrance of dreams, direction and acceptance of sexual identification, parental roles in authority, and symbolization of symptoms.

Finally, it is suggested that new areas of study might include certain aspects of the concept of self, social mobility factors, and religious practices and expressions.

9   SOCIAL STRESSES AND RESOURCES AMONG

MIDDLE MANAGEMENT MEN

By John and Ruth Useem

I. SETTING OF THE STUDY

Over the past decade a new literature has emerged on the problems of the individual in American society that stem from recent changes in the patterns of social behavior and in the organizational arrangements of group life. Con-

Supported by a grant from the National Institute of Mental Health, United States Public Health Service, administered by the Social Research Service of the Department of Sociology and Anthropology of Michigan State University. We are indebted to a number of persons who at one time or another participated on the project. Particularly we wish to mention Duane L. Gibson who was co-chairman of the project and who was largely responsible for the development of the scales. For the analysis and interpretation of the materials, the present authors assume full responsibility.

tributions have come from a number of quarters, including social science research publications, popular novels, and broad, sociologically-oriented essays.

Although this literature varies in approach, form and scope, it shares at least three distinctive features. First, much of it focuses on that segment of American society which falls roughly in the middle and upper-middle classes, particularly on those who aspire to upward mobility and have a fair probability of achieving their life goals. Present emphasis differs, in this respect, from a primary concern of two decades ago with persons in the lower social ranks, persons who faced bleak prospects of attaining their minimal needs and who at best were surviving on precarious margins. It also is a departure from the emphasis of the previous decade on the adjustments of men to the exigencies of military life.

Second, the accounts concentrate on the world of work of American males. More specifically, the managerial hierarchies are depicted as gigantic collectivities swallowing up the individual, demanding conformance to narrow grooves, constricting freedom of choice, muting individuality and emphasizing interpersonal adjustment.

Third, the literature is concerned with the dysfunctional consequences of the world of work for the individuals who compose it. The men are seen as experiencing tensions, stresses and anxieties precipitated by the present occupational style of life. Whereas the common worker may be deemed a transparent victim of depersonalization due to mass production and automation, the executive is presented as one who by the very process of adjusting to his immediate world has become vulnerable to personality distortion.

In this article we shall report on some of the results of an empirical investigation of selective aspects of the three features noted above. More particularly, the study explores the social and cultural resources available to and used by men in middle management positions in meeting and preventing stress.[1]

II. RESEARCH DESIGN AND THEORETICAL ORIENTATION

Early in our study we selected as primary variables the social and cultural aspects of interpersonal behavior and excluded purely intrapersonal variables unique to the individual. The core disciplines represented are sociology and anthropology, which is another way of saying that we had greater interest in what a group of persons of comparable social status have in common with respect to their social selves than in the unique total personality of each individual. Preliminary work in the area of our main concern disclosed sufficient complexity to untangle without undertaking the even more ambitious task of working in the interstitial zones of human behavior where the disciplines of sociology and anthropology need the help of clinical psychology, psychiatry and medicine. This decision does limit the generalizations which we can make and of necessity leaves unanswered certain relevant questions.

For the purposes of this paper, we are confining ourselves to a report of the social stresses and resources connected therewith found in the world of work and excluding those related to the family and other institutions.

From our reconnaissance interviews we soon found that what was a stressful circumstance to one was not stressful to another and further that determining the overall amount of stress experienced by the individual gave us fewer leads than delineating the critical areas of social life in which the person was having difficulties. After considerable analysis of the trial interviews, we concluded that social stress could be most effectively approached by determining not the individual's degree of total stress but rather the degree of stress experienced in particular areas of behavior highly valued by the individual.

From the trial interviews we empirically derived twenty-five aspects of men's occupational roles in which the men had some interest. Of these, eleven were studied in detail. The titles and a short description of the eleven are: "Self-Fulfillment"—a job which makes real use of your initiative, skills and abilities; "Occupational Mobility"—a job from which it is possible to advance and move ahead; "Time for Family"—a job which leaves sufficient time and energy to devote to your family; "Limitation of Job Demands"—a job which has a relatively fixed time schedule and does not make excessive demands on your time; "Self Direction"—a job in which you are free to make most decisions connected with your work; "Job Prestige"—a job that is respected and considered important by other people; "Support from Others: Understanding"—a job in which there are friendly and understanding people who are sympathetic to the problems of your job; "Social Value of the Job" —a job which is recognized by others as valuable to society or beneficial to humanity; "Task Closure"—a job in which tasks can be satisfactorily completed and in which there are a minimum of interferences and overlapping tasks; "Freedom for Affective Expression"—a job on which you can freely express your thoughts and feelings to those whom you contact; "Support from Others: Help"—a job in which there are persons upon whom you can rely for assistance and advice when you are in need of them.

In each of these and other areas, the amount of stress experienced by an individual varies both with the degree of his interest in the area and with the degree to which there are factors perceived as interfering with obtaining the goal. These two variables were labeled "involvement" and "blockage." Guttman-type scales were developed for measuring the degree of involvement and degree of blockage for each of the eleven areas.[2]

To illustrate the point somewhat more concretely, let us take the job aspect of "occupational mobility." A man can vary from low to high in his involvement in this area; likewise, he can perceive from none to a great amount of blockage. Social stress, then, is a function of these two combined. Thus, a man experiences high stress if he is intensely desirous of getting ahead (high involvement) but he sees his organizational environment as affording him little opportunity for upward mobility (high blockage). The man has low stress if he wants to advance and he sees his environment as allowing fulfillment of this aim (a combination of high involvement-low blockage). Furthermore, if he is relatively uninterested in advancement, he is not upset whether he assesses the environment as permitting or not permitting his improving his occupational status (i.e., a combination of either low involvement-low blockage or low involvement-high blockage). Between these extremes, are degrees of stress.

We found no practical means for scaling social resources and instead developed an open-ended questionnaire to trace this dimension as well as other stresses not encompassed in the scales.

To give perspective to our study, the "involvement-blockage scales" were administered to approximately one thousand administrators selected in a random manner from a number of different bureaucratic organizations.

To maximize our chances of securing and delineating the meaning of relevant social facts, we decided to interview in depth a small sample. For the latter interviews, three kinds of social structures were selected: an automotive industry, an insurance company and a combined state-community educational system. They were similar in that each had a sizable aggregate of administrators engaged in middle management activities but differed somewhat with respect to their organizational environments. All three were in a period of expansive growth.

Within each of these three organizations a random sample of twenty-five men (a total of seventy-five) was chosen from lists compiled according to several criteria: the men had to fall between twenty-five and fifty years of age, occupy positions of authority with at least two echelons of superiors above them and as many ranks of subordinates below them, and to have been employed for a minimum of a year in the organization. In addition, the men were checked for their general reputation in their organization in order to assure the inclusion of persons known to be reasonably effective and normally adjusted in their work roles.

The contact with each informant was subdivided into an initial session during which he filled out the twelve "involvement-blockage scales" and a subsequent meeting lasting approximately three hours during which he responded to a series of open-ended questions. The latter interview was tape-recorded and typed off verbatim.

III. THE RESULTS

We summarize the findings of our study relative to the world of work under three main topics: incidence of social stress as measured by the scales; the high involvements and high blockages of middle management men derived from the depth interviews; social and cultural resources.

A. Incidence of Social Stress. In the absence of any absolute measure of stress, we have relied on a relative one by comparing the scale results of the sample of seventy-five men (who had the reputation of being reasonably "successful" in their occupational roles) with the norms derived from the larger group of administrators picked at random. A massive amount of quantitative data can be telescoped into a few generalizations which have special pertinence for this report. Conventional statistical tests of significance were used but are omitted here for reasons of economy.

(1) In comparison with the larger group, an appreciably lower proportion of the sample of seventy-five are in the "stress" category of eleven of the twelve job aspects—that is, they were experiencing both high involvement and high blockage. The one exception was in the aspect, "Time for Family"

in which they did not differ significantly from the larger group. To give some concrete instances: only four percent of the sample group *both* were highly involved in upward mobility *and* perceived serious blockage to this goal in contrast to one-fourth of the larger group; less than seven percent felt both highly desirous of making decisions on their jobs and seriously blocked in so doing, again in contrast to roughly a fourth of the larger group.

A lower incidence of stress in various job aspects might be interpreted as the "expected" for men who have earned a reputation of being successful—but if so, it runs counter to the literature which depicts the more successful as experiencing the greater stress.

(2) The seventy-five men have high involvements in aspects of their work for which they perceive least blockage. Again to cite an instance, sixty-five percent of the sample *both* want intensely to use their initiative, skills and abilities in their work *and* assess their environments as facilitating these ends (low blockage) in contrast to one-fourth of the larger group.

(3) On the other hand, in comparison with the larger group, the smaller sample has proportionately more who are low-involved in those aspects of their working role which they apprize as being difficult to realize in their work world. For example, eighty percent of the "successful" group view their jobs as making great demands on their time and energy and at the same time are uninterested in a job which would make fewer demands on them. Less than a third of the larger sample fell in this category.

(4) Comparing the results of the men from each of the three organizations with each other, it is evident that there is not a homogeneous subculture of administration but rather variations among organizations. For instance, men in the educational field are both highly involved in wanting a work role which is recognized as being valuable to society and beneficial to humanity and feel their organizational environment enables them to achieve this goal. Men in the automotive and insurance fields, on the other hand, see their jobs as giving them little opportunity to contribute to humanity but they are not highly involved in wanting to make such a contribution.

(5) Upon comparing the scale results of the seventy-five men with each other, it was clear that even a single organizational environment does not impinge equally on all of its members; for, within the three structures, the men do not have identical assessments of the situational environment within which they work. Depending upon the position of the person and the part of the substructure to which he is exposed, the social situation is appraised differently (i.e., they have differing perceptions of degree of blockage).

To put the scale results in a slightly different way: inherent in bureaucratic structures are many conditions which have the potentiality of precipitating stress in middle management man and any one of these conditions does, in fact, distress some individuals who perceive the condition as a blockage to a highly desired goal. However, if our findings are sound, then we may conclude that a composite portrait of "a middle management *man*" into which is incorporated all the stresses which middle management *men* collectively experience and which, thereby, creates the impression that middle-range executives are entrapped in anxiety-producing situations, is a distortion of the true incidence and distribution of stress.

In giving some perspective on the incidence of stress, our purpose has not been to lead the reader into thinking that the bureaucratic world is without its situations which can precipitate stress in individuals; nor has our aim been to belittle or dismiss as unimportant the problems faced by middle-ranking administrators. Rather our intent has been to refocus attention on our original question—how do these men function reasonably effectively and maintain their self-identity despite the numerous instabilities, pressures, and conflicts with which they presumably are faced? Material for the following sections has been drawn from our depth interviews.

B. Areas of High Involvement and Conditions Which Constitute High Blockage in the Work World. Every culture poses for its members a distinctive set of personal problems related to its own unique style of life and social imperatives. A subculture, also, has its characteristic problems for the individual which are endemic to its specialized style of life and sub-cultural norms. Each subculture (e.g., academic people, housewives, middle-management men) will have certain distinctive problems although all may share some common problems growing out of the fact that they share certain larger cultural norms. In the following we are trying to identify the problems only of middle-management men growing out of their subculture.

Since social stress is a function of both personal involvement and perceived social blockage, perhaps an instructive way of relating our findings on this issue is to first summarize the high involvements which are characteristic of the sample men and delineate the conditions which the men themselves say induce worry, tensions and frustrations. Some of these "high blockage" conditions the men have experienced in their own past or present, of others they are cognizant through observations of their fellow men, and still others they anticipate because of their knowledge of themselves and their social environment.

1. *A work role which is a challenge.* Ranked first in importance to these men is a work role which offers them a "challenge," a chance to use their own skills, initiative and abilities. The men make a distinction between that which is their "job"—the formal description of prescribed duties, and that which they actually "do"—or what we have called the "work role." The men are stressed if they have few or no opportunities to innovate and propose new ideas, no scope for expanding the areas of their work in which they feel their talents are outstanding and no possibility of minimizing those areas in which they have no particular interest or skills. A "no challenge" job is one which has ready-made solutions for all the problems which the men are asked to solve; it matters little whether the available answers are given by the social organization in the form of detailed rules and regulations or whether the solution are the precipitates of the men's own actions. Thus a once challenging work role ceases to be so if the man has worked out answers covering all the contingencies likely to arise and is circumscribed in finding new challenges. Some satisfaction is felt in the competent performance of the basic duties of their jobs but greater involvement lies in the "self-made" aspects of the work role and situations which allow no latitude in this area are considered stress-producing.

It should be mentioned that the crucial point is not the amount of time which is spent in these "challenging" activities, since quantitatively the satisfied man may spend the vast majority of his day in the details and routine of his job, but rather that there is some opportunity for a creative approach to his work role.

2. *A work role which has a future.* Another high involvement for these men is the desire for continuous growth. They want to feel that they are "getting ahead" or "getting someplace." The significant expression, "there's no future in it," is used to cover a set of work conditions they find upsetting. A "no future" job is one that does not allow him to learn, to develop new skills and abilities which can eventually be recognized by assumption of a more important position or by upgrading in importance his present position. Particularly stressful is to be told that he has proved himself so indispensible in his present office that he will be kept there indefinitely instead of being advanced to a more important one.

Special note should be taken of what the "future" signifies. The future, as a frame of reference, is not a specified long-term goal (e.g., vice-president of the company, making a certain income, or retirement at a given age) nor is it even a set number of years; rather the future is the "next step" or the next two steps and this future is seen as having ties into the present work role. The man feels stressed if he can see no relationship between his present activities and the next step or two steps.

3. *Support from others.* As many students of administration have noted, the locus of authority in American organizations is simultaneously centralized and diffused and the formal charts do not adequately designate the actual distribution of control. Our follow up on this lead took us into the way the men play their roles within the intricate matrices of the structure. We soon found that the men function in a continuing state of interdependency as a result of the constellation of persons with whom they share authority. Besides their immediate superior, most had direct contacts with others in levels higher than their own, some with widely scattered publics and other organizations outside their own bureaucratic structure, and all with associates in various substructures of their organization. Moreover, the higher their status, the more the men were dependent on their subordinates for the achievement of their ends. Many decisions, therefore, are made within a network which combines both formal lines of authority and informal relationships between the men.

For these reasons, a high involvement for these men is having the support and understanding of others where mutual action is necessary. Tension beyond the normal level is engendered in the individual when he cannot count on others for the backing and cooperation necessary for the successful accomplishment of his own work role.

More specifically, the men mention the following actions of their immediate superiors as upsetting to them: the superior's not backing up his own subordinate when interacting with outsiders; offering but vague guidance so that the assigned responsibility is unclear; giving complete minute directions on how every action is to be done so that there is no subdelegation of responsibility; subdelegating authority for decision making but snatching it back without warning; failing to communicate changes in higher echelon policies and in the superior's own decisions which are relevant to the man's responsibilities; having no understanding of the content of the man's job and hence being unable to evaluate what comprises real achievement or even what is required to accomplish the work; being inaccessible when crucial decisions demanding the superior's action have to be made; or, if accessible, not permitting the man to express his opinions fully and to have a full hearing on the reasons for his proposals.

The behavior of subordinates which the men find particularly vexing are: unresponsiveness to guidance; reluctance to assume responsibility for the full range of their duties; carrying out their duties to the letter but with little imagination; learning their jobs slowly and seldom under self direction; acting in a manner that precipitates doubts in the minds of middle management men as to the loyalty and integrity of their subordinates; engaging in interpersonal feuds among themselves which require intervention by middle-ranking executives to settle; lacking discrimination in communication upwards—either telling all or keeping everything bottled up inside themselves; needing open reprimands in order to be properly motivated. In relationship with his subordinates, the most distasteful job which a man has to perform is the actual firing of a subordinate for incompetence.

Associates usually cannot stimulate as much tension in the man but they can contribute. Colleagues who cannot be approached in good faith because of their tendencies to be tricky, argumentative over small points, inarticulate in exchanging opinions on decisions, inflexible and unwilling to compromise, and personally so uncongenial that every contact is an ordeal—all can cause stress in middle management men. Especially difficult are colleagues who make decisions which reverberate into a man's area of responsibility without clearing these decisions before they are finalized.

4. *Personal recognition and respect.* Underlying all of the above is a high involvement in developing and maintaining a self-image which is recognized by significant others in their environment. The men want to think of themselves and have others view them as individuals who have sound judgments, foresight, and ability to get out of difficult situations; as men who because of their skills and capabilities can make a contribution; as persons whose sincerity, integrity and loyalty enables them to get along with others.

The form of recognition most prized is being given increased responsibility and authority. Official position or rank is one way in which the organization may reward the man but it is highly valued only if accompanied by more important duties. Financial remuneration, also, is important but the actual amount is of less significance than is its being a tangible expression of the organization's recognition of the man's worth. Thus, automatic increments and "across the board" raises are less prized than are individual merit or "jump" raises; and the amount is appraised within a restricted system of comparison with significant others rather than within the larger economic system.

There are also a number of non-income perquisites which are forms of recognition—having a company car, having one's own secretary, being able to determine the time for taking a coffee break, being recommended by the organization as its representative to civic endeavors, etc. Often these latter items are in and of themselves not wanted (e.g., the man who finds he can't keep his weight down if he eats in the restricted "executives dining room" or the man who doesn't want to help with the local community chest drive) but their symbolic meaning as "yardsticks" by which he can measure his worth are important. Compliments which are received third-hand are more highly valued than are effusive direct compliments.

"No recognition" or high blockage situations which threaten a man and may precipitate stress in this area of high involvement are: having a major assignment withdrawn at a time when it becomes an object of great attention in the organization; being left out of group discussions and decisions on matters relevant to his work; having his authority and responsibilities redistributed to peers or others with no satisfactory explanations forthcoming; having others refrain from asking his opinion or not taking his views seriously; "getting the word" only through formal channels and not through informal "grapevines"; hearing rumors that his superior or colleagues no longer trust his competence, or even worse, being so isolated from the informal structure that he hears nothing at all; and, of course, the worst ultimate possibility, being (in the men's own words) " put on ice"—that is, not being fired outright but, although still on the payroll, having all responsibility and authority withdrawn until the man finds it so intolerable that he either resigns or laboriously and painfully builds a new set of relationships in the organization.

Social Resources. Just as social stress is the outcome of men's behavior within social patterns, so, too, social resources are related both to the individual and his environment. Unlike stress, social resources, particularly those which maintain conditions of non-stress, are not always consciously perceived or are recognized as resources only if they no longer obtain. The fact that the men are not always aware of their resources need not deter us from analyzing them as such.

Social resources might be defined simply as those factors which alleviate stress or prevent the rise of stress. Put in terms of our framework, social resources are those factors which serve to alleviate conditions of experienced stress (i.e., high involvement-high blockage): (a) by reducing involvement although blockage remains the same (changing a condition of high involvement-high blockage to one of low involvement-high blockage); (b) by reducing blockage although involvement remains high (high involvement-high blockage to high involvement-low blockage); or (c) by reducing to some extent both blockage and involvement.

Social resources are also those factors which serve to prevent the rise of stress (i.e., a potential high involvement-high blockage situation): (a) by preventing high involvement from occupying in an area in which there is high blockage; (b) by preventing high blockage from occurring in an area in which there is high involvement; or (c) by preventing to some extent both high blockage and high involvement from occurring.

From the point of view of the individual, resources might be classified according to the degree to which the individual feels that he has control over them. Thus some resources the person may consider as being at his disposal for the alleviation or prevention of stress, others he may view as being only partially subject to his control, while still others he may consider as being outside his control entirely.

In looking at the following social resources, we shall use the above schema implicitly but not follow them point by point.

1. *Interiorization of involvements and perceptions of blockages—the work-role self.* Students of personality and culture have long pointed out that the self is developed in social interaction. Considerable research has shown that an individual's conception of himself is in keeping with the emphases of the particular culture in which he is socialized; and, although there are unique elements in each individual's self growth, certain generalized patterns are discernible which mark off the type of self which emerges within one milieu as against that which is produced in another. The men we studied have a number of selves growing out of the various subcultures of which they are a part. The two most important ones which came out of our interview material are the "family self" and the "work-role self." For the purposes of this paper we shall analyze only the latter, making but passing references to the former where it is of importance for understanding the work-role self.

The subculture of middle management socializes a man to fulfill the expectancies of his role; or, to put it another way, he develops a work-role self congruent with his status. The rather unique aspect of the work-role self is not that its process of development differs significantly from the way other self conceptions emerge but rather that the period in which it evolves is somewhat unusual.

In modern urban civilization, there is relatively little carryover of the forms of social behavior learned in childhood and adolescence to adult behavior in the bureaucratic world of work. Most of the men of our sample were reared in families in which no member had a position comparable to their present one and those few whose fathers had similar statuses claimed they had little understanding of the intricacies of their father's role, seeing only the impact of it on the family. Very few had even heard in school about the existence of their current roles; those who are now school superintendents say they knew such a position existed but for the most part it was outside the periphery of their interests while they were in high school. Few of the men in our sample even started out in their work life to be what they have become; they had goals such as engineers, architects, teachers, lawyers, football coaches, accountants, and technical specialists of various sorts—very few were interested in becoming an administrator in a bureaucratic organization. Parental and educational influences can be traced in some of the general values instilled (such as improving one's position in life, making a contribution to society, being honest and reliable) but the ways for realizing these values remained unshaped until they entered their adult work roles; and the values themselves have been reinterpreted and rescaled in importance and new values interiorized.

The crucial things we learned about the work-role self are that it is no less "real" and no less important than other selves even though the etiology is relatively late in the individual's life history; that stress experienced in areas of high involvement is no less intense because the high involvement is recent; that size of problems is a matter of perspective and is not diminished because the perspective is relatively new.

The involvements and aspirations of the men in their work role and also those conditions which can precipitate stress can be predicted better from knowledge of the subcultural milieu within which they work than they can from background factors. In those areas in which the men of the three organizational structures differ in their involvements and their blockages, the variations can be traced to considerable degree to organizational environmental differences. Thus social class background, parental family influences, occupation of father, relationship with siblings, educational exposures, armed forces experiences have less predictive value in determining involvements and blockages in the world of work than has the work world itself. This is not to say that the background factors have no importance but rather it is to say that a man's work-role self is not completely established prior to a man's role but is developed coevally with it.

The socialization process of the men to their current positions began after they entered the working world but in advance of occupying the particular statuses they now hold. They had passed through the culture shock of discovering conflicts between the stated ideals of their occupation and its actual practices and had learned to live with the "politics" of organized group life. They had learned the fine art of the organized man for getting along with others with whom they shared authority and had developed talents for determining the location of power, including their own, within a structure. They no longer were amateurs in the committee system of decision making or in the strategies for making innovations that get group support, and they had interiorized subcultural norms for evaluating criticisms and complaints.

Our life histories show that much of the learning in advance of occupying a particular position takes place through informal observation of the acts of significant others—often an individual of higher rank but close enough to study first hand; and, just as important, in fulfilling their present role they are already anticipating their next step. "I watch my immediate superior operate in a meeting and I see that he is effective and I want to see why; if he is ineffective, I want to understand that. I see a colleague handle a problem and I hope to learn and improve by it." As the man takes in his own mind the role he hopes some day to assume, he internalizes new attitudes and values. The anticipatory learning centers not on a specific "job" but on the behavior and style of life connected with the work role; furthermore, the men are highly selective; they note those personal characteristics of others which they wish to emulate and those which they wish to eschew, they observe successful techniques which they want to copy and unsuccessful techniques which they want to avoid.

The socialization of the men within the middle and upper ranks of the hierarchy is organized primarily around self-directed and continuous learning. The organizations take for granted that any competent member of the ingroup has both the potentialities for self growth and the motivation to develop himself. The amount of formal indoctrination is confined to a brief review of the formal organization and official procedures. The informal structures within which much of his work revolves—the personal alignments of individuals in key positions, the ways and circumstances under which rules can be bypassed, how decisions are actually made—he must learn on his own initiative without upsetting the mores. A man who moves up the social ladder learns that he has to exert greater self control over the expression of his opinions and feelings for all his acts have wider ramifications and he is more dependent on others for the accomplishment of his work. The person who has been preoccupied with his technical performance or norms of his professional field pays increasing attention to his social performance and his orientation is enlarged from the concerns of a substructure to the interests of the wider structures of the organization.

The man's conception of himself changes as the socialization process continues. He gains confidence in his ability to evaluate issues and relies more on intuitive judgments in decision making. He not only finds the means for establishing an acceptable social identity within the group, he incorporates them into his own self. During the early stages of this learning, the men report that they are especially sensitive and mindful of their changes in social character, outlook and behavior. But once well established in their roles, they tend to become less self conscious of their learning even though continuous growth is a central part of their daily lives.

The subculture not only socializes the man; it has also socialized others who are significant to him. The higher he moves in the bureaucratic world the more he interacts with others who are "predictable" and hence rather than becoming increasingly stressed, he finds fewer blockages in the attainment of his central goals and interests—goals and interests which themselves have been derived from the subcultural milieu. Subordinates, particularly women, who are not as socialized to the expectations of the bureaucratic world continue to be problems to him. However, the middle management man finds especially rewarding opportunities for contributing to the socialization of younger persons, for being instrumental in furthering the careers of his subordinates, for helping others coming along to have the chance to grow, learn and become successful in their own right and not as appendages of himself. The middle management man thus contributes to the continuation of the subcultural norms by aiding in the socialization of those below him.

We feel that the "work-role self" development of the men and their significant others is a major social resource contributing to the lower incidence of stress noted earlier in the paper among "successful" middle management persons. Their involvements are high and blockages low in salient areas emphasized by the subculture of middle management; and involvements are minimized even though blockages may exist in aspects less emphasized by the bureaucratic world.

2. *Reduction of blockages—self actions.* A fundamental resource for these men is the perception of blockages, especially in the work world, as challenges calling for self action in their resolution rather than inevitable obstructions beyond their control. In other words, the men think that experienced stress can be lessened or potential stress avoided by the individual himself actively reducing the blockages while still maintaining high involvements.

Beneath the surface and rarely verbalized as a formal code of belief, lies a basic faith in the American conception that a man can help shape his environment and, more specifically, that a man can to a considerable degree determine his own life chances. Although they do not regard themselves as supermen, the vast majority consider their achievements in life to be results of their own acts. Nine out of ten give a categorical or qualified "yes" to the question, "Do you feel that fate is pretty much in your own hands?" A typical answer is, "It's almost completely. What happens to me is the result of the way I conduct myself. I may get a little help along the way but it's up to me and nobody else."

Their world outlook is optimistic in the sense that the men view their work world as one in which they are more likely to have favorable than unfavorable "breaks" in life and they consider that they have had and will have their fair share of life's opportunities. But they quickly add that the man himself must actively engage in creating the breaks and when they occur through no effort on his part, then it is up to him to take advantage of fortunate circumstances. "You must have the breaks and they will come your way, but you also must have the ability to take advantage of opportunities."

With this view of their world of work and with this orientation to their role as an active agent, it is not surprising that many blockages are viewed as "challenges" which can be reduced through self effort. Two out of three rate themselves as superior to others in being "resourceful" in handling blockage situations, referring concretely to instances in which they have improvised solutions, have discovered alternative approaches for getting around obstacles, have changed their approaches to gain cooperation from others, have taken the initiative in overcoming impediments. As put by one man, "I seldom find myself in a position where I'm at a loss for an avenue of exit or entry. If I can't attack a problem one way, I start looking for other ways to attack it. I pride myself on being able to take a new problem and come up with an answer which is workable."

An even higher proportion, nine out of ten, regard themselves as superior to others in preventing problems from taking place or from becoming serious when they do occur. They attribute to themselves considerable skills in foreseeing difficulties that are likely to appear, anticipating troubles before they emerge, and quickly assessing the possible serious implications of small problems. Foresight and anticipation not only alert them to pending issues but motivate them to figure out in advance possible ways of solving the problems —to initiate self action for keeping blockages low in areas in which they are highly involved.

The scope of individual control over blockages which can produce stress is not unlimited. All have some qualifications concerning their capacities; some say they are less ingenious in dealing with routine problems than with crises, some claim the reverse, others consider their self efforts are more successful in controlling blockages in the arena of organizational arrangements than in the control of artifacts. Although not germane to our main orientation in this paper, all claim greater control by the self over blockages in the world of work than in the home or community.

3. *Reduction of involvements—flexibility and rigidity.* We have already noted in the development of the work role self that through participation in the subculture of middle management the primary involvements of these

men have undergone some changes. In general the trend is from specific involvements to more generalized involvements. But once crystallized we could
note no diminution (at least during the working years we studied) in their
commitments to the broadly defined goals of desiring a work role that is a
challenge, of eagerness to grow and get ahead, of needing the support of
others, and of wanting personal respect and recognition. Perhaps there will be
changes as the men approach retirement but anything we could say on future
changes in involvements would be pure speculation.

A number of writers have noted that one of the characteristics of successful executives is their "flexibility," but few have delineated what flexibility is.
Often it has been thought of as a "personality component" and some have
even recommended that executives be picked on the basis of this rather
statically conceived, personality characteristic. We shall try to point out here
what we have found to be some of the facets of flexibility.

The term "rigid" describes these men only in the sense that they hold
firmly to those broad goals which we have termed areas of high involvement
in the work world. In relationship to these broad goals, however, the men
exhibit considerable flexibility in their commitments.

A careful screening of their life histories shows that flexibility in commitments is not the outgrowth solely of a predisposing personality attribute,
but that it, too, is socially learned in the bureaucratic world. Those who claim
that they always "rolled with the punches" even in childhood, learn adaptability in the work role easily; for others, who say their personality in earlier
years was more inelastic, flexibility was somewhat more painfully achieved.
The latter type almost invariably use the term "introvert" to describe what
they were and "extrovert" to indicate what they are now—and give lengthy
accounts of the process of change. But whether they achieved present flexibility easily or with difficulty, all cite instances from their working past of
how they learned to be less rigid in their approach to their jobs, less committed to particular techniques or operations, less stereotyped in their assessments of others, less narrowly moralistic in their judgments and more
tolerant of alternative means.

It is significant to note in this connection that "inflexibility" as an early
personality characteristic is more likely to be maintained within the family
role than within the work role—which is another way of saying that the family self has more roots in childhood and adolescent behavior whereas the
work-role self has less continuity with earlier years.

One of the most striking features of work-role flexibility is what we have
termed "tolerance of irrational authority." In essence this refers to a readiness
to accept and work constructively with high policy decisions that may not fit
the logical needs of a man's task, to an ability to relate oneself to a superior
whose decisions may not appear sound, and to skills in adapting to the actions of colleagues whose stands on issues seem unwarranted. This tolerance
is not submissiveness or merely giving in to others who "count"; it includes an
ability to find means for achieving one's overall goals in a social system that
at times appears disorganized and with men whose conduct seems peculiar
without becoming enmeshed in feuds or moralizing about the state of affairs
or rejecting completely the existing structures and men. It means maximizing

what can be done within one's own sphere even when the policies and actions of others seem irrational.

Another feature of flexibility is the apparent freedom from a compelling need for certainty. In a sense this is the reverse side of their high involvement in wanting a work role that is a challenge. Eighty-four percent of the men say that they must take risks in their decisions or actions either occasionally or often. The taking of calculated risks is viewed as a necessity, or in the words of one informant, "It is better to lose doing something than nothing." The men have learned to make decisions with incomplete facts, to live with the intermittent reorganization of offices, departments and functions so characteristic of American bureaucracies and to take in stride the accompanying confusion. There is recognition of their part that not only is this the way dynamic organizations work but, more important, that it is a necessary accompaniment to their being able to achieve their salient values from the environment. They have internalized a tolerance for complexity.

A third feature of flexibility is the dissociation of past troubles from current interests. Over and over the men made such statements as: "I'm pretty good at bouncing back by figuring that if anything happens why that's that and I go on from there. There is no point in worrying about it any longer, I don't cry over spilt milk very much, but just start fresh and forget the rest." Or again, "Well, I fluff off on some situations and yet I have a pretty fair average of making a reasonable score on situations as they arise. When I do a poor job I count if off and it doesn't disturb me."

The clue to the process of "forgetting" past mistakes and problems grew out of analysis of the major troubles which the men identified from their life histories. Major problems were conceived of as being of two types—"unresolvable serious" and "resolvable critical." An unresolvable serious problem is one in which the man believes he lacks control over the events, cannot solve at least partially by his own efforts, has no way of predicting or controlling its effect on his future, and for which he can see no acceptable solution. Resolvable critical problems, on the other hand, are those which can jeopardize the future of the individual and those closely associated with him if they are not resolved satisfactorily, but the man is aware of the ramifications, is of the opinion that he can have some part in controlling the outcome, and thinks there are possible solutions which are to some extent acceptable to him. Both types of problems can occur in both the family and the work-world, but the men identified more of the unresolvable serious type as occurring in the family context and more of the resolvable critical type as occurring in the occupational sphere. Continuous, unresolved problems in the family could not be "forgotten" whereas shorter-termed, eventually resolved problems in the work role were more likely to be dismissed.

Further probing in the area of remembered "achievements" of the past also gives clues to the process of dissociating the past from the present. In answer to a series of questions on the "most pleasant thing which has ever happened to you," and "the most important decision you ever made," the vast majority of answers referred to family affairs—choice of a mate, birth of a child, marriage of a daughter, etc. At first blush it might seem that the family self is "really" more important and that the work-role self is but of secondary interest; but all of our data attest to the crucial importance of the work-role self.

We think that the explanation for what is a seeming paradox lies in the difference between the nature of the work-role self and the nature of the family self. The identity of the man in his family is related closely to what he "was" in the family; and the identity of the man in the world of work is related to what he "is" and what he "can become." Not only can a man forget his past troubles in the world of work but he is also put in the position of having to ignore his past achievements; there is continuous need to revalidate the self in the present and future in dynamic organizations characterized by changing structures and functions and by changing significant others. In the family a man is in a network which covers the full time-span of his relationship with a relatively few significant others; he can rely on his past achievements to tie him to these few others and he is also forced to live with his mistakes. In the family, then, there are not the same pressures for continuous revalidation of the self which there are in the work world. Families which emphasize a long segment of a man's life have "long memories" of the man whereas bureaucratic structures have "short memories." The self which is developed in each of these systems reflects the system itself.

To summarize then, a social resource of importance to the men in the world of work which tends to minimize stresses is the flexibility of dissociating past troubles from present concerns; and this flexibility is not so much a predisposing personality characteristic as it is a characteristic derived from the occupational system within which the man works. Thus stresses in the family have to be sought from a longer time perspective whereas stresses in the world of work are more likely to stem from the present and anticipated future.

One final point on flexibility. When we pursued their outlook towards the problems they face, we found there were outer limits as to how much a man will accept before he begins to consider alternatives. These probings offer guidelines for understanding a valuable resource for men in the status position we studied. Although the men are firmly committed to the rather broad involvements which we earlier noted, they are not so entrapped or so overcommitted to a particular job, organization or community as to be willing to endure stresses beyond their capacity to control blockage situations. The vast majority consider they have marketable skills, capabilities and talents which would enable them to find another job, and that if their present one becomes intolerable they would rather leave than suffer continuing deprivations. This is said with no lack of feelings of loyalty or identification with their present role and organization but as an objective way of scaling the relative value of things in life to them. Some have changed jobs in the past, most have contemplated alternative positions, and a few at present are waiting to see what changes are likely to eventuate in the near future before they actively search out another position. These few think that "things will turn out all right" on their present position but reassure themselves that if they don't they can and will move.

The seriousness of a job change lies not so much in the actual change of position as it does in the meaning of the change to the man's family. Ordinarily, a man's involvement in his family is to some degree insulated from his involvements in his work role. A job change which does not uproot his family (for example, change to a job in another local division in the same company, or another company in the same city) may be made on the relative merits of the position alone. Job changes which precipitate family movement force the man to assess together his involvements in family and work and such decisions rest on a number of factors not inherent in the position itself—unwillingness or willingness of the wife to move, age and involvements of children in their activities, possibilities of suitable housing, schools, religious institutions and community relationships in the place under consideration in comparison with what he now has. Ordinarily it takes the man's family longer to adjust to a new community than it takes the man to adjust to his new job. The length of time necessary for family adjustment is a function of the availability of institutions and voluntary associations which are ready to accept newcomers. Although to some extent the men and their families can seek out and activate these resources, the control over blockages in these areas tends to be low.

IV. SPECULATION

Probably no responsible social scientist would assert that a single empirical investigation of a limited universe offers a conclusive test of a major theory or lends itself to the construction of an overall new theoretical orientation. While we do not wish to make such claims for the results of this pilot study, our findings do indicate the need for more critical appraisals of current theories and generalizations.

If our facts for the sample population are valid and if our tentative theoretical orientation is sound, then questions need to be raised as to the assumptions, criteria, subcultures and norms used in current interpretations of the organization man and his problems. Has the mode of our times motivated social analysts to overstate the case for personal anxieties of the organization man in somewhat the same fashion as post World War I writers dramatized the "lost generation" rather than measured the true incidence of the "lost?" Have the present critics of American middle class life tacitly and nostalgically invoked norms out of the past in their evaluation of the contemporary similar to the way in which earlier critics invoked the traditional ideals of rural life to assess the meaning of growing uzbanization? Is it possible that the problem itself has been in part misconstrued by assuming that the structural tensions and rough and jagged edges of bureaucratic social structures have a one-to-one relationship with tensions experienced by individuals? Has there been an overemphasis upon the stresses and a neglect of the resources latent in American culture and existing in bureaucratic structures for dealing with problems that face the individual?

Is it improbable that there has been a tendency toward oversimplification of reality by taking as representative of middle class Americans, samples that mirror only particular subcultures? Our narrowly selected sample does not allow for broad generalizations about American men in middle management, to say nothing about American executives as a whole or middle class life in general. We are inclined to believe that some of the contrasts between our data and those of other reports may be due less to the methods of gathering relevant facts than to sampling different groupings of men.

Thus, we cannot say that the social resources we found will *per se* assure that all individuals who have access to them will have mental health. Rather, we can say that these are the social resources commonly found among men who are considered to be within the range of normally well-adjusted and from which we infer that these social factors will serve to alleviate experienced stress and prevent stress from occurring within this particular social environment.

10   RELIGIOUS PRACTICE AND CARDIOVASCULAR REACTIONS DURING STRESS

By Stanley H. King and Daniel Funkenstein

Recent research has pointed to a number of psychological and sociological correlates of physiological reactions during acute stress. In terms of cardiovascular response we have demonstrated a positive association between anger directed outward and a nor-epinephrine-like cardiovascular pattern and between anger directed inward or anxiety and an epinephrine-like pattern. (3) We have also shown that the perception by the subject of his father as stern and dominant in discipline was associated with a nor-epinephrine-like cardiovascular reaction while perception of father as mild and non-dominant in discipline was associated wtih an epinephrine-like pattern. (6) This report describes a third correlate of cardiovascular reactions in acute stress, that of religious practice and attitudes.

Procedure. The data on which these findings are based were gathered in a two-year study of healthy college students during acute laboratory stress. The details of this study have been reported elsewhere (2, 3, 7) but in brief, the procedure was as follows. One hundred twenty-five randomly selected male students were placed in laboratory stress situations where they were given arithmetical problems to do in their heads while being hurried and criticized by the experimenter, or they were asked to repeat a story from memory while talking into an auditory feedback device. Cardiovascular measurements by means of a blood pressure cuff and a ballistocardiograph were obtained before and after each session and the subjects were interviewed at the end of the stress situation for a measure of their emotional reactions. In addition to this each subject was seen by the experimenters on other occasions where a bat-

Grateful acknowledgement is given for support of this work to the School of Aviation Medicine, Randolph Field, Texas, under Contract AF 33(038)20142, the Russell Sage Foundation, the Supreme Council, 33rd Degree, Scottish Rite, Northern Masonic Jurisdiction, U.S.A., through the National Association for Mental Health, and the Laboratory of Social Relations, Harvard University.

From *The Journal of Abnormal and Social Psychology*, 55, (1957), 135–137. Copyright 1957 by The American Psychological Association.

tery of psychological tests and a biographical questionnaire were administered.

On the basis of relative changes between the pre-stress and stress measures of blood pressure and ballistocardiograph tracings the subjects could be
divided into two main groups. These groups were comparable to ones which
had been described earlier by Funkenstein and Meade (4). In their study
healthy subjects were studied under two conditions, during the infusion of
nor-epinephrine and during the infusion of epinephrine, using blood pressure
and ballistocardiograph tracings. The various physiological measures fell
into two distinct patterns under each condition, characterized by changes
in pulse, mean IJ wave on the ballistocardiograph, and mean blood pressure.
The exact procedure for the determination of these two patterns can be
found elsewhere (4, 5). It is important here to note that the pattern of physiological variables in one group of our subjects was like that found by Funkenstein and Meade during the infusion of nor-epinephrine and has been termed
by us nor-epinephrine-*like*. The other group had a pattern of variables comparable to that found during the infusion of epinephrine, and we have termed
it epinephrine-*like*.

Data on religious practice and attitudes were obtained from the personal
history questionnaire and the Religious Conventionalism Scale of Levinson.

On the questionnaire each subject was asked about the church-going behavior of his parents through the following questions:

How frequently does your father attend church?
  a)   Frequently
  b)   Occasionally
  c)   Seldom
How frequently does your mother attend church?
  a)   Frequently
  b)   Occasionally
  c)   Seldom

These questions were then combined into a single measure of parental
church attendance, as follows:

Regular attendance (both attend frequently or one attends
    frequently and the other occasionally)
Occasional attendance (both attend occasionally or one at-
    tends frequently and the other seldom)
Infrequent attendance (both attend seldom or one attends
    seldom and the other occasionally)

Further data in the area of religion were available from the scores on the
Religious Conventionalism Scale which had been administered as part of the
battery of attitude scales developed by Levinson out of the work described
in *The Authoritarian Personality* (1). Levinson has described this particular
scale as follows(8):

The *Religious Conventionalism* (RC) Scale contains a variety of ideas about the
church, the Bible, God, prayer and the like. High scores reflect a conception of God

as punishing power figure and of the church as absolute moral authority, as well as a marked emphasis on faith, tradition, and conformity to institutional forms. Low scores, on the other hand, represent a religious humanistic or a nontheistic approach which emphasizes reason, personally derived values, and a naturalistic rather than supernaturalistic view of the world.

The subject is presented with 12 statements in the area of religious conventionalism and asked to indicate the degree of agreement or disagreement with each statement on a seven point scale ranging from strongly agree to strongly disagree. The subject can receive a score of 1–7 on each statement or a range of 12–84 on the total.

Results. The association between the measure of parental church attendance and the cardiovascular reactions of the subjects in stress can be seen in Table 1. Subjects whose parents were regular attenders were more inclined to have nor-epinephrine-like cardiovascular reactions while those whose parents were occasional or infrequent attenders had epinephrine-like patterns. This difference was especially striking between the subjects with regularly attending parents and those with infrequently attending parents. The Chi-square in this table was 8.719 which with 2 degrees of freedom is significant at the .02 level of confidence.

Table 1—Parental Church Attendance and Cardiovascular Reactions of Subjects During Stress

Parental Church Attendance	Cardiovascular Pattern of Subject		Total
	Nor-epinephrine-like	Epinephrine-like	
Regular	20	11	31
Occasional	13	19	32
Infrequent	3	12	15
Total	36	42	78

$$\chi^2 = 8.719 \quad P < .02$$

The mean RC Scale scores for the nor-epinephrine-like and epinephrine-like groups are shown in Table 2. It will be noted that even though the standard deviation was large there was still a significant difference between the means with the use of a t test. Those with N patterns had higher RC Scale scores than those with E patterns.

Table 2—Mean Scores of the Cardiovascular Reaction Groups on the Religious Conventionalism Scale

Cardiovascular Reaction Group	Number	Mean Score	Standard Deviation
Nor-epinephrine-like	36	42.94	19.00
Epinephrine-like	41*	33.63	18.79

$$t = 2.13 \quad P < .05$$

* One subject became unavailable for testing after filling out the personal history questionnaire and before taking the RC Scale.

Discussion. These data when combined with those on which we have reported previously indicate that there is a constellation of psychological and sociological factors which are associated with the cardiovascular reactions of healthy subjects in acute stress. This constellation includes the immediate emotional reaction of the subject, his attitudes in the area of religious values, his perception of parental behavior in discipline, and the church-going behavior of his parents. Subjects who responded to acute stress with a nor-epinephrine-like cardiovascular reaction tended to also respond with anger directed at the experimenter. In addition they were individuals who perceived their father as the principal disciplinarian in the family and stern in his discipline, they had conservative attitudes in the area of religious faith and belief, and they came from families where the church attendance habits were regular. On the other hand, those subjects who responded to acute stress with an epinephrine-like reaction tended to respond with anger directed against themselves or anxiety. In addition they perceived their fathers as non-dominant in discipline, had moderate to liberal attitudes in the area of religious faith and belief, and came from families where the pattern of church attendance was occasional or infrequent.

These factors come from a number of levels, not only the immediate biological (physiological and emotional), but the more enduring organization of perceptions (perception of father and attitudes toward religion), and even the surrounding family milieu (church attendance of parents).

We leave it to future research to spell out the manifold implications of these associations. We do suggest that they are of sufficient strength to encourage further interdisciplinary research among the fields of physiology, psychology and sociology.

11   CULTURAL FACTORS IN HEALTH AND DISEASE

By John M. Maclachlan

Neither health nor disease may be considered, by the social scientist, as a universal absolute. A medical definition of health,[1] satisfactory as it may be for the practitioner, leaves much to be said on the part of the sociologist and the anthropologist. This is because the maintenance of norms of all types is an essential function of cultures, and because of the great variation of concepts of *normal* health among the world's many culture groups. "Normal" is what is usual, expected, understood in its frame of reference, and generally regarded as desirable.

Again, 'disease' may appear to have an absolute meaning,[2] but on closer examination becomes subject to the same stricture. If definitions common to the medical dictionaries are followed, two necessities occur. First, the condition must be known for its "train of symptoms" and, second, it must be regarded as abnormal, as a condition of ill health. A single disease, to exist in a culture group as such, must come within the purview of the contemporary diagnostics. Otherwise it can exist only as a part of the general malaise known as "feeling bad" or, alternatively, may even be considered a desirable departure from normality. At one time none of the major diseases recognized today was known as a separate entity, and in some culture groups—the Arunta of Australia, for instance—almost none are defined even today.

At this juncture some exploration of the concept of culture is necessary. Anthropologically, a culture is the whole fabric of ways of living which distinguishes a human society. The term subsumes the modes of communication, the pattern of organization or structure, the complexes of roles and statuses which interrelate the individual members of the group, and the technologies which serve to manipulate the physical world—including, needless to say, the human body itself.

Viewed so broadly, culture appears as a dynamic factor related to virtually every state of health or disease. The ministrations of the witch doctor, the dietary preferences of the folk, the prevalent notions concerning housing, clothing and sanitation, as well as the very definitions of health and disease, are all cultural phenomena. The degree of contact of the culture group with others is less a matter of geography than of the extent to which the technology of travel and communication are developed and utilized.

At this time, especially in the literate societies, a negative approach to the concept of ill health is justified by the use of a null measurement: where ill health is known to be absent, one presumes that good health exists; it only remains to isolate social and cultural factors connected exclusively with one or the other.

Thus, a semantic, or perhaps only terminological, difficulty confronts the student who inquiries into the phenomenon of ill health in society. Ill health is multi-faceted, and confusion may result if one facet is taken for another. Modern medical science comes close to a defensible definition of a state of good health, and does so through reliable techniques of test and diagnosis. The individual who comes through the elaborate and exhaustive, not to say exhausting, physical examination of the modern major clinic with a verdict of good health may feel reasonably sure that he is a physically sound specimen. While diagnosis and classification of mental illness has not yet reached the same level of exactitude, similar criteria can now be applied to the individual to determine the state of his mental health.[3] When every organ and portion of the body and mind passes muster, good health is present and ill health absent.

This, however, is not the criterion used by most of the human race today. "Being sick" is a cultural phenomenon in itself, and may or may not accompany clinically definable ill health. Primitive peoples, and great numbers of those who participate in contemporary civilized cultures, persist in other views of the matter. One may instance cases in which clinically very serious ill health—schizophrenia or epilepsy, to name only two—is evaluated culturally as an enviable state. Again, disorders which are so thoroughly endemic as to saturate a society may be taken as a matter of course and, even though they are recognized, regarded as concomitant with normal good health. Still again, the limitations of a culture may make its participants simply oblivious to a given kind of ill health.

Areas of southern North Africa in which hookworm infestation was universal, in the early years of the century, had no other children with whom to contrast their own anemic youngsters. Efforts to eradicate the hookworm in some isolated places encountered resistance analagous with the open warfare which the cattle-tick eradication program brought on in the same localities. Even leading newspapers took up the cudgel to defend their communities against the activities of Stiles[4] and his associates. A still more contemporary example is the opposition to the fluoridation of public water supplies. The prevention of dental caries has little meaning to those who do not accept the concept of the debilitating effects of this affliction.

It may seem too much to assert that "a man is as sick as he feels," but there is considerable evidence to support such a statement. In any event, a clear discussion of health and culture requires a distinction between scientifically definable ill health and culturally defined states of health. "Sick" and "well" are antonyms unrelated to test tube and stethoscope. The patient who starts "feeling sick" only after his symptoms are interpreted to him may have his counterparts in whole communities or culture groups. "Being sick" is a process with both subjective and objective components, although it may in a given instance lack one or the other.

This follows from the fact that hypochondria in the individual may have a cultural counterpart. The "swooning" of the Victorian lady, like the induced hysteria of the Dyonisian Amerindians, may have been a very real experience to its victims even without any prime physiological basis. Such disorders might well be described as *sociosomatic*. Possible examples to be cited later range from the thanatomanic disorders of certain primitives to the disturbed behavior patterns of some adolescents, women during the "change of life" period, frustrated elders, and others in civilized communities.

Cultural Influences on Physical Health. By operational definition, disease to the social scientist must be ill health which is either (a) experienced consciously by the participants in a culture, or (b) ill health which is observed in a population by competent diagnosis or analysis, or both of these.

It might be ventured that the existence of virtually all communicable and infectious disease, and of illness occasioned by faulty diet, clothing or housing, is dependent upon cultural factors. Furthermore, it can be shown that even organic disease has at least an indirect cultural origin. Senile dementia would be rare in a society whose mean age at death, like that of medieval Europe, stood at about twenty-five years. In such a society deaths from heart disease would likewise occur infrequently, simply because the diseases of middle and later life would have fewer likely victims available. The practice of geronticide, again, could conceivably relieve the vital statistics of the society from most of these instances of organic disease.

The modes of cultural impact on health should be kept in mind at this juncture. Just as most individual human beings do not use scientific criteria in evaluating their own health, most human societies use crude cultural yardsticks to measure the physical well being of the whole group. Moreover, dysgenic customs may be clung to as stubbornly as the tobacco addict clings to his cigarette. To demonstrate that customs do not yield to the principle of the survival of the fittest—that is, that the customs which persist most strongly are not necessarily those which contribute most to the welfare of the community—is easy.

Except among the scientifically informed, and often not even there, diet patterns are matters of like and dislike, of acculturation. The kinds of foods eaten, and their preparation, are integral parts of culture. The same thing may be said concerning clothing, whose basic function is that of symbolizing sex and status rather than that of either modesty or protection against sun and rain. While housing may be thought of as having primarily a protective function, it nevertheless follows that the kind and quality of the dwelling lived in are dictated by custom. However drafty the *tipi*, the occupant seldom thought of building a sod hut. The fact that few dwellings have ever been more inhospitable to a human frame than the medieval castle was unimportant in the light of its cultural utility as a symbol of power.

Man's physiological orientation is largely a cultural phenomenon, and deficiencies of diet, clothing and housing become prime causes of ill health. Patterns of settlement, defining as they do relative population densities, arise from the culture and affect health. Where the village type of settlement exists, rural populations do not benefit from the protective factor of low population density per square mile. The Amerindians who crowded together in their 'long houses' provided apt incubators for the micro-organisms brought them by the white man, albeit they were surrounded by wide open spaces. Peoples who migrate tend to carry with them their customary pattern of settlement, along with their cooking utensils, their garments and their mating systems, and are as likely to resist change in one as in another of these. That the geographic pattern of settlement persists as the physical skeleton of the cultural community is demonstrated conclusively by Murdock's demonstration that location and place of residence always precede changes in kinship systems.[5]

So it is that technological components of culture, those concerned with the manipulation of the physical world, relate quite recently to health. A broad concept of *technology* includes the modes of treatment of recognized physical ill health as well as those of producing food and clothing. Occupational hazards and fatigue levels are afferents of technology, and determine what proportions of human energy must be expended for subsistance, and what may be left over for other considerations. Cooking practices, geared to the tastes of the people who eat the food, may affect profoundly the dietetic quality of what is prepared. The introduction of the cheap iron cook-stove in the United States late in the 19th century was an important precursor of the wave of dietary deficiency diseases which later swept large areas of the countryside.[6]

Culture and Mental Health. What has been reviewed to this point is perhaps self-evident, but must be kept in mind. It is no less important to point, for purposes of this discussion, to the intimate relation of culture to mental well-being. Like physical disease, mental disease is subject to cultural definition and may even more readily be seen in a given culture group as either negligible or desirable.

In this connection a useful concept is that of the "modal," "social," or "normal" personality pattern of a culture group or society. While there is a wide range of variation of personalities within even small societies, certain components are shared by all or nearly all of their members. These constitute the characteristics which distinguish members of the society from those of any other group. If Ruth Benedict's effort to classify cultures in terms of a single broad and basic quality of personality, as "Dyonisian" or "Apolonian"[7] leaves something to be desired, it is at least a good point of departure. A society, thus, possesses some cultural attributes which mark off its members in terms of characteristic emotional tones, with appropriate variations appertaining to differences of sex, age and status.

Moreover, the system of symbolic communication of a society sets limits of conceptualization beyond which individual members cannot go. Just as Latin numerals make arithmetic difficult and algebra impossible,[8] so the possession or lack of word-symbols governs the "ability to think" of the participants. What cannot be phrased cannot be thought, while highly efficient word-symbols provide short cuts to insight and analysis.

The "normal" or usual emotional patterns and the systematized language of words and numbers set up a framework on which individual-personal personality patterns must be structured. In turn, cultural predispositions to given ways of behaving in specific situations occur, along with generalized tendencies. A significant by-product here is what Sutherland calls the "run of attention" characteristic of a culture group.[9] A major illustration of this phenomenon contrasts the traditional Hindu culture with that of western Europe or the United States. During the centuries when the westerners were exploring the labyrinths of physical science, concentrating on the conquest of matter and the creation of modern technology, the Hindu, although contemporary in the chronological sense, was still bemused by the intricacies of cosmic philosophy. The forces affecting western culture combined to turn the attention of its leading minds to science while those affecting Hindu life faced in precisely the opposite direction.

This is to say that not only the ability to conceptualize but also the determination of life will be addressed by the individuals in the group, depends upon the basic culture pattern. Since there does not appear at present to be any evidence of physiologic differences among ethnic stocks, or cultural subdivisions of those stocks, to explain differences in mental focal points or in the phenomena of mental health, it seems at least plausible to assume that these differences are more likely to follow the greatly variable cultural factor than the apparently relatively constant physiological one.

Social Structure and Mental Health. The structured relationships of age-, sex-, status-, and kin-groups dictate patterns of individual response in a society. The attributes we see as those of masculinity are not linked physiologically with maleness, nor are those regarded in our culture as feminine ineluctable qualities of the human female. Our patterning of the individual life span into infancy, childhood, adolescence, maturity and old-age, a five-age pattern, is far from universal. At least as common is a three-age pattern of childhood,[10] maturity abruptly entered through initiatory rites in the early teens, and old age. Teknonymy, the practice of renaming all members of the immediate family to celebrate the arrival of the newest infant, emphasizes the importance of youth as certainly as gerontocratic practices give value to old-age.

Modes of behavior within the nuclear family begin to put the impress of the culture group upon the individual very early in life. The view that the modes of handling the infant, such as feeding practices, sphincter training, swaddling, means and levels of discipline, lay permanent foundations in the innermost recesses of the personality, has wide current acceptance.[11] Strong enforcement of parental authority, insistance upon the domination of male over female in the family and community, culturally patterned tones of casual interpersonal association which create high levels of nervous tension, and other such cultural factors may have a great deal to do with the development of any prepotent tendency towards mental disorder.

It is through these multitudinous, structured interpersonal relationships that psycho-social stresses, repressions, frustrations and their positive counterparts come to be. Neurosis and the stimulation of predisposition to psychosis, looked at in this way, take on a definitely cultural air. If they are produced in individual personalities, and in terms of psychological function, they are nevertheless of the very essence of cultural phenomena.

The binding influences of customary relationships between class and class, caste and caste, overlaid upon the patterns of interpersonal behavior, may, because they are essentially non-rational and hence indefensible in the eyes of the subordinate groups, be a source of even more stress than the latter. Other things being equal, members of a minority group regarded as inferior could thus be expected to show higher levels of stress and hence higher incidence of stress-induced disorders. The high incidence of infectious and communicable disease among the nonwhite population of the United States is paralleled, when the age factor is controlled, by comparably high incidence of organic diseases. To use diseases of the heart as an example, the age-adjusted death rates[12] of the white and nonwhite population show 1940–1953 arithmetic means of 304 per 100,000 white persons and 363 per 100,000 for the nonwhite population. To show that the sex factor does not override this contrast, the white male rates for the 1940–1953 period averaged 27 heart deaths per 100,000 in the 25–34 year age group, while the nonwhite female rate for the same ages averaged 59 deaths per 100,000 persons. In the 35–44 age group the white male average was 119 deaths per 100,000 persons, and that of the nonwhite females 201 per 100,000. If the nonwhite female heart death rates in the ages from 25 to 44 were double the white male rates, the nonwhite males produced an even greater contrast with 62 and 210 deaths per 100,000 for the age groups.

Such differences in the incidence of physical disease cannot be demonstrated as clearly with reference to mental ill health, since the latter is not covered by comparable reporting. However, the very high rates of crimes of violence among the nonwhite population and the disproportionate share of admissions to mental hospitals attributable to it may be taken as indirect evidence of high levels of maladjustment.

It is obvious that many factors contribute to differences in health, mental and physical, between social classes. Mental health is related more directly to patterns of culture, perhaps with differences which are not always favorable to the upper classes. Hollingshead has shown[13] that the American social classes tend towards different psychoses, and it may be that neurosis based on anxiety or guilt feelings tends to be a middle- or upper-class specialty. The findings of Kinsey[14] concerning the attitudes towards sexuality of lower-class males are definitely less productive of emotional upset than those of middle and upper-middle class men. The apparently lower incidence of chronic alcoholism among Negroes than among white persons in a Florida study[15] can be associated with cultural differences from the white population. Since the latter group shows its highest rates among unskilled laborers and high-level managerial executives, with much lower rates in the intervening middle-class, sub-cultural differences within the white population appear to be effective.

Culture and the Range of Mental Disturbance. The range of conditions which may be regarded as levels of mental ill health is a wide one. Granting that the relation between medically defined psychosis and cultural factors has not been given any final consensus, it remains to consider the range of disorders in which the cultural factor is clear. These vary from the extremes of thanatomania and compulsive cannibalism to the relatively unspectacular psychoneurosis of civilized man. In order to emphasize the cross-cultural dimensions of this range, examples will be cited more or less in order of the severity of the disorder.

Culture and the Trauma in Extremis. Most extreme of the disorders which might be labelled thus is *thanatomania,* as defined anthropologically (illness or death resulting from belief in magic)[16] and distinguished from the medical use of the same term (i.e., suicidal or homicidal mania).[17] Here the victim may waste away and die, even with competent medical care. Instances of such self-induced death have been recorded in South America, Africa and Oceania.[18] Honigmann calls attention to W. B. Cannon's hypothesis that the profound physiologic consequences of continued intense fear may account for the phenomenon.[19] Inability to eat or drink while under such fear, however, is sufficient as a total explanation, since some reported thanatomanic deaths have occurred too swiftly for such deprivation to have an important role.

While a number of thanatomanic deaths have been reported by reliable sources, relatively few have occurred under clinical or hospital conditions which permitted close examination of the victim during the process. One of these latter is reported by Simmons and Wolff[20] as occurring in an Australian military hospital. At no time did the patient exhibit "the tachycardia, the cold and clammy skin, and the hypertension characteristic of shock, except perhaps during the terminal moments."[21]

W. Lloyd Warner[22] suggests that the behavior of the friends and relatives of the victim, strongly re-enforcing his conviction of impending death, may have a strategic place in thanatomanic death. The people around him, that is, assume that his fate is settled, and that he is as good as dead. As he weakens under the multiple impact of stress, suggestion and self-induced starvation, preparations are made to bury the victim, and appropriate last rites are performed. Under the circumstances the occupant of the center of the stage has little choice as to what to do next.

W. E. Roth, quoted in Cannon's "Voodo Death," makes much the same report concerning the 'bone pointing' black magic of the primitives in north central Queensland, as does Herbert Basedow. Since everyone is convinced of the efficacy of the magic, the victim becomes resigned to his fate and soon meets it. A special case of thanatomanic death has been reported in the Philippines. Here the victim becomes obsessed with the idea that he will have a death-dream, one so terrible that it will kill him. At the appropriate time he does so, and dies with promptitude. Another instance in which thanatomanic death is not the direct product of an enemy-induced curse is the Maori conviction that improper contact with sacred vessels will bring down upon one a fatal curse.

Compulsive Cannibalism. Some culture groups show a predisposition towards compulsive cannibalism, unrelated both to dietary needs and ritual practices. Kardiner[23] comments on this as occurring among the Marquesans, and reports it as an outgrowth of the fear of being eaten by neighbors, who thereupon are instead themselves consumed. Herman Melville dramatizes a related episode in his graphic novel *Typee*.[24] John M. Cooper is cited by Honigmann[25] for his description of the *Wiitiko* psychosis among the Cree and Ojibwa Indians of northern Canada. The victim is seized by a fear that he will develop a craving for human flesh, or that he will actually eat it. This fear becomes so intense that, finally, he accedes to the compulsion. Thereupon he is obsessed with the belief that he has become a *wiitiko*, an icy-hearted, cannibalistic ogre, and as a result turns into a ruthless homicidal maniac.

The same source describes Ruth Landes' summary of *windigo*, seen as a somewhat broader term embracing melancholia, violence and ultimate obsessive cannibalism among the Ojibwa,[26] again not directly related to cannibalism forced by hunger. The latter, fairly common among peoples who live in extremely inhospitable regions, has had at least two instances in the history of white North America.

Without specific supporting elements in the culture pattern, none of these behaviors could occur with regularity. Belief in magic and unreasoning fear of the supernatural are far more widespread than thanatomania or cannibalism, and cannot in themselves suffice to explain the phenomena. Rather, a specific myth[27] and a resulting death-related complex of attitudes, must prepare the potential victim for his mania over a long period of prior conditioning.

Culture and Psychopathology. It is a matter of debate as to whether behaviors such as those already described should be classified as "abnormal," since they are outgrowths of cultural forces rather than of any specific pathology in the individual. Thus a behavior pattern may be "normal" in its culture group in two sharply contrasted ways. One of these is the familiar *typical* behavior, which occurs frequently and is emulated by all or nearly all of the members of the group. The other may be designated as *archetypical*, as representing an extreme essence of the culture, a *reductio ad absurdum*. Looking at the first, stresses the tendencies towards uniformity in the group, while reference to the latter emphasizes, through the extreme case, the unique characteristics of its culture. While archetypical behavior may actually happen infrequently, and may be limited to a few members of the group, it nevertheless springs from deep roots in the culture. To use a pair of literary examples, Booth Tarkington's *Penrod* portrays American boyhood through a picturization of typical behaviors. In contrast, the characters in Erskine Caldwell's *Tobacco Road*, far from being typical southerners, may be seen as archtypes demonstrating the extremes of cultural disorganization in the deep South.

A complete list of the known instances in which culture groups believe in, and therefore experience, psychic possession would require more space than can be allotted here. West African and Haitian zombi-ism undoubtedly falls into some such category. *Amok*, which leads its victims into a homicidal frenzy, occurs in widely scattered groups throughout the Far East and in Siberia and in the Philippines, with similar results. Among the Eskimo groups it appears to be limited to women, and to involve both echolalia and echopraxia.[28] A similar seizure, called *pibloktoq*, is reported among the pre-literates of western Greenland. Like the thanatomanic disorders, these may be regarded as archetypical behaviors, but also like them they are regarded among the peoples affected as being specific conditions of ill health, with usually some prescribed treatment designed to cure the sufferer. It is questionable, however, whether the concept of disease can be extended to the condition of members of a culture group among whom psychic dysfunctioning, which we would regard as neurotic, is usual and expected.

Culture groups whose patterned behavior induces high levels of nervous tension; whose culture pairs deeply contradictory values and attitudes with resulting internal conflict among its possessors; or induces prolonged conflict patterns between the sexes or among the kin groups, bring about obvious predisposing tendencies towards neurosis. Chronic alcoholism, as a possible symptom of neurosis, has been shown by Horton[29] to occur more frequently among such groups than among more stable peoples. Studies of alcoholism in the modern world have demonstrated significant differences between cultural groups such as the Irish-Americans and Jewish-Americans. Neurosis may not be universal in any culture group, but considerable evidence demonstrates its relative frequency in some, and its comparative absence among others.[30]

Addiction and Culture. Virtually every culture group has available in its environment one or more of the substances which form a basis for addictions, but the actual occurrence of the latter is very unevenly distributed through the world's peoples, suggesting that cultural factors underlie the addictive pattern. Ruth Benedict's observation that addiction is unknown among the Apollonian Zuni, and common among the Dyonisian tribes,[31] is supported by a considerable literature relating to other peoples. Donald Horton in his excellent cross-cultural study of alcoholism referred to above demonstrates conclusively that cultural stress is related to the phenomenon. The opium addiction of the Orient, often explained as simply a product of the greed of westerners, could not have been brought about without a culturally receptive market, and has never been approximated in the Occident. The use of *hashish*, *marijuana* and *peyote* is far from equally experienced by the peoples living in regions where the plants are readily available, but rather is concentrated in specific tribes, culture groups, castes and classes.

The Cultivation of Disease. While it would appear logical that a state of good physical and mental health should be regarded as desirable everywhere, there is evidence that this is not the case, or perhaps it should be said that conditions which in our culture are considered undesirable departures from basic good health are not so regarded elsewhere. The deliberate inducement of hysterias such as the 'dancing madness' of the middle ages, the painful attainment of hallucinations among some American Indian tribes, the adulation of addicts in some of the societies in which addiction is related to ritual, are all instances of a positive search for states of mental ill-being as we would define it.

It is clear, too, that deviations from physiological normality can be considered desirable. The conception that obesity is esthetically desirable has been reported in Africa and the near East, with the expectable effects on feminine contours. The former custom of foot-binding among the upper class Chinese, the attenuation of the neck among the Congoese of Africa to make their women more beautiful, the stretching of the lip among the Ubangi, and the flattening of the skull among several northwestern Indians, are examples. Scarification and tattooing, carried to extremes in various cultures, provide more evidence that man can place more value on purely esthetic satisfaction than upon keeping a whole skin.

Culture and Neurosis. Many peoples among world culture groups possess basic personalities which, within the frame of reference of western life, would be considered definitely neurotic. Contrariwise, however, the well adjusted New Yorker might seem so to them in turn. Such behavior as being too 'finicky' to eat insects, or obsessed with the belief that frequent bathing is a necessity, or showing nausea at the prospect of eating human flesh, would immediately brand the westerner as at the very least a neurotic.

While this is undoubtedly true, the important present consideration is the phenomenon of neurosis in the contemporary modern world. Neuroses based on feelings of anxiety, insecurity, frustration or guilt are prevalent and, according to many authorities, increasing rapidly. Certainly admissions to mental hospitals for treatment of psychotic or psycho-neurotic conditions have increased at a more rapid rate than the total population. Although it is not clear to what extent increased facilities, changes in diagnosis and public awareness of the importance of treatment contribute currently to the trend, the fact itself cannot be ignored.

The rapid changes which have characterized American life in recent decades might be expected to produce ample opportunity for individual maladjustment to occur. The nation as a whole has become largely urban within less than a generation, and largely through the migration of rural people to urban areas. A highly important factor is interregional migration, which has carried a large proportion of Americans long distances from their cultural bases. A third of the adult population of the United States lived outside the state of birth in 1950, and migration from rural to urban areas drained off a fourth of the rural farm population between 1940 and 1950. During the same period more than a million nonwhite persons migrated from the South to other regions, and it is estimated that this number was equalled again between 1950 and 1956. Growing rates of delinquency and interracial friction in non-southern cities testify to the unsettling effects of such a rapid movement, and such a basic change in social environments.

Adolescent Neurosis and Culture. It has been pointed out that adolescence, a state of transition between childhood and maturity, is limited in its occurrence among world cultures. The "three age" cultures already mentioned include no adolescents among their members, nor do exotic groups as the Peruvian culture with ten recognized age-status segments. Forced to remain non-adult past physiological maturity because he has yet to prepare himself for a vocation, and to prepare himself in general to meet the challenges and demands of adulthood, he has reason for feelings of frustration, insecurity and incompleteness.

Too often these tensions are looked upon as results of nothing more basic than personality clashes between parent and offspring, or between a youth and adults encountered outside the home. Neither understanding nor resolution of the especial problem of the adolescent can be had without a prior realization that the actors in such episodes are merely following a major theme of our culture. Wholesale inventory of the social attitudes and values surrounding the concept of adolescence would be needed for such an accomplishment.

The "Marginal" Woman. A generation ago the migrant caught between two cultures, one in the 'old country' and the other in the 'new world,' was characterized as "the marginal man." In much the same sense an indeterminate, but large, proportion of middle-class women in the modern world can be seen as marginal. In times when the patriarchal tradition still held, woman's role as wife-mother gave her a clear-cut place and responsibility, with psychic and personal security to match the well-defined limits beyond which she could not function without penalty. The profound changes in modern life which have made continuation of this role impossible have not, as yet, produced an altogether effective substitute.

Two archetypical results follow. One is the woman who drops all effort to act the traditional role, and attempts with only limited success to make for herself a way of life on the masculine pattern. The other is the woman who, in continuing to be simply wife-and-mother, nevertheless feels either that life has led her into a *cul-de-sac* or, alternatively that she herself has failed to meet the challenge of life, to realize her potentialities.

In either instance prime material for neurosis is produced, and by the middle years its fruits, if we are to believe the literature, mature. The 'career woman' and the 'frustrated housewife' alike, confronting the difficult period of menopause and self-evaluation characteristic of middle age, may in such circumstances encounter the most severe psychic trauma.

The Concept of a "Sick" Society. If all the members of a society share the same identifiable malady, an observer may be justified in describing it as a "sick" society, one in which good, rather than bad, health would be "abnormal." Erich Fromm has pursued this concept through three volumes.[32] His concern has been with contemporary civilization, and his premise that:

. . . The basic passions of man are not rooted in his instinctive needs, but in the specific conditions of human existence, in the need to find a new relatedness to man and nature after having lost the primary relatedness of the prehuman stage.[33]

This, the main thesis of 'humanistic psychoanalysis,' is basic to the view that mental health and ill health are phenomena shared by the individual and his society, and may be accepted as valid without necessarily accepting Fromm's conclusion that modern society is very sick indeed. His contention that modern man has created for himself a profound sense of insecurity by reaching 'freedom from' the arcane sureties of the middle ages, without gaining 'freedom to' live a full life, has point. Lawrence K. Frank[34] sets up a similar thesis in *Society as the Patient,* if from a different point of view. Essentially Fromm looks through the individual towards the social order while Frank examines the latter to arrive at conclusions as to its effects upon the psychosocial comfort of the former. The two offer a view of the range of such recent literature.

Margaret Mead's *Growing Up in New Guinea* and Gordon Macgregor's[35] monograph on the Pine Ridge Sious are comparable critiques of tribal societies. Here are social orders in which behavior patterns regarded as normal resemble what would be called neurotic patterns in western life. Similarly, the life pattern of large segments of our own culture group may appear as neurotic in tone to other, better adjusted elements in the group. The professional student of man in society, observing a sufficient proportion of maladjusted individuals in the world around him, may thus come to the diagnosis of the society, itself, as indeed "sick."

It would seem difficult to arrive at any quantitative estimate as to the proportion of a population which must be maladjusted before the society may be so characterized, or at any such estimate for contemporary American life. Estimates of the frequency of specific disorders, with chronic alcoholism as a single instance, offer difficulty enough, but immeasurably less than would be involved in trying to guess at the numbers of persons suffering from all forms of maladjustment. Meanwhile, the current literature suggests several archetypical cases, representing broad groups in the modern community who, because of certain characteristics of our culture, undergo pressures or tensions highly favorable to neurosis.

We have already discussed the adolescent, subject as he is to a paradoxical and contradictory social-cultural orientation; and the middle class woman, who has cast off much of her former feminine role without taking on a satisfactory replacement for it. A third is the elder citizen who finds himself confronted by anachronistic ideas about the social-economic significance of aging. A fourth is the member of the minority group who becomes defensively aware of oppression and subordination. A considerable bibliography of writing, autobiographical or analytical, could be submitted regarding each of these cases.

The dysfunctioning of personality illustrated in each instance could well be labelled as *sociosomatic,* in an extension of the psychosomatic concept. That they may be widespread, and often deadly, has been shown. Just as psychosomatic illness must be distinguished from the imagined and nonexistent ills of the hypochondriac, so the sociosomatic ailment must be. While individuals in these groups are no less than other kinds of persons subject to the general pattern of stresses and tensions, they also have unique problems of adjustment.

II

Health and the

Community

ONE of the most puzzling problems confronting the medical profession is the fact that despite the accessibility of medical treatment, there still remain large segments of the community who do not take advantage thereof. Health, as well as illness, have been found to be related to many living conditions of the community apart from what have been viewed customarily as medical factors. This section deals with studies of those conditions to which individuals are exposed and which in turn bring about disease itself, such as the existence of sanitary health practices, poor dietary habits, ignorance of preventive health techniques and practices, and laxity in obtaining proper medical treatment because of a failure to recognize symptoms of illness. Also included are those studies dealing with the success or failure of health programs in the community.

Ozzie Simmons shows in his article that the social class of the population affected by certain diseases is a factor that very often stimulates medical research toward the controlling of that disease. One of the most extensive surveys of the use of medical services in an urban community is reported in the study by Earl Koos. The effectiveness of inducing participation in a recent experiment in polio vaccine trials is evaluated in the article by John Clausen, Morton Seidenfeld, and Leila Deasy. A comparative study between two communities in their use of medical facilities is presented by Saxon Graham in pointing up many similarities and differences between the communities.

Too often the terms "diet" and "nutrition" are intermixed. Diet can be regarded as the type of food-intake of a particular culture or group of people, while nutrition is the biochemical composition of diet. John Cassel discusses some of the important connections between human culture and food intake, indicating how the cultural background of the dietitian or nutritionist often serves as a stumbling block in their efforts to improve the nutritional level of groups of people with whom they are unacquainted.

Walter Boek presents some problems of the community power structure as it affects the outcome of community health programs. He presents two models for community action to serve as guides for obtaining desirable goals for health programs. A case study of an effort to organize several community health projects is presented and analyzed in the original contribution by Charles Willie and Herbert Notkin, M.D.

Some stimulating research hypotheses concerning apathy of families toward health care are presented in the original paper by H. Ashley Weeks, Marjorie Davis, and Howard Freeman.

Talcott Parsons, in an original article, analyzes the intricate relationships between various conceptions of health and illness and the cultural values and social structure of American society.

12   IMPLICATIONS OF SOCIAL CLASS FOR PUBLIC HEALTH[1]

By Ozzie Simmons

This paper will consider three areas in which social class and status have important implications for public health: 1) the differential distribution of disease and consequent evaluations of appropriate foci of public-health interest and activity, 2) the functioning of interpersonal relations within the health team and between team and public, 3) the congruence between public-health precepts and felt needs of the public at whom these precepts are directed.

For present purposes, "status" and "class" will be employed as generic terms, the former to refer simply to rank, or relative position in a status hierarchy, and the latter to refer to a group of individuals who occupy a broadly similar position in a status hierarchy. When the term "class status" is used, it refers to membership in a given stratum of a status hierarchy, whether this stratum be a statistical aggregate or a real group. When class value differences are discussed in terms of middle-class and lower-class, the reference is to modal types which higher and lower status people may manifest in different degrees; it does not necessarily follow that all higher status people adhere to the middle-class modal type, and all lower status people to the other. Presumably, many members of both these strata may not incorporate the corresponding class values and may deviate from the modal type in other respects. It may be noted that the character of modal types is determined by common economic and power situations and cultural experiences, which offer more or less similar life chances or opportunities. In discussing interpersonal relations, the primary focus will be on the ways in which orientations to relative status affect the functioning of a given relationship. In discussing congruence and divergence between public-health precepts and felt needs of the public, the primary focus will be on modal subcultural types.

Like the social welfare movement, the public-health movement has been conceived and implemented primarily by middle-class people, and directed primarily at lower-class people. As in most social movements, the public health movement was mainly activiated by motives of social uplift and self

From *Human Organization*, 16, (Fall, 1957). Copyright 1957 by The Society for Applied Anthropology.

protection. The conclusion, in 1830, that if cholera were not stamped out it might move from the slums to within the middle-class gates led to a sudden increase in interest in public health both in Europe and the United States. According to Shryock, "Fear now combined with humanitarianism to demand investigations, cleanups, and general sanitary reform."[2]

Public health has traditionally focused on the control of the mass diseases which, by and large, have had their greatest incidence and prevalence among the lower-classes, as, e.g., smallpox, typhus, typhoid, the nutritional deficiency disorders, and tuberculosis. With increasing control of these diseases, new mass diseases, such as the cardiovascular disorders and poliomyelitis, have claimed not only the attention of public-health personnel but have excited great public interest among our higher status groups as well, as currently reflected in the great annual fund-raising drives.[3] Taking as a specific case the contrast between polio and tuberculosis, we find that when the treatments for the latter were developed, professional interest far exceeded public interest; yet, when the Salk polio vaccine was developed, public interest far exceeded professional, and Salk became a national hero. There is an inverse correlation between degree of public interest and incidences connected with these two diseases. Polio rates are relatively low compared to those of other mass diseases, and tuberculosis rates continue relatively high.[4]

This striking difference between polio and tuberculosis may be regarded in large part as a function of class distributions and perceptions of disease.[5] Tuberculosis, like many of the older mass diseases, is primarily identified with lack of personal and environmental hygiene, poverty, overcrowding, and malnutrition, but in the case of polio, as in that of the cardiovascular ailments, no such identification has been established. In fact, there is some evidence to indicate that higher polio rates are to be found among those who enjoy quite the opposite set of conditions.[6] Tuberculosis and polio are both public threats, but the crucial difference here seems to be that tuberculosis is pretty well confined to our lower status groups, while polio is within the middle-class gates.

The practice of public health is carried on within two main interpersonal relations systems, the intrateam and team-public systems. Participants in either system may be members of the same or different societies, but in either case, class, as it refers to subcultural differences, may add an important dimension. Although there has been some research on interpersonal relations in the practice of clinical medicine and psychiatry, investigations in the public-health field have scarcely yet gone beyond impressions and casual observations. We will consider here only a few of the possibilities in intrateam relations in the intercultural situation, and in team-public relations in the intracultural situation.

The most common instance of public-health teams where members belong to different societies is to be found in technical assistance programs in "underdeveloped" countries. In this intercultural situation, class considerations can minimize or enhance major cultural differences that obtain between team members. With regard to class factors that serve to reduce cultural differences, it has been noted that class cultures tend to go beyond societal boundaries. As Saunders has pointed out, an upper-class Mexican-American may feel more at ease with an upper status Anglo American than with a lower-class

Mexican-American in a situation involving some degree of intimacy, since their awareness of cultural group distinctions is minimized, even though it may not be entirely superseded, by their social class identification.[7] In Latin America, upper-class groups in different countries, due to similar positions of dominance, possession of power and wealth, and the common experience of travel and education in Europe and America, tend to have value systems which not only approximate those of higher status Americans, but are more similar to each other than to those of lower-class Latin Americans in their respective countries.

With regard to the role of class factors in enhancing cultural differences among team members, it may be that, despite the cross-societal bond, tensions will be engendered, e.g., between Americans and their local collaborators due to failure of the American to understand and acknowledge what may often be substantial differences in status between the two relative to their own class hierarchies. Thus, in contrast to the American, who will only in the rare case be descended from a top status family and have held a high level position in his own country, local collaborators are likely to be members of ruling class families and to occupy high-ranking positions in their government's ministry of health. Americans, by virtue of their tendency to play down class differences, as well as of pronounced ethnocentric tendencies, are not likely to overtly manifest the degree of respect for their collaborators which the latter may expect as their due. For the same reasons, they are likely to reject or ignore the subordinating and deference devices traditionally used by upper-class people in conducting their relations with lower status people in those countries where status differences are generally explicitly acknowledged and taken for granted. One of the more pervasive grievances nursed by upper-class people abroad with respect to Americans concerns the latter's treatment of servants as near-equals by giving them the same food, paying them "too much," and so on.

Ideally, the doctor's role in the therapeutic relationship focuses on his performance of a technical specialty, on his impartially serving the patient's health needs independently of whether he likes the patient as a person, and on his obligation to give priority to the patient's well-being over his own personal interests. This ideal seems to hold across the board in most Western societies, although it may not always hold in non-Western societies.[8] This role definition is calculated to inspire trust, respect, and confidence between doctor and patient, and thus insure cooperation. In practice, however, it seems that the ideal is seldom approximated in professional-patient relationships, and that it is precisely in the doctor-patient relationship where it is likely to be achieved.

Studies in intracultural situations, both here and in other societies, indicate a tendency for class considerations to overshadow therapeutic considerations in the professional-patient relationship. It appears that the degree to which the qualities ideally defined as essential to the therapeutic relationship, namely mutual trust, respect, and cooperation, will be present in a given professional-patient relationship varies inversely with the amount of social distance. Conversely, the greater the social distance, the less likely that participants will perceive each other in terms of the ideal type roles of professional and patient, and the more likely that they will perceive each other in terms of their social status in the larger society.

The therapeutic relationship should function at its optimum where professional and patient are of the same class status. Studies of the psychotherapeutic relationship in this country indicate that the patients who most nearly approach the therapist's status are accorded the best treatment and the most sympathy.[9] In the public-health context, it is possible that, although professionals may deem it easier to relate to patients who are of the same class status, higher status patients may reject the health worker not because of his class status as such but because they perceive his attempts to serve them at all as identifying them with the lower status people typically served by public health, and thus regard him as a threat to their social position. In a Peruvian village, an auxiliary health worker was rejected by higher status people because "she was perceived as equating them with the unwashed and uneducated poor."[10] In Chile, health center nurses were extremely reluctant to approach middle-class families in their sectors because they anticipated a poor reception.[11]

In public health, where the typical case is that of higher status professional and lower status patient, the available evidence indicates that doctors and patients do not "get along" as well as do nurses and patients, but this need not mean that the respective class statuses of doctor, nurse, and patient are the sole or even principal factors in determining the difference in quality of doctor-patient and nurse-patient relations. Such factors as differences in professional training and expected role performance must also be weighed.[12]

In attempting to specify the varying roles that class perceptions and values may play in the functioning of professional-patient relations, it would be worthwhile to investigate whether status considerations loom larger for the professional or for the patient. In Regionville, e.g., there was considerable feeling on the part of lower status people that physicians did not want them as patients.[13] On the other side, some of the factors that influence professionals to inject status considerations into their relations with patients may be related to the professional's orientations to upward mobility. In Colombia, e.g., the cities have been flooded by rural immigrants who no longer classify themselves according to the traditional status system. As a result of the competition to rise socially, individuals with some small position of authority press their weight on others to force a recognition of their status. Thus, doctors and nurses in the Colombian government health centers are often overbearing in their treatment of the public.[14]

To the extent that it may be characterized as a social movement, public health has inevitably incorporated the dominant middle-class values of our society, primarily those that stem from the "Protestant ethic" core.[15] It follows that public-health precepts are formulated in terms of these values, and applied on the assumption that they are universally meaningful and desirable. However, class differences may set substantial limits to the degree of congruence possible between these precepts and the felt needs of a lower-class public.[16] We may ask: 1) To what extent do public-health workers apply their middle-class norms in working with lower status groups? 2) Are lower-class norms significantly different in those areas where middle-class norms are imposed? 3) If there are such points of difference, how relevant are they for the effective functioning of public-health activities?

Lower status families are beset by greater economic insecurity than higher status families, and their "scientific" knowledge about modern medicine is apparently less extensive than that of higher status people, but beyond these reality factors, classes also vary in their behavioral characteristics and value orientations.

In view of the prominent public-health emphasis on personal and environmental hygiene, possible class differences in the importance attached to cleanliness is an area that readily comes to mind. For middle-class people, cleanliness is not simply a matter of keeping clean but also an index to the morals and virtues of the individual. It has been frequently observed that middle-class valuations of cleanliness approach compulsive proportions, and that lower status people are much more casual in this matter. It is possible that the stress placed on cleanliness in health education and other public-health activities far overshoots any felt needs in this area on the part of lower status people.

Middle-class norms place great emphasis on the ability to defer gratifications in the interest of long-run goals. Readiness to sacrifice the present for possible gain in the future may not be nearly so pervasive a pattern among lower status people, who may accord priority to immediate rewards. This suggests some questions with regard to the public-health emphasis on prevention. Is acceptance of the value of prevention contingent upon ability to defer gratification, and, if so, do lower-class norms in this area set limits to such acceptance? Are lower status people as willing as higher status people may be to inconvenience themselves by adoption now of practices aimed at avoiding possible consequences in the future?

Middle-class norms accord high value to rationality, as it refers to use of foresight, deliberate planning, and allocation of resources in the most efficient way.[17] This again places an emphasis on future time orientations that may not be particularly meaningful to lower status people. However, public-health teachings assume that this value does hold for lower status people when they emphasize the development of regular health habits and the expenditure of the domestic budget in ways best caluculated to insure a balanced diet for the family.

Middle-class norms prescribe a strong sense of individual responsibility, which sets a high premium on resourcefulness and self-reliance. This value is frequently built into public-health goals. For example, the principal objective of health education is often expressed as the "inculcation in each individual of a sense of responsibility for his own health." This ideal pattern of individual responsibility can be contrasted with one of reciprocity, particularly within the family, that seems more characteristic of lower-class norms. The lower status individual may be much less likely to think that responsibility for his well-being rests solely with himself, and more likely to think that if something does happen, the kin group will see him through.

An individual's definitions of and responses to health and illness have import for a wide range of public-health problems, and these are usually class-linked. Throughout Latin American, e.g., lower status groups adhere to a vigorously functioning medical tradition which health workers and other medical people do not share.[18] The gulf is in part maintained by the health worker's rejection of this folk medicine tradition as "superstition," and in part by the fact that lower status people reserve for folk medicine a wide variety of illnesses defined as inaccessible to scientific medicine because doctors do not "know" them and therefore cannot cure them.

Finally, we may briefly consider class differences in child training patterns as these are relevant for public health. Middle-class socialization patterns tend to be consistently organized in accordance with the middle-class emphases on effort and achievement, which are thought to be good in themselves or good because they are instrumental to long-run goals, and, as a consequence, the middle-class child is subjected to considerable close supervision and control.[19] On the other hand, lower-class socialization patterns are relatively easygoing, and allow the child much more latitude with respect to eating, sleeping, cleanliness, dress, work, school, and play. Lower status parents may be much more rigid about obedience, but the imposition of authority is usually arbitrary and inconsistent. Maternal and child health programs are considered to be one of the most crucial in any large-scale public-health effort, and the mother is generally regarded as the most strategic person to reach in health education. Much of the education of lower status mothers seems to be based on the premise that the latter are as motivated to controlling and molding their children as are higher status mothers, and if this is not actually the case, it would mean that these teachings stand relatively less chance of being implemented. Moreover, if lower-class socialization is so likely to be governed by the child's own inclinations, his parents' convenience, and fortuitous circumstances, it is probable that the health worker must cope with much greater variation in practices than he may be aware of.

This discussion has considered three areas in which social class has important implications for public health. Social class differences are associated with the differential distribution of disease and consequent definitions of appropriate foci of public-health interest and activity, with variations in quality of interpersonal relations and the health team and between the team and the public it serves, and with divergences in goals and perceptions between the health worker and his client.

By virtue of the fact that the situation of action in the public-health field typically involves the higher status practitioner and lower status patient, class differences in realistic conditions, value orientations, and behavioral characteristics may have a substantial role to play in determining the outcome of public-health programs. Acceptance or rejection of the goods and services that public health has to offer in large part depends upon how these are perceived by the recipient. Such perceptions vary with one's class membership, and attempts to change them are likely to collide with the individual's investment in his group affiliations. A social class constitutes a membership group, and promoting and maintaining one's acceptance by the group calls for conformity with the perceptions and behavior deemed correct and desirable by the group, whether it be in relation to health and illness or anything else.

13   "METROPOLIS"—WHAT CITY PEOPLE THINK OF THEIR MEDICAL SERVICES*

By Earl Koos

"Metropolis" is a city of approximately 350,000 population located in the industrial northeastern United States. It has a medical school, a half-dozen approved hospitals, a full complement of medical specialists, a sprinkling of general practitioners—and the usual assortment of quasimedical manipulators, in spite of whom the American people seem to survive. Its expenditures for hospital facilities and services are at least average and its public health services are certainly above average. Its foreign-born and Negro populations are not disproportionate in either size or characteristic. It is a city characterized by some sophistication, and it is proud of that fact. Metropolis is probably not entirely representative of cities of its size, but it is surely not so different as to make the findings of this study meaningless.

This study was concerned with an economically stratified but randomly selected sample of 1,000 families. Sampling was centrally controlled and was based upon decennial census city-block data, aerial survey maps, and city directory listings; the characteristics of the sample were not markedly different from those of the city's total population.

As in the case of Regionville,[1] the findings are reported upon the basis of the family's membership in one of three social strata. These are designated, for present purposes, as Classes I, II, and III, in descending order of socioeconomic position in the community. Here, too, X^2 was used to ascertain the significance of the relation between what people thought and did about health and their socioeconomic position.

Incidentally, the term "medical services," as used here, is broadly interpreted and includes not only the paramedical team but such other services as are used by the population—whether within the professional groups or not. Also, this whole research project centers upon the philosophy that health is the concern of all members of the community and not solely that of the medical profession.

We can report briefly upon only five aspects of the total medical care program.

Medical Care. *What Did Metropolis Think of Its Medical Care?*—There was, surprisingly enough, little criticism expressed regarding the cost of medical care. Only 19 percent of the respondents believed that medical care cost too much and these were distributed among all three social classes. From the content of the interviews it was evident that costs were thought not to be out of line with the general high cost of living.

Pronounced dissatisfaction with the medical care as available or received (and these two are closely related) was found in only 17 percent of the interviews. There was a significant difference among the social classes, however, with dissatisfaction, as might be expected, found among those families which

From *American Journal of Public Health*, 45, (December, 1955), 1551–1557. Copyright 1955 by The American Public Health Association, Inc.

made use of nonmedical personnel in the treatment of illness. This is not to say, however, that there was no dissatisfaction with certain aspects of medical care, for special criticisms were equally in evidence among all three social classes. Fifty-one percent of the respondents criticized the physicians of Metropolis for being unwilling to make house calls, or for the counterpart— the insistence of the physician that a sick individual be brought to the office or taken to the hospital for examination in all but the most serious cases. Dissatisfaction was expressed, too, in 47 percent of the responses with the physicians' handling of his office practice—with "having a two o'clock appointment and having to wait until three-thirty to see him."

The greatest criticism centered, however, upon the nature of today's patient-physician relationship. Sixty-four percent of the replies indicated that modern, technic-centered medical practice lacked the human warmth of the old-time general practitioner (who possibly knew less about medicine but more about his patients). Those who are defensive regarding criticisms of modern medical care have been known to charge that this attitude exists only among the older age groups who view the passing of the family doctor with nostalgia. Our data do not bear this out, for the respondents in the families with husbands under 40 years of age were even more definite in this criticism than were those in the older age group. In the words of a young Class II matron: "We're new at this (raising a family). If we could feel that we mean something to Dr.—, I'd be happy with him. But I'm sure he has to look at baby's history, or have his nurse tell him who we are, so he'll know what to call me. . . . It's like running through an assembly line to go to his office. . . . I'm sure, though, that he knows his medicine—from that point I'm satisfied."

We can probably best sum up the position of the people of Metropolis regarding their medical care in these words: they tend to be satisfied with what they get and to accept its cost, but they dislike the way it is provided.

It is futile to belabor the physicians of Metropolis for providing an office-centered and impersonal type of medical care, for they are very often caught in a social matrix not of their own making. It should not be futile, however, to suggest that the physician alter his technics and attitudes—in so far as is humanly possible—in order to provide what the people feel they need and want from medical care. Certainly, the direction of such a change is in accord with the current trend in medical education,* and with the developing emphasis upon the psychosomatic aspects of medical care.

Hospital Care. *What Did Metropolis Think of the Care Provided in Its Hospitals?*—In answering this question from our data the picture seems to be almost the reverse of that presented in the preceding section. Hospital costs were believed to be too high, in 82 percent of the answers, and there appeared to be no mitigating factors so far as these respondents were concerned. Equally important, however, was the pronounced unfavorable reaction regarding the care given by the hospitals. This negative attitude was confined to no one hospital, nor was it significantly associated with any one socio-economic stratum. Seventy-one percent of the respondents believed the hospital care available to them to be unsatisfactory, but many then qualified their response, as is illustrated in the following abstract from an interview: "I don't say our hospitals don't turn you out alive—at least they most often don't kill you—but the way they treat you while you are in their hands is pitiful. . . . I was in —Hospital for four weeks last spring. They didn't do anything to hurt me, but they certainly didn't do anything to help me psychologically to get well. . . . I can't put my finger on it, exactly. I think what I'm trying to say is nobody just gave a darn about me as a person. I was just somebody filling a bed."

The uncertainty expressed here as to what was undesirable about the care received was characteristic of eight out of 10 of the respondents who believed hospital care to be inadequate. Some were able to identify particular events, or to name persons who caused them to feel as they did; the failure to receive a prescribed treatment on time, or the crotchety behavior of a nurse or aid, are examples. Others, and they were in the majority, could only report a virulent dislike for the care they had received or would expect to receive without being able to pinpoint the cause of their attitude.

Further discussion in each interview, using open-end questions, did elicit some data which seem important. It appears, for example, that the hospitals' changing social structure—in which the old and relatively simple hierarchy of doctor-nurse-orderly-kitchen maid has been replaced by one including all manner of aides, technicians, floor clerks, and so on—has created confusion and frustration for the patient and his family. Nursing, in the old sense of the word—a highly personal one-to-one relationship—appeared from the data to have been replaced with a highly specialized division of labor in which the patient had an unrecognized and sometimes an uncertain place. The same respondent quoted above had this to say: "Now that you get me to talk it out, maybe I see what disturbed me. It was that I never knew exactly who did what for me. . . . If I rang my bell, someone came and then said, "I'll have so-and-so do that." But maybe so-and-so never came, so I was just left to lie there."

Here, too, it is necessary to admit that the hospital—as well as the physician—is caught in the coils of an advancing medical technology, as well as faced with pressing problems of labor and economics. But it is also necessary to state our belief that many of the ills current in hospital-patient-family relations are present simply because, as the respondents imply, the patient has been somehow forgotten in the course of hospital progress.

Since the two topics just discussed are somewhat different from those which are to follow, we may well look briefly at their implications. Whether or not the people of Metropolis have favorable attitudes toward the care afforded them is important. There is no place in modern medical care for "the devil take them if they don't like what we have to offer" attitude on the part of the paramedical team. If the patient's needs are to be met, if he is to be kept healthy or returned to health—these can be accomplished only if he has a favorable relation to the sources of this medical care and some accepting understanding of what is being done to and for him. The data in other portions of the study strongly imply that many illnesses go untreated and the patient and his family muddle through to an unsatisfactory solution of a health problem simply because of their negative attitudes which inhibit the use of modern medicine.

Public Health Services. *What Did Metropolis Think of the Care Provided by Its Public Health Personnel?*—Metropolis has a health department upon which it spends considerable money and to which it could point with pride; its services, also, were of such a nature that they reached into all levels of the population. Despite all of these qualifications, the data show that there was no great consciousness of the value, the effectiveness, or even the functions of the health department. This ignorance, furthermore, was proportionately distributed among all three social strata.

More than two-thirds of the respondents in each of the classes viewed the health department's functions as solely those of a health police force. Such functions as "keeping the water pure," "being sure that sewage is taken care of," "quarantining people who have infected (sic) diseases," "being sure that restaurants are clean," etc., were interpreted by respondents in all three classes as the only functions of the health department. (Were the director of that department responsible only for such activities in Metropolis his job would indeed be a much easier one). The other and more positive (although less dramatic) functions—promoting and coordinating the health functions of the schools and other agencies, educating special groups, etc., were apparently unrecognized by the very public which supported them through taxation. This seems to indicate that Metropolis views its medical care in a very limited way—as simply a matter of physician's services, hospital care, and certain policing functions.

Time and again, Haven Emerson, M.D., and others have raised questions in meetings such as this as to why we have not progressed farther and faster in our community health programs in all of the 48 states. May not one of the answers be found in these data? If the population of a sophisticated urban community of better than average economic status is as devoid of knowledge of its health department's activities as these data indicate, we may well expect a similar or greater lack of appreciation of the health department's functions —and the need for them—in communities with less advantages.

The reverse of the above is equally significant. When presented with a question regarding any health needs which were not being met but might be met through health department activities there was a decided lack of fruitful answers (only 2 per cent in Class I, 3 percent in Classes II and III), and the needs suggested were already being met, at least in part, in a majority of cases. These findings suggest either a magnificent complacency about the health of the community, or an acute unawareness of what the term health really means, or an unawareness of what public health personnel have to offer. Any of the three gives professional health workers the right to be disturbed.

Nonmedical Health Care. *What Did Metropolis Think of the Quasiprofessional Health Care Provided by Nonmedical Personnel?*—Since people do turn to nonmedical and quasiprofessional people for help in meeting their health needs, it is legitimate and important that we understand how these extramural services are regarded. In the present writing, the greatest importance lies not so much in the actual care given, however unscientific or damaging it may be, for this care is not numerically too important—only 9 percent of the families were reported in this category—but in how the total population regards these services. For this regard constitutes, in our opinion, something of an index of how the total population conceptualizes its health needs and services.

First, the data show that the use of nonmedical personnel, in both the treatment of illness and in its prevention, was a phenomenon confined primarily to Class III, with very little use by Class II, and practically none by Class I. The data suggest, as did those in the Regionville study,[2] that the use of such personnel was not primarily for economic reasons, but because of the psychological values which the patients appeared to gain from such care. In other words, the anonymity characteristic of the care in teaching clinics and outpatient departments and the impersonality of the physician's office (especially as reported by Class III respondents) were in sharp contrast to the care afforded by the nonmedical practitioner.

The real importance of the data in this section seems to lie, however, in the noncritical attitude, especially of Classes I and II, toward such care. It had been hypothesized that these classes would reject the idea of such care being available and on a variety of grounds. Actually, 73 percent of Class I and 67 percent of Class II respondents either knew nothing of such care (and therefore had no attitude regarding it) or saw no reason why it should be strictly controlled or prohibited. This seems, again, to mean that a large portion of the population of Metropolis is either indifferent to standards of medical care as they relate to the total population, or that people lack the background for a critical evaluation of medical care. If adequate medical care is to be the concern and responsibility of the whole population, rather than of the medical profession alone, these findings give us cause for reflection—and for some form of educational activity.

Health Insurances. *What Did Metropolis Think of the Nonprofit Services Which Provided It with Insurance Against Medical and Hospital Costs?*—If the family is to be bulwarked against the economic pressures of medical services in a satisfying manner, the data on this topic are important. (Metropolis has an unusually high participation in both Blue Cross and Blue Shield because of the nature of its industrial organizations.) Seventy-eight percent of the respondents reported satisfaction with Blue Cross, but only 49 percent with Blue Shield. The data indicate that the difference lies in the fact that Blue Cross more nearly provides complete coverage than does Blue Shield. Class II (which might be termed representative of the "great American middle class") was especially critical of the fact that there was a considerable gap between what the insurance paid for and what the physician or surgeon charged. "If we're going to be insured, then we ought to be completely covered" was the sentiment most often expressed by Class II respondents. The Class II respondents were also most concerned with the need for the extension of insurance services to include long-time illness (both acute and chronic). This might be expected, since Class I was able to meet its own needs in this regard and Class III had available a number of institutional aids in time of such illnesses. When we realize that nonprofit insurance against the economic costs of illness has been in existence only within our own lifetimes we can view with some satisfaction the coverages already provided. We need, however, to recognize that medical care costs still outrun the protection available and to view realistically John Doe's desire for more protection against the cost of illness.

Implications of These Findings. No social research is worth its salt if it does not give some insights into the workings of society. In this paper we have indicated the findings very briefly and can only sketch lightly the insights.

A first of these insights is known to all of us, but worthy of reemphasis: to wit, that modern medical care, whether in the physician's office, the clinic, or the hospital, appears to move—consciously or not—away from the needs of the consumer of that care. The data show that this population viewed adversely the aura of impersonality which (at least in their opinions) pervaded the highly technical medical care available today. These adverse attitudes were directed toward the physician in his office and toward the hospital and the clinic. These adverse atttiudes might be of little importance except for the fact that they are strongly prescriptive or proscriptive for the behavior of the individual when he needs medical care. We recognize, for example, that the pregnant mother should have prenatal care from an early date; we must also recognize that how she and her associates view the available care determines in good measure whether or not she will seek that early prenatal care, and how she will accept its dictates if she does seek it.

It appears that too strong an emphasis cannot be placed upon this aspect of medical care. Certainly there are tremendous advances yet to be made in medicine, but the advances to this point do guarantee to our people preventive or successful treatment of much of what can ail us. (Vital statistics trends are a constant reminder of this fact). If Metropolis is to use its medical care to the full extent necessary for "good" health, then that medical care must be of such a nature (aside from its technical aspects) that it is viewed favorably by the consumer. To create this favorable view demands revisions, not of the technics of medicine (for only rarely does the prospective patient set himself up as a judge of these), but of the technics of human relations in medicine —wherever medicine is practiced.

A second of these insights focuses squarely upon the roles of the physician, nurse, technician, sanitarian, or other member of the paramedical team. Here, I can only repeat what has previously been said in connection with our findings in Regionville. Each of these professional persons accepts his primary role without question, each performs it within the limits of his ability or perception, but each may fail in so doing to broaden adequately the patient's or family's perceptions of what health is, because each may fail somewhat to assume the role of teacher. As a result, the patient still sees the physician as a "healer of symptoms" rather than as what John R. Paul has called a "clinical epidemiologist."[3] And the same appears to be true for the other technical personnel involved in the health activity. Is it not highly probable that the reason the average citizen shows so little knowledge of, or interest in, the broader aspects of health care is because in the physician's office, the hospital, or the clinic he is helped only to focus his attention on the symptom and the services related to it? May it not be that the taking for granted attitude expressed toward public health services and the limited knowledge shown are products of this symptom-focused attention?

This involves, of course the significant question of how much the people of Metropolis should know about illness—an old question in the world of medicine. We need only to look at any popular magazine today to realize that people are being given information on medical developments—sometimes in an unduly optimistic fashion. It seems inconsistent for the paramedical team to withhold itself from the teaching role, only to have that role assumed by every slick-paper magazine.

Summary. It may be said, then, that Metropolis views its medical services with mixed emotions. It accepts its medical care, in general, without undue reaction against the cost, but with strong reservations regarding the emphasis upon technical medicine given without regard for human relationships. It accepts hospital care, but with strong reservations both regarding costs and hospital-patient relations. It takes for granted public health services and has little recognition of what public health really has to offer in mid-20th century. It views with remarkable complacency the nonmedical services which attempt so feebly to substitute for medical services. In short, despite the excellence of its medical personnel, its hospitals, and its public health department, Metropolis is, in the opinion of these respondents, as yet some distance from the millenium in regard to medical care.

14   PARENT ATTITUDES TOWARD PARTICIPATION OF THEIR CHILDREN IN POLIO VACCINE TRIALS*

By John Clausen, Morton Seidenfeld, and Leila Deasy

The public health officer is frequently faced with the task of securing public cooperation for programs or measures which much be established or carried through in very short order. He knows in a general way which segments of the population are likely to support particular measures and which segments are likely to be resistant or hostile. Data secured from a study of parental reactions to polio vaccine trials may be useful in indicating in somewhat greater detail than is usually available the factors influencing participation in such a program and the attitudes and characteristics of participants and non-participants.

Testing the Salk polio vaccine by inoculating hundreds of thousands of school children during 1954 entailed an intensive task of local organization in a relatively short period of time. After selection of the counties in which vaccinations were to be carried out, it was the task of local health officers to orient school officials and parents to the proposed program and to arrange for the administration of the vaccine (by local physicians) and the maintenance of the necessary records. As in the case of other new vaccines, there were a number of unanswered questions about the Salk vaccine and some differences of opinion as to its probable effectiveness. It was taken for granted that some parents would have reservations about having their children vac-

From *American Journal of Public Health*, 44, (December, 1954), 1526–1536. Copyright 1954 by the American Public Health Association, Inc.

cinated, and participation was invited on a voluntary basis with a presentation of the facts about the vaccine as the only means of inducing such participation.

This paper presents data on the factors influencing parental consent to participate in the vaccine trials, drawn primarily from interviews with mothers of second-grade children in five schools in a single county in Virginia. The county is partially suburban to Washington, partly rural. Although the area was not selected as "typical" in any specified respects, it is believed that the factors that influenced parents in this county were, on the whole, relevant to the decision of parents in other areas. The uncertainty facing parents in this county was, however, markedly intensified by the fact that several other counties in the immediate area had planned to participate in the vaccine trials but, for reasons relating to the scheduling of the trials, had decided to postpone them indefinitely. Indeed, this was the only county in the United States in which four neighboring areas withdrew from participation.

A brief chronology of the events and communications preceding the vaccine trial will provide a background for the data to be presented. General announcements (without mention of specific areas) were carried in major news magazines and in Washington papers in the fall of 1953. The first mention in Washington papers that counties in the area might participate came early in March, 1954. It was indicated that several cities and counties suburban to Washington might be involved, though early coverage dealt largely with a Maryland county where plans were most fully developed. The scheduling of inoculations in this country had been predicted upon availability of the vaccine prior to the spring recess of the schools. The vaccine could not be made available at the desired time, however, and the trial of the vaccine was first postponed and subsequently abandoned in the suburban Maryland county, even though orientation sessions had been held and consent slips distributed. Major metropolitan papers gave prominent space to this sequence of events and decisions. During March and early April several papers also carried feature articles by science writers describing the rationale for the vaccine tests, the nature of the Salk vaccine, and the methods of preparing and safety testing it.

Following abandonment of the tests in suburban Maryland, press attention focused upon the Virginia county in which the present study was conducted. Shortly thereafter, a nationally known radio commentator told his listeners that the vaccine had been found to contain live virus and warned them not to permit their children to receive the shots. In the county under study, the medical society and the health officer issued a joint statement squarely facing the charges of the commentator, expressing confidence that a safe vaccine would be available and assuring parents that the vaccine would not be used if any doubts about safety remained unresolved. This statement was carried in full in the local suburban press and was prominently featured in abridged form in the metropolitan dailies. At the same time editorials in the major papers expressed confidence in the program and in the safety measures, specifically decrying the emotional attack made by the commentator. In short, the press reported some controversy over the use of the Salk vaccine, but was preponderantly favorable in its presentations about the program. In the following two weeks, however, one other city and one county which had considered participating in the program decided not to do so. This fact was known to many parents in the county studied and was clearly a source of doubt about the program for some of them.

To assess the factors influencing parental decision, mothers were interviewed in the week between the deadline for returning the consent slips to the school and the commencement of inoculations. Interviewers used a previously pretested questionnaire; the interview averaged 20 minutes to a half an hour in length. The sample consisted of every third name from the rosters of second-grade children.[1] In the schools selected the proportion of parents giving consent ranged from 30 to 71 percent.[2] In the larger suburban schools, the high proportion of parents giving consent made it desirable to increase the subsample of parents who did not give consent. This was done by taking every other name from the roster of those who had not given consent.

The total sample interviewed comprised 175 mothers, of whom 101 had given consent and 74 had withheld consent. Interviews were conducted in the home. If the mother was not at home a single return call was made. Only three persons designated for interviews refused to cooperate.

In addition to the interviews, data were secured from observation of the meetings held in the schools to inform parents about the vaccine tests. All questions raised by parents in these meetings were listed and analyzed as to content.

Hypotheses Underlying the Research. Numerous factors enter into a decision that involves permitting one's child to participate in a frankly experimental program aimed at preventing disease. While such decisions are seldom made wholly on logical grounds, many parents may be expected to balance the probability of gain against the possibility of harmful effect. Familiarity with the idea and practice of inoculations for prevention of communicable disease and the acceptance by parents of the importance of the scientific approach in medicine may be expected to exert favorable influences. On the other hand, misconceptions about the objectives and procedures of the vaccine trials may lead to withholding of consent. Of considerable interest was the question of how parents would attempt to increase their knowledge of relevant aspects of the vaccine trials and how they might resolve uncertainties.

Data relating to the following variables were secured through the interview schedule:

Sources of information about the vaccine itself
Sources of information about the local vaccine trials
Attendance at orientation meetings at the school
Amount of consultation with medical and nonmedical personnel
Precautions usually taken to protect family from polio
The child's feelings about the shots
Attitudes toward the program and its objectives

Factors Influencing Parental Consent. Reasons for deciding whether or not to participate in a health program designed to test a new vaccine may be quite complicated. Further, while people may be aware of some of the considerations which led them to a particular conclusion, they may not be at all aware of considerations which might have reversed their decision. Nor, for that matter, may they be aware of the fact that they have certain misconceptions and that they are therefore reasoning from false premises. Nevertheless, it is useful to know the reasons to which they themselves ascribe their decision.

Mothers who consented to their children's receiving the vaccine reported as their main reason the belief that the vaccine would be effective. Most of those who withheld consent said they did so because of particular health conditions of the child or because they were uncertain as to the safety of the vaccine. Thus, the ultimate physical well-being of their children seemed the overwhelmingly important consideration influencing parents regardless of their decisions (Table 1).

Table 1—Reasons Reported by Mothers for Giving or Withholding Consent (Per cent)

Main Reason for Consenting (101 Mothers)		Main Reason for Not Consenting (74 Mothers)	
May prevent polio	66	Physical condition of child	30
Contribute to medical research	24	Parent believes shots unsafe	24
Medical authorities approve	2	Opposes "experimentation"	11
Other reasons	8	Controversy over program	9
		No proof of effectiveness	7
		Opposition of child	4
		Other reasons	15

It is obvious that many of the considerations which led some parents to give consent were accepted also by parents who withheld consent; yet they were not regarded by them as compelling toward approval in the face of their doubts and fears. What then influenced these two groups? Two types of data are available: (1) data on certain characteristics, beliefs, and attitudes of the two groups, and (2) the mothers' reports on the factors that influenced their decision.[3]

Educational-Informational Level. Mothers who gave consent for their children to receive the vaccine tended to have a higher educational level (Table

Table 2—Educational Level of Mothers by Consent Group (Per cent)

	Mothers Who Gave Consent	Mothers Who Withheld Consent
Grade school	8	26
Some high school	13	22
High school graduate	32	25
College (any amount)	47	27
Total	100	100

2) and to be better informed about the vaccine than were those who withheld consent (Table 3). The marked difference in educational levels was associated with many differences in belief and attitude between the two groups as will be seen.

Table 3—Over-all Sources of Information About Polio Vaccine (Per cent)

	Mothers Who Gave Consent	Mothers Who Withheld Consent
NFIP leaflets sent home from the school	99	92
Newspapers (alone or in combination with other sources)	90	74
Radio-TV (alone or in combination)	40	54
Magazines (alone or in combination)	29	16
Other sources	13	3
No sources of information reported, other than school	5	15
Number of cases	(101)	(74)

Leaflets describing the vaccine trials were sent home via the children at the time the consent slips were distributed and all but a few of the parents reported that they had received this material. Most parents received some information from other sources as well.

A large part of the difference in the proportions of the two groups who derived information from various sources, of course, is related to educational background. Among respondents whose education had not extended as far as high school graduation, however, those giving consent were significantly more likely to have received information from other sources than were those withholding consent (e.g., on newspaper readership about the vaccine, the relative percentages were 77 and 54.) It is noteworthy that more of the mothers who gave consent derived information from printed sources, while more of those who withheld consent heard some information over radio and television. The latter media had not been systematically used for presenting information about the program. A larger proportion of those who said they had received information through radio and television also reported that they had heard the commentator who warned listeners against the vaccine. For many, then, this may have been the sole source of information through these channels.

The differences between consent groups in initial source of information about local participation in the program are striking. Of parents who gave consent, two-thirds first heard about the participation of their county through newspapers. Of those who did not give consent, only a third derived their initial information from this source. The major part of this difference reflects the difference in educational levels as will be seen in Table 4.

Table 4—Source of Initial Information on Polio Vaccine Trials in Local County by Consent Group and by Education (Per cent)

Source of Initial Information	Less than High School Graduation	High School Graduate	College	Less than High School Graduation	High School Graduate	College
The school	57	32	8	50	45	20
The child	..	..	2	8	..	..
Friends and neighbors	..	3	4	8	..	15
Newspapers	38	62	82	20	50	55
Radio-TV	..	3	4	8	..	5
Other	5	..	..	6	5	5
Total	100	100	100	100	100	100
Number of cases	(21)	(31)	(48)	(35)	(18)	(20)

This table does indicate, however, that for each educational level those who gave consent were more likely to have learned about the local program through the newspapers than were those who withheld consent. This finding is probably a reflection both of when parents learned about the trials and of the more favorable orientation of those parents who were well informed. Those who had read about the program seem to have been better prepared to assess favorably the materials brought home from school by the child.

Consultation with Medical and Nonmedical Personnel. Parents who gave consent were much more likely to have talked with others about the polio vaccine shots than were parents who withheld consent. This was true not only with respect to consulting the family physician, but also with respect to discussing the matters with friends, relatives and neighbors, or with personnel in the schools (Table 5).

Table 5—Extent to Which Mothers Discussed Shots with Others by Consent Group (Per cent)

Persons with Whom Shots were Discussed	Mothers Who Gave Consent	Mothers Who Withheld Consent
Doctor or nurse	41	27
Friends, relatives, neighbors	61	39
School personnel	15	8
Talked with no one	28	47

Again, the differences with reference to consultation reflect in part the different educational distribution of the two groups, since college graduates were much more likely to consult others than were persons with only a grade school education. Among those who had not been graduated from high school, however, twice as many of the parents who gave consent, as of those who withheld consent, had consulted a physician.

Attendance at Orientation Meetings. One-third of the parents who gave consent attended the meetings conducted by the Health Department for parents, but less than one-sixth of the parents who withheld consent attended. This immediately raises the question of whether it was primarily the favorably disposed parents who attended the meeting or whether attendance actually induced parents to decide favorably. The first alternative seems more largely to have been the case, as is evidenced by the fact that regardless of final decision 34 per cent of those whose initial impressions had been favorable went to the meetings but only 14 percent of those whose initial impressions were unfavorable attended.

It cannot be assumed that the meetings did not serve a positive function. Among parents who had initially been undecided, those who attended an orientation session at one of the schools were significantly more likely subsequently to give consent than were parents who did not attend (75 percent of the former group versus 41 percent of the latter gave consent). Moreover, many parents favorably disposed toward the program, yet harboring some uncertainties and anxiety, were apparently reassured by the answers given to their questions at these meetings conducted by the health officer and his staff.

Feelings About Polio and Personal Contact with Polio. Whether or not they consented to their children's participation in the test, most mothers regarded polio as the most serious of the diseases that afflict children. More than four-fifths agreed that "most people worry more about polio than abut any other disease that strikes children." Those parents who gave consent were slightly more likely to report that a close friend or relative had had polio, but the difference was not significant (36 percent versus 28 percent). Most likely this difference reflects the persons of higher socio-economic and educational status.

Table 6—Reported Precautions Taken to Protect Against Polio by Consent and by Educational Level (Per cent)*

Precautions Reported by Mother	Less than High School Graduation	High School Graduate	College	Less than High School Graduation	High School Graduate	College
Avoidance of crowded areas in season	33	61	61	20	39	80
Avoidance of epidemic areas	..	13	23	6	17	15
Special attention to health care	33	71	73	26	61	80
Polio insurance	5	10	10	3	11	5
Other	5	3	..	3	..	..
No precautions	43	16	6	66	22	5
Number of cases	(21)	(31)	(48)	(35)	(18)	(20)

* Percentages add to more than 100 since many parents took more than one type of precaution.

On the other hand, four-fifths of the parents who gave consent said they took some precautions to protect their children against polio, while the comparable proportion for parents who withheld consent was about three-fifths. Nowhere else are differences between educational levels more striking (Table 6). It appears, then, that concern about polio is slightly related to the giving of consent for vaccine shots, but is of minor significance except perhaps for those parents whose education did not extend as far as high school graduation.

Doubts About the Safety of the Vaccine. Doubts as to the safety of the vaccine were clearly the most pressing reason for withholding consent. More than four-fifths of the mothers who withheld consent expressed doubt about safety in answer to a direct question (Table 7).

Table 7—Responses to Question on Safety by Consent Group (Per cent)

Are You Completely Convinced that Shots Will Be Perfectly Safe?	Mothers Who Gave Consent	Mothers Who Withheld Consent
Yes	82	18
No	12	67
Undecided	6	15
	100	100

Why were so many parents in doubt on this score? True, there were widely circulated public statements from certain sources which were negative to the program. On the other hand, the weight of medical opinion, both nationally and in the local county, was strongly favorable. Some parents had very cogent reasons for feeling that their own children should not be involved (because of allergic conditions, for example). Others had consulted the family physician or other authority figures and had been left with just enough doubt so that they decided against the child's participation.

It is significant that doubts about the safety of the vaccine were equally frequent at all educational levels. Mothers who were college graduates were more likely to have heard specifically that live virus had been found in the vaccine, but were also more likely to have checked with their physicians and to have consulted other sources of information about the program. Thus, those high school and college graduates who were dubious about the safety of the vaccine were on the whole not simply reacting to rumors or to emotional statements against the vaccine, but were making reasoned judgments based on a substantial amount of information. This was not as true of the respondents with less education who expressed doubt about the safety of the vaccine. To a considerable extent they seem to have made up their minds with relatively little information.

Eighteen percent of those who gave consent nevertheless had some doubts about safety. It appears these these persons were definitely of two minds about this matter, but resolved the conflict because of the strong hope that the shots would yield positive protection against polio (voiced by 78 percent as their main reason for consent). Two-thirds had consulted their physicians about the shots—as against 37 percent of those who were perfectly convinced that the shots were safe.

Opposition of Child to Taking Shots. One-tenth of the parents who gave consent and one-fourth of those who withheld consent reported that their child in the second grade was "very much against" the shots. Although only a few mothers gave this as the main reason for not approving of the child's receiving the shots, it may well have been a contributing factor in a number of instances. Opposition by the child was reported most frequently by parents whose initial impression was unfavorable and who withheld consent (38 percent reported the child strongly opposed). It will be recalled that these parents most often received their initial information about the program when the child brought home the announcement from school.

General Attitudes Toward the Program and Its Objectives. Responses to five statements with which the mothers were asked to express agreement or disagreement afford an indication of favorability to several of the major ideas embodied in the vaccine trials (Table 8).

The proportion of favorable responses to individual items, on the part of mothers who had withheld consent, indicates that withholding consent was not a matter of disapproval of all aspects of the vaccine trials. Indeed, the responses to those items indicate that consent and nonconsent should not be viewed as a sharp dichotomy, but rather as the reflection of different weightings of the issues involved and of the evidence with reference to these issues. In part the responses to these "agree-disagree" items reflect the orientations that led to one decision or another; in part, also, however, they probably represent rationalizations of the decision arrived at, whether or not the mother had previously been influenced by such considerations. The interrelationship between items 2 and 4 in this series is instructive in this respect. The two really bear upon the same point—that the vaccine must be tried out on many children before it is proved to be effective. To be consistent, then, any

Table 8—Responses to Items Reflecting Favorability to Program by Consent Group (Per cent)

Statement	Favorable Response	Per cent Giving Favorable Response	
		Mothers Who Gave Consent	Mothers Who Withheld Consent
1. "Since the shots may not be effective, I don't think my child should go through the discomfort of having them."	Disagree	92	56
2. "A vaccine for polio can't be proved effective until it is tried out on many thousands of children."	Agree	89	77
3. "I don't like the idea of my child getting the shots from anyone but our family doctor."	Disagree	94	65
4. "They shouldn't try out this vaccine on children unless they know it will prevent polio."	Disagree	81	41
5. "I would want my child to have the shots even if the chances of their preventing polio were slight."	Agree	92	43

parent who agreed with item 2 should disagree with item 4. The latter item, however, is worded more emotionally, the former more in "objective" terms.

It is not surprising that those who consented to their children's receiving the shots tended to be consistent in agreeing with item 2 and disagreeing with item 4. Of those who withheld consent, however, roughly half were inconsistent, agreeing with the objectively worded item (an argument for their participation), but not disagreeing with the emotionally worded item (an argument against their participation). This illustrates one of the major problems in putting across new health measures, or for that matter any other type of measures; communicating the abstract idea behind a measure does not insure that the public will be able to dismiss a negative argument stated in emotional terms. The suggestion that a program involves "trying something out without knowing whether it will work" may cause distrust, particularly among those unfamiliar with the scientific method. In such instances a frank discussion of the complex nature of the problem in terms of the experience of the participants is often useful in achieving conviction which will withstand emotional attacks.

Responses to the five items are even more highly related to educational background than was giving or witholding of consent. Of those mothers who withheld consent, yet who had relatively favorable attitudes toward various aspects of the vaccine trials, four-fifths had graduated from high school, while of the mothers with less favorable attitudes, only one-third had graduated from high school. Further examination of the differences between mothers whose attitudes are generally favorable and those with unfavorable attitudes among the groups who gave and who withheld consent reveals that the "favorable" mothers who withheld consent are more like the "favorable" mothers who gave consent than like the remainder of those who withheld consent. In other words, higher proportions of the two "favorable" groups were initially favorable to the idea of their own child's receiving the shots, attended meetings at the school, took precautions against polio, consulted their physicians, etc.

Why, then, did the one group not give consent? The reasons most frequently reported were classified under these headings: "Some physical condition of the child makes it unsafe for him to take the shots" (35 percent); "controversy over the program" (19 percent); and "general fears about the safety of the vaccine" (15 percent). It is likely, also, that in some instances the attitudes of the father were less generally favorable and that his voice in the process of decision accounted for the withholding of consent.

Discussion and Summary. Interviews were conducted with a sample of mothers of second-grade children in five schools participating in polio vaccine trials in a single Virginia county. The county is partially suburban to Washington; its population is characterized by an appreciably higher educational level than the United States population as a whole. The local situation with reference to the polio vaccine trials was markedly atypical in that several surrounding counties and cities which had considered participating in the trials withdrew when it appeared that the vaccine would be ready somewhat later than had been anticipated. Despite these differences, it is believed that information derived from mothers interviewed in this county illuminates the factors which influenced the decision of parents in other parts of the county as to their participation in the vaccine trials.

The level of participation achieved in this county—nearly two-thirds of the eligible children—represents an exceedingly favorable response in view of the withdrawal of other suburban areas which were to have been involved. Further, a number of parents who did not give consent refrained because of health reasons which they or their family physician regarded as cogent. Indeed, the overwhelming desire of parents interviewed was to do what would be best for their children. The major point of interest in the present research has been to analyze the various bases of assessment which lead to favorable or unfavorable response.

Mothers who had given consent to the participation of their children were found to be better informed about the nature of the trials, having read more and consulted more widely with medical and with nonmedical sources about the vaccine. On the whole, those who gave consent had been initially favorable to the idea. Attendance at orientation meetings in the schools was both an expression of favorable attitudes and a means of resolving uncertainties. Parents who consented were also more likely to have taken precautions to protect their children against polio in the past. Most of the differences in attitude and general orientation of parents who gave consent were associated with a very considerable difference in educational level and general socioeconomic status between the two groups.

In the instance of the polio vaccine trials, the chief consideration was that participation be sufficiently high to yield an adequate sample for assessing the effectiveness of the vaccine. It frequently happens, however, that programs for which there is a more impelling need for complete participation encounter the same source of resistances and the same apathetic responses from some segments of the population that was evidenced by a portion of the non-participants in the polio vaccine trials. Using the technics of social science research, it would seem fruitful to investigate further the methods of reaching and influencing those segments of the population which tend to be non-participants in such public health programs.

15   SOCIO-ECONOMIC STATUS, ILLNESS, AND THE USE OF MEDICAL SERVICES*

By Saxon Graham

A survey of past studies on the subject with which this paper deals generally reveals that the greatest amount of illness is found amongst those socio-economic classes which are least able to pay for it. The work of Sydenstricker in Hagerstown, Maryland as early as 1921 revealed an increase in illness with a decrease in socio-economic status (1). Despite differences in definitions of illness and socio-economic status, most of the subsequent studies had findings consistent with those in Hagerstown. They further discovered that the lower socio-economic classes, those with the greatest proportion ill, consulted physicians and were hospitalized least (2). One important exception, the study by the Committee on the Costs of Medical Care, suggested that persons in upper strata had highest illness rates, but concurred with other investigations in finding that lower strata use physicians and hospitals least (3).

The purpose of this paper is to examine the relationship of socio-economic status, illness, and use of physicians and hospitals in Butler Country, Pennsylvania in 1954. In the last fifteen years, America has seen continuing and increasing economic prosperity. Concurrently, it has witnessed a growth in the use of health insurance and increasing control of communicable diseases. It seems particularly important at this time, therefore, that the relationship between social stratification and health be re-examined to discover whether the traditional picture has changed in response to new conditions.

The data utilized in this investigation were gathered in June and July of 1954 by personal interviews on a probability sample developed through the area sampling technique, combined with geographic stratification and proportionate representation of urban, rural-place, and open country population.[1] The sample, consisting of 3,403 persons, represented roughly three per cent of the County's population, all of the white race. Butler County, it was found, is about 28 per cent urban, 20 per cent rural-place and 52 per cent open

From *The Milbank Memorial Fund Quarterly* (New York: Milbank Memorial Fund, 1957), 35, (January, 1957), 58–66.

country population. Two kinds of evidence can be used to evaluate the estimates developed in this survey. First, comparisons of the survey results with those of the 1950 census, show close similarities in estimates on age, sex, education, and rural-urban distributions. Secondly, computations of sampling variation of estimates based on the survey indicate a relatively small margin of error.

The Findings. Using Edwards' Occupational Categories to establish socioeconomic status, six classes were devised: professionals in Class A, proprietors and managers in class B, clerks and sales personnel in class C, skilled in class D, semi-skilled in class E, un-skilled in Class F. The 236 farmers in the sample were excluded from this analysis. The definitions of illness and of use of services must be carefully grasped. Respondents were first queried as to whether they or any members of their households had at the time of interview any of nine chronic diseases, rheumatic fever, high blood pressure, diabetes, asthma, kidney trouble, arteriosclerosis, or hernia. Later they were asked whether anyone in their households had consulted a physician, had been hospitalized, or had lost time from work or other usual activity in the month prior to interview. Questions were also asked to determine hospitalization in the year prior to survey. In each case of an affirmative answer, questions were asked as to whether a medical condition had been responsible, and if so, further questioning was undertaken to discover the nature of the medical condition. A final question had to do with whether any individual had been ill but had not seen a doctor, been hospitalized, or lost time from work. A count of the total number of people who affirmatively answered any of the questions and cited medical conditions as being responsible, furnished an estimate of the total illness in Butler County. Our analyses are in terms of numbers of people ill rather than in terms of attacks of illness.

It was found that no discernible differences existed among the classes in the total percentage of persons ill of any cause during the month preceding survey. Because of variations in age distribution of the classes, and of the importance of age in illness, proportions are age-adjusted. Class A reported 25 percent ill, as did class F. (*See* Table 1) This is at odds with traditional findings. In the proportions consulting with physicians regarding their illnesses, however, some differences were discovered. Fifty-eight percent of class A

Table 1—III persons and ill persons consulting physicians in the month prior to survey, in percentages (age-adjusted)

	CLASSES							
	High			Low			Total	X² Prob-ability
	A	B	C	D	E	F		
Total Persons III	40	69	66	205	179	176	735	.75
Percentage (Age-Adjusted)	25.3	22.8	24.2	25.3	23.3	25.5		
N	163	294	270	843	809	686	3,065	
III Persons Consulting Physicians in the Month Prior to Survey	23	23	30	93	69	74	312	.15
Percentage (Age-Adjusted)	58.3	34.5	40.4	43.8	36.6	40.6		
N	40	69	66	205	179	176	735	

individuals consulted with physicians and this decreased to around 40 percent of class F.

Dividing illnesses into acute and chronic conditions, we find only small differences. (*See* Table 2) Class A had the highest proportion of acutely ill individuals with 13.3 percent. Class F, however, had a somewhat smaller proportion with 9.8 percent. This increase of acute illness with increase in class rank is at odds with the inverse relationship discovered in the National Health Survey (4). But the differences observed in Butler were not significant by the

Table 2—Persons having acute illness and acutely ill persons consulting physicians in the month prior to survey, in percentages (Age-Adjusted)

		High			Low		Total	X^2 Prob- ability
	A	B	C	D	E	F		
Persons with Acute Illness	19	23	28	79	59	68	276	.25
Percentage (Age-Adjusted)	13.3	8.1	10.3	9.4	7.3	9.8		
N	163	294	270	843	809	686	3,065	
Acutely Ill Consulting Physicians	17	14	23	64	45	46	209	.15
Percentage (Age-Adjusted)	87.0	50.0	63.3	78.8	74.8	70.6		
N	19	23	28	79	59	68	276	

chi-square test.[2] With regard to acutely ill persons who consulted physicians relative to their illness, however, the traditional pattern was suggested. Thus, almost 90 percent of class A persons who were acutely ill saw their doctors, only half of class B, and around 70 percent in class F consulted their physicians. But although class F consulted less than class A, no regular decline from one to the other was observed, nor were differences statistically significant.

Table 3—Persons having chronic illness and chronic ill persons consulting physicians in month prior to survey, in percentages (age-adjusted)

		High			Low		Total	X^2 Prob- ability
	A	B	C	D	E	F		
Persons with Chronic Illness	22	50	45	145	136	130	528	.60
Percentage (Age-Adjusted)	12.7	15.8	16.5	17.7	18.1	19.0		
N	163	294	270	843	809	686	3,065	
Chronically Ill persons Consulting Physicians		17		36		52	105	.75
Percentage (Age Adjusted)		22.4		18.8		18.6		
N		72		190		266	528	

Table 4—Persons having impairments, in percentages (age-adjusted)

		High			Low		Total	X^2 Prob- ability
	A	B	C	D	E	F		
Persons Having Impairments		25		57		69	151	.75
Percentage (Age-Adjusted)		5.1		6.1		4.9		
N		457		1,113		1,495	3,065	

Persons having chronic disease were defined by considering those who answered affirmatively to the specific questions regarding whether household members had certain chronic diseases; also included were persons who reported an acute attack of a chronic disease in the month prior to survey.

Only insignificant differences in persons having chronic diseases amongst the classes were discovered. (*See* Table 3) Thirteen percent of class A were afflicted with chronic diseases in the month prior to survey as opposed to 19 per cent of class F. Thus, the traditional picture was again discovered. The number of persons consulting physicians for their chronic illness was very small, and estimates, therefore, are less reliable than in the cases already cited. Nevertheless, it was found that around 22 percent of classes A and B consulted their physicians as compared with around 19 per cent of classes C, D, E, and F.

With regard to reporting of impairments such as loss of arms or legs and vision or hearing defects, the upper, middle and lower classes were almost identical. (*See* Table 4). Roughly 5 percent in all classes reported an impairment.

Analyses of the use of health services among the classes revealed other differences which were small. (*See* Table 5). Thus the proportion of persons who saw a doctor for any reason, i.e., consultation for illness or for routine physical examinations was 18 percent of Class A as compared to 13 percent of class F. We have already seen that in consultation for illness, there was a small decline with class rank. An almost infinitesimal decline with rank also was recorded in proportions consulting physicians for examinations. The differences, of course, were not statistically significant.

Table 5—Persons consulting physicians in month prior to survey, and persons hospitalized in year prior to survey by percentages (age-adjusted)

	CLASSES							
	High			Low			Total	X² Prob-ability
	A	B	C	D	E	F		
Persons Consulting Physicians for Any Reason	28	37	37	109	94	87	392	.60
Percentage (Age-Adjusted)	17.5	12.5	13.6	13.0	12.1	12.5		
N	163	294	270	843	809	686	3,065	
Persons Consulting Physicians for Examination		15		21		40	76	.15
Percentage (Age-Adjusted)		3.0		1.9		2.7		
N		457		1,113		1,495	3,065	

Table 6—Persons hospitalized in past year by percentage (age-adjusted)

	CLASSES							
	High			Low			Total	X² Prob-ability
	A	B	C	D	E	F		
Persons Hospitalized in Past Year	13	16	20	56	43	44	192	.60
Percentage (Age-Adjusted)	7.8	5.2	7.2	6.8	5.5	6.5		
N	163	294	270	843	809	686	3,065	

Again, in the use of another type of health service, hospitals, no significant differences were revealed. Roughly 8 percent of class A persons were hospitalized in the year preceding survey as compared to around 7 percent of class F persons. (*See* Table 6). It was felt that the effect of possession of health insurance might have some influence on the use of hospitals by individuals in Butler County. Analysis revealed, however, that persons with health insurance are not much more likely to have been hospitalized than those without it.

We can conclude that when the variables are defined as they were in Butler County in 1954, the relationship of socio-economic status to illness differs in some degree from that found in past studies. Only minor differences were discovered in illness rates and in use of hospitals. The only relationships similar to those found earlier were in the slightly smaller use of physicians and the somewhat larger proportion of persons with chronic disease in the lower part of the socio-economic continuum. It is true that definitions of socio-economic status and of illness differ in the various studies. Some are based on income, others on categories such as "well-to-do" and "comfortable," and others, like the present study, on occupation. Nevertheless, the definitions are roughly similar. In view of the findings of the present study, then, we suggest that the whole problem of the relationship between socio-economic status, illness, and use of services should be re-examined in future studies.

It is possible that socio-economic differences in illness as defined in this paper never existed in Butler County, or that if they did in the past, as intimated by earlier studies, they have disappeared. If the latter alternative is the case, and this possibility exists, they may have disappeared because of the prosperity America has enjoyed in the last fifteen years, because of the proliferation of health insurance, and because of the increasing control of those illnesses which are fostered by low socio-economic status.

Increasing prosperity could make more universally available the material prerequisites for health, i.e., good food, housing, and the like, and thus help to reduce class differences in illness. Again, the greatest advances of medical science and public health have been in the direction of controlling communicable diseases. These are the diseases which are fostered by the crowding, filth, and other factors associated with low socio-economic status. The new control measures may be so effective that disease is reduced regardless of illness-producing conditions in some classes, and class differences in illness thus are reduced. Finally, the spread of health insurance protects all classes from the costs of illness, and this may promote the use of hospitals in equal degree by all classes. The possibility that the lower classes still consult physicians less may be a reflection of the less effective insurance provided for the costs of physicians' services.

All of these are suppositions only. We have no evidence that Butler County is peculiar in its conditions because of any change. The situation revealed may be a long-standing one. It is interesting, however, that Butler County does not appear to be aberrant from others in Pennsylvania in education, housing characteristics, or in medical care facilities. A study comparing illness and use of medical care facilities in Butler County and the Arsenal Health District of Pittsburgh revealed no important differences between the two areas (5). The one unequivocal statement that may be made is that in Butler County, while

some traditional relationships were suggested, no appreciable differences, as
we defined them, existed among socio-economic status groups in illness and
use of hospitals. This indicates the need for further examinations of the relationship.

16   **SOCIAL AND CULTURAL IMPLICATIONS OF**
        FOOD AND FOOD HABITS

By John Cassel

The last few decades have witnessed a rediscovery by the health professions
that man cannot be understood out of the context of his total environment.
The concept that the social and cultural components of this environment are
of equal if not of greater significance than the physical is not entirely new, but
only recently have attempts been made to organize and formalize this knowledge. Recent articles have indicated that these social and cultural factors may
play crucial roles in the whole broad area of interest to health workers, from
the dynamics of disease processes in the individual[1-3] to the development of
community-wide health promotion programs.[4, 5]

It is no coincidence that one of the major areas of interest common to
both the health professions and the social sciences should center round the
topic of food. From the dawn of medical history the role of food in health and
disease has been under investigation by health workers, and its significance
increases as further advances in nutritional knowledge are made. For social
scientists a study of food ways and the system of attitudes, beliefs, and practices surrounding food may constitute an important technic in unraveling
the complexities of the over-all culture pattern of a community.[6] Health workers are, in addition, now learning that food habits are among the oldest and
most deeply entrenched aspects of many cultures, and cannot therefore be
easily changed, or if changed, can produce a further series of unexpected and
often unwelcome reactions.

With this degree of interest in common food to social scientists and health
workers it is perhaps surprising that so little effective application of social
science concepts has been made to nutrition programs. Two major reasons
may account for this. The first is the lack of effective communication between
the two sciences; the second the degree to which we as health workers are
"culture bound" and tend to reject concepts and patterns of behavior different
from our own.

Lack of effective communication relates not only to the difficulties resulting from specialized terminology, although there is little doubt that this is a
problem. Of greater moment is the fact that health workers and social scientists approach their common goal, in this case a study of food, from two entirely different frames of reference without any common meeting ground.

From *American Journal of Public Health*, 47, (June, 1957), 732–740. Copyright 1957
by The American Public Health Association, Inc.

Social scientists, usually untrained in the field of health, cannot be expected to interpret the possible relationship of many of their findings to health programs, nor is this necessarily of particular interest to the majority of them. Health workers not being aware of the areas of competence of the social sciences cannot specify the contributions they might expect from these disciplines, especially in initiating or evaluating programs.

This paper is an attempt to illustrate by means of a case study some of these social and cultural factors of significance in programs designed to change food habits; an attempt will be made to derive certain general principles from this illustration; and finally some of the specific contributions that social scientists could make in such programs will be indicated.

Before considering these factors, however, it is desirable to elaborate somewhat on the degree to which we as health workers are "culture bound." The type of training the majority of us receive makes it difficult for us to see any merit in points of view or patterns of behavior different from our own. Food patterns for example which differ from our concepts of "good" practices are automatically labeled "bad." Attitudes and beliefs differing from ours are regarded as "illogical," "misinformed" or "wrong." The people who hold these different concepts are regarded as "ignorant" or perhaps "superstitious," "childlike" or plain "stupid."

Unfortunately, there are still too many of us who are convinced that our own particular set of beliefs, attitudes, and practices is the only correct way of life and one that should be emulated by people of all cultures and all social classes. Such a philosophy on our part presumes that only we as professional health workers know what is good for all people. Furthermore, it is frequently our fond belief that our nutritional education is being executed in a "knowledge vacuum" (to use the words of Edward Wellin[7]) as far as the recipients are concerned; that because the population we are serving knows nothing of our nutritional concepts, they therefore have no concepts whatever about nutrition. It is evident that documentation of the relevance of social and cultural factors to health programs is unlikely to lead to any effective application of these concepts as long as such attitudes are maintained by the majority of health workers.

The Case Study.* In 1940 the Pholela Health Centre was established on a "native reserve" in the Union of South Africa. Health conditions among the Zulu tribesmen to be served by this center were extremely poor. The crude mortality rate was 38 per 1,000 population and the infant mortality rate 276 per 1,000 live births. Poor environmental sanitation and communicable diseases represented two major health problems, but of greater significance, perhaps, was the extensive malnutrition that existed. Eighty percent of the people exhibited marked stigmata of this malnutrition and evidence of gross nutritional failure in the form of pellagra or kwashiorkor was common.

The Pholela Health Centre, charged with the responsibility of providing comprehensive medical care and health services to the population, was organized on the basis of a number of multidisciplined teams. Each team, consisting of a family physician, a family nurse, and a community health educator (health assistant), was responsible for the health of a number of families living in a defined geographical area. The major health problems of the area were defined by the teams and broadly classified into "unfelt" and "felt" needs. Health programs to meet these needs were then initiated on two planes in which the promotive-preventive and curative aspects of the services could be integrated. Basically the function of the health assistants was to develop community health education programs whereby the "unfelt" needs could be made apparent to the community, and members of the community stimulated to change aspects of their way of life to meet these needs. Simultaneously curative and preventive services to individuals within their family units was the responsibility of the doctor and nurse on the team. Each individual was offered periodic health examinations, followed by a family conference to discuss the health problems of that family, and any illness in any family member would similarly be treated by his family doctor and nurse. At the clinical sessions the community health education programs were reinforced in the specific advice given the individual patients.**

The case study to be presented here is a description of one program which was designed to change the food habits of mothers and infants. Dietary surveys revealed that the existing diet consisted principally of a single staple, corn, prepared in numerous ways, supplemented by dried beans, negligible amounts of milk and occasionally meat and wild greens. Potatoes and pumpkins were eaten seasonally, and millet (sorghum) was fermented to brew beer which was consumed in large quantities. Whenever funds allowed, sugar and white bread were also bought. Even though this was a rural agricultural community, poor farming methods and poverty of the soil made it impossible for the vast majority of the people to raise adequate food supplies. Consequently a large percentage of the food consisted of refined corn meal purchased with money sent home by the migrant laborers. Furthermore, during the best month of the year, if all the milk had been equally distributed, only one-twentieth pint per head per day would have been available. Having determined the existing food patterns an analysis was then made of the major factors responsible for the inadequacy of the diet. These included the extreme poverty of the people, the extensive soil erosion, certain traditions as to which foods were customary, and inefficient use of available resources. In addition prevailing cooking methods frequently destroyed a large fraction of what nutrients were present.

As anticipated, early attempts at group meetings and home visits to demonstrate the causal relationship between a poor diet and a low standard of health encountered considerable skepticism. People maintained that their diet had always been the diet of their people. On this same diet, they maintained, their ancestors had been virile and healthy and consequently there could be no possible relationship between the present diet and ill health.

It was difficult to refute this point without having any reliable information about the health of their ancestors.

A search of the available literature, however, revealed that the present diet had not always been the traditional diet of the Zulus and other Bantu-speaking tribes. Prior to the arrival of the whites, the indigenous cereal had been millet, corn having been brought into the country by the early white settlers. Because of its greater yield, corn had gradually supplanted millet as the staple cereal, millet being reserved solely for brewing. Furthermore, historically the Zulus were a roving pastoral people owning large herds of cattle; milk and meat had played a prominent part in their diet. So important was milk as an article of food that no meal was considered complete unless milk was included. The relatively fertile nature of the land at that time and the extensive wild game resulted in further additions of meat to the diet and a plentiful supply of wild greens. Roots and berries gathered from the forests were also extensively used.

These facts were presented to the community at the regular small group meetings initiated by the health assistants and discussion invited. In particular, confirmation was sought from the older members of the tribe, and in most instances such confirmation was received. This endorsement by the prestigeful and usually most conservative segment of the population insured that interest in the topic of food would remain high. Realization that the modern diet was not as traditional as had been supposed assisted in reducing resistance to the changes that were later advocated.

At subsequent meetings concepts of digestion and the functions of different foodstuffs were discussed. It was widely, though not universally, held that in some manner food entered the blood stream, but what happened to it thereafter was unspecified. Greatest interest was aroused by considering how a fetus was nourished in utero; discussion on this point would sometimes continue for hours. Many women were of the opinion that there must be a breast in the uterus from which the fetus suckled, but others indicated that calves in utero must be receiving nourishment in the same way, and no one had ever seen a breast in a cow's uterus. Some women maintained that the fetus was nourished by the placenta as the Zulu term for placenta literally means "the nurse." But when challenged, they were unable to explain how the placenta could feed the baby.

The result of these and similar discussions was to arouse a desire for further knowledge. When the functions of the placenta and umbilical cord were explained by use of posters and models, the interpretation was readily accepted. Over a period of time the concept that body tissues were nourished by the food via the blood stream became generally agreed upon.

As the concepts about the digestion and absorption of food began to change, it was possible to direct discussion to the function of different types of foods. The view generally held was that all food had only one function, to fill the stomach and relieve hunger. This view was challenged, however, by a number of people who maintained that certain foods gave strength and others were fattening—fat being a bodily attribute much valued in this community.

Gradually it became more generally accepted that different foods had different functions, particularly in regard to infant health and nutrition. In attempts to improve infant nutrition, and in view of the existing resources, it appeared that green vegetables, eggs, and milk were the foods on which greatest emphasis should be laid.

Introduction of Green Vegetables. Even though green vegetables had rarely formed part of the diet, and then only in a few families, their introduction for a number of reasons appeared to be a promising first step. Wild greens gathered from the forests had always been eaten and were enjoyed, but due to soil erosion these were becoming increasingly difficult to find. There were no very strong feelings or set of beliefs about green vegetables. The climate was suitable for their cultivation and each home had adequate space for use as a garden. Thus no marked objections to green vegetables was anticipated, their similarity to wild greens could be usefully exploited, and resources, at present unused, could be brought into use to make the vegetables available. In view of these circumstances the procedures that appeared to be necessary consisted of attempts to:

1. Increase the motivation of the people to eat vegetables—These included emphasis on their nutritional value in terms of concepts previously discussed; relating to their taste to that of familiar wild greens; and emphasis on the financial savings that could be made by replacing part of the purchased food by homegrown vegetables. These views were presented at the group discussions held in the homes of the people and reinforced at the clinical sessions, particularly the prenatal and mother and baby sessions.

2. Demonstrate the means by which these vegetables could be obtained by the families—A demonstration vegetable garden was developed at the Health Centre where members of the staff could themselves gain practical gardening experience and where the families could have the methods of growing vegetables demonstrated. Vegetables from this garden were made available to certain families on prescription. The more cooperative families were assisted in starting their own gardens and as the number increased a seed-buying cooperative was initiatied. Over the years a small market was established where families could sell their surplus produce, and annual garden competitions and an annual agricultural show were organized. As members of the Health Centre staff, particularly the health assistants, became more proficient gardeners themselves they were able to give practical advice and assistance to any of their families who desired it.

3. Demonstrate the palatability of the vegetables and the best means of incorporating them into the diet without destroying their nutrient values— Cooking demonstrations were organized both at the discussion groups and for the waiting patients at the Health Centre sessions. As far as possible, traditional means of preparing food were adhered to. Over the years different recipes were introduced and women from the area who were successfully incorporating vegetables into their families' diets were encouraged to organize these demonstrations.

The response of the community to those programs was satisfactory. In 1941 the first garden survey revealed that only 3 per cent of the homes had any form of vegetable garden, and that a total of five varieties of vegetables were growing. By 1951, 80 per cent of the homes had gardens and were growing more than 25 varieties of vegetables. This response was all the more gratifying as the size of the area served had been increased sixfold over the course of the 10-year period, so that some families had had only relatively recent contact with the program.

Increasing Egg Consumption. The attempts to increase the consumption of eggs encountered somewhat greater resistance than did the vegetable program. Surveys revealed that over 95 per cent of the families had poultry, and that eggs were relatively plentiful at certain seasons of the year. Eggs were infrequently eaten, however, but in contrast to vegetables, very definite views were held about them. It was considered uneconomical to eat an egg that would later hatch and become a chicken; egg eating was regarded as a sign of greed; and finally eggs were thought by some people to make girls licentious.

After prolonged staff meetings the consensus of team opinion was that none of these beliefs had any deep emotional associations and that probably the concept of it being poor economy to eat eggs was the most important of the factors preventing further use being made of eggs. The program based on this analysis therefore was patterned on the same general lines as the vegetable program. Technics for improving the egg yield whereby eggs could both be eaten and leave sufficient for breeding were discussed; the nutritional value and palatability of eggs were stressed both in the community education programs and for each specific patient at the prenatal and mother and baby session; and various methods for incorporating eggs into the diet without any marked modification of prevailing receipes were demonstrated. The fact that certain adverse views were held about eggs was of importance, however. Even though these views were not strongly held they indicated that relatively greater effort would be required to motivate the community to use eggs.

As might have been anticipated, therefore, response to this program was slower than to the vegetable garden program. In the course of 12 years, however, the technics proved relatively successful, and the consumption of eggs, particularly in infant diets, steadily increased. Furthermore, toward the later years of the program, families began to put excess eggs on the local market and found purchasers among their neighbors, a phenomenon totally foreign to this community.

The Milk Program. Increasing milk consumption proved to be a considerably more difficult and complex problem. Not only was the supply extremely limited, but frequently the available milk was not being consumed. In particular, women took no milk whatsoever, and this became a matter of some concern to the Health Centre in regard to expectant and lactating mothers. Investigation disclosed that milk drinking was associated with very deep-seated beliefs and customs. Only members of the kin group of the head of a household could use milk produced by that man's cattle. This restriction applied equally to men, women, and children, so that no family could supplement its milk supply from another family outside the kin group, but the situation was more complex in the case of women.

During her menses or when pregnant, a woman was thought to exert an evil influence on cattle and was not allowed to pass near the cattle enclosure or partake of any milk. This applied even in her own home. Since it was usually impossible for men to know when a woman was menstruating, it was customary to exclude milk from the diet of the majority of girls once they had passed puberty. When a woman married and went to live with her husband's family group she fell under a double restriction. Not only was she a woman, but she was now in the home of a different kin group. Consequently, of all people in the community, married women were most rigidly excluded from partaking of milk. Under two conditions only might she have milk. If her father presented her with her own cow at the time of her marriage she could use milk from that cow, or if her husband performed a special ceremony involving the slaying of a goat, she would be free to use any milk in his home. Because of the general poverty of the area neither of these two procedures was common although several decades ago they were not uncommon in certain families.

The reasons for these customs were lost in the mists of antiquity, not even the oldest people in this community being able to explain them. "This is our custom, and this is how it has always been" was the only explanation offered. In all probability the customs are closely related to native religious beliefs centered around ancestors. Even today when some 60 per cent of the community are Christians, ancestors play a very important part, protecting a person from all manner of misfortune and ill health. The link between man and his ancestors is his cattle, and ceremonies of propitiation involve the slaying of cattle. Accordingly, anything that might have an evil influence on the cattle would endanger the relationship between a man and his ancestors. In addition, a married woman continues to have her own set of ancestors derived from her family and may not interfere in any way with her husband's.

The degree to which concepts concerning milk were enmeshed in the overall cultural pattern made it obvious that the general approach used for increasing vegetable and egg consumption would be of little avail. Considerable motivation for drinking milk already existed in the community, and attempts to increase this motivation would be unlikely to change existing practices. Attempts were nevertheless made on several occasions to change these practices by stressing the importance of milk as an ideal food for lactating and expectant mothers, but were futile.

Analysis of the underlying beliefs indicated clearly that the barrier to greater milk consumption lay in the link between milk and the specific cattle from which it came. If milk from cows which did not belong to any member of the tribe or any other related groups could be introduced into the community, presumably the barrier would be overcome. The most practical method of accomplishing this was to make powdered milk available. Accordingly, supplies of powdered milk were obtained by the Health Centre and offered to families on prescription. No secret was made of the fact that this powder was a form of milk, but it was stressed that this milk did not originate from cows belonging to any of the Bantu people.

From the inception of this program it was clear that no stigma was attached to the use of the powdered milk. Even the most orthodox of mothers-in-law or husbands had no objection to this powder being used by the young women of their families. The only barrier that remained was that it was an unfamiliar food stuff with a strange taste. To overcome this, the familiar formula—increase the motivation, help make the product easily available and demonstrate methods for incorporation into the diet—proved all that was necessary. The application of these technics produced a demand for the powdered milk that, over the years, steadily outgrew the Health Centre supply. Families were then encouraged to budget their slender incomes to allow for its purchase from the local stores. By 1954 it became apparent that in some families the demand for milk had become too great to be met from either of these two sources. To the gratification of the Health Centre staff permission was given in a number of the more educated families for women to consume milk from the family cows without any marked reaction from the rest of the community.

Some of the results of the Health Centre's programs are of interest. In the course of 12 years the infant mortality rate dropped from 276 to 96, pellagra and kwashiorkor all but disappeared from this area and the average weight of the babies at one year had increased by two pounds. This trend, as far as was known, was not occurring elsewhere in the country, and in fact in neighboring areas where the Health Centre provided only medical care but no community health education program, no such changes were discernible.

Some General Principles. From this illustration it is now possible to derive some guiding principles indicating the significance of social and cultural factors to health programs in general.

The first is self-evident. Health workers should have an intimate detailed knowledge of the people's beliefs, attitudes, knowledge and behavior before attempting to introduce any innovation into an area. While this principle is frequently violated in practice it is certainly no new concept in public health. What it not so well recognized however, is that the intimate knowledge of these factors is but the initial step in the evaluation of cultural factors.

The second principle, which is usually more difficult to apply, is that the psychologic and social functions of these practices, beliefs, and attitudes need to be evaluated. As stated by Benjamin Paul,[4] "It is relatively easy to perceive that others have different customs and beliefs, especially if they are 'odd' or 'curious.' It is generally more difficult to perceive the pattern or system into which these customs or beliefs fit." It is in this area of determining the pattern or system into which these customs or beliefs fit that social scientists can probably make their greatest contribution to health programs. This is the knowledge that will help determine why certain practices obtain, help predict how difficult it will be to change them, and give indications of the technics that can be expected to be most helpful.

A third principle that should be emphasized was unfortunately not well illustrated in the example but is of fundamental importance in the United States. It should be appreciated that while it is permissible for some purposes to consider an over-all "American Culture," numerous distinct subcultures exist, sometimes even within a single county. These subcultural groups must be carefully defined, as programs based on premises, true for one group, will not necessarily be successful in a neighboring group. This also is an area in which we as health workers can receive invaluable assistance from social scientists.

There are a number of very interesting illustrations of the importance of these subcultural groupings in regard to food habits in the United States, of which only two will be mentioned. Margaret Cussler and Mary De Give[8] differentiate five major subcultural groupings in the South, white owners, white sharecroppers, Negro owners, Negro sharecroppers and wage laborers. To a greater or lesser degree each of these groups had different attitudes, beliefs, knowledge, and practices in regard to food, and for different reasons.

John Bennet, Harvey Smith, and Herbert Passin[9] have distinguished in the southern part of Illinois eight separate and distinct subcultural groups, each with its own set of attitudes toward food. Interestingly enough, none of these attitudes were based on a knowledge or interest in the nutritional value of the foods.

Many nutrition programs today are designed for application to the total area under the jurisdiction of the nutritionist—an area that is often very large. The underlying premise would be that this total area—region, state, district, or even county—has a completely homogeneous culture. Greater concentration of a nutritionist's time in a carefully defined subcultural group with the development of programs specifically designed for that group would eventually be more efficient in effecting permanent changes in food habits.

There are a number of other social and cultural factors, some of which have been implied in the case study and which, though important, have not been emphasized. These include a determination of the leadership patterns within a community, a definition of the decision makers in a family or larger institution, and determination of the status of various groups within the community and the status of the health worker in comparison to these groups. The importance of these factors has been well recognized by health workers in planning and executing programs and requires little further emphasis here. In this connection it is of interest to note however that several investigators[8, 10] report that in the majority of American homes all major food decisions are made by the housewife. Concentration of the nutritional education on the housewife alone therefore would probably be more beneficial than attempts to educate the total community in many subcultures in the United States.

A further area in which profitable collaboration between social science and health could occur is concerned with the prediction of the long-range effects of any program. Following a program two interrelated series of questions would be of interest to all health workers. Are there likely to be any unanticipated repercussions of the program and, secondly, how permanent can the changes introduced be expected to be?

The answers to these questions will be largely determined by the degree to which the innovations are absorbed into the cultural framework and the impact they have on other facets of the culture. For example, in our illustration the effect of the acceptance of new dietary patterns by the Zulu women might conceivably eventually threaten the status of males as decision makers in that society. Similarly permission given to women to take milk might eventually be one of the factors changing the intensity of religious beliefs.

By indicating the possible effects on other segments of the culture, and by determining the degree to which the concepts embodied by the new program have been absorbed into the existing cultural framework, social scientists would have a significant contribution to make in sensitizing health workers to the possible long-range effects of their programs.

The concluding consideration is the degree to which we as health workers are "culture bound." Unless we can avoid cultural bias or ethnocentricity in our dealings with people, much of the crucial data will not even be made available to us by members of the community. Even should we be fortunate enough to have access to some of these facts, our analysis of the situation will continually be distorted through imposition of our own culturally determined system of values onto the behavior of others. In this regard social scientists can perhaps help us to become somewhat less "culture bound," but fundamentally for many of us that requires a major reorientation of our own philosophy which only we ourselves can achieve.

17   SOCIAL SCIENCE APPLIED TO THE DYNAMICS OF COMMUNITY PROCESS

By Walter Boek

Many ideas for social change germinate in the minds of professional workers in educational systems, health departments, planning commissions, and other community agencies, both voluntary and governmental. Even when ideas are originated by non-professional citizens, they are usually handed over to the professional to be implemented.

There are two fundamental reasons for this: (1) People in Western society increasingly tend to see the function of maintenance and improvement of their communities as being the role of a professional. (2) In order to show they are earning their money and to gain status within the community and in their professions, the county agent, health officers, executive secretary of the Chamber of Commerce, and all the rest must be constantly thinking of new projects to develop and new ways to expand their domains.

In their role of innovators and agents for carrying out new ideas, community action professionals may sometimes be humbled and perhaps even frustrated by the complexity of their problems. In spite of this, many are successful in their endeavors even when reasons for success are not entirely clear. The purpose of this article, therefore, is to present two models for community action developed with the use of social science knowledge which may serve as a guide for obtaining program goals.

The First Model. Our first example is concerned with action on a community service desired by a county health officer whom we shall call Dr. Page. Dr. Page wanted to obtain approval and financial support from the County Board of Supervisors for setting up a mental health center.

His first step was to tell his Health Board that he expected to emphasize mental health during the next year, since each year he and his staff put special concentration on one problem area in their educational program.

The doctor's second step was to bring up the mental health problem in a conversation with the top leader in his community's power structure. His manner of handling this was to tell the leader that some people had begun to talk about the problem and that he felt the leader should know about it.

Reprinted from the Spring 1957 issue of *Adult Education,* a publication of the Adult Education Association of the U.S.A. Copyright 1957 by the Adult Education Association of the U.S.A.

This allowed Dr. Page to follow through after the session by sending literature to the community leader about the local situation, about the State local financial assistance laws, and about what other communities were doing. A similar procedure was used with the Chairman of the Health Committee of the County Board of Supervisors and with other community leaders.

Step three was to contact all the other community professionals who headed organizations like his own, and to tell them his feeling about the need for a mental health center. The system of reciprocal obligations, usual among these agencies, insured their support. Several months were required to complete these first three steps, as Dr. Page had planned, for he estimated 18 months for his strategy to be carried through.

Dr. Page then got himself and his staff ready for the fourth step. Mental health consultants, both physicians and nurses, as well as literature were obtained from the State to give his staff the background they needed for their role, which was to emphasize mental health on every possible occasion during the next 12 months. When nurses made home visits, they discussed the adjustment of junior to the coming of sister. Sanitary engineers on inspection rounds talked about good human relations as a means whereby an employer could get better cooperation from his restaurant workers on sanitary measures.

Every speaking engagement of the health officer and his staff either was on mental health or had a section on mental health. In addition to the large groups before which professionals like the health officer customarily appear, such as service clubs, Granges, and church groups, he and his staff met with many small groups such as garden and bridge clubs, home bureau units, and mothers' clubs. A concerted effort was made to cover every township in the county. When questions arose during the talks about doing something to combat the disease of men's minds, the speaker would mention what another county had done and suggest they discuss it with their township supervisor.

Before long, citizens began talking about mental health in their different organizations. Professionals other than the health officer felt this citizen-demand and relayed it to their board members and to the major and minor leaders in the power structure. Members of the Board of Supervisors also began to be asked questions. The man at the apex of power who had been receiving information from the health department was grateful to the health officer for it, because it meant he could give informed answers to people asking his opinion.

The Clincher. It was now time for Dr. Page to take the last two steps. As step five, he visited the top leader again to ask for advice on handling the demands made on him to meet the community's mental health needs. During this visit, he brought up the possibility that the Board of Supervisors might use State aid to set up a local mental health center. This meeting resulted in Dr. Page receiving the support of his community's big wheel.

Right afterwards, Dr. Page got the Chairman of the Board of Supervisor's Health Committee to bring up at the next Board meeting the business of establishing a center. This was done, and the Board, with little debate, voted the funds. However, this was not what Dr. Page had planned for his sixth step.

He wanted Board members to discuss it, but to delay a decision until they had talked with people in their own townships. He was interested in continued support, and he knew township supervisors would feel more sure about supporting a center if they first had an opportunity to talk with their constituents. As it happened, the Board thought about it a little more during the rest of their meeting and rescinded their action before they adjourned. At a later meeting they again gave the necessary approval.

Figure 1 has been prepared to provide a clearer conception of this model for community action. As can be seen, the steps in this idea that originated in the health department are:

(1) The Board of Health is told about the stress to be placed on mental health.

(2) The top leader and secondary leaders are informed.

(3) Community action professionals are contacted and their support ensured.

(4) Interest is stimulated among citizens who then demand action directly from their leaders and indirectly through their agencies.

(5) Support from leaders is solicited. These leaders cooperate by giving orders down the line to sub-leaders and their representatives on the policy-making health boards and on the Board of Supervisors.

(6) The suggestion is brought up for the policy makers to consider. Policy makers then take action desired by their leaders, other citizens, and the health officer.

A facsimile of this model for community action was tested in one community of 35,000 people on one activity. It is hoped that it will be tested by others many more times.

It is postulated that for large communities of 100,000 or more, and for those in which there is open resistance to the innovation, a model would differ in placing more emphasis on power leaders and less on citizen participation in obtaining the objectives.

An issue which has aroused interest and emotion of citizens in many communities is the possibility of fluoridating municipal water supplies to prevent tooth decay. In most communities proponents of this public dental health measure must develop a careful plan or strategy to achieve necessary approval from the governing officers.

The Second Model. The model that will now be presented was developed for use in a campaign to have fluorine added to water in a large city. The Dental Societies' Fluoridation Committee and the City health officer were to carry out the plan listed here from (a) to (1).

(a) Support from all dentists was to be assessed and strengthened through the use of an opinion questionnaire, followed by dental society meetings, personal contacts between pro-fluoridation Dental Society leaders and anti-fluoridation or neutral dentists, and the sending of research literature to the dentists.

(b) Leaders in the medical society were to be informed and their support secured.

(c) Cooperation of the city engineer, who would draw up plans to be

Figure I

A MODEL FOR COMMUNITY ACTION

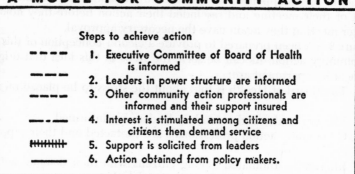

Steps to achieve action

- - - -   1. Executive Committee of Board of Health
           is informed
— — —   2. Leaders in power structure are informed
- - - -   3. Other community action professionals are
           informed and their support insured
—·—   4. Interest is stimulated among citizens and
           citizens then demand service
++++++   5. Support is solicited from leaders
———   6. Action obtained from policy makers.

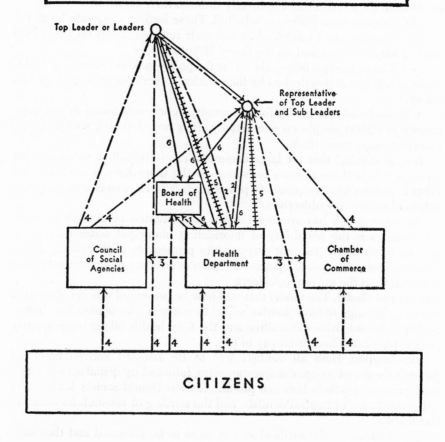

Top Leader or Leaders

Representative
of Top Leader
and Sub Leaders

Board of
Health

Council
of Social
Agencies

Health
Department

Chamber
of
Commerce

CITIZENS

submitted with the health officer's proposal to the City Council, was to be obtained by having a leading dentist and a leading physician visit him.

(d) The chairman of the City Council and the Mayor were to be asked when they would like to bring fluoridation before the Council by the Chairman of the Dental Societies' Fluoridation Committee and the City Health Officer.

(e) Editors and leaders in the newspapers and radio and television stations were to be contacted and asked to name reporters who would prepare news items about fluoridation in cooperation with a free lance writer to be paid by the dental society. This was one means of delaying news announcements until the appropriate time in the campaign and of insuring more complete news coverage.

(f) Top social strata leaders in the dental and medical societies were to discuss the issue with community power structure leaders, and their support obtained.

(g) All relevant community organizations were to be contacted to get their cooperation, but they were not to be asked to take an active part in the campaign at this time.

(h) Dentists were to discuss fluoridation with City Councilmen individually. Either the Councilman's personal dentist or the dental leaders would talk with them in a pair situation.

Again—The Clincher. If a satisfactory margin in the Council could be predicted from individual contacts with Councilmen, the plan would move on to its last phases. (If a satisfactory margin could not be expected, a reappraisal of the opposition would be made and a plan developed to meet it.)

(i) News items and articles were to be released in the mass media.

(j) Parents in the various organizations would be asked to phone and visit their Councilmen.

(k) Parents and representatives of organizations would be encouraged to attend a public hearing, since a public hearing is a necessary part of the legislative process in many cities.

(l) If the final decision were favorable, follow-up support would be given to Councilmen and City officials by having dentists and physicians publicly commend the Mayor, community leaders, and Council members, and by providing some speaking services to community groups until fluorine was entering the water. If the decision was negative, a second long range plan would be developed.

It can be seen that this strategy varies from the procedure usually recommended by community organization specialists who often suggest that a community-wide campaign committee be organized, along with initiation of a mass media and speakers program. In the model outlined, however, mass media were not to be used until near the end of the campaign, nor were the citizens and citizen organizations to be actively involved until that time. Neither was a committee of citizens to be set up representing all community organizations to promote fluoridation. Instead, this was pretty much a behind-the-scenes attack on the decision-making power structure because of the organized opposition. The hypothesis tested was that the issue could be settled through already established decision-making processes that were used for other problems by the leaders.

Summarizing. Models for obtaining community action have been advanced; one for a medium sized community and one for an especially large community. Community action professionals have many more techniques acquired from their experiences. Much more could be learned by observing professionals work to achieve their goals, since with their similar thinking about the type of change that should be initiated and their similar methods of achieving objectives, they are a much stronger force in maintaining the cultural values of the middle class than generally may be realized. Much remains to be done to develop reliable models for there certainly will be many variations from the two described.

18   COMMUNITY ORGANIZATION FOR HEALTH: A CASE STUDY

By Charles V. Willie, and Herbert Notkin

For more than three years, a research and study group known as the Community Seminar has functioned at the Upstate Medical Center of the State University of New York. The Seminar consists of faculty members from the State Medical College, Syracuse University, and officials of several state, county, and city governmental agencies as well as of some local voluntary associations. Its purpose is to study the processes of community organization, with particular reference to health. Special emphasis is given to the power system and its role in resolving community health issues. To study these processes the seminar traces the development of current or recent issues, identifying the persons (and their positions in the community) who effectively block or help to solve a problem. It also attempts to determine the specific correlates of resolved and unresolved problems.

The Seminar has analyzed such issues as proposals (1) for community hospital construction, (2) to fluoridate the common water supply, (3) to establish a County Health Department, and (4) to erect public housing.

For seven years, Syracuse has been trying to evolve an acceptable plan to improve inadequate and insufficient hospital facilities. The study of this issue and its pending resolution are reported herein. The analysis and data are presented as (1) a case study of the community organizational process in solving a health problem, and (2) an example of how the seminar operates.

Case History. Syracuse, with a population of 213,945 (according to a 1956 special census), is the hub city of a metropolitan area of 394,802. The largest proportion of the labor force works in manufacturing—there are more than 500 plants in the metropolitan area. In addition, there is one large university, an expanding medical center, and a smaller liberal arts college.

Critical review of an earlier draft of this discussion by Dr. Robert Straus, Professor of Medical Sociology at the University of Kentucky Medical Center, is acknowledged with appreciation.

In the spring of 1950, the Syracuse Regional Hospital Planning Council was faced with six applications from institutions in the Syracuse metropolitan area for federal (Hill-Burton Act) funds for construction of community hospital facilities. To help determine the merit of these applications, the Council of Social Agencies was requested to appoint a citizen's committee to undertake a survey of community hospital facilities. Thus, the Citizen's Committee on Health and Hospital Facilities was appointed, and held its first meeting in 1951.

The committee obtained Community Chest funds for professional consultants and staff. By 1954, the study phase of the task was completed. In a preliminary report, it estimated that 1,625 general hospital beds were required to serve the community adequately. Of the existing 1,150 beds, only 717 were acceptable, according to the committee's evaluation.

To overcome this deficit in hospital beds, it was recommended that one of the general hospitals (whose beds were excluded from the above 717 total because of its poor physical structure) should be assisted in erecting a 300-bed facility to replace its existing plant. It was also recommended that the community should assist another general hospital with a relatively modern physical plant to add a 400-bed wing. The report also explained that the remaining bed requirements probably would be available in the general hospital planned as part of the expanding State University Medical Center.

It is estimated that the plan proposed by the Citizen's Committee would cost $9,000,000, of which the federal government would provide $2,000,000—the balance to be raised from voluntary gifts of corporations, organizations, and individuals.

Before these recommendations were made public, the committee chairman—an attorney—turned to the senior partner in his law firm (a civic leader, well respected resident of the community, and a member of an old, established, and important family) for advice on implementation of the plan. His advisor suggested that the board chairman of a large local industry might wish to call together some 30 to 40 people to discuss the recommendations before they were made public. This approach was suggested because these individuals were persons whose endorsement and contributions would be essential to the success of any large-scale fund raising effort. At such a meeting, these key citizens could become familiar with the facts in order to facilitate their later support, particularly in fund-raising.

In this private meeting and in other informal discussions, it was decided that the plan proposed by the committee was too expensive and that further study was needed to refine the recommendations—possibly through reorganization of existing private hospitals, and by linking community hospital development more closely to plans for the expansion of the State Medical Center.

Hence, a second committee (The Citizens Hospital Committee) was organized in 1954; and publication of the first committee's report was deferred. This committee was organized under the chairmanship of the industrial executive who had called the informal assembly of commercial, financial, and industrial leaders referred to above. The chairman was appointed by the president of the Community Chest and Council.

The second committee assumed two responsibilities: (1) of further planning for the improvement of health and hospital facilities, and (2) of determining how objectives could be achieved within attainable financial limits. Hence, the Citizens Hospital Committee—with the aid of professional consultants and staff also financed by Community Chest funds—first determined the community's capacity to finance improved hospital facilities. Proposals were formulated in the light of this estimated financial capacity.

In the Autumn of 1955 the committee's recommendations were presented to the public. The report of the first committee was also released at this time; but these findings were in a separate document stamped (presumably after decision to withhold an earlier release) "tentative and preliminary only." This message was signed by the chairman of that committee. Before release of the second committee's report, there was no informal assembly of industrial, financial, and commercial leaders. This was probably not considered necessary because these interests were represented on the committee. Nor were there preliminary planning meetings with other special interest groups, such as nurses, physicians, social workers, hospital administrators, and Boards of Trustees. The new recommendations came as a surprise to most of these persons, many of whom had helped formulate the plans of the first committee.

The second committee's report recommended that three of the existing general hospitals abandon their structures, sell their properties to the state for the Medical Center hospital, merge their organizations, and incorporate as a single board of trustees to supervise the erection and operation of a new 400-bed community hospital that could eventually expand to 600 beds.

It was explained that this plan, providing for a single modern hospital to replace three of varying quality in physical plant, was superior to the first plan, described as a "patchwork program" of adding to existing structures. And finally, the Committee stated that "merging of the three hospitals . . . will create a united front. Special interests will vanish."

Ironically, special interests caused the eventual abandonment of this plan. One of the three general hospitals involved opposed the merger. This is the hospital that was to have erected its own new plant, according to recommendations of the first committee. Another was reluctant to accept the plan and reserved decision, pending a thorough study. The third hospital involved accepted the plan in principle only. In the midst of this indecision, the State Medical Center took option on other sites for the eventual erection of its own hospital. Finally, many physicians in private practice—particularly general practitioners and some surgeons—were concerned about staff privileges in the proposed single community hospital and thus hesitated to endorse the plan.

Unable to harmonize these dissenting reactions, the Citizens Hospital Committee disbanded. Two committees had now failed to devise acceptable plans for improved hospital facilities. The community organizational process for the solution of this problem was stalled. The problem had become an issue, and those seeking ways to solve the issue had reached an impasse.

Urgency was attached to the solution of this problem, because the community risked the loss of $2,000,000 in federal aid for hospital construction. Communities are given priority ratings for federal assistance, based on need for hospital facilities. While Syracuse had a high priority, its ability to obtain Hill-Burton Act funds would be jeopardized when contracts were let for construction of the new Medical Center hospital, as this facility would lower its priority rating. Yet, the community bed shortage would not be greatly relieved because (1) a state general hospital is obliged to accept patients from outside the Syracuse metropolitan area, and (2) a teaching hospital must exercise control over admissions to provide certain kinds of teaching experiences to medical students. The State predicted that a contract for its new hospital would be let in 1958 or 1959. Another deadline was seen in the fact that the Hill-Burton Act expires in June, 1958. Although there is general belief that it will be re-enacted by Congress, the possibility of non-passage always exists. Community leaders were well aware that too much delay in solving this issue might result in great financial loss for the community.

In an effort to fill the hospital planning vacuum, the accredited hospitals formed a study group which had no formal name but which we shall call the Joint Hospital Planning Committee. This third committee was organized in 1956 under the chairmanship of an attorney who is also a hospital trustee and a member of the Regional Hospital Planning Council, which receives applications for federal aid to hospital construction. The Joint Hospital Planning Committee consisted of trustees and administrators, but its proceedings were dominated by the professional hospital administrators. The Community Chest and Council neither appointed nor sanctioned the work of this committee, which had no funds for staff and consultants. The Joint Hospital Planning Committee was short-lived and disbanded without public explanation only a few months after its formation. In fact, its dissolution was so abrupt that some members were first informed by newspaper.

Deliberations of the third committee never reached the stage of even a preliminary written report. It is known that Committee discussions involved expansion of the existing hospitals—a modification of the rejected plan of the first committee. The estimated cost of these preliminary proposals far exceeded the community's ability to finance the program. Hence, efforts of the third committee contributed little to resolving the issue.

In the Spring of 1957, the mayor of Syracuse announced that he would submit a plan under which hospital leaders and representative citizens could work toward a solution of the "log-jam" in community hospital development. Shortly thereafter, he appointed the City Planning Commission as his official Hospital Advisory Committee. The Common Council was requested to appropriate funds for staff and consultants for this committee—which now became the fourth group to try to evolve an acceptable plan.

The mayor's Hospital Advisory Committee proceeded by scheduling five days of public hearings. Approximately 60 organizations concerned with the hospital bed shortage were invited to send representatives to speak at the hearings. Testimony was taken under advisement; existing facilities were visited; previous reports were studied; and community leaders were consulted.

In the Autumn of 1957, the mayor made the committee recommendations public. The report identified two categories of community hospital needs: (1) the addition of more hospital beds, and (2) the replacement of hospitals which had inadequate structures. The first need was described as short-range and the second as long-range. Recommendations were restricted to the short-range need, but suggested that a County Regional Hospital Council be established for long-range planning.

To increase the number of hospital beds, the Hospital Advisory Committee recommended construction of a new 300-bed community hospital independent of existing hospitals. The cost of this plan was estimated as $8,-500,000, of which approximately $6,000,000 would have to come from local voluntary contributions. The Community Chest and Council gave "enthusiastic approval" to the plan two days after it had been published. The President of the Community Chest and Council commended the mayor for his "foresight and initiative," and congratulated the Committee and its chairman for "outstanding work." Following this action, the mayor discharged his Hospital Advisory Committee.

Immediately, fifth and sixth committees were appointed by the president of the Community Chest and Council and charged with the development and execution of this plan. Primary responsibility was assigned to a group known as the Community Hospital Committee. This fifth committee is to receive assistance and advice from a sixth group designated as a Board of Counselors. The County Medical Society was also asked to appoint representatives to consult with the Community Hospital Committee.

Less than one week after the plan was published, the County Medical Society approved it. Endorsements were also received from the four major nursing groups in the community. Ten days after the plan was announced, the newly appointed Community Hospital Committee held its first meeting and decided to retain professional fund raisers to launch the campaign for voluntary gifts.

In the light of these rapid developments, a local daily newspaper commented "that after seven years of study of the knotty hospital problem, a plan has been presented which almost certainly will become a reality."

In addition to reviewing the chronology of events, it is necessary to examine the membership of the various committees which contributed to the evolution of an acceptable hospital construction plan, if perspective is to be gained on this community organizational process for health.

A total of six committees have been involved in this seven year process, five voluntary and one official. Of the five voluntary committees, four were appointed by the Community Chest and Council.

Membership of the four Community Chest appointed committees was investigated to determine the positions occupied by the principal persons associated with implementation of a major health program through the local system of voluntary organizations. The Citizen's Committee on Health and Hospital Facilities (organized in 1951) consisted of 19 members. Nine members formed the Citizens Hospital Committee appointed in 1954. The Community Hospital Committee is a 15 member unit; and it is advised by a 17 member Board of Counselors; both appointed in 1957.

A total of 60 positions comprising 51 different persons is observed for these four committees, indicating that nine individuals have served on more than one committee. An investigation of these nine individuals was made to determine the continuing interests that have been associated with this problem. Of the persons serving on two or more appointed committees, three are in banking or finance; two are lawyers; two are officials of retail department stores; and two are industrialists.

Table 1—Occupation of Persons on Four Committees Concerned with the Hospital Construction Issue, Syracuse, 1951–1957

Occupation	Citizen's Committee on Health & Health Facilities 1951	Citizen's Hospital Committee 1954	Community Hospital Committee 1957	Board of Counselors to the Community Hospital Committee 1957	Total Number	Per Cent
Industrial official	4	3	9	5	20	33.2
Bank or finance official	1	2	2	4	9	15.0
Retail or wholesale official	2	3	3	1	9	15.0
Attorney	1	1	1	3	6	10.0
Clergyman or rabbi	1	..	..	3	4	6.7
University prof. or official[a]	3	..	..	1	4	6.7
Wife of industrialist	3	..	..	..	3	5.0
Labor official	1	..	1	..	2	3.3
Physician	1	..	..	..[b]	1	1.7
Wife of physician	1	..	..	..	1	1.7
Contractor	1	..	..	..	1	1.7
TOTAL	19	9	16	17	60	100.0

[a] Although physicians, the medical college dean and the full-time department chairman are recorded as university professor or official.
[b] The Community Chest requested the County Medical Society to appoint a special committee to consult with the Community Hospital Committee.

That these are the four major categories of power in this particular voluntary community organizational effort for health is revealed by investigating the occupations held by persons filling all 60 positions. Table 1 indicates that one-third of the combined committees is composed of industrial officials; fifteen per cent of banking or finance officials; fifteen percent of retail or wholesale company officials, and 10 percent of attorneys. These four categories represent nearly three-fourths of the 60 positions. In fact, a majority is obtainable with only three of the four groups, provided industrialists comprise one of the three.

Further investigation was made of the four Community Chest appointed committees to determine the representation of industrial, financial, commercial, and legal interests on each. The first committee (whose report was rejected) consisted of persons representing many occupations. In addition to these four categories of interest (a minority of this committee), other members were contractor, physician, labor official, university professor, clergyman, and wife or homemaker.

Rejected also was the report of the second committee whose membership consisted exclusively of industrial, banking or finance, retail or wholesale officials; and one attorney.

The fifth and sixth committees appointed to implement the plan of the mayor's committee which "almost certainly will become a reality," according to a local newspaper have, an overwhelming majority of members associated with industrial, financial, commercial, and legal interests. However, religious, educational, and labor interests are also represented. In fact, nearly one-fourth of the Board of Counselors (the sixth committee) consists of persons who represent occupations other than banking, industrial or commercial management, and law. Moreover, the County Medical Society was requested to appoint a committee of physicians (with dental society representation) to consult with the fifth committee which has basic responsibility for implementing the mayor's committee's plan.

Business men in finance, manufacturing industry, and commerce are found on all four committees. Attorneys, however, are the only professional men on all four committees, despite the fact that the issue was the development of *health* and *hospital facilities.* Attorneys are also chairmen of two of the Chest-appointed committees.

It was also decided to determine which individuals on the four voluntary committees contributed most in time and responsibility to solving the hospital construction problem. A rating method was constructed for this aspect of the study, based on the assumption that committee membership becomes increasingly important as the problem of inadequate and insufficient hospital facilities becomes more basic following several unacceptable solutions. In the rating scheme, varying values were arbitrarily assigned to the four voluntary committees sanctioned by the Community Chest and Council. For participation on the first committee (1951) a value of one was assigned; a value of two was given to participants on the second committee (1954); and a value of three was attached to positions on either the fifth or sixth committees (1957). Officers other than chairman received one additional credit. Committee chairmen received two additional credits. Theoretically, one could receive a maximum of 12 credits and a minimum of one. A person would receive the maximum participation score were he both a member of three of the voluntary committees and chairman of each committee. No one received the maximum score. Because one could receive three credits simply by being a member of either the fifth or sixth committees, only those persons with four or more credits are identified as major contributors to solution of the hospital construction issue.

Of the 51 individuals who served on one or more of the four committees, only 13 have four or more credits. Four are industrialists; four are in banking or finance; three are attorneys; and two are in commerce. Hence, it is observed that industrial and banking or finance officials comprise nearly two-thirds of those who contributed most in time and responsibility to the development of an acceptable plan.

Additional investigations of these thirteen individuals reveal the following facts. All are male. Three-fourths of the men are business executives. At least half are board chairmen or presidents of their respective organizations. Most of the 13 leaders live either in a small, old, exclusive Syracuse neighborhood—about five tenths of a square mile in size—or in the suburban areas.

According to this rating method, the individual who contributed most to the evolution and implementation of a plan to solve the problem of hospital facilities is an attorney. The second highest contribution was made by an industrialist. The attorney had eight credits and the industrialist had seven.

This attorney with the highest participation score was observed in terms of his affiliations with committees that made significant contributions toward a resolution of the hospital construction issue. He is a board-member of the Community Chest and Council. He is a law-firm partner with the chairman of the first committee; he was vice-chairman of the second committee; he is a law-firm partner with the chairman of the fourth committee (the mayor's committee); and he is chairman of the sixth committee—the Board of Counselors.

Case Analysis. This case history of community health organization demonstrates the presence of a system of voluntary organizations that may be brought into intensive activity when problems occur which are beyond the regular scope of responsibility of other institutions, such as government, religion, education and economics. Hospital construction was one such issue.

While this configuration of organized and interconnected groups and individuals is a *voluntary* system, it is contemporarily thought of as a *power* system because it has no continuous program responsibilities—as do economic and governmental institutions—but frequently undertakes tasks which other institutional systems are unable to handle. The diversity of issues and tasks confronted by the voluntary system has reinforced the concept of it as a power system, a sort of "community court of last resort."

In this analysis deference will be made to the contemporary conception; but it is also emphasized that the power system is not an ultimate. Its flexibility and ubiquity brings the power system into close and frequent contact with all the organized systems of a community. But this characteristic of omnipresence does not represent omnipotence.[1] While the power system exerts a considerable influence upon community organizational processes, it, in turn, is influenced by the multiple operations within the community. To view the power system as the supreme community institution distorts the perspective necessary to understanding its actual function.

Reference has been made to the power *system* rather than to the power *structure*.[2] Power system is a more inclusive concept and is preferred. Systems have both structural and functional components. Systems also are in movement—in homeostatic balance.[3] The approach to a solution of the hospital construction issue in Syracuse was in a state of flux from 1951 through 1957, with each new move compensating for past mistakes in an effort to maintain the delicate balance which permits the continuation of a search for a solution. The major structural components of the lower system for this effort were members of the four voluntary committees and the major functional component was the Community Chest and Council which facilitated continuous movement toward an acceptable solution.

Apparently, a balance of certain kinds of positions among the structural components of the power system is required for effective action. The voluntary committee in which industrial, financial, commercial, and legal interests were a minority failed, but so did the committee in which the same interests were an exclusive majority. Predictions for success have been made for those groups attempting to solve the hospital construction issue with committees consisting of a majority of industrial, financial, commercial, and legal interests but with minorities representing religious, educational, medical, (The Medical Society was asked to appoint a consulting committee, even though it had no direct committee representation.) and labor interests. Hence, the structure of the power system concerned with the hospital construction issue in Syracuse involved majority and minority positions. Two committees were doomed to failure; one, because of an inappropriate majority, and the other, because of a non-existent minority. Too frequently, the minority component is omitted in analyses of power structure. However, the Syracuse experience suggests that a minority component is as essential for the effective operation of the power system as an appropriate majority.

That the Community Chest served as a sieve through which the power system functioned in the process of solving the hospital construction issue is clearly seen in several actions. Four of the hospital planning committees were appointed by Chest officers. Two of these committees were financed by Chest funds. The report formulated by the mayor's committee was transmitted to the Community Chest and Council for action. And, of course, the committees established to implement the plan were appointed by the Chest. In short Community Chest sanction made legitimate the many efforts designed to solve the hospital construction issue.[4]

Additional evidence that the Community Chest and Council was a functional component of the power system is seen in the ineffective and short-lived existence of the Joint Hospital Planning Committee. It was neither appointed, sanctioned or supported by the Chest. As a voluntary committee which attempted to operate outside the functional order of the power system, it disbanded only a few months after its organization. In short, this committee was not legitimized by the Chest. It is probable that the disintegration of this effort outside the functional direction of Community Chest was due also to faulty structural composition. The committee was a special interest group dominated by professional hospital administrators. This was an inappropriate majority, according to the findings of this analysis.

The community is a social system consisting of several interrelated and interdependent sub-systems.[5] The interrelatedness of the institutional systems within a community is well recognized, especially when mention is made of the pervasiveness of government, the power system, or compulsory public education. It is equally important to recognize the interdependency of institutional systems in understanding the processes of community health organization. That the power system is not the supreme community institution is indicated by the fact that its hospital planning efforts reached an impasse and were stalled. The interdependence of the political and power sub-systems was illustrated in the aid which government gave the power system to break the "log-jam," as the mayor described the stalled hospital planning efforts. Two Chest appointed and one non-Chest appointed voluntary committees had failed. It was then that the mayor appointed the City Planning Commission to serve as his official Hospital Advisory Committee. After it developed a plan, the governmental institution returned the task to the power system, which once more began effective and purposeful movement. The interdependence of these two institutional systems is specifically demonstrated by the hospital construction issue in Syracuse.

No social system is a closed one. Just as the political and power systems feed one into the other, so is the community interrelated with the larger society. The Syracuse community is not a closed social system; it is inter-related with the State and the Nation. This principle is well illustrated in the hospital construction issue.

Community efforts to solve this local problem were affected by non-local circumstances.[6] Because the State planned to erect a teaching and research facility in Syracuse, the second committee proposed a plan which would involve the sale of some existing hospital properties to the state for Medical Center expansion, thereby reducing the funds required of the community. Further evidence of extra-community influence is seen in the federal criteria for the distribution of Hill-Burton Act funds to localities. In addition, the priority of the Syracuse community to receive federal aid would be greatly lowered when contracts were let for construction of the State Medical Center hospital. Although the proposal to tie the community hospital construction plan more closely to the state's Medical Center expansion plans was abandoned, the extra-community influence remained in such matters as priority rating. Urgency for solution of this community problem stemmed from the fact that the federal law authorizing financial help for community hospital construction would expire within a few years and might not be renewed. The Syracuse metropolitan area is interrelated with the larger state and national society, in many ways, like the sub-systems within the community are interrelated. It is revealed in this analysis that extra-community influences must be recognized in any adequate study of community health organization.

The community as a social system has its reality in the interacting people who are the basis of social organization. Parsons has stated that ". . . the motivational processes of the social are *always* processes within the personalities of the component individual actors."[7] The thirteen individuals with participation scores greater than three may be considered the fundamental structural components of the community power system with reference to the hospital construction issue. It is noted that none of the four major interests in the power system constituted a majority of these thirteen. In fact, eight of this number were divided equally between industrialists and financiers, with attorneys and retail merchants accounting for the remainder. Although industrial and financial interests are equally represented, an indication of the ascendancy of industry as the major interest in the power system is seen in the affiliations of those four individuals with participation scores greater than three who had served on only one voluntary committee. These are the persons whom official positions were entrusted on the fifth and sixth Chest appointed committees, although they had no prior committee association with the hospital construction plan. Two of these four are industrial officials.

An individual's position within the power system is based not only upon his participation in various associations, but also upon the existence of certain obligatory relationships with others. For example, the person with the highest participation score had direct association with the Community Chest as a member of its board and served as vice-chairman and chairman of the second and sixth Chest appointed committees. He also had an obligatory relationship with chairmen of the first and fourth committees, who are his law firm partners. Hence, it may be said that the person who contributed most in time and responsibility to a solution of the hospital construction issue in the Syracuse community had direct and indirect access to the leadership of four of the six committees that concerned themselves with hospital construction between 1951 and 1957.

Finally, this case study indicates the effect of sentiment in community action. Much of the unanticipated resistance to the hospital construction plan of the second committee was due to sentimental attachments to the existing hospitals and to the separate identity each had attained in the community. Hospital administrators, Boards of Trustees, medical staffs, and women of the auxiliaries have great emotional investments in "their" hospitals. The second committee recommended that three of the existing hospitals merge into a single institution. While some objections to merger may have been rational and well-founded, others were thinly disguised but deeply ingrained sentiments attached to a particular institution. And thus, the merger proposal was abandoned.

Conclusions. The extent to which these findings illustrate existing social theory and correspond with findings in other communities will be pointed out.

Bierstedt theorizes that "the sources and necessary components of power reside in a combination of numbers (especially majorities), social organization, and resources."[8] In explaining these three, he states that "the power of a majority . . . either threatens or sustains the stability of the associational structure."[9] Numbers, then, are a primary source of power. But they are insufficient unless accompanied by a well organized and disciplined body; it is known that "an organized minority can control an unorganized majority."[10] When there are two groups ". . . equal or nearly equal in numbers and comparable in organization, the one with access to the greater resources will have the superior power. Hence, "resources constitute the third source of social power."[11] Bierstedt also states that "resources may be of many kinds—money, property, prestige, knowledge, competence . . ." and so on.[12] He concludes that ". . . no one of these sources in itself constitutes power. . . . Power appears only in the combination of all three—numbers, organization, and resources."[13]

The failure of the first and second Chest-appointed committees illustrate this theory of social power. The first committee was well organized with several sub-committees designed to stimulate community involvement; but it commanded insufficient financial resources. A majority of the second committee was associated with organizations with large financial resources. But this committee was deficient because of inadequate organization which limited community consultation and advice. Hence, absence of one of the above power sources rendered these two committees ineffective.

Several findings of the Syracuse analysis correspond to findings of a national study of 218 communities which had been involved in hospital construction activity. Major differences between Syracuse and these communities are that they are small, with populations of less than 7,500 and are mostly rural. Nevertheless, many similarities in community organization for health persist. Those instances in which the Syracuse experience in hospital construction corresponds with that of other communities are presented below:

1. Most communities reported a long and gradual period of development

of from two to ten years between first interest and initial action toward hospital construction.[14]

2. The task of new hospital development was primarily a masculine enterprise.[15]

3. Approximately two-thirds of the active participants in projects to construct new hospitals were either businessmen, professionals, employed managers or executives. However, a small portion of sponsoring committees consisted of non-supervisory employees. Seldom were projects initiated by a single individual.[16]

4. Usually, campaigns for a new hospital were launched by voluntary associations organized for this specific purpose.[17] Seldom were existing community groups asked to assume the responsibility of implementing a project as gigantic as that of hospital constuction.[18]

5. The proper and appropriate representation on a sponsoring group was always a difficult problem in the early stages of community organization for hospital construction.[19]

6. Most communities recommended the careful use of community surveys and outside consultants as worthy devices in implementing a project.[20, 21]

7. Most sponsoring groups had a persistent problem of justifying to the community the need for a new hospital.[22]

To summarize the experiences of community organization for hospital construction in these 218 towns scattered throughout the nation, it is stated that "the hospital was not like the easy agreements of doing good for one's home town. It was 'sticking one's neck out.' The people who did so were for the most part, neither farmers, social workers, nor doctors. They were people who knew about dollars and banks and bookkeeping. They were the people who knew about the wealth of the community and, for the most part, possessed it."[28] This may well be an apt summary of the Syracuse experience.

19 APATHY OF FAMILIES TOWARD MEDICAL CARE: AN EXPLORATORY STUDY

By H. Ashley Weeks, Marjorie Davis, and Howard Freeman

Introduction. Over the past seventy-five years efforts have been made to provide clinical resources for families unable to meet the costs of medical care. More recently pre-payment health insurance has been made available to the general population. Various health education efforts have been directed toward promoting the use of health resources, the value of periodic examinations, and the desirability of planning for health needs.

At the present time well over half the country is covered by some form of hospital insurance and the extent of coverage is increasing. In most urban centers there is no shortage of medical practitioners. Today most families of all income levels take advantage of the medical knowledge available to them for pre-natal and post-partum care and the care of infants. Furthermore, even many so-called low income families have cars, radios, television sets and other once considered luxury goods. The concept of the American family as a unit grubbing for a bare existence is becoming obsolete.

Yet, despite all this, a significant proportion of young men are continually found unfit for military service. A recent survey in Michigan reported that about half of five hundred businessmen who came to the university hospital for company paid check-ups were sick and did not know it. With all the emphasis on the need for good health care in a time of rising living standards, why do not more people take advantage of the facilities and services that are available?

Most frequently, the answer to this question has been sought through simple correlations between the total amount of family income and the amount of income expended for health care; or sometimes between lack of foresight or planning for health care and good health practices. This study, on an exploratory level, attempted to question such simple correlations. While it was believed necessary to investigate whether or not income, *per se*, is crucial in explaining the differences in health care among families, the primary concern was to examine the values that families place on their health. The particular aim was to study the economic value the family places upon health in comparison to other financial outlays and in relation to economic planning. This exploratory study tried to survey some of the attitudes related to health care, current spending patterns, and economic planning in an attempt to develop working hypotheses to explain why families behave as they do in terms of their medical care.

Methodology. In this exploratory study, it was decided to control some of the variables which might contribute to spurious correlations between health care and income. Sixty white, native born, Protestant, intact families, residing in Yonkers, N.Y., who had children of school age, were selected through the cooperation of several of the local ministers. Thus all were church goers. The original intention was to obtain thirty families with incomes around three-thousand dollars and thirty families with incomes around five-thousand dollars. However, the ministers underestimated the total family incomes and the sixty families in the sample were divided into two groups, one with a mean of 3,900 dollars and the other a mean of 6,800 dollars. The incomes for the sample ranged from 3,000 dollars to 12,000 dollars. Information obtained from the local Welfare service director indicated that families of four members are likely to be subsidized unless they have an income of over 3,000 dollars. The spouses in both groups have been married about fourteen years, average two children and the husbands are mainly skilled and semi-skilled workers.

An interview guide was constructed covering a brief medical history of the spouses' childhood families, income and budget data, and attitudinal data in the areas of health, income and planning. In one-quarter of the families both spouses were interviewed. The differences between the responses of the spouses were insignificant.

Influence of Income. On the average, the thirty families in the lower income group spend slightly less for health services, some seventy dollars less for medical care and some fifty dollars less for dental care. In proportion to their income, however, the lower income group spends considerably more. Both groups spend about the same amount for medications. Few in either group had any unpaid medical bills at the time of the interviews, although about two-fifths of each group reported that they had to cut down other expenditures to pay their health bills. Lower income families are more likely to cut down on the quality of food; upper income families on recreation. A few more of the lower income families had unmet medical needs, although in both groups these unmet needs could frequently be traced back to fear of treatment rather than to amount of income.

Dental checkups were slightly more common in the higher income group but medical checkups were somewhat more frequent in the lower income group. Children were much more likely than adults to receive complete medical and dental care in both groups. Almost all the families subscribed to some form of health insurance. All but one of the families reported that they were either very "healthy" or "average." Families in both groups claim they have a "family physician" but in practice individual members visit different doctors. Self diagnosis followed by a visit to a specialist is common in both groups. A larger proportion of lower income families are interested in extended health coverage. More of the lower, than upper, income families said they would be willing to subscribe to a plan which included medical and dental bills, medications and eyeglasses providing the cost was within their means.

There is no difference between the income groups in regard to planning expenditures. Various types of budgeting were common in both groups. Economic pressures operate so that the lower income family selects cheaper foods, cheaper and fewer clothes and saves less money. They are more likely to say that if they had to they would use additional income to supplement their food and clothing allotments while the upper group would use additional funds for recreation and vacations. It is to be noted that when so queried not one family in either group mentioned applying additional income for health needs. In general, the lower income families are not so optimistic as the upper income families in terms of their economic future and feel they have more problems than most people in the U.S., their friends, brothers, and sisters.

Although there is an income level below which a particular family cannot afford to take care of its own health needs, among the families studied it seems fairly certain that health care is neglected in favor of obtaining other goods and services and that the motivations for such goods and services are similar in both income groups. When a family in either group has an alternative of buying a car or using the money for dental or medical care, the choice is almost invariably in favor of the car unless physical pain or incapacity is present. Apathy towards health care is present and is likely to remain even if our society becomes one in which fewer and fewer families live at the poverty level of subsistence. The analysis indicates that there is much more variation in terms of health care and attitudes within the two income groups than between them.

Moreover, attempts made to teach individuals to plan for health care do not seem to be particularly effective. Most families do not anticipate serious illness, therefore, they do not plan for health care; when they become ill they are forced to find some way to meet the costs involved. Even families with rigid budgeting habits avoid setting aside contingency funds for health care. It is doubtful that health insurance of any kind would be purchased by such a large proportion of the families if the breadwinner's job or work situation did not include it as an employee benefit. Most of the health insurance carried by the sample families is paid for through payroll deductions and health care is provided by the company in many cases. The families did not plan for it themselves; it was planned for them.

There were some relatively non-apathetic families found among the sixty interviewed. What accounts for the differences among these families? The tentative inference is that differential past experience, cultural and situational backgrounds, and differences in personality offer possible explanations. This paper now turns to some tentative hypotheses in these areas.

Tentative Hypotheses. Tentative hypotheses were developed by first classifying the families into three groups and comparing the differences reported in the interviews. The sixty cases were classified into: 1) families who are concerned only when a member becomes ill; 2) families who consciously maintain what they consider to be a reasonably good state of health; and 3) families who consciously strive to improve the health of their members. Despite the limited data, it seems reasonably certain that social and psychological variables offer many fruitful clues to the behavior and attitudes of the families in these three groups.

A. *Past and Present Experience.* The interviews suggest that some of the marked differences in health care are associated with childhood or some prior adult experience.

Hypothesis 1. The non-apathetic family is more likely to have a member, usually the mother, who had had either an extremely favorable or unfavorable socialization with respect to health care. If the experience was favorable the pattern is continued, if negative the family behaves differently in its current health practices.

For example, the comments of the wife of a 6,000-dollar-a-year oil burner installer:

"We children never saw a doctor, . . . my mother thought it was a waste of money. We only saw a doctor when we needed one desperately. . . . I think I had polio but never saw a doctor. My family is much healthier. I first went to the dentist when I was twelve years old and never brushed my teeth. I see to it that my children do."

Hypothesis 2. The non-apathetic family is likely to have had adult experience, particularly periods of economic deprivation occasioned by health costs, which tend to be associated with an increased concern with health.

B. *Interpersonal Relations.* There seems to be little doubt that agreement among the spouses makes it easier to plan and carry out health care for the entire family.

Hypothesis 3. The non-apathetic family is more likely to operate as a unit and have stronger affectual bonds between its members.

In families where there is limited cohesiveness, health is apparently regarded as an individual matter and there is a lack of stimulation on the part of one of the spouses to get the other spouse, or for that matter the children, to attend to their health needs.

Hypothesis 4. The non-apathetic family is less likely to be one in which a spouse (usually the husband) dominates and controls the family spending pattern.

For example, in one very apathetic family the wife commented:

"I usually ask my husband, he decides everything. I never spend anything unless he tells me to. We see a doctor if he thinks we are sick."

In a much less apathetic family the wife reported:

"We have a joint checking account. We consult one another when we want to buy or spend any money. We really don't want for anything. I am more concerned about the health of the family so I take care of medical costs as well as food."

Hypothesis 5. The non-apathetic family is less likely to perceive its economic problems as hopeless.

For example, one of the few families without health insurance had an income of well over six-thousand dollars and had experienced a series of illnesses. The wife suffers from a cardiac condition and the husband from tuberculosis. They felt that they would never be able to get out of debt and their philosophy was one of "We take the bills as they come."

Hypothesis 6. Families having intense achievement desires are more likely to be apathetic toward health.

For example, in one of our cases the husband was trying to build up his business. He noted:

". . . I'm a thick-headed Dutchman and can pay my way. I'm simply out of luck if something terrible happens . . . if we get sick . . . right now we must put aside everything else; it's my business and I've got to build it up."

Hypothesis 7. Families with spouses more suggestable to current marketing practices are more likely to be apathetic.

One such family on the apathetic end of the continuum actually bought a cemetery plot with space for two more than they could use. (They later relinquished their plot and bought part of a lot from a friend.)

C. *Cultural and Situational Influences.* Like all other social behavior, a family's concern with health seems to be associated with a concern over the opinion of others.

Hypothesis 8. Families whose members are concerned with the purchase of goods and services that elicit favorable responses from others are more likely to be apathetic.

This last hypothesis in part may explain the superior health care received by the children in the families under study. In our society, it is important to have young children who are healthy. The health of a child brings forth expressions of approval or disapproval from friends, neighbors, and relatives. There is not the same approval for adults or even older children. Especially for males, health care is at variance with values associated with strength and virility; to acknowledge sickness is a sign of weakness. A large expenditure for a trip overseas, a television set or a newer car is much more likely to call forth expressions of approval than an equal amount spent for health care.

Hypothesis 9. Families in which the mother takes the role of diagnostician and therapist are more likely to be apathetic.

Many families still seem to operate through magical though rationalized treatment, frequently supported by the advice of the druggist.

Hypothesis 10. Apathetic families are more likely to be uncertain as to the business relationship between their family and the practitioner.

There is some evidence that the cultural traditions regarding the business relationship between the physician and the patient are changing. Uncertainty of whether the physician also takes the role of the businessman or whether "the doctor's is different from other expenses" seems to be related to the postponement of medical care.

Hypothesis 11. Families who have extensive payroll deductions and who use postponed payment plans are likely to be apathetic.

Many of the families in the sample have accepted an imposed pattern of planning. More and more, families have deductions taken from their pay. When fixed obligations such as rent are added to taxes, health and life insurance, union dues, war bond and retirement deductions, and the family is buying also on credit a car, a television set, or a rug, it can easily be seen why the family avoids such areas of expense as medical care.

D. *Personality.* Personality factors, conditioned as they are, may also explain some of the differences among the families in the sample.

Hypothesis 12. Lessened anxiety regarding pain or serious illness among family members is related to apathy. The non-apathetic family is more likely to be anxious about illness.

In some families there is considerable motivation to go to a physician or dentist since there is concern about illness. However, if there is fear of a physician or dentist, as in many of the cases, then there is an avoidance or postponement of these services.

Hypothesis 13. Families whose members are socialized to gratify immediately their material needs are more likely to be apathetic.

With the occurrence of "super-market" buying in all areas of consumer purchasing and with the availability of postponed payment plans, those individuals who tend to regulate their behavior in terms of immediate solutions are more likely to be less concerned with medical care, unless in pain. For example, one father bought a new television set rather than get his old one repaired because the children were annoying their grandfather who lived with them and he just "couldn't stand it any longer" without the TV set to amuse the kids and ease the family strain.

Conclusions. There are many variables operating in present-day society to influence families in the spending of their income and in the attention they pay to their health needs. The results of this study cast doubt on the idea that income is the crucial variable. However, the tentative hypotheses which have been set forth need to be tested under more rigid conditions.

20   **DEFINITIONS OF HEALTH AND ILLNESS
       IN THE LIGHT OF AMERICAN VALUES
       AND SOCIAL STRUCTURE**

By Talcott Parsons

The aim of the present paper is to try to consider the socio-cultural definition of health and illness in the United States in the light, in the first instance, of American values, but also in terms of the ways in which the relevant aspects of the value system have come to be institutionalized in the social structure. I shall give primary attention to mental health, but will also attempt to define its relation to somatic health and illness as carefully as possible. I shall also try to place the American case in comparative perspective.

First, it is important to try to define the respects in which health and illness can be considered to be universal categories applying to all human beings in all societies and to distinguish them from the respects in which they may be treated as socially and culturally relative. It will be possible here to say only a few rather general things, but the development of social science does, I think, permit us to be somewhat more definite than it has been possible to be until rather recently.

There is clearly a set of common human features of health and illness; indeed more broadly there is probably a set of components which apply perhaps to all mammalian species. There is no general reason to believe that these common components are confined to somatic illness; my view would be that there are also such components for mental illness. It does, however, seem to be a tenable view that there is a range, roughly, from the "purely somatic" to the "purely mental"—both of course, being limiting concepts—and that as one progresses along that range the prominence of the factors of relativity as a function of culture and social structure increases. The importance of the "interpenetration" between somatic and mental aspects is so great, however, that it would be a mistake to draw a rigid line, in any empirical term, between them.

One point is relatively clear. This is that the primary criteria for mental illness must be defined with reference to the social *role-performance* of the individual.[1] Since it is at the level of role-structure that the principal direct interpenetration of social systems and personalities come to focus, it is as an incapacity to meet the expectations of social roles, that mental illness becomes a problem in social relationships and that criteria of its presence or absence should be formulated. This is of course not at all to say that the state which we refer to as mental, as of somatic, illness is not a state of the individual; of course it is. But that state is manifest to and presents problems for both the sick person and others with whom he associates in the context of social relationships, and it is with reference to this problem that I am making the point about role-performance.

At the same time I would not like to treat mental health as involving a state of commitment to the performance of *particular* roles. Such a commitment would involve specific memberships in specific relational systems, i.e., collectivities. Mental health is rather concerned with *capacity* to enter into such relationships and to fulfill the expectations of such memberships. In terms of the organization of the motivational system of the individual, it therefore stands at a more "general level" than do the more specific social commitments.

There is a set of mechanisms in the operation of which social system and personality aspects are interwoven, which make possible the many complex adjustments to changing situations which always occur continually in the course of social processes. It is when the mechanisms involved in these adjustive processes break down ("adjustive" as between personalities involved in social interaction with each other) that mental illness becomes a possibility, that is, it constitutes one way in which the individual can react to the "strains" imposed upon him in the course of social process. This can, of course, occur at any point in his own life cycle from the earliest infancy on. Also, I take for granted that mental illness is only one of several alternative forms which "deviance" can take, again at every stage. Mental illness, then, including its therapies, is a kind of "second line of defense" of the social system vis-à-vis the problems of the "control" of the behavior of its members. It involves a set of mechanisms which take over when the primary ones prove inadequate. In this connection it can also be readily seen that there are two main aspects of the operation of the mechanisms involved. First, the individual who is incapacitated from performing his role-functions would be a disturbing element in the system if he still attempted to perform them. Hence we may say that it is important to have some way of preventing him from attempting to do so, both in his own interest and in that of the system itself. Secondly, however, there is the therapeutic problem, namely of how it is possible to restore him to full capacity and return him to role-performance after an interval.

So far, I have been speaking of mental health with special reference to its place in the articulation between social system and personality. Mental health—and illness—are states of the personality defined in terms of their relevance to the capacity of the personality to perform institutionalized roles. For analytical purposes, however, I have found it necessary to make a distinction, which a good many psychologists do not make, between the personality and the organism. They are, of course, not concretely separable entities, but they are analytically distinguishable systems. There would be various ways of making the distinction, but for present purposes I think it is best to put it that the personality is that part of the mechanisms involved in the control of concrete behavior which genetically goes back to the internalization of social objects and cultural patterns in the course of the process of socialization. The organism, as distinguished from this, consists of that part of the concrete living individual which is attributable to hereditary constitution and to the conditioning processes of the physical environment. Hence, from the point of view of its relation to the personality, it is that aspect of the mechanisms controlling behavior which is not attributable to the experience of socialization in and through processes of social interaction.[2]

It will be noted that I have been careful not to say that the mechanisms

through which the personality component of the concrete individual functions are not "physiological." In my opinion, it is not the distinction between
physiological and in some sense "mental" processes which is the significant
one here. Indeed, I think that *all* processes of behavior on whatever level are
mediated through physiological mechanisms. The physiological mechanisms
which are most significant in relation to the more complex forms of behavior
are, however, mainly of the nature of systems of "communication" where the
physiological mechanisms are similar to the physical media and channels of
communication. Hence, in both cases the content of "messages" cannot be
deduced from the physical properties of the media. In the higher organisms,
including man, it seems clear that the focus of these mechanisms rests in the
central nervous system, particularly the brain, and that the next level down
in the order of systems of control, has to do with the hormones which circu-
late through the blood stream.

It is important to stress this "interpenetration" of personality and organism, because, without it, the complex phenomena usually referred to as
"psychosomatic" are not understandable. Correspondingly, I do not think
that the way in which *both* somatic and mental health and illness can fit into
a common sociological framework are understandable without both the distinction between personality and organism and the extreme intimacy of their
interpenetrating relationship.

Coming back to the relation of both to the social system, I should like to
introduce a distinction which has not been consistently made by sociologists
either in this or in other connections, but which I think is very important for
present purposes. This is the distinction between *role* and *task*. There are
many different definitions of the concept role in the sociological literature.
For my present purpose, however, I think one very simple one is adequate,
namely a role is the organized system of participation of an individual in a
social system, with special reference to the organization of that social system
as a collectivity.[3] Roles, looked at in this way, constitute the primary focus
of the articulation and hence interpenetration between personalities and
social systems. Tasks, on the other hand, are both more differentiated and
more highly specified than roles; one role is capable of being analyzed into a
plurality of different tasks.

Seen in these terms I think it is legitimate to consider the task to define
the level at which the action of the individual articulates with the *physical*
world, i.e., the level at which the organism in the above analytical sense is
involved in interaction with its environment in the usual sense of biological
theory. A task, then, may be regarded as that subsystem of a role which is defined by a definite set of *physical* operations which perform some function or
functions in relation to a role and/or the personality of the individual performing it. It is very important that processes of communication, the *meanings* of which are by no means adequately defined by the physical processes
involved at the task level, are not only included in the concept of task, but
constitute at least one of the most important, if not *the* most important, categories of tasks, or of components of them.[4]

Coming back to the problem of health and illness, I should now like to
suggest that somatic illness may be defined in terms of incapacity for relevant

task-performance in a sense parallel to that in which mental illness was thought of as incapacity for role-performance. In the somatic case the reference is not to any particular task, but rather to categories of tasks, though of course, sudden illness may force abandonment of level rather than any particular task.[5] Put the other way around, *somatic health is, sociologically defined, the state of optimum capacity for the effective performance of valued tasks.*

The relation between somatic and mental health, and correspondingly, illness, seen in this way, bears directly on the problem of levels of organization of the control of behavior. It implies that the "mind" is not a separate "substance" but essentially a level of organization, the components of which are "nonmental," in the same basic sense in which for example, the hypothetical isolated individual is "non-social." It further implies that the mental level "controls" the somatic, or in this sense, physical, aspect of the individual, the "organism." Somatic states are therefore necessary, but in general *not* sufficient conditions of effective mental functioning.[6]

The Problem of "Cultural Relativity" in Health and Illness. Our present concern is with the relation of personality and organism on the one hand, the social system and its culture on the other. It is now possible to say something on the question of the relations between the universal human elements and the socioculturally variable ones in health and illness on both levels. Clearly, by the above definition, *all* human groups have highly organized personalities which must be built up by complex processes of the sort we call socialization and which are subject to various sorts of malfunctioning at the level of social adjustment which has been referred to. All human societies have language, a relatively complex social organization, complex systems of cultural symbols and the like. The individual in such a society, however "primitive," is always involved in a plurality of different roles which are the organizing matrix of the various tasks he performs.

Clearly this personality element of the structure of the individual person is closely interpenetrating and interdependent with the organic-somatic aspect. Hence, there are clearly "problems" of both somatic and mental illness and health for all human groups. Furthermore, all of them are deeply involved with the structures of the social system and the culture.

That there are uniformities in the constitutions of all human groups at the organic level goes without saying, and hence that many of the problems of somatic medicine are independent of social and cultural variability. Thus such things as the consequences and possibilities of control of infection by specific bacterial agents, the consequences of and liability to cancerous growths and many other things are clearly general across the board. This is not, however, to say that the *incidence* and probably degrees of severity of many somatic diseases are not functions of social and cultural conditions, through many different channels. But within considerable ranges, independent of the part played by such factors etiologically, the medical problems presented are essentially the same, though of course, how to implement medical techniques effectively is again partly a socio-cultural problem.

It follows from the conception of personality put forward here, that constancies in the field of mental health are intimately related to uniformities in the character of culture and social structure. Here it is particularly important that, after a period in which a rather undiscriminating version of the doctrine of "cultural relativity" was in the ascendant, much greater attention has recently come to be paid to the universals which are identifiable on these levels. It is not possible here to enter into any sort of detail in this field, but a few highlights may be mentioned.

Most fundamental, I think, is the fact that every known human society possesses a culture which reaches quite high levels of generalization in terms of symbolic systems, including particularly values and cognitive patterns, and that its social structure is sufficiently complex so that it comprises collectivities at several different levels of scope and differentiation. Even though, as is the case with most of the more "primitive" societies known, there is scarcely any important social structure which is not, on a concrete level, a kinship structure, such kinship systems are clearly highly differentiated into a variety of subsystems which are functionally different from each other.

With minimal exceptions, the nuclear family of parents and still dependent children is a constant unit in all kinship systems, though structural emphases within it vary.[7] It is clearly the focal starting point for the process of socialization and the source of the primary bases of human personality organization. But the nuclear family *never* stands alone as a social structure, it is always articulated in complex ways with other structures which are both outside it and stand on a higher level of organization than it does. This involvement of the nuclear family with the wider social structure is, from the structural point of view, the primary basis of the importance of the incest taboo, which, as applying to the nuclear family, is known to be a near universal.[8] Put in psychological terms, this means that the internalization of the object systems and the values of the nuclear family and its subsystems, starting with the mother-child relation, constitutes the *foundation* of personality structure in all human societies. There are, of course, very important variations, but they are all variations on a single set of themes. Because the internalization of the nuclear family is the foundation of personality structure, I suggest that *all mental* pathology roots in disturbances of the relationship structure of the nuclear family as impinging on the child. This is not in the least to say that there are not somatic factors in mental pathology; some children may well be constitutionally impossible to socialize adequately. But the *structure* of pathological syndromes which can legitimately be called mental will always involve responses to family relationships.

It is, however, equally true and important that in no society is the socialization of an adult exhausted by his experience in the nuclear family, and hence is his personality *only* a function of the familial object systems he has internalized. Correspondingly, mental pathology will always involve elements in addition to disturbances of the nuclear family relations, especially perhaps those centering about peer-group relations in the latency period and in adolescence. These other factors involve his relations to social groups other than the nuclear family and to higher levels of cultural generalization and social responsibility than any of those involved in the family.

It is thus, I think, fully justified to think of both mental and somatic pathology as involving common elements for all human groups. But at the same time both of them would be expected to vary as a function of social and cultural conditions, in important ways, and probably the more so as one progresses from the more "vegetative" aspects of organic function and its disturbances to the more behavioral aspects and then from the "deeper" layers of personality structure to the "higher" more "ego-structured" layers. It is also probable that the lower in this range, the more the variation is one of incidence rather than character of pathology, the higher the more it penetrates into the "constitution" of the illness itself.

Health Among the Problems of Social Control. Health and illness, however, are not only "conditions" or "states" of the human individual viewed on both personality and organic levels. They are also states evaluated and institutionally recognized in the culture and social structure of societies. Can anything be said about the ways in which the constancy-variability problem works out at these levels?

Clearly the institutionalization of expectations with respect both to role and to task performance is fundamental in all human societies. There must, therefore, always be standards of "adequacy" of such performance and of the "capacities" underlying it which must be taken into account, and hence, a corresponding set of distinctions between states of individuals which are and are not "satisfactory" from the point of view of these standards. But by no means all types of "conformity" with performance-standards can be called "health" nor all types or modes of deviation from such conformity "illness." Are the categories health and illness, as we conceive them, altogether "culture-bound" or is there something about them which can be generalized on the social role-definition level? To answer this question, it will be necessary to enter a little more fully into the sociological problems presented by these definitions.

Since I am attempting to deal with illness in the context of "social control," I should like to approach the problem in terms of an attempt to classify ways in which individuals can deviate from the expectations for statuses and roles which have been institutionalized in the structure of their societies. In spite of the fact that it will complicate matters, it seems unavoidable to deal with the problem on two different levels.

The first of these two levels concerns the relation of the problem of health and illness to the whole range of categories of deviant behavior. In this connection, I shall attempt to assess the relative importance given to the health complex in different types of society and to show that it is particularly important in the American case. The second level will take up the problem of selectivity and variation *within* the health-illness complex itself. Here, I shall discuss how this relates to selective emphasis on the different components of the role of illness and of the therapeutic process, and will attempt to show that, not only does American society put greater stress on the problem of illness that do other societies, but that its emphases in defining the role and in therapy are also characteristically different.

I shall outline the classification I have in mind on the first level in terms of the way it looks in our own society and then raise the question of how universally it may be assumed that the relevant categories are in fact, differentiated from each other in different societies. The first category is that of the control of the capacities of units in the social structure in the sense in which this conception has been discussed above in connection with the definition of health and illness. Every society must have important concern for the level of these capacities. The present context, however, is that of social control, not socialization, so it is not a question of how these capacities come to be developed in the first place, but rather of how tendencies to their disturbance can be forestalled, or, once having occurred, can be rectified.

Though comparable considerations apply to collectivities as units, in the present context the relevant unit is the human individual, and with reference to him we must consider both of the two aspects which have been distinguished, namely, somatic and mental health. Capacity, it will be remembered, is thought of as standing on a more "general" level than commitment to any particular role or task obligations. It does, however, include the motivation to accept such obligations given suitable situation and opportunity.

There is a second category of problem of social control in relation to the individual which in another sense also stands on a more general level than any particular action-commitments. This may be called the problem of *morality*. This concerns the state of the individual person, but not with respect to his capacities in the same sense as these are involved in the problem of health, but with respect to his commitment to the *values* of the society. This is the area of social control which has traditionally been most closely associated with religion, especially when the reference is to the person, rather than to any collective unit of the society. When I associate the problem with religion, I do not wish to imply that every attachment to a religion or religious movement automatically implies reinforcement of commitment to the values of a *society*. This is by no means necessarily the case. The point is, rather, that it is in the sphere of religious orientation, or its "functional equivalents" at the level of what Tillich calls "ultimate concern," that the individual must work out the problem of how far he is or is not committed to the values of his society.

There is, of course, a great deal of historical and cross-cultural variation in the ways in which individuals may be treated as standing in religious states which need to be remedied or rectified. It seems, however, to be sound to distinguish two very broad types, namely, those involving "ritual impurity" of some sort, and those involving the problem of "salvation" or "state of grace" in a sense comparable to the meanings of these terms within the Christian tradition. In speaking of religion in this connection, I also do not wish to rule out cases which do not include an explicitly "supernatural" reference in the meaning we would tend to give that term. Thus from a "humanistic" point of view the problem still exists of ensuring commitment to the humanistic values. Perhaps the best single example of this reference is the ritualistic aspect of classical Chinese culture with its "secular" ideal of the "superior man."

Both the above two contexts of the problem of social control of individuals refer to rather generalized states of individuals which may be conceived to "lie behind" their commitments to more differentiated and particularized role-obligations and norms. If both of these latter categories be interpreted in the context of social system involvement, then it is a problem in every society how far different elements in its population maintain operative commitments on both these levels which are compatible with the social interest.

The reference to norms, which I have in mind in the first instance in a society as a whole, focuses on the legal system. Any going society must cultivate a rather generalized "respect for law," and this must be specified in several directions to come down to the level of particular legal obligations.

It is important to note that commitment to law-observance stands on a level more general than that involved in any particular role. Such principles as honesty in the sense of respect for the property rights of others, "responsibility" in the sense of the obligation to fulfill contractual obligations once entered into, or recognition of the general legitimacy of political authority; none of these is specific to any particular role in a particular collectivity. In a highly differentiated society like our own, the practicing legal profession may be said to carry out functions of social control in this field which are in some ways parallel to those of the medical profession in the field of health.[9]

Of course, commitment to norms is by no means confined to the norms which in a modern type of society are given the "force of law." But the law first may serve as a prototype, and second is, in a well-integrated society, necessarily the paramount system of norms with respect to the society as a system, though norms of "morality" may as noted above, take precedence on a religious or purely "ethical" level. "Below" the legal level, however, every collectivity in the society has some set of rules, more or less formalized, to which it is essential to secure some order of commitment on the part of its members.

The last of the four contexts in which the problem of social control in the present sense arises is that of commitment to role-obligations in particular collectivities. This also is a broad category running all the way from the obligations of marriage, to a particular spouse, and of occupational commitment in a particular "job" to the obligations of the citizen of loyalty to his national government. One would expect mechanisms of social control to cluster about this area. In our own society, this is the least differentiated of the four, but certain relatively specialized agencies have begun to emerge. On the "lower" levels, social work is one of the more prominent. "Industrial sociology," so far as it is oriented to the problem of the individual worker as a member of a formal organization, is another. This is the area of which Chester Barnard spoke[10] as that of "efficiency" in the technical meaning he gave to that term.

I have taken the space to review these four different contexts of the problem of social control, because I think it is essential to have such a classification as a basis for placing the treatment of any of these problems in a comparative setting. In a highly differentiated society like our own, these four functions have become relatively clearly differentiated from each other, and the operative processes of social control are, with certain indefinite borderlines, of course, to be found in the hands of different organizational agencies. The last of the four I outlined is by a good deal the least firmly institutionalized as a distinct function and it is probably significant that, in our society, it is most fully worked out, through social work, for the lower status-levels of the society.

The present situation with respect to differentiation cannot, however, be said to be typical of all societies; indeed, I doubt whether any case can be found where a comparably close approach to completeness in this differentiation can be found.

Two major "axes" of differentiation were implicit in the classification I have just presented. Both need to be taken into account in placing the problem of health and illness relative to the others. The first of these may be called the differentiation in terms of orientation, on the one hand, to the exigencies of the *situation* in which the person must act; on the other hand, orientation to or through *normative patterns*. The second axis concerns not this problem, but that of whether the "problem" lies in the state of the person as a whole, at a level deeper than the problem of his acceptance of particular obligations, or whether it lies in the question of his "willingness" to accept certain more specific obligations, to particular norms and classes of norms, and to particular roles in particular collectivities.

The first of these two axes differentiates the types of deviance involved in illness and disturbance of commitments to collectivities on the one hand from those involved in disturbance of commitments to norms and to values on the other. The second axis differentiates the problems of illness and of disturbance of commitment to values on the one hand from the problems of commitment to collectivities and to normative patterns (rules and law) on the other. The following tabular arrangement may be helpful to the reader.

	Disturbance of Total Person	Disturbance of Particular Expectations
"Situational" Focus	Problem of "capacities" for task and role performance	Problem of commitments to collectivities (Barnard's "efficiency")
	Illness as deviance Health as "conformity"	Disloyalty as deviance Loyalty as conformity
"Normative" Focus	Problem of commitments to values, or of "morality" "Sin" and "immorality" as deviance	Problem of commitments to norms, or of "legality" "Crime" and "illegality" as deviance
	State of grace or "good character" as conformity	Law-observance as conformity

It is in terms of the first axis that one fundamental type of differentiation involving health can be made, that which treats health as a "naturalistic" state which is not to be explained by or treated through religio-magical media. It is of course a commonplace that in all nonliterate societies, with relatively minor exceptions such as fractures, this differentiation has not yet taken place, and much the same can be said about the high civilizations of the Orient such as India and China until touched by Western medicine. This of course, is in no way to say that "therapies" which are couched in magico-religious terms are necessarily ineffective. On the contrary, there is much evidence that they have been very effective in certain cases. It would, however, hardly be denied that with the clear differentiation of roles in this area which has taken place in the modern world, much greater effectiveness has been made possible over at least a very large part of the range.

Though differentiation on the first axis discriminates the problem of health from that of the "ritual" state of the individual, or his state of grace or, more generally, commitment to values, it fails to discriminate between the more general level of his state "as a person" and his commitment to the more specific obligations of societal membership and activity. Here a problem which has been very central in the modern world in drawing the line between problems of mental health and of law seems to be a major one. This is the question of whether and how far the "deviance" of the individual from conformity with social expectations can be considered to be "intentional" i.e., the question of how far he may legitimately be held *responsible* for his actions. In one area, at least, this has in fact come to be accepted as a main differentiating criterion and, I think, rightly so.

Let me try to elucidate a little some of its implications in the present context. It has long been one of the principal criteria of illness that the sick person "couldn't help it." Even though he may have become ill or disabled through some sort of carelessness or negligence, he cannot legitimately be expected to get well simply by deciding to be well, or by "pulling himself together." Some kind of underlying reorganizing process has to take place, biological or "mental," which can be guided or controlled in various ways, but cannot simply be eliminated by an "act of will." In this sense the state of illness is involuntary. On the other hand, both obedience to norms and fulfillment of obligations to collectivities in roles are ordinarily treated as involving "voluntary" decisions; the normal individual can legitimately be "held responsible."

Certainly both in fields such as law and in that of collectivity obligations, there are many cases where failure to live up fully to "formal" obligations is not "blamed on" the individual. But the distinction is, on the whole, clear; if he is not "ill" (or in a state of ritual impurity, or "sin"), or willfully recalcitrant, it must be the fault of somebody else or of "the system." The essential basis of this possibility of "holding responsible" is the particularity of specific norms and role-obligations. A normal person has the capacity to accept or reject particular obligations without involving a reorganization of the major structures of his personality or of his body. It is only when there is a "disturbance" which goes beyond these particularities that we can speak of illness, or of disturbed commitment to values.[11]

This same problem occurs in the relation to the commitment to values as operating through religion and cognate mechanisms. It is very clear that among many nonliterate peoples, states of ritual impurity are treated as outside the control of the individual victim. They are states for which he may not legitimately be held responsible, except, and this is a most important exception which applies to illness as well, for subjecting himself to the proper treatment institutionally prescribed for those in such a state. In general, some ritual performance is called for, which may even sometimes be self-administered, to "rectify" his state.

Without attempting to discuss the situation in other major religions, it is a very important fact that the conception of original sin in the Christian tradition defines the situation in a cognate way. Though retroactively and mythologically Adam is held to have sinned "voluntarily," the burden of original sin on mankind is held not to be the responsibility of the individual, but something which is inherent in the human condition. Conversely, it cannot be escaped from without outside help.

Here it is important to distinguish original sin from the infraction of the norms and role-obligations of a religious collectivity. I think it can fairly be said that that aspect of "sin" which is treated by religious authorities as *within* the responsibility of the individual is strictly analogous to the civil responsibility for law-observance and/or the responsibility for living up to the obligations of a particular role, in this case of church-membership. Christianity thus has institutionalized the differentiation of these two aspects of the problem of social control. Original sin belongs, with respect to *this* axis of differentiation, on the same side as does illness.

With respect to the major categories I have been discussing for the last few pages, societies may be expected to differ in two major respects. The first I have already been stressing, namely with respect to the *degree* to which these major types of deviance are *differentiated from each other* and the functions of social control with respect to them institutionalized in differentiated agencies. In an evolutionary sense (with societal, not organic reference) they may be said all to have originated in religion.[12] Priests and magicians have thus been the "original" agents of social control everywhere. The roles of physician, of lawyer and, if you will, of "administrator" and social worker have only gradually and unevenly differentiated off from the religious roles.

The second range of variation concerns the relative stress put on conformity with social expectations in each of these categories and hence the seriousness with which deviance in each is viewed, and the importance given to building up effective mechanisms of social control in the area in question as distinguished from others. Thus in a society like that of Hindu caste in India, the overwhelming emphasis seems to have been religious, with ritual purity on one level, the problem of control of and emancipation from the Hindu counterpart of Christian original sin on another as the primary preoccupations. The neglect of health as Westerners understand it in India (until very recently) is too well-known to need emphasizing. Soviet society may be said to be a type which puts primary emphasis on effective role-performance in the socialist state and hence to bend its primary efforts to controlling the commitments of the population (above all through "propaganda" and "agitation")[13] to exerting the utmost effort, especially in production. Finally, with differences, of course, it may be suggested that both classical Rome and modern England have laid more stress on law and integration through the legal system than any other of the major features with which this discussion has been concerned.

Seen in this perspective, contemporary American Society is, with respect to the institutionalization of mechanisms of social control, probably as highly differentiated as any known, certainly as any outside the modern Western world. But among those which are highly differentiated, it is also one which places a very heavy emphasis on the field and problems of health and illness relative to the others, probably as high as any. It is also clear that our concern with problems of health has increased greatly since about the turn of the present century, and furthermore, that the emergence of the problem of mental health into a position of salience, on anything like the scale which has actually developed, is a new phenomenon.

A Restatement of the Criteria of Health and Illness. Before attempting to relate this emphasis systematically to American values and social structure, it would be well to attempt to state somewhat more precisely what seem to be the principal general characteristics of health and illness seen in the context of social role structure and social control.

Health may be defined as the state of optimum *capacity* of an individual for the effective performance of the roles and tasks for which he has been socialized. It is thus defined with reference to the individual's participation in the social system. It is also defined as *relative* to his "status" in the society, i.e. to differentiated type of role and corresponding task structure, e.g., by sex or age, and by level of education which he has attained and the like. Naturally, also there are qualitative ranges in the differentiation of capacities, within sex groups and at given levels of education. Finally, let me repeat that I am defining health as concerned with capacity, not with commitment to *particular* roles, tasks, norms or even values as such. The question of whether a man wants to remain with his wife or likes his particular job or even feels committed to refrain from highway robbery is not *as such* a health problem, though a health problem may underlie and be interwoven with problems of this sort.

Illness, then, is also a socially institutionalized role-type. It is most generally characterized by some imputed generalized disturbance of the capacity of the individual for normally expected task or role-performance, which is not specific to his commitments to any particular task, role, collectivity, norm or value. Under this general heading of the recognition of a state of disturbance of capacity, there are then the following four more specific features of the *role* of the sick person: 1) This incapacity is interpreted as beyond his powers to overcome by the process of decision-making alone; in this sense he cannot be "held responsible" for the incapacity. Some kind of "therapeutic" process, spontaneous or aided, is conceived to be necessary to recovery. 2) Incapacity defined as illness is interpreted as a legitimate basis for the *exemption* of the sick individual, to varying degrees, in varying ways and for varying periods according to the nature of the illness, from his normal role and task obligations. 3) To be ill is thus to be in a partially and conditionally *legitimated* state. The essential condition of its legitimation, however, is the recognition by the sick person that to be ill is inherently *undesirable*, that he therefore has an obligation to try to "get well" and to cooperate with others to this end. 4) So far as spontaneous forces, the *vis medicatrix naturae*, cannot be expected to operate adequately and quickly, the sick person and those with responsibility for his welfare, above all, members of his family, have an obligation to *seek competent help* and to cooperate with competent agencies in their attempts to help him get well; in our society, of course, principally medical agencies. The valuation of health, of course, also implies that it is an obligation to try to *prevent* threatened illness where this is possible.

These criteria seem very nearly obvious on a common sense level in our society, but some aspects of their subtler significance become evident when we consider the way in which, through the channels of mental and psycho-somatic illness, the balance of health and illness comes to be bound up with the balance of control of the motivation of individuals in their relation to the society as a system. This is what I had in mind in discussing illness in the context of the problems of deviance and social control in the first place. I shall not take space to go into this set of problems here, since they have been dealt with elsewhere, but will only call attention to them, and draw a few inferences.[14]

The most important inferences for present purposes concern the importance of *two* related but distinct functions for the society of the health-illness role structure. The first of these is the *insulation* of the sick person from certain types of mutual influence with those who are not sick, and from association with each other. The essential reason for this insulation being important in the present context is not the need of the sick person for special "care" so much as it is that, motivationally as well as bacteriologically, illness may well be "contagious." The motives which enter into illness as deviant behavior are partially identical with those entering into other types of deviance, such as crime and the breakdown of commitment to the values of the society, partly they are dynamically interrelated with these so that stimulation of one set of motives may tend to stimulate others as well.

In the light of the motivational problem the important feature of insulation is the deprivation, for the sick person, of any claim to a more general legitimacy for his pattern of deviance. As noted above, the conditional legitimation which he enjoys is brought at a "price," namely, the recognition that illness itself is an undesirable state, to be recovered from as expeditiously as possible. It is at this price that he is permitted to enjoy the often very powerful gratifications of secondary gain. But the importance of the institutionalization of the role of illness is not confined to its bearing on the motivational balance of the sick person. As Durkheim pointed out for the case of crime, the designation of illness as illegitimate is of the greatest importance to the healthy, in that it reinforces their own motivation *not* to fall ill, thus to avoid falling into a pattern of deviant behavior. The stigmatizing of illness as undesirable, and the mobilization of considerable resources of the community to combat illness is a reaffirmation of the valuation of health and a countervailing influence against the temptation for illness, and hence the various components which go into its motivation, to grow and spread. Thus, the sick person is prevented from setting an example which others might be tempted to follow.

The second important implication of institutionalization of the roles is that being categorized as ill puts the individual in the position of being defined as "needing help" and as obligated to accept help and to cooperate actively with the agency which proffers it. The role of illness, that is to say, channels those categorized as belonging in it into contact with therapeutic agencies. It is therefore involved in both negative and positive mechanisms of social control, negative in that the spread of certain types of deviance is inhibited, positive in that remedial processes are facilitated.

An interesting and important intermediate aspect may also be noted. By defining the sick person as in need of help and tending to bring him into relation to therapeutic agencies, the role of illness tends to place him in a position of *dependency on* persons who are *not* sick. The structural alignment, hence, is of each sick person with certain categories of nonsick, not of groups of sick persons with each other.[15]

American Values and the Health Problem. Now let us turn to the question of the way in which American values and social structure may be said to operate selectively with reference both to the place of the health-illness complex among other mechanisms of social control and with respect to emphases within the health-illness complex itself. To start with it will be necessary to sketch the main outline of the American value system in the relevant respects.

I would like to suggest that even so complex and highly differentiated a society as our own can be said to have a relatively well-integrated system of institutionalized common values at the societal level. Ours I shall characterize as a pattern emphasizing "activism" in a certain particular sense, "worldliness" and "instrumentalism." Let me try, briefly, to explain these terms.

In the first place, a societal value system concerns the orientations of members to conceptions of what is desirable for the society itself and as a whole as a system or object of evaluation. Only derivatively, does it provide patterns of evaluation of the individual. When I refer to activism, I mean that in relation to *its* situation or environment, the society should be oriented to mastery over that environment in the name of ideals and goals which are transcendental with reference to it. The relevant environment may be either physical or social, but because of our relative isolation from other societies until the last generation or so, the physical environment has been particularly prominent in our case. The reference point for exerting "leverage" on the environment has been, historically, in the first instance religious. It will not be possible here to go into the question of the sense in which, or degree to which this is still the case; nevertheless, the main orientation clearly is one of maintaining the pattern of mastery, not of "adjustment" to the inevitable. In no field has this been more conspicuous than that of health where illness has presented a challenge to be met by mobilizing the resources of research, science, etc., to the full.

When I speak of the "worldliness" of the American value system, I mean that, in spite of its religious roots, the *field* of primarily valued activity is in practical secular pursuits, not in contemplation or devotions, or aesthetic gratifications. In its societal application this means a conception of an ideal *society,* originally the Kingdom of God *on Earth,* in a secularized version a good society in which such ideals as liberty, justice, welfare and equality of opportunity prevail.

Finally, when I speak of "instrumentalism," I refer to the fact that, in the first instance for the society as a system, there is no definitive "consummatory" state which is idealized, no definitive societal goal state which is either attained or not—as in the case of "communism." There is rather an indefinite perspective of possible improvement, of "progress" which fulfills by degrees the ideal by moving in the right *direction*.

The absence of a definitive goal for the system as a whole, places the primary active achievement emphasis on the level of the goals of *units* and measures their achievements in appropriate terms. There is a kind of "liberal" pluralism in that any unit in the society, individual or collective, has liberty to pursue goals which to it may seem worthwhile, but more importantly, there are standards of *contribution* to the progress of the society. Perhaps the most obvious (though not the only) field of such contribution is that of economic productivity, for it is the productivity of the economy which is the basis of the availability of facilities for attaining *whatever* goals may seem most worthwhile, since income as generalized purchasing power is nonspecific with respect to particular uses. This is the most generalized basis of opportunity to do "good things." But equally important is the provision of the society with units which have the *capacity* for valued achievement.

I may note that collective units and their achievements are of the utmost importance in the American system, for example, the business firm. But their achievements are fundamentally dependent on the capacities and commitments of the human individuals who perform roles and tasks within them. It is in this connection that the relevance of the valuation of health appears. For the individual, the primary focus of evaluation is universalistically judged *achievement*. The possibility of achievement is, of course, a function of opportunity at any given point in his life cycle, which in turn is a function of the economic level of the community, because openings both for self-employment, e.g. in independent business, and for employment by others, are a function of markets and of funds available through whatever channels. But on a "deeper" and in a sense more generalized level, this achievement is dependent on two basic sets of prior conditions which underlie his capacities, namely, on education in the broadest sense, and on health. It is in the first instance as an essential condition of valued achievement, that the health of the individual is itself valued.

There is another very central strand in the pattern of our evaluation in both respects. This is the relation of both education and health to the valuation of *equality* of opportunity. For reasons which cannot be gone into here, but which bear above all on the high level of structural differentiation of our society, it is one which shows a great deal of mobility of resources. Ascribed status is relatively minimized. The "pluralism of goals" which has to do with the instrumental emphasis in our value system raises the problem of "justice" with great acuteness. One aspect of this is distributive justice with references to the allocation of rewards. But with the emphasis on active achievement, even more crucial than justice of reward distribution is that of *opportunity*

for value achievement. But education and health are clearly more fundamental conditions of achievement than is access to investment funds or to
employment, since they condition capacity to exploit opportunity in this narrower sense. Hence, *access* to education and to health services becomes, in a
society like our own, a peculiarly central focus of the problem of justice in
the society.

On technical grounds I do not classify education as a function of social
control in a society.[16] Within the field of problems of social control, as discussed above, the problem of health clearly constitutes the "rock bottom" of
the series. There seem, when the problem is seen in this light, to be a number
of reasons which I may review briefly, why it has emerged into a position of
special prominence in contemporary America.

First, and of course a very important point, the development of medicine
and of the health sciences underlying and associated with it, has made possible an entirely new level of control of illness, both preventive and therapeutic, far higher than has ever existed before in history. There is, of course,
interdependence. American medicine did not just take over a medical science
ready-made, but has developed the European beginnings with an energy
and resourcefulness probably matched only in the field of industrial technology. There is, hence, interdependence between the development, on the
one hand, of medical science and technology, and on the other, of interest
in, and concern for, effective handling of health problems.

Secondly, the order of significance of the problems of social control, starting with commitment to paramount values themselves, running through commitment to norms, then to roles and tasks, is probably, in a very broad sense,
of evolutionary significance. This is to say that there is a tendency for a
problem area to emerge into salience only when, to a degree, the ones ahead
of it in the priority list have in some sense been "solved." This is not to say
that any of them ever are definitively solved, but in a relative sense one can
speak of solution.

It is not possible to discuss this question here in detail. But it may be suggested that by the mid-nineteenth century, with the very important exception of the problem of the South, a certain national unity had been achieved
in terms of values and norms.[17] It can then be further suggested that in the
latter half of the nineteenth century there was concentration on the problems
of setting up the new industrial system with the institutionalization of the
principal role-categories which have to go into that, notably, of course, an
occupational role system which was structurally quite different from that of
the earlier society of "farmers and mechanics." Not least important in this
connection was the institutionalization of the repercussions of these changes
on the family, because of the drastic nature of the differentiation of occupational from familial roles. From the point of view of the individual, it may be
said that the development of the industrial economy provided, in terms of a
structural type congruent with American values, a new level of solution of the
problem of opportunity.

From this point of view, one might say that after the turn of the century
the stage was set for a new level of concern with the problems of education

and health, which have indeed figured very prominently in this period, though not by any means to the exclusion of the others. Their importance is, I think, further accentuated by another feature of the development of the society. This is the fact that, with the development of industrialization, urbanism, high technology, mass communications and many other features of our society, there has been a general *upgrading* to higher levels of responsibility. Life has necessarily become more complex and has made greater demands on the typical individual, though different ones at different levels. The sheer problem of capacity to meet these demands has, therefore, become more urgent. The motivation to retreat into ill-health through mental or psychosomatic channels, has become accentuated and with it the importance of effective mechanisms for coping with those who do so retreat.

Seen in terms of this kind of historical perspective, it makes sense, I think, that *the first major wave of development of the health institutions was in the field of somatic illness and the techniques of dealing with it, and that this has been followed by a wave of interest in problems of mental health.* This is partly, but by no means wholly, because the scientific basis for handling somatic illness has developed earlier and farther. In addition to this, it is well known that the resistances to recognizing the existence of health problems are stronger in the field of mental than of somatic health. Furthermore, a larger component of the phenomena of mental illness presumably operates through motivation and is hence related to the problems and mechanisms of social control. Social changes, however, have not only increased the strain on individuals, thus accentuating the need for mechanisms in this area, but some of the older mechanisms have been destroyed or weakened and a restructuring has been necessary.

For one thing, levels of mental pathology which could be tolerated under pre-industrial conditions, have become intolerable under the more stringent pressures of modern life; this probably includes the pushing of many types of personality over the borderline into overt psychosis, who otherwise would have been able to "get along." Furthermore, the family, for example, has undertaken a greatly increased burden in the socialization and personality-management fields, and new institutional arrangements for dealing with the health problems of its members are required. This seems, for example, to be one major factor in the rapid spread of hospitalization.[18]

I may sum up this aspect of the discussion by saying that both by virtue of its value system, and by virtue of the high level of differentiation of its social structure, American society has been one in which it could be expected that the problem of health, and within this more particularly of mental health, would become particularly salient. Its "liberal" cast which militates against highly stringent integration with reference to a system goal tends to emphasize the problem of getting units to "come along." The human individual is the end of the series of units on which the functioning of the society depends, and is hence the "last resort" in this connection. At the same time, the activistic orientation of the society militates against any orientation which would be inclined to let individuals "rest on their oars," but puts very much of a premium on the protection and development of capacity in the sense in which I have discussed it here.

The same factors, particularly seen in the context of the stage of development of the society, tend to prevent too strong an emphasis on any of the other primary problems and modes of social control. Generally, I think, contrary to much opinion, it can be said that the American society is very firmly attached to its primary values, so much so that they tend to be placed outside the field of serious concern. There is, to be sure, much controversy about what are alleged to be changes in values. But a careful analysis, which cannot be entered into here, will reveal that very much, at least, of this does not lie at this level, but rather at ideological levels.

A very good example of this is the amount of concern displayed over the developing salience of problems of mental health, and the scope given to the permissive and supportive elements in the orientation to the mentally ill. But people who show this concern often forget to emphasize the other side of the coin, namely, the equally prominent concern with therapy, with bringing the mentally ill back into full social participation, which above all, means into full capacity for achievement. Particularly revealing, I think, is the conception that the therapeutic process involves active *work* on the part of the patient, his seriously *trying* to get well. He is conceived of as anything but a passive object of the manipulations of the therapeutic personnel.

American Selectivity within the Patterns of Health and Illness. I have argued above, that among the problems and mechanisms of social control, both the values and the social structure of American society will tend to place emphasis on the problems of health and illness which concern commitment to roles, as compared with those of commitment to collectivities, to normative rules, or to the values themselves. This essentially is to say that it is *capacity* which is the primary focus of the problem of social control for us. With the increasing complexity and "maturity" of the society in turn, the problem of motivation to adequate role-performance and hence, to mental health becomes a salient one.

The problem now arises of what kind of selectivity we may expect, on the basis of the above analysis, *within* the complex of illness, and the corresponding attitudes toward therapy, relative to other ways of treating the problem of illness as such. In order to approach this question, I would like to use the formulation of the main components of the definition of illness, as stated previously herein, as my main point of reference. The first point, namely, a disturbance of capacity, is general, and is the link with the foregoing discussion of selectivity among the problems of social control. This is to say that in the United States we are more likely to interpret a difficulty in an individual's fulfilling social role-expectations as a disturbance in capacity, i.e., as illness, than is true in other types of society with other types of value systems.

The other four criteria, it will be remembered, were exemption from role-obligations, holding the patient not responsible for his state, conditional legitimation of the state, and acceptance of the need for help and of the obligation to cooperate with the source of the help.

My suggestion is that, compared with other societies in which other value systems have been institutionalized, in the American case the heaviest emphasis among these tends to go to the last. Essentially, this derives from the element in the American value system which I have called "activism" above. The implication of that element, in the context of the others to which it relates, is for the personality of the individual, the valuation of *achievement*. This in turn, as was developed above, implies a strong valuation of the capacities which underlie achievement, capacities which are primarily developed through education or socialization and protected and restored through health education or socialization and protected and restored through health services. But in the American case, this does not imply that the primary stress is on the dependency aspect of the "need for help"—I shall return to the question of the role of dependency presently. It is rather, from the point of view of the society, the attitude which asserts the desirability of *mastery* of the problems of health, and from that for the individual sick person, the obligation to cooperate fully with the therapeutic agency, that is to *work* to achieve his own recovery. The rationale of this is plainly that, if he is not motivated to work to attain the conditions of effective achievement, he cannot very well be considered to be motivated to the achievements which require good health as a condition.

It might then be said that the other three components of the role of illness are institutionalized as subsidiary to, and instrumental to, this one. With respect to legitimation there is a particularly strong emphasis on its *conditional* aspect, that illness is only legitimized so long as it is clearly recognized that it is intrinsically an undesirable state, to be recovered from as expeditiously as possible. Similarly, with the factor of exemption from role-performance and the "admission" that the patient cannot be held responsible in the sense discussed above. In this connection, there is a very important relation to the scientific aspect of our cultural tradition. That the patient "can't help it" is simply one of the facts of life, demonstrated by medical science. Where scientific evidence is not available, the tendency is to give the benefit of the doubt to the possibility that he can help it. Thus, we tend to be relatively suspicious of plans for "free" health care because of the readiness to impute malingering wherever objective possibility for it exists.

I shall wish to suggest very tentatively how this American emphasis on active therapy differs from emphases in other societies, but before taking this up, I would like to try broadly to answer two other sets of questions about the American case. The first of these is how the patterning of illness in our society relates to the problem of the *directions* of deviant behavior, the second to selective emphases among the social components involved in the therapeutic process.

In a previous publication, I attempted to classify the directions which deviant orientations might take in terms of three major dimensions, two of which were very close to, if not identical with, those set forth by Merton.[19] These were first the variation between *alienation* from social expectations and *compulsive conformity* with them, second between *activity* and *passivity*, and third between *object*-primacy and *pattern*-primacy. The first two of these are the ones also selected by Merton.

In terms of these first two dimensions, illness clearly belongs in the general category of a type of deviance categorized by alienation and by passivity. This general type I have designated as withdrawal whereas Merton calls it "retreatism." This tendency to withdrawal as the most prominent type of deviance is typical of American society generally. But some of the dynamics of it are relevant to the questions of selectivity within the components of the pattern of illness.

Before entering into these, however, it may be noted that with respect to the American pattern of illness, I think it can be said that the primary focus is object-oriented rather than pattern-oriented. This is above all because illness focuses at the level of capacity for role and task performance, not at the level of norms or values and conformity with them. This would also be true of illness generally but for reasons which will be discussed presently. I think it likely that it is more accentuated in the American case than others.[20]

What then, can be said to be some of the main patterns of motivational dynamics relevant to the problem of illness in American society and their relation in turn to these features of the role of illness as an institutionalized role? I may start by suggesting that all patterns of deviant behavior, as distinguished from creative alteration of the cultural or normative tradition, involves the primacy of elements of *regressive* motivational structure in the psychological sense.[21] But for different types of deviance and within the category of illness as a type of deviance there will be selective emphases on different phases of psychological regression.

It is not possible to enter into all the complications here, but I suggest that in the American case, the primary focus lies in the residues of the pre-oedipal mother-child relationship, that phase of which Freud spoke as involving the "first true object-attachment." The basis on which this develops goes back to the very great, and increasing prominence in socialization of the relatively *isolated* nuclear family. The "American dilemma" in this case is that the child is, typically, encouraged to form an extremely intense attachment to the mother at this time, while at the same time he is required later to break more radically with this early dependency because the process of emancipation from the family of orientation is pushed farther and faster than in other systems. Independence training, that is to say, forms a particularly prominent part of our socialization process and the strength of the mother attachment is an essential condition of its successful carrying out.

The alienation involved in the motivation to illness may then be interpreted to involve alienation from a set of expectations which put particular stress on independent achievement. Because of this complex, the importance of the passivity component of the deviance expressed in illness is particularly great, because the ambivalent motivational structure about the dependency-independence problem is particularly prominent. Therapy then focuses on the strengthening of the motivation to independence relative to dependency and on overcoming the alienation, focussing on the expectations of independence and, through it, achievement.[22]

I suggest, then, that the American pattern of illness is focussed on the problem of capacity for achievement for the individual person. Therapeutically, recovery is defined for him as a *job* to be done in cooperation with those who are technically qualified to help him. This focus then operates to polarize the components of the "problem" in such a way that *the primary threat to his achievement capacity which must be overcome is dependency.* The element of exemption from ordinary role-obligations may then be interpreted as permissiveness for temporary relief from the strains of trying hard to achieve. The patient is permitted to indulge his dependency needs under strictly regulated conditions, notably his recognition of the conditional nature of the legitimacy of his state, and exposure to the therapeutic task.[23]

These elements of the situation relate in turn to the components of the therapeutic process. I have elsewhere[24] designated these, in terms of role-pattern, as permissiveness, support, selective rewarding and reinforcement. An essential point is that the dependency component of the deviance of illness is used constructively in the therapeutic pattern, essentially through what is in certain respects a recapitulation of the socializing experience. This is to say that through permissiveness to express dependency, both in exemption from role-obligations and in supportive relations to others, the patient is encouraged to form a dependent attachment to others. The permissive and supportive treatment of the sick person, by giving him what he wants, undercuts the alienative component of the motivational structure of his illness. He finds it much more difficult to feel alienated toward social objects who treat him with kindness and consideration than he would otherwise be disposed to feel—though, of course, there may be a problem, particularly with some types of mental illness of getting him to accept such kindness and consideration, even to accept his need for the exemptions permitted by virtue of illness.

At the same time the element of dependency, through "transference," is the basis of a strong attachment to therapeutic personnel, which can then be used as a basis of leverage to motivate the therapeutic "work" which eventually should result in overcoming the dependency itself, or mitigating it sufficiently so that it no longer interferes so seriously with his capacities. Building on this, then, the active work of therapy, adapting to the fundamental conditions of the biological and psychological states of the patient, can take hold and operate to propel toward recovery.[25]

I should finally like to turn to a brief and very tentative suggestion of the main differences between the orientations to illness in the United States and in two other modern societies, namely Soviet Russia and Great Britain. Let us take the Soviet case first.[26]

Whereas in the American case I suggested that our concern with capacity for role-achievement put the primary emphasis on the restoration of that capacity through therapeutic work, the general orientation of Soviet society is different; it is to the attainment of a collective goal for the society as a whole, the "building of socialism." With reference to the problem of illness this tends to shift the emphasis from the obligation to cooperate in therapy to the problem of responsibility and non-responsibility. This is most conspicuous in the field of mental illness where the Soviet attitude is an extreme antithesis of our own precisely on this point.[27] One very telling expression of it is the complete prohibition of psychoanalysis, whereas psychoanalysis has had greater success in the United States than in any other country. My interpretation of this would be that psychoanalysis is a threat from the Soviet point of view, because through the theory of the unconscious, it so strongly emphasizes the elements in the personality of the individual which are outside his voluntary control. It would give too plausible excuses for too many for the evasion of responsibility. In the American case, on the other hand, psychoanalysis is defined more as offering *opportunity* for constructive therapeutic work, to the patient as well as the therapist.[28]

The same general strain seems to be conspicuous, from Field's account, in the field of somatic medicine. The attitude seems to be one of reluctant concession to human frailties. Of course, it is part of socialism to have a national medical service, but at the same time party and administrative personnel keep strict watch on the medical people to be sure that they do not connive in malingering which—because of the great severity of labor discipline—they have been under strong pressure to do. To American eyes the Soviet treatment of illness seems to be marked by a certain perfunctoriness, as if it were up to the patient to prove that he is "really" sick rather than it being the physician's role to investigate the possibilities on his own. I suggest that this may be more than a matter of scarcity of personnel and resources; it is probably at least in part an authentic expression of Soviet values.

Reinforcing this conclusion is the probability that illness is not the primary type of deviance for Soviet society in the sense that I have argued it is in the American case. I think it probable that what I have called "compulsive acquiescence in status-expectations" is the most prominent type. This, of course, very generally does not appear overtly as deviance at all and hence is difficult to detect.[29]

There is, however, another side of the Soviet picture, just as there is in the American case of polarity between the emphasis on active mastery and the problem of dependency. This is that in medical care, especially in the hospital, there seems to be a particularly strong supportive emphasis. This is to say that, once the status of being sick is granted, there is not nearly so strong an emphasis on the conditional character of its legitimacy as in the American case, and patients are encouraged to relax and to enjoy being taken care of.[30]

This suggests a permissiveness for regression, but one which is differently structured from the American. It is less the need to express dependency on particular social objects which does not threaten essential acceptance or belongingness. Psychologically it suggests primacy of oral components rather than of the mother-child love-attachment.

Thus, on the one hand, the role of illness is not given nearly so wide a scope in Soviet Russia as in the United States, particularly in the direction of mental illness. At the same time, it is also differently structured in that the primary focus is the problem of the responsibility of the individual rather than his capacity in our sense to achieve and to cooperate in recovery. The permissive element is more for "rest," for relaxation from responsibility, than it is for the direct expression of object-oriented dependency.

The British case does not seem to be quite so clear, but I think it is different in important ways from either the American or the Soviet. By contrast, with the other two, British society has a particularly strong integrative emphasis. From this point of view, illness is not so much a threat to the achievement of the individual or to his responsibility as it is a threat to his *status* as an acceptable member of the society and its various relevant subgroupings. The main emphasis in treatment then would be on reintegration, an element which is always present, but is more strongly stressed in the British case than in others.

One important type of evidence is the particularly strong British feeling that the sick individual has a *right* to care in case of illness. The whole welfare state is related to the integrative emphasis in the society, but the particularly full coverage provided by the National Health Service for the whole population is one very salient aspect of this general orientation. On the part of the nation and its health agencies then, it is strongly declared that illness, far from jeopardizing the individual's status, gives him special claims on the collectivity. The burden of proof is not nearly so much on him that he is "really" sick as in either the American or the Soviet cases. One might speak of a scale of decreasing "tolerance of the possibility of malingering" in the order, British, American, Soviet.

Another interesting point is that, with respect to the scope given to the recognition of mental illness, the British case is intermediate between the American and the Soviet; this includes the position of psychoanalysis. I suggest that this has to do with the very strong British emphasis on the importance of self-control in social relations. Somatic illness is generally clearly beyond the responsibility of the individual, and generally the legitimacy of illness is not made so highly conditional as in the American case. But capacity is not so highly valued and mental disturbance is not to the same extent seen as an opportunity for therapeutic achievement. The deliberately encouraged regression which, with all the differences, is shared by the Soviet and American cases, is substantially less conspicuous in the British.

The above are, as I have emphasized, extremely tentative and sketchy impressions of relatively systematic differences between American, Soviet, and British selectivities in the definition of health and illness, and in the roles of patient and of therapeutic agencies. I have introduced them and carried the analysis as far as I have, only to try to give some empirical substance to the general view of the nature of variability from one society to another in those respects that have been presented herein.

III

Socio-Cultural Aspects of
Medical Care and
Treatment

THIS SECTION deals with the impact of culture upon the process of medical care and treatment and upon societal attempts at healing of a non-medical nature. Medicine is a social institution in its own right, with many norms, rituals and values of its own. The treatment process itself is affected by cultural conditions and not free from processes of social control.

Modes of healing by persons other than physicians, such as "folk-practitioners," comprise an area of behavioral science investigation becoming known as the study of folk and primitive medicine. Lyle Saunders presents a chapter from his larger treatise on modes of healing peculiar to the Spanish-speaking people of the American Southwest, one of the most extensive studies of folk medicine. The obstetrical and pediatric practices of a non-medical nature of a different sub-cultural group, the Hutterites, are analyzed in the original contribution of Joseph Eaton.

Some interesting aspects of the patient-physician relationship, in terms of the level of medical information revealed, is the subject of the paper by Lois Pratt, Arthur Seligmann, M.D., and George Reader, M.D. Julius Roth presents an intriguing analysis of some of the normative components of certain hygienic practices in a tuberculosis hospital.

Some socio-cultural and social psychological aspects of illness and treatment as they relate to changes in the American family system are discussed at length in the contribution by Talcott Parsons and Renée Fox.

21   HEALING WAYS IN THE SPANISH SOUTHWEST

By Lyle Saunders

With regard to illness and its treatment, as in other aspects of their culture, the Spanish-speaking people of the Southwest have many traits in common with the Anglos. Like most other people, they have minor ailments that they tend to disregard. Like all people, they occasionally have aches and pains, chills and fever, and other insistent symptoms that force them to seek relief. And, as in the case of most other people, what they do, how they do it, and when, are determined by the "knowledge" they have of the meaning and cause of their symptoms, and of what can or should be done about them. Such knowledge is a product of association with other people and may be as restricted or expansive, as consistent or contradictory, as the range of their associations permits it to be.

Medical Knowledge of Spanish-Speaking People. In varying degree, depending on who he is, where he lives, and what his personal experience has been, the Spanish-speaking individual draws his knowledge of illness and its treatment from four widely separated sources: (1) from the folk medical lore of medieval Spain as refined in several centuries of relative isolation from its source; (2) from the cultures of one or more American Indian tribes; (3) from Anglo folk medicine as practiced in both rural and urban areas; and (4) from "scientific" medical sources. In a given instance of illness, elements from any or all of the four sources may be utilized in any sequence that may seem appropriate to the individual or to those who may advise or otherwise try to help him. In a case recently observed, a young Spanish-American couple first attempted to treat the husband's digestive difficulties with popular remedies purchased from an Anglo drugstore. When that failed to bring the desired results they used concoctions suggested by the wife's mother, which were prepared from anise, sagebrush, and horsemint. Dissatisfied with the results of this therapy, they next consulted an Anglo physician. When, after two visits to his office, the husband's discomfort persisted, they sought the services of a *curandera* who was reputed to know a good deal about stomach disorders. Another woman, the daughter of a Pueblo Indian mother and a "full-blooded Mexican" father, who now lives in an Anglo city, prides herself in possessing considerable medical knowledge, most of which she obtained from an uncle living in one of the New Mexico pueblos. Although she has been a regular patient at an Anglo cardiac clinic, this woman feels that Anglo doctors do not really help anybody and are frequently too stubborn to take advantage of the superior wisdom of some of their patients. She treats herself, her family, and neighbors who seek her advice, from a pharmacopoeia that includes Anglo patent preparations, household remedies from both the Anglo and Spanish folk medical traditions, and herbs, the preparation and the use of which she learned from her Indian uncle.

Adapted from *Cultural Difference and Medical Care* (New York: Russell Sage Foundation, 1954). Copyright 1954 by The Russell Sage Foundation of New York.

Illness and disease are social as well as biological phenomena. On the biological level they consist of adaptations of the organism to environmental influences; on the social level they include meanings, roles, relationships, attitudes, and techniques that enable members of a cultural group to identify various types of illness and disease, to behave appropriately, and to call upon a body of knowledge for coping with the condition defined as an illness. What is recognized as disease or illness is a matter of cultural prescription, and a given biological condition may or may not be considered an "illness," depending on the particular cultural group in which it occurs.[1] Infestation by intestinal worms is generally regarded as a type of disease by people in the United States. Among other people, for example the inhabitants of the island of Yap, worms are thought to be a necessary component of the digestive process. *Mal ojo, susto,* and *empacho* are examples of diseases that are common in Latin America but unknown in the United States—with the exception of the Spanish-speaking Southwest—although the symptoms which give rise to diagnoses of any or all of these are fairly common in this country. What should be done about a given condition defined culturally as "illness" and the proper relationships of a sick person to other people are also culturally prescribed. An individual thus has cultural guides that enable him to know when he or others may be regarded as sick, something about the cause and nature of the sickness, what may be done to alleviate or remedy the condition, and the behavior expected of him and of others in the situation.

The Spanish-speaking people, having drawn from many cultures their understandings of illness and disease and of the proper behavior associated with their various manifestations, have a somewhat incongruous set of notions which, in a given individual, may range from an uncritical belief in witchcraft or magic as etiological factors to complete acceptance of the latest "scientific" methods of diagnosis and therapy. It is not uncommon to find elderly Spanish-speaking patients in the most modern of Anglo hospitals wearing bracelets of copper wire to prevent rheumatism or similar painful conditions of the joints, or other amulets or charms believed to have therapeutic value. As in the case of other cultural elements, no valid generalization can be made that will be applicable to the entire Spanish-speaking population, since the range of experiences within the group is extremely wide and the opportunities for differential participation in two or more cultures varied. It is probable, however, that age and degree of participation in Anglo culture are the most important variables associated with differences in belief, knowledge, and practice with respect to illness and disease. Older persons and those having relatively little effective contact with Anglo culture can reasonably be expected to have drawn much of their knowledge and belief about sickness and its treatment from Spanish or Indian cultural sources. Younger persons and those with a relatively large degree of effective participation in the Anglo culture are more likely to share Anglo beliefs and attitudes about sickness and to utilize Anglo techniques for dealing with it.

In adopting new ideas about illness and new materials and techniques for treating it, the Spanish-speaking people have not necessarily abandoned any of their old ideas or healing methods. Some individuals may have dropped certain practices used by their parents or grandparents in treating certain disease conditions, or may have failed to learn them, but in the Spanish-speaking population viewed as a whole most of the old ways persist in some form. Drugstores in the "Mexican" sections of Anglo cities in the Southwest do a thriving business in herbs and other folk remedies. *Parteras, curanderas, médicas, albolarias,* and even *brujas*² still find a demand for their services in both rural and urban areas. Alternative types of medical service and methods of treatment are seldom mutually exclusive, so that the adoption of the new does not necessitate giving up the old. The new is merely added to the old body of knowledge or belief, and either or both are drawn upon, depending on the circumstances. The Spanish-speaking person who puts himself in the hands of an Anglo institution and practitioner for a surgical operation expects to receive the utmost benefit from Anglo knowledge and skill. If, subsequently, he wears a piece of *oshá* over the incision, this does not necessarily indicate any lack of faith in Anglo methods but rather his reliance on a wider range of "knowledge" than that possessed by the Anglos who are treating him. Penicillin and the other antibiotics admittedly reduce or prevent infection, but so, in his opinion, does *oshá,* and it does no harm to be doubly certain of results by using both.

Folk Medicine. Three of the four sources from which the Spanish-speaking people derive their ideas about sickness and its treatment provide them with types of knowledge, belief, and practice that may be classified as folk medicine.³ Folk medicine differs from "scientific" medicine in a number of ways. In any culture, it is generally the common possession of the group. In a folk culture, there is relatively little division of knowledge with respect to medicine, so that what one adult knows about illness and its treatment is usually known by all other adults. Although knowledge of the origins of folk medical practices and beliefs may have largely been lost, the practices and beliefs themselves are often so rooted in tradition that they seem a part of the natural order of things and are as much taken for granted as is the daily rising and setting of the sun. Folk medical lore is transmitted from person to person and generation to generation by informal methods and through what sociologists like to call unstructured situations. One learns it, much as he learns other elements of his culture, as an incidental part of his everyday associations. Folk medicine is usually well integrated with other elements of a folk culture and is reinforced by them. The expected attitude toward a given element of folk medicine is one of uncritical acceptance. Failure does not invalidate a practice or shake the belief on which it is based. A remedy is tried, and if it works no surprise is evinced, since that is what was expected. If it does not work, the failure is rationalized and something else tried. In most illnesses the patient ultimately either recovers or dies. If he gets well, the remedial technique is credited with effecting the cure. If he dies, the reason is not that the remedy was inappropriate, but that the patient was beyond help.⁴ Folk medicine, like scientific medicine, undoubtedly derives much of its prestige and authority from the fact that the majority of sick persons get well regardless of what is done.

If practitioners of scientific medicine think of folk medicine at all, they are likely to regard it as mere superstition or as a somewhat curious and outdated survival, having about the same relationship to medical science that astrology has to astronomy. But folk medicine, even in cultures with a well-developed tradition of scientific medicine, is a flourishing institution, and many folk practices have survived because they undoubtedly do get results. Although they are in general uncritically accepted by those using them, folk medical practices are subjected over a period of time to a rough empirical evaluation. Those that seem successful frequently come to be more and more used and thus firmly entrench themselves in the minds and behaviors of the group using them. Those that consistently fail to do what is expected of them tend to be used less and less frequently and, in time, may be dropped altogether. There thus operates a selective process that tends to weed out the ineffective practices and to strengthen those that prove to be effective.

Between scientific medicine and folk medicine there is a constant two-way interchange. Remedies that have been developed by scientific medicine become a part of the pharmacopoeia of folk medicine (for example, aspirin to relieve headaches or other minor aches and pains) and others with a long history of folk use are "discovered," analyzed, tested, and ultimately become a part of scientific medicine (for example, curare, quinine, cocaine). It is not the materials or procedures that determine whether a given technique represents folk or scientific medicine, but rather the way in which they are used and the body of knowledge or belief that lies behind the use. Scientific medicine is rooted in a precise knowledge of cause and effect relationships and a critical attitude toward both practices and results. Folk medicine is neither precise nor critical. It is rooted in belief, not knowledge, and it requires only occasional success to maintain its vigor.

The folk medicine of a given people, however, is usually not a random collection of beliefs and practices; rather, it constitutes a fairly well-organized and fairly consistent theory of medicine. The body of "knowledge" on which it is based often includes ideas about the nature of man and his relationships with the natural, supernatural, and human environments. Folk medicine flourishes because it is a functional and integrated part of the whole culture, and because it enables members of cultural groups to meet their health needs, as they define them, in ways that are at least minimally acceptable.

The Spanish-speaking people of the Southwest, as has been indicated, draw their medical beliefs and practices from many sources. One of these, and one that particularly influences the medical beliefs and practices of the two groups we have called Mexicans and Mexican-Americans, is the folk medicine of Mexico.

Mexican Folk Medicine. There is probably no single body of medical knowledge and practice that is common to all persons of Mexican origin. The isolation of many areas and the poor communication existing between them until recently have undoubtedly contributed to the development of somewhat different bodies of medical lore in different parts of the country. Varying degrees of contact with indigenous Indian cultures have also resulted in variations in medical knowledge and practice. But there are a few elements, common to a number of different areas in Mexico and other parts of Latin America, that have influenced the medical behavior of Spanish-speaking persons in the Southwest.

One widely dispersed body of knowledge and practice is that related to concepts of heat and cold as qualities both of disease conditions and of materials used in therapy.[5] These concepts provide a means of determining what remedy may be used for a particular illness and what the consequences are likely to be if the wrong treatment is used. Illnesses are classified as hot and cold, without respect to the presence or absence of fever, and the correct therapy is to attain a balance by treating "hot" diseases with "cold" remedies and "cold" diseases with "hot" remedies. Food, beverages, animals, and people possess the characteristics of "heat" or "cold" in varying degree, and it is thought wise always to maintain a proper regard for the principles of balance.[6] "Hot" foods, for example, should never be combined, but rather should be taken in conjunction with something "cold," with care being used to see that extremes of heat and cold are not taken together. A person with a "cold" disease is endangered by being given "cold" remedies or foods, since these are likely to aggravate his condition. There is no general agreement on exactly what is "hot" or "cold"; therefore, the classification of a given material or condition may vary from place to place.

Another fairly common body of belief and practice in Mexico relates to the concept of the clean stomach and includes the idea that the maintenance of health requires a periodic purging of the stomach and intestinal tract. At least one disease, *empacho*, is thought to be directly due to failure to achieve a clean stomach, and the rather large number of purgatives used are evidence of the extent to which the concept is accepted.[7]

Blood is considered important in the balance of health and disease and many folk remedies serve the function of purifying the blood or otherwise improving its quality. Loss of blood for any reason, even in the small amounts necessary for laboratory tests, is thought to have a weakening effect, particularly on males, whose sexual vigor is thereby believed to be impaired.

Illness is conceived primarily in terms of not feeling well. Conditions that are not accompanied by subjective feelings or discomfort are generally not classified as illness; hence, there is no obligation to do anything about them. Health is looked upon as a matter of chance, and it is felt that there is very little that a person can do to keep it. Minor discomforts usually are not sufficient motivations to seek treatment, and frequently persons are seriously ill before they begin to seek or accept help. There is a tendency to conceal illness, partly deriving from the idea that to be sick is a manifestation of weakness.

Air is considered potentially dangerous, particularly if cold or if it is blowing over one. Night air is more dangerous than day air, and persons already ill are thought to be particularly susceptible to the harm that air can bring. Consequently, sickrooms are not ventilated, and special care is taken to see that all windows and doors are closed at night.

Pregnancy requires adherence to many dietary restrictions and a reduction in the amount of water drunk, lest the head of the foetus grow too large for an easy delivery. Frequent bathing and regular exercise in the prenatal period are thought to facilitate the delivery process, which frequently takes place with the woman in a squatting or kneeling position. After the delivery the mother remains in bed for an extended period of time, and then she takes or is given a steam bath. During the first three days following delivery the diet is restricted to a small amount of "cold" foods. Thereafter, "hot" foods again may be eaten.

With respect to etiological factors, three types of causation are recognized: empirical, magical, and psychological. Empirical or "natural" diseases are those in which a known external factor operates directly on the organism to produce the illness. Anything resulting from exposure to bad air, invasion by microorganisms, contact with an infected person, eating improper foods, failure to keep a clean stomach, and similar hazards are considered "natural" diseases. A long list of illnesses, including pneumonia, rheumatism, diarrhea, colds, smallpox, worms, tuberculosis, and venereal disease, are placed in this category. Magical diseases are those in which the causative factors lie outside the realm of empirical knowledge and cannot be thus verified. Such a disease is *mal ojo*, or evil eye, which is produced in young children, often without intention, by persons who have a "strong glance." Some kinds of *susto*, a type of illness resulting from fright, are of magical etiology in that they are felt to be caused by the possession of an individual by an evil spirit. And there are, of course, many kinds of bewitchment in which a person with evil intent and magical power can cause illness symptoms in another. Psychological diseases are those in which a strong emotional experience causes the appearance of the disease symptoms. Examples are *susto* when it occurs in young children who have suffered a severe fright, or epilepsy, which is believed to result from strong emotional feelings.

For most illnesses there are appropriate remedies. The number and range of remedial measures is so great that only some of the major categories can be indicated here. Herbs are widely used in a variety of ways and for a large number of conditions. Tea made by boiling leaves or stems in water is a common remedy. Herbs are also taken with foods, are used in aromatic preparations whose fumes may be inhaled, are applied to external surfaces in the form of powder, and are worn in bags or cachets over parts of the body, much as the Anglos not so many years ago wore asafedita to ward off colds. Massage or some form of manipulation of body parts is considered efficacious for some illnesses, and poultices and plasters of various kinds are used to produce both mechanical and magical effects. Salves and ointments are not uncommon; foods are both prescribed and withheld for remedial purposes; and various types of bathing are practiced. Prayer and the reciting of religious formulas are common forms of dealing with sickness, and where the illness is thought to be magical in nature, spells, charms, incantations, and other ritualistic practices may be utilized. In recent times, practices and materials have been borrowed from scientific medicine, and injections or "shots" have become a common form of treatment.

Mild disorders are treated by the afflicted person or by some member of his family. More serious cases, or those that do not yield to home treatment, may require calling in someone with more specialized knowledge. Who is called and when, depends on the type and seriousness of the disease, the degree of discomfort, the availability of specialized help, and the probable cost of obtaining assistance. If the disease is a "natural" one that is fairly serious or uncomfortable, a physician may be called in to assist rather early in its course, provided a doctor is available and the problem of payment is not insuperable. Physicians, it is felt, understand "natural" diseases and are able to do something about them. But if the disease is thought to be of magical or psychological origin, assistance is more likely to be sought from a *curandera*, a *bruja*, or some other type of folk specialist, since they are assumed to be more familiar with and, hence, better able to treat such diseases. A complaint of *susto* or *mal ojo* will be listened to understandingly by a folk specialist, and the patient will be assured that his ailment is being treated. But to make such a complaint to a practitioner of scientific medicine would be to expose oneself to the possibility of skeptical disbelief, condemnation, or even ridicule, a circumstance that most patients and their families prefer to avoid.

The folk medical beliefs and practices of Mexicans do not stop at the Rio Grande. Many of them find their way across the border and can be found, even far inland, in areas where Mexicans and Mexican-Americans are living. A welfare worker in California is told by a Mexican-American family that they cannot eat grapefruit because it thins the blood and increases the possibility of their contracting tuberculosis. A visiting nurse in Colorado is accused by a mother of inadvertently causing illness in a small child by having smiled and spoken pleasantly to him. A sociological investigator in South Texas finds *susto* and *mal ojo* to be two of the major causes of illness among Mexican-Americans there.[10] A tuberculosis patient receives a portable one-room dwelling from the county health department in order that he may live in it and not infect his family. Not considering himself ill, he invites his mother to come to live in the portable dwelling, while he moves back with the family.[11] A Mexican-American woman seeks a blood test from a public health agency because she believes she has "bad blood" and that the test is a cure for it. Old Mexican-American women wrap their faces tightly in *rebozos*, lest they be endangered by contact with the air.[12]

Many of these and other people who still believe in and practice Mexican folk medicine also accept many of the ideas and procedures of scientific medicine. They permit their children to be immunized against specific disease conditions. They seek the services of professionals practicing scientific medicine. They attend clinics and enter hospitals. So long as there is no basic conflict with any of the more deeply held beliefs of the old culture and scientific medical practices continue to give observable results, there is no reason why Mexican-Americans should not more and more avail themselves of the techniques of scientific medicine. The extent to which they do so will be determined by such factors as the extent and nature of their exposure to new medical ways, the degree to which they may be motivated by the failure of old ways to meet their medical needs, and the degree to which their experiences with scientific medical and health personnel are pleasant or unpleasant. Scientific medicine will not soon be entirely substituted for folk medicine among the Mexican-Americans, but if properly presented it can come to play a larger and larger part in their responses to illness and the threat of illness, with resulting benefits to the Anglo as well as the Spanish-speaking population.

Spanish-American Folk Medicine. The Spanish-Americans, like the Mexicans, have been exposed to a number of streams of medical influence, and their behavior with respect to illness and its treatment also includes a mixture of elements from several sources. In the villages during centuries of isolation, the folk medical notions of sixteenth-century Spain were blended with those of the several Indian tribal groups with whom the villagers came into contact, and with ideas and practices brought from Mexico by the occasional traders, government officials, or others who had occasion to pass back and forth between the two areas. With the coming of Anglos into the Southwest, a new source of influence developed and Anglo folk medical ways began to be used in the villages. More recently, opportunities for drawing upon the resources and methods of scientific medicine have been made available and have been accepted, so that, both in parent villages and Anglo cities to which many Spanish-Americans have migrated, the medical beliefs and practices of the Spanish-American population now represent a mixture, if not always a blend, of widely diverse elements.

"Faith and fatalism," says Mrs. L. S. M. Curtin in the introduction to her *Healing Herbs of the Upper Rio Grande*, "are the first ingredients in folk medicine."[13] And faith and fatalism are qualities that the Spanish-American villagers had, and to an extent still have, in abundance. They are qualities that have served the people well in enabling them to adjust to the uncertainties and hardships of village life, qualities that have been of particular value in dealing with illness. However extensive folk medical knowledge may be and however effective the content of a given cultural group's medical bag of tricks, folk medicine is limited in many ways, and those who must rely on it alone for diagnosis and treatment have many opportunities for the exercise of both faith and fatalism.

Considering their long isolation and the resources with which they had to work, the medical knowledge of Spanish-American villagers and the range of treatment materials and procedures were quite extensive.

"The Spanish people of New Mexico," as Mrs. Curtin has pointed out, "live on the soil; they live simply and they have long memories. They can remember the language of Spain three hundred years ago and they have not yet forgotten the ways and customs of those times. . . . They are a people accustomed to the harvest of their yearly nourishment from the earth, from the fields about their homes, and it is without strangeness that they also draw medicines from the same source. The ever-present earth supplies the needs of its children here, as elsewhere; it is the grocer and the druggist for those who belong to the earth."[14]

That the earth was bountiful and the Spanish-Americans ingenious in making use of its offerings can be seen in the list of remedies Mrs. Curtin has compiled and the illnesses for which they were, or are, used. The latter include many of the ills of the flesh known to scientific medicine and a few others, such as pains due to witchcraft or tarantula bite, which are peculiar to the region. Among the more common illnesses for which the village folk had numerous remedies were arthritis, asthma, bone fractures, bronchitis, cancer, colds, colic, diarrhea, earache, goiter, gonorrhea, headache, heart trouble, measles, mumps, nosebleed, paralysis, pneumonia, rheumatism, skin diseases, sore throat, stomach trouble, tonsillitis, tuberculosis, and whooping cough. As in the case of Mexican folk medicine, the range of techniques for utilizing remedies was somewhat limited, so that most treatments called for the drink-

ing of an infusion, a medication in the form of a salve or powder, bathing in
or applying medicated fluids, or mixing remedies with foods. Alternative
treatment procedures were available for many diseases—Mrs. Curtin lists
46 remedies for rheumatism!—so that if one failed to give the expected relief
others might be tried.

Probably one of the most widely used, and certainly one of the most
efficacious, remedies of the Spanish-American villages was *oshá*, a plant of the
parsley family, to which reference has already been made, whose properties
were probably learned from the Indians. The healing qualities of *oshá* are
largely concentrated in the root, which may be used in many ways to treat a
wide variety of illnesses. Chewed raw or ground into a powder and made into
a tea, it was thought to prevent flatulency and to soothe the stomach. Drunk in
hot water with sugar and whiskey, it will break up a cold and help to cure
such respiratory illnesses as influenza, pneumonia, and pulmonary tuberculosis. Taken internally it will also reduce fevers. Applied directly to a wound in
powdered form, or worn over a wound, *oshá* promotes healing. An ointment
for the relief and cure of cuts and sores can be made from mutton fat, candle
wax, and turpentine into which is mixed some powdered *oshá* root, *manzanilla*
(camomile), and *contrayerba* (caltrop). Mixed with olive oil, *oshá* can be
used as a liniment in the treatment of rheumatic pains, and it is also useful, in
the form of a paste, to draw out the poison from snakebites. In addition, this
highly versatile plant is used as the basis of an enema, as a remedy for colic in
children, and as a means of protection against snakes, which are believed to
be repelled by its pungent odor. *Oshá* has recently entered into Anglo folk
medicine as an ingredient in a cough remedy prepared and sold by a Denver
druggist. It is also useful as a seasoning for soups and stews.

The familiar onion of Anglo home remedies is also put to many uses by the
Spanish-Americans. Roasted and applied hot, *cebollas* are thought to be
effective in treating chilblains. Teething babies are allowed to chew the leaves
and stems to relieve the pain of swollen gums. A cough syrup made of the juice
of fried or roasted onions sweetened with honey or sugar is thought to be an
excellent treatment for colds, particularly in the case of babies. *Inmortal*
(spider milkweed) likewise has many uses. Powdered and mixed with water,
it can be drunk to reduce headache or chest pains or to bring down a fever.
Made into a paste and used as a poultice, it will relieve pains of various kinds.
It is also useful in childbirth. Rubbed on the abdomen or taken with cold
water it will reduce labor pains, and drunk with hot water after delivery it
helps to expel the placenta. Asthma, shortness of breath, and similar afflictions
may be helped by drinking a tea made of *inmortal*.

Not even a representative sample of the many plants used in the folk
medicine of Spanish-Americans can be given here. But some indication of the
extent of the list and of the familiarity to Anglos of many items on it may be
obtained from a brief mention of the popular Anglo names of a few of the
plants used: cattails, garlic, cottonwood, basil, apricot, camphor, alfalfa,
lavender, aster, licorice, sunflower, anise, sagebrush, cocklebur, pumpkin,
thistle, elderberry, lupine, algae, oleander, milkweed, corn, mustard, golden-
rod, tansy, and mint. And not only plants but animals, animal products, and
nonorganic substances find their place in the list of remedies, as can be seen in

a mention of rattlesnake oil, cowhide, lime, rennet, milk, red ants, bones, alum, earth, and rock of various kinds, each of which, along with many other substances, is used in the treatment of some type of illness.

Folk Medical Practices at Ranchos de Taos. One of the few reports focused on the medical practices of Spanish-Americans is that of Sister Mary Lucia van der Eerden,[15] who in 1944 completed the field work for a study of patterns of maternity care as they exist in the village of Ranchos de Taos in northern New Mexico. Since Sister Mary Lucia's observations are accurate, extensive, and reasonably representative of rural Spanish-American medical care today, after some years of exposure to Anglo medical ways, both folk and scientific, it may be useful to review her findings.

Ranchos de Taos is a sprawling village of about 1,400 inhabitants, mostly Spanish-speaking, located a few miles southwest of Taos on the Santa Fe highway. The center of the village is the much-photographed Church of St. Francis, which stands on a site occupied by a Catholic church since 1733. Spanish is the everyday language of the village, and English is known mainly by school-age children, adults under thirty years, and a small proportion of those between the ages of thirty and fifty. Young people marry early, children are welcomed, and families tend to be large.

Pregnancy and childbirth are looked upon as part of the natural and normal life experience of women. Consequently, there is no generally held notion that the period of pregnancy preceding delivery requires the intervention of any persons with specialized medical knowledge or skill. Advice and information may be sought from one's mother or grandmother, and, in any case, such counsel will undoubtedly be offered once the fact of pregnancy becomes apparent. In general, however, the pregnant woman continues to follow her regular routine, taking care only to observe a few precautions to prevent harm to herself and the baby. She avoids moonlight while in bed, and, should there be an eclipse during her pregnancy, takes the prophylactic precaution of hanging some keys on a string around her waist, lest the baby be deformed by the effect of the moon's shadow falling on the mother.[16] Some months before her confinement regular bowel evacuations are advised. For attaining regularity, a cathartic in the form of castor oil or the powdered root of *inmortal* or *yerba del lobo* may be taken. About the time that the first movements of the baby are felt, the mother begins wearing a *muñeco,* a cord or cloth band which is wrapped tightly around the waist to keep the foetus in place and prevent its damaging the upper organs of the mother. A series of prayers designed to assure safe delivery through the intercession of Saint Ramon Nonnato are begun nine days before the expected date of confinement. These activities constitute the common prenatal observances. Few of the married women of Ranchos, at the time of Sister Mary Lucia's study, consulted a physician during pregnancy, although several were available in nearby Taos.

The period of labor and the subsequent time of enforced inactivity following delivery require some outside assistance for the mother. In Ranchos at least two choices are open: to use a *partera,* or midwife, or to go to the hospital at Taos or Embudo, where the delivery can be handled by a physician and the follow-up care given by trained nurses. In 1944, as perhaps today, many of the women of Ranchos preferred the *partera*.[17]

Village lore required that a woman in labor not be permitted to go to bed until after the birth of her baby. It was felt necessary that she keep in motion during the progress of labor, supporting herself by clinging to a chair or some other solid object during pains, but walking about in the intervals between them. To hasten delivery one or another of a number of medicinal plants might be used, depending on the knowledge of the *partera* and her judgment as to the condition of the patient. *Canela en raja*, powdered sticks of cinnamon, were usually given first, and if delivery did not follow soon, other herbs might be given. *Alvacar* (sweet basil), *yerba buena* (spearmint), *yerba del sapo* (an herb of the aster family), *pimienta* (black pepper) were all thought to be useful, as were garlic water or a raw onion. Fried onions sprinkled with dried *manzanilla* (camomile) and rubbed over the woman's body were also considered effective in speeding delivery. It was felt important that the delivery room be kept cheerful and happy, and that anything disturbing, exciting, or unpleasant be prevented from reaching the mother, lest she be placed in serious jeopardy.

The expectant mother usually was fully clothed, including stockings and shoes. The baby was born on a sheepskin or quilt spread on the floor, with the mother in a kneeling position, supporting herself by holding onto a chair or being held under the arms by her husband, the *partera*, or a female relative.[18] After delivery, the umbilical cord was cut with a pair of scissors, and the mother was permitted to go to bed, where the placenta was delivered. The baby was given an oil bath, and the stump of the cord treated with olive oil or a mixture of baking powder and olive oil or lard. The placenta was usually burned. Postpartum hemorrhage was treated with *alhucema* (lavender), either by spreading dried petals over burning coals and having the woman stand in the smoke, or by applying powdered lavender to the bleeding area. *Yerba buena* was a supplementary remedy.

Folk Medicine and Scientific Medicine Compared. Anglo practice and village practice with regard to childbirth differ in several important respects. Anglo physicians, who are in a position to advise practicing midwives, recommend that the patient be delivered in bed to lessen the possibility of postpartum hemorrhage.[19] They advise that the mother should remove her clothing, that the *partera* should scrub her hands and arms with strong soap before approaching the mother, that the scissors used for severing the cord be washed in soapy water, that the mother be given a sponge bath soon after delivery. There has been a strong tendency, however, for many of the *parteras* to look upon Anglo medical ways as different from but not appreciably better than their traditional medicine and to continue to use their own more familiar methods. Or, if the Anglo methods are adopted, their efficacy may be reduced by the failure of the *partera* to grasp the reasons behind their use. The scissors, after being washed with soap, may be dried with an unsterile cloth or placed on a table that has not been cleaned. Water that has been boiled may be poured when cool into an unsterile container. The acceptance of Anglo ways may represent merely the adoption of new elements into an old pattern in which the new procedures are not understood in terms of the Anglo reasons for their use, but instead are fitted into the already existing pattern of understanding with respect to causation and healing of illness and disease. Just as Anglo medical personnel tend to see many of the Spanish-American folk practices as either worthless or dangerous, so Spanish-Americans are inclined to be skeptical about the efficacy, necessity, and safety of some of the Anglo healing practices, and may be at times reluctant to accept them. Surgical procedures, in particular, are frequently regarded as harmful, dangerous, and unnecessary, and many villagers can tell of someone who was done irreparable damage by an operation or who, being advised by an Anglo physician that an operation was absolutely necessary, was thereafter cured by some folk procedure.

The transition from Spanish-American folkways to the acceptance and use of Anglo scientific medicine is complicated by the fact that folk medical knowledge is widely disseminated, so that anyone giving medical care is subject to the critical attention of relatives and friends of the patient, who are always ready to step in and insist on changes in treatment or to add to what is being done if they feel that proper care is not being given. Thus, the *partera* who has learned some new techniques from a physician or from the training program of the State Department of Public Health may find herself constrained by the pressure of family opinion to forego her new knowledge and to continue with old ways. Knowing as well as she what herbs may be used to hasten delivery or check postpartum bleeding, the family has provided them, and they are likely to interpret the failure of the *partera* to use them as resulting from ignorance or indifference to the welfare of the patient. They *know* these traditional remedies assure comfort and safety for the patient, and they are likely to feel that no treatment process can be good which withholds them.

Among many Spanish-American villagers, Anglo medicine is regarded as something to be used chiefly as a last resort when all other known procedures have failed. Consequently, for a long time, the Anglo record of successful treatment was less good than it need have been because too frequently Anglo practitioners were not consulted until the case was practically hopeless. Most of the successes in treatment were thus credited to folk practices; many of the failures were charged to Anglo medicine. As a result, another barrier to the acceptance of Anglo medicine was raised through the development of the belief, which could be supported by reference to known cases, that Anglo medical institutions were places where people went to die.

The continued use of their own medical practices by Spanish-Americans sometimes leads the Anglo, who knows his ways are better, to characterize Spanish-Americans as ignorant or superstitious, to accuse them of being indifferent to the well-being of their families and friends, and to become impatient and annoyed at their failure to see the obvious benefits to Anglo procedures. What such Anglos fail to appreciate is that Spanish-Americans also *know* that their ways are superior and that their use, far from constituting neglect of or indifference to the needs of sick relatives and friends, actually constitutes the provision of first-rate medical care. The Anglo may argue that by the pragmatic test of results his *is* the best medicine and that the Spanish-American ought to have enough sense to see it. But the evidence of the superiority of Anglo medicine is not always available to the Spanish-American in a form that has meaning to him and, in any case, what is or is not "good sense" is relative to culture. In utilizing his own knowledge and that of his friends, relatives, and neighbors, and when that fails, in calling in a *médica* or *curandera* or even a *bruja,* the Spanish-American villager is acting in a way that is eminently sensible in the light of his convictions about the nature of disease and the proper ways to deal with it. To behave otherwise, to disregard what he knows and subject himself or a member of his family to a course of treatment that may bear no particular relationship to his understanding of disease, simply because some Anglos say that it is what he should do, would constitute a very strange kind of behavior indeed.

Sickness, particularly if it be serious, is likely to be viewed as a crisis, and in situations of crisis people in all cultures tend to resort to those patterns of thinking and acting that have been most deeply ingrained in them as a result of their cultural experiences. To meet a crisis with the resources of one's culture, whatever they may be, is to behave in a manner that is both sensible and sound; it is, in fact, to behave in the only way that most human beings can under such circumstances. The Spanish-American, in utilizing the medical ways of his culture is neither ignorant nor indifferent. If he knew no way of dealing with illness, he might be called ignorant. But he does know something to do, frequently many things. If he did nothing, he might be called indifferent. But he does something, and continues to do something while his resources remain undepleted or until he achieves results. The sequence in which he does things is determined by the differential value he places on the various procedures as they apply to the particular situation. If the seeking of Anglo medical care is, for a given illness, well down on the list, it is because this is the way he sees the particular procedure in relation to the others that are available to him. That an Anglo, in a similar situation, might have a different set of resources and a different order of importance for them, cannot be expected to have any considerable influence on his behavior.

Folk Practitioners. Although folk medicine is in general known by all members of a cultural group, some persons, because of age, experience, or special interest, may have a more extensive knowledge than their neighbors and friends and thus acquire a somewhat specialized status. The *partera,* or midwife, is an example of such a person. In the field of general medicine, *médicas* and *curanderas,* whose knowledge of herbs and household remedies is somewhat greater than that of the general population, perform a similar function, being called upon for assistance when a medical problem gets beyond the competence of the patient or his relatives. None of them, of course, is a specialist in the Anglo sense of having a specialized kind of training and being given distinctive formal recognition (licensure) for their skill. But they are specialists in the sense that they are considered to have a greater knowledge of medical matters than other people in the population and perform a specialized function. Like *parteras, médicas* and *curanderas* expect to be paid for their services, either in goods or in cash, and, like Anglo practitioners, they are called upon to do a certain amount of "charity" work for which they are not paid. In most instances, the commercial part of the transaction is definitely subordinated, although in urban areas where close village relationships are no longer possible, *médicas* and *curanderas* are likely to regard themselves and to be regarded as impersonal purveyors of medicines and services, and the commercial element in the relationship is quite prominent.

One type of "specialist" with no exact counterpart in Anglo folk or scientific medicine is the *bruja* or witch, whose extensive command of both the malevolent and benevolent techniques of witchcraft makes her a person both sought after and feared. Although a belief in magical powers is becoming less and less respectable, there are few Spanish-speaking communities in the Southwest that do not include among their inhabitants one or more persons known to be witches. Their continued activity has made possible the rise of another "specialty," that of the *albolaria* whose particular skill is the ability to thwart or render harmless the evil powers of *brujas*. Not many Spanish-speaking will admit a belief in witches anymore, but nearly everyone can tell about someone else who believes in them, and it can be noted that the services of *albolarias* continue to be in demand.

The general patterns of behavior of both rural and urban Spanish-Americans with respect to illness and therapy are almost always a mixture of elements from their own and Anglo culture. A number of Spanish-Americans interviewed in the San Luis Valley of Colorado in 1952 indicated that in general they utilized the services of both folk and Anglo scientific medical practitioners, and that their knowledge of remedies for various conditions included items drawn from both cultures. One *médica*, who also performs as a *partera*, serves patients from many surrounding communities and works closely with an Anglo physician in caring for her maternity cases. When pregnant women come to her, they are sent to the doctor for a blood test and a "check-up" after which, if everything seems normal, they return to her for the actual delivery. Most of the deliveries take place in her home. Difficult cases are delivered by the doctor and in a hospital. For the treatment of other than maternity cases the *médica* uses remedies that she obtains by mail from supply houses in San Antonio and Trinidad.[20]

Nearly everyone interviewed knew of *médicas* and *curanderas* practicing in the vicinity, and many made no particular distinction between the services they offered and those available from Anglo physicians. The *médica* mentioned above thinks that many people do not like doctors and hospitals because they are afraid of both. Many women who come to see her, she said, refuse to go to the physician for a check-up and can be persuaded to do so only when she threatens to withhold her assistance. A man who was interviewed said that he does not consult a doctor until he is "about dead." He and his wife have four children, two of whom were delivered by *parteras* and two by physicians. He knows a good deal about folk remedies and uses them for himself and his family when indicated. A large proportion of his acquaintances use folk remedies, and a few have told him that they would not go to a doctor under any circumstances. One woman reported that a physician who came into the area just before the turn of the century used to take her mother, a *médica*, with him on his calls. By allowing her to make diagnosis and prescribe treatments, the mother said, he was able to learn the value of her *remedios* and later to use them in his own practice.

In cities, as well as in rural areas, the medical practices of Spanish-

Americans continue to be a mixture of elements of both cultures, although because of greater availability of Anglo medicine, the somewhat better financial status of many Spanish speaking persons, and a higher level of acculturation, Anglo medicine is used proportionately more in cities than in the country. *Remedios,* including both Anglo patent preparations and medicinal herbs, are sold in the "Mexican" sections of cities and large towns, and one who has need of the services of a *médica* or *curandera* does not have far to look for them. In addition to giving service, they will also prescribe and sell medicine.

No precise studies have been made of the extent to which Spanish-speaking people of the Southwest use one or another of the several types of medical aid available to them for particular kinds of illnesses. One small survey of a group of families living in Fort Collins, Colorado, showed a greater acceptance of Anglo practices by young people than by the older folk, but a rather large use of Anglo procedures by persons of all ages.[21] Another study of Colorado migrant families living in four agricultural areas of Colorado gives some evidence on the observed and reported use of Anglo medical personnel, facilities, and practices, but no comparative information on the use of folk medicine.[22] In this report a physician is quoted as saying, "We know that communicable diseases are present among the migrants. The fatalistic acceptance of the situation, plus their poverty, makes the problem of medical care a critical one. Tuberculosis, enteritis, smallpox, typhoid fever, dysentery, and venereal diseases have been more often detected by accident or search by public health officials than by patients voluntarily seeking medical assistance."[23] A conspicuous finding of this study was that health and medical care services were not widely used by the migrants observed. Of 1,098 persons from whom information was obtained, 947 had not seen a doctor during the preceding year, and 955 of 1,101 persons giving information had not visited a dentist during that period. Of those who had consulted a dentist, the majority wanted extractions or went to get relief for a toothache. Of the few who had gone for prophylactic reasons, all were persons who had served in the armed forces or were members of households where there were ex-army personnel. Just over 42 per cent of the 631 children reported on had been vaccinated for smallpox; only a fifth had been immunized against whooping cough, and about the same proportion against diphtheria. Nine out of ten migrants above seven years of age had not been hospitalized at any time during the previous five years, and only 15 per cent had undergone physical examinations during that period, the majority of these having occurred during an illness or as a requirement for a job.

Reasons for Anglo Medicine Not Being More Extensively Used. A number of explanations can be found for the failure of Spanish-speaking people in close contact with Anglo culture to adopt completely its medical ways. One such factor is certainly the extent to which Anglo medical services and facilities are urbanized, many of them still live in rural areas where medical personnel and facilities are not readily available. Large numbers of Spanish-speaking people live in sparsely settled areas where one has to drive many miles to see a physician or enter a hospital. A map of health facilities in New Mexico, prepared in 1946 for the New Mexico Health Council, showed four counties to be completely without medical facilities and a large part of the state to lie outside a 30-mile radius from any type of health facility.[24] In parts of Colorado, Arizona, and Texas, similar conditions exist. The present widespread distribution of automobiles and recent improvements in rural roads have done much to make Anglo medicine more readily available to rural Spanish-speaking people and have undoubtedly contributed to its somewhat greater use. But there still remain many areas where, either because of sparseness of population or a high concentration of Spanish-speaking people among the residents of the areas, it would be quite difficult to get to an Anglo doctor or hospital even if one were highly motivated to do so.

Another factor related to availability is that of cost. Anglo medical care is expensive and the Spanish-speaking, as a group, are poor. In many instances they cannot afford, or do not feel that they can afford, the services of a physician or a sojourn in a hospital. Anglo medicine involves bills from home or office calls, some likelihood of being given an expensive prescription, and the possibility of surgery, or hospitalization for some other reason, which may be very costly. A *médica* usually does not charge much and under certain circumstances can be paid with products instead of cash, a definite advantage to those living in rural areas. Her medicines are not likely to cost much, and there is little likelihood that she will recommend hospitalization or an operation. Diagnosis and treatment by oneself and one's family cost little or nothing, and for many minor illnesses can be quite satisfactory. These differences in costs certainly constitute an influence in the readiness or reluctance with which an individual or family makes the decision to seek any given type of medical care.

Lack of knowledge of Anglo medical ways is probably another factor in the extent to which Spanish-speaking people do or do not use Anglo practitioners and facilities. The simple matter of getting in touch with a doctor and putting oneself under his care can seem complicated to a person who is not at ease in either the English language or Anglo medical culture. How does one find a doctor? How can one be sure that the chosen doctor will be either competent or *simpatico*? How is a doctor approached? How can one know in advance how much the treatment will cost or what will be the expected manner of payment? What illnesses may properly be taken to a physician? These and other questions, the answers to which most of us take for granted, can be puzzling to persons not wholly familiar with Anglo culture, and can be effective barriers to the initiation of a doctor-patient relationship, particularly when the potential patient may not be highly motivated in the direction of wanting Anglo medicine.

Closely related to a lack of knowledge of Anglo medical ways as a deterrent to seeking Anglo medical care is the factor of fear. That which is strange or unknown is often feared, and there is much in Anglo medicine that is strange and fear inducing even to Anglo laymen. The instruments used, the pain that sometimes accompanies their use, and the unfamiliar surroundings of the office, clinic, or hospital in which they are used, all can arouse fear. So can the unfamiliar elements in the medical routine—the examination procedure, the invasion of one's physical and mental privacy, the uncertainty of the diagnostic procedure, the incomprehensible language that may be used. For a Spanish-speaking person, for example, a physical examination can be a very unpleasant experience, particularly if it involves the participation of persons of the opposite sex. The fear of being examined by a man is sometimes enough to keep Spanish-speaking women away from Anglo medical practitioners and to make traumatic for others the contact they have with Anglo medicine. Foster reports the failure of a considerable proportion of women coming to a prenatal clinic in Mexico City to return for a follow-up visit after their initial examination.[25] It is not without significance for the medical relations of Spanish-speaking and Anglos in the Southwest that most of the healing personnel in the culture of the Spanish-speaking are women, whereas proportionately more of those in the Anglo culture are men. Spanish-speaking men, too, are likely to have some reluctance to subjecting themselves to examination by Anglo physicians and to being placed in potentially embarrassing situations with Anglo nurses.

Another possible factor that may operate is resistance to being separated from one's family and being isolated for an indefinite time in an Anglo institution, where all relationships are likely to be impersonal. Good medical care, from the Anglo point of view, requires hospitalization for many conditions. Good medical care, as defined in the culture of the Spanish-Americans, requires that the patient be treated for almost any condition at home by relatives and friends, who are constantly in attendance and who provide emotional support as well as the technical skills required in treatment. In time of sickness one expects his family to surround and support him, and to supervise closely and critically, if not actually carry on, the treatment process. Members of the family, in turn, feel obligated to remain close to the patient, to take charge of his treatment, and to reassure him as to his place in and importance to the family group. The Anglo practice of hospitalization, with the treatment being taken over by professional strangers and the family relegated to the meager role permitted by the visiting regulations, runs counter to the expectation patterns of the Spanish-speaking and, thus, may be a factor in the reluctance of some members of the group to seek or accept Anglo medical care.

There are some illnesses for which Anglo medical care is not sought because, as has already been noted, the type of sickness is not ordinarily known to Anglo practitioners. A patient suffering from *mal ojo, susto,* and similar conditions seeks relief, if at all, from someone who is familiar with these diseases and who, therefore, may be expected to know something about the proper method of treatment. This difference between the two cultures in the conceptualization of disease serves to restrict the range of conditions for which Anglo medical assistance might be sought to those recognized by both cultural groups and gives to the folk practitioner almost exclusive influence in dealing with those conditions that are recognized only by the Spanish-speaking group.

A final factor that may be mentioned as possibly contributing to the hesitancy of Spanish-speaking people to use Anglo medicine is that such attempts as are made often do not provide the satisfactions that the Spanish-speaking expect. With the *curandera* and *médica* the whole process of diagnosis and treatment moves along in an atmosphere of informal cooperation and collaboration between patient, family, and the healer. Alternative procedures are discussed and courses of treatment agreed upon, with the opinions of patient and family frequently being given much weight in the final decisions. The folk practitioner works less as an independent specialist than as a consultant and technician who implements the therapeutic plans of the patient or his family, all of whom remain very much in the picture throughout the treatment period. All know what is going on and why. All are free to offer suggestions and criticisms. The diagnosis and treatment of illness thus involve active participation by the patient and members of his family in a situation in which the relationships are mainly personal and informal. Diagnosis is usually easy and swift, and treatment follows immediately.

By contrast, Anglo medicine is likely to be somewhat impersonal and formal. It is expected that the patient will be turned over to the physician, who will then direct the diagnostic and treatment procedures, largely without the benefit of advice or suggestion from either the patient or his family. Information may be sought from both, but usually only for the purpose of getting at the present complaints or learning the patient's medical history. Diagnosis may be slow and may involve techniques that are not understood by the patient or his family. Treatment may be delayed pending the establishment of a definite diagnosis and, when instituted, may involve hospitalization of the patient. The patient and his family are expected to be relatively passive participants in a situation in which most of the new relationships established are impersonal, businesslike, and, frequently, very unsatisfactory. In treatment by either folk practitioner or physician the possible range of outcomes is about the same. The patient may get better, may remain as he is, may get worse, may die. There being no conclusive evidence of the relatively greater frequency of desirable results when using Anglo medicine than when relying on folk healers, the amount of satisfaction that patient and family get in the medical relationship becomes an important factor in determining which of the two types of medicine they will select.

The most important differences between Spanish-American folk medicine and Anglo scientific medicine that influence the choice of one or the other are these: Anglo scientific medicine involves largely impersonal relations, procedures unfamiliar to laymen, a passive role for family members, hospital care, considerable control of the situation by professional healers, and high costs; by contrast the folk medicine of Spanish-American villagers is largely a matter of personal relations, familiar procedures, active family participation, home care, a large degree of control of the situation by the patient or his family, and relatively low costs. Given these differences, it is easy to understand why a considerable motivation would be necessary for a Spanish-American to have any strong preference for Anglo medicine over that which is not only more familiar and possibly psychologically more rewarding—or at least less punishing—but also less expensive.

Despite the many factors that operate to hinder the seeking and acceptance of Anglo medical care by Spanish-speaking people of the Southwest, however, Anglo medicine is rapidly coming to play an increasingly larger part in the total complex of attitudes and activities of the Spanish-speaking people with respect to illness and health.

22   FOLK OBSTETRICS AND PEDIATRICS MEET THE M.D.: A CASE STUDY OF SOCIAL ANTHROPOLOGY AND MEDICINE*

By Joseph W. Eaton

Why Study the Hutterite? Hutterite child care methods afford an opportunity to doctors to examine what they believe and what they know about obstetrics and pediatrics against the background of practices of a contemporary folk culture with a respectable record for its parents. The average mother has close to 11 live births, not counting miscarriages and still births. This record fertility is accompanied by fairly good health practices. This sect has what may be the world's record of reproduction. The 443 members counted by the United States Census in 1880 multiplied to 8542 in 1950, with the doubling of population about every 16 years.[5]

The Hutterites value children. Their large family system is supported by an economy of Christian communism. Each of the self-contained hamlets or colonies, as the Hutterites call their over 100 settlements, owns a large ranch. All income is shared on the basis of "to each according to his needs." The number of children does not affect a family's standard of living.

Child rearing practices still show the impact of the group's Tyrolese-Austrian origin in the early 16th century. They serve to support the transmission of important religious values, including an emphasis on simple and austere living, pacifism and an anabaptist creed of Christianity. There is well defined division of labor between sexes and age groups to guide mortals in the all important goal of Hutterite existence: earning one's way to heaven.

What are the obstetric and pediatric practices of a group in which few children are viewed by their parents as having problems requiring special help? Even by the somewhat different standards of their American neighbors, Hutterite youngsters have an extraordinary high probability of growing up under conditions of satisfactory physical and mental health. Functional mental diseases tend to be labile; crime, delinquency, personal violence, divorce, unusual sexual practices and suicides are rare.[6, 14]

Hutterites differ from their American and Canadian fellow citizens in many ways, but interact with them. They are sufficiently within the periphery of the Euro-American culture stream to make cross-cultural comparisons somewhat more directly relevant to the middle class American scene than the interesting studies of American Indians or Balinese non-literates.[26] Hutterite children attend schools taught by American teachers. The adults speak English in addition to their native Hutterite German. They use many modern machines. But when they drive the colony truck into town to sell cattle, their European peasant garb will remind them and their neighbors of their differences.

Every patient has culturally determined expectations about children and child-rearing. They affect his readiness to ask for obstetric and pediatric advice. They influence his willingness to use it. A doctor must learn to identify what these sub-cultural patterns are if he is to understand a patient's medical history and make an effective plan for treatment. A study of the Hutterites can help Americans to see telescopically how much we are changing and to estimate some of the possible consequences of these changes for child care.

Sex and Reproduction. Few are the secrets Hutterites try to keep from each other. Pregnancy is one of them. Only the husband and mother, a sister, older daughter, or other close friend know of the "blessed event" before its physical manifestations become obvious. Some of the older Hutterite women recall that they were bashful about telling their husband about being pregnant. It takes special effort among the Hutterites to keep anything hidden from neighbors who share your meals three times a day in the colony dining room and who have known you intimately since birth. What is the social function of this effort to keep secret something that must in due time become public knowledge?

Hutterites react positively to birth, but feel uncertain about its prerequisite: sex. Adult Hutterites were close to unanimous in stating verbally that they preferred to avoid thinking about sex when they were young. This claim to effective and wide-spread repression is confirmed by much data from interviews and projective tests. Special efforts are made to keep an awareness of pregnancy from smaller children. Those who ask questions about what is going on will get no explanation. "She's having a baby and don't you trouble yourself with things which are only for grown-ups" is a likely answer.

The Hutterite religious value system suggests an explanation of this social emphasis on "secrecy." Pregnancy is closely associated with sex. It is public evidence that sex relations have taken place. Among the Hutterites, as among other Christian religious groups in America, the physical aspects of sex are considered inherently evil. They are only tolerated, after sanctification through a religious marriage ceremony. This ambivalence about sexual needs is well documented in the Hutterite religious literature:[21]

> There are three degrees of marriage. First there is the marriage of God and the Human Soul; second there is the marriage of the human soul to its body; and third there is the marriage of the body of a man to that of a woman. The latter is the least and the crudest form of marriage, but it also is a symbol of the higher and abstract forms of marriage.

Sexual urges are viewed as a concession of God to man for the expression of higher spiritual values. This religious outlook permits expression of sex needs within the marriage bond, while keeping guilt feelings quiescent.

Preparation for Motherhood. Education for future motherhood begins everywhere as soon as the young girl is old enough to watch her mother with a still younger baby. Among the Hutterites this goal is planfully pursued. Even before the age of six, girls are sometimes entrusted with the care of a younger sibling. As baby-sitters they share the mother's responsibility for the household, except during school hours. Here is an almost verbatim account of an interview with a 14 year old baby-sitter:

> I only got my brother John to take care of. He is three. He minds me. I give him toys to play with, I wash him and I see that he gets his supper. He still eats at home. (In most colonies children at the age of three eat in the kindergarten.) He eats good

—he's got a fine appetite. (She hugs him affectionately.) I like him very much, but he's scared now. He's bashful. He never cries except when he wants water. He sleeps well at night and in the morning, I wake him after we have eaten our breakfast. I took care of four others until they reached the kindergarten. I was six years old when I started. My mother learned me how to change diapers, how to put clean sheets on the bed, and how to hold him. I had to stand on a little stool at first to reach the baby crib when I started this work.

I work. I don't play. I knit, sew, and spin, too. I am too old to play. Mother takes care of the two tinier ones. We take the baby for walks in pushcarts. I put something clean over a pillow at the bottom.

I have brothers. They help if I ask them. They get me water, coal, or take out dirty things, the ashes, and clean up the baby's shoes. Sometimes I give them the baby to hold, but I fear they might let him fall. It never happened in our family, but it happens.

Most Hutterites girls feel adequate as mothers when they reach adulthood, but the opposite is true of their preparation for the biology of pregnancy. The Hutterite educational system is negative and repressive in this area. Mothers of the older generation reported to have been "too ashamed" to talk to their daughters about the meaning of menstruation, except perhaps to give reassurance that it is something "natural." Many mature men and women avow a hardly credible degree of sexual ignorance at the time of their marriage. "I did not find out much about how babies are born until I had my own; my mother told me some things just before I got married, but not any details" were some of the comments. Some older women thought as girls that babies are born through the mouth or come through the abdomen. Only in the present generation of young Hutterites is there evidence of willingness to admit to knowledge about the connection between conception, pregnancy, and the sex organs.

It would be logical to expect an association of considerable anxiety with pregnancy and birth in view of these claims to premarital ignorance of the "facts of life." Evidence fails to support this plausible assumption. Hutterite women seem to approach the pregnancy with confidence and self-assurance. The physical dangers and pains are not something they talk about, in either their free-association interviews or their projective tests. The bodily changes of pregnancy seem to be accepted without much concern.

The contradiction between the lack of anxiety and the evidence that sex and pregnancy are tabooed subjects may be related to the strong cultural support given by the Hutterite religion to the child-bearing function. There is much ambivalence about sex, but when it leads to delivery of an infant the parents assume a highly respected role, that of being a mother and father. Having a baby is more important than maintaining a figure. Pregnancy and birth resolve anxiety in this group where children are viewed to be the most important source of "wealth," and the only one on which parents may claim a proprietary right.

Pre-Natal Care. Pregnancy is considered a good reason for being relieved from all communal work chores, such as cooking, baking, dishwashing, and gardening. Young husbands of the present generation often insist on taking over such household chores as floor washing and laundering, something their fathers were much less likely to do. During the later months preceding the birth, women are expected to be somewhat careful not to lift heavy objects or to do hard work.

Hutterites have some understanding for the importance of special diets during pregnancy. Mothers drink more milk and eat more eggs. One midwife mentioned the belief that foods like raw carrots, radishes, and fried potatoes are not good for expectant mothers. No effort used to be made to supplement the intake of vitamins and minerals or to keep the weight down, but these dietary attitudes are in the process of modification through the influence of doctors.

Certain superstitions related to pregnancy and birth are widespread. There is a belief that a mother's thoughts and visual impressions can affect the baby in her womb. "Mice and rats can cause birthmarks." One midwife thought that her first baby was born "blue in the face" because she had seen many Negroes on a trip to Bigtown. Most babies wear a red ribbon around their right wrists to "ward off the evil eye." When asked how else a baby could be protected against it, an older woman picked up her little nephew and licked him all across his face, saying, "This is how we clean it if the evil eyes are thrown at it."

Despite the existence of these superstitions, no one seemed to be very afraid of them. They seem to be taken as a matter of course by those who believe them, with an increasing number of young people questioning their validity.

A non-anxious reaction to pregnancy is strongly supported by the Hutterite culture pattern which regards motherhood as a woman's most suitable and valuable contribution to the communal welfare. Through it she lives up to the religious dictum which God gave to Adam and Eve in Genesis.[8] "Be fruitful and multiply!" She helps to assure the survival and continuity of the group. She perpetuates the family strain, a fact valued highly by Hutterites who are relatively familio-centric. She becomes the heroine in a drama, in which her husband, her family, and her community play subordinate and supporting roles.

The non-anxious approach creates a problem for the physician. How can he motivate Hutterite women to come in for prenatal examinations? Some welcome a doctor's appointment, if for no other reason than that it justifies a trip to town with her husband. Among the Hutterites, travel for its own sake is regarded to be a "luxury." Certain doctors have tried to secure patient interest in regular obstetric care by worrying them about the hazards of pregnancy. In recent years as many as perhaps one woman out of five sees a doctor at least once, particularly if it is her first pregnancy or if she has had difficulties with past deliveries. This practice may function to prevent a few cases of infant mortality and maternal deaths, but is "paid" for in part by an increase in anxiety of Hutterite women.

Relaxed Childbirth. At the first sign of labor, the husband usually sends someone to the home of the village manager to make two telephone calls. The first is to the midwife at another colony, unless there is a woman on the place who is considered well trained. The second call is to the mother or sister of his wife, who will visit for a month to serve as practical nurse. Both have been previously alerted for the occasion by mail or telephone. The colony will send out its trucks or hire a taxi to bring both of these ladies to the colony.

In a special survey of 110 children on this subject, only 13% or 14 women were delivered by a doctor and in a hospital. Hutterites spend their entire lives in the familiarity of a closely integrated community. This fact probably accounts for much of their preference for having babies delivered at home, despite the recognition by many women that hospital facilities for treatment are superior.

At home, there is never any separation of mother and infant. The husband and other children are on call at any time. She need feel no anxiety about what is happening at home during her lying-in period. One young Hutterite mother, whose first baby was born in the hospital because no midwife was available, gave the following typical description of her hospital confinement:

When I had Sarah, I went to the hospital only because our midwife was away on a visit. I had not seen a doctor except early in pregnancy, when I wanted to check that I was pregnant because I vomited badly. The doctor did not see me during the entire period, but came after me in his car when he was asked to deliver me. My husband and mother-in-law went to the hospital with me. If I had wings I would have flown home after I got to the hospital, because the nurses took me away and my people had to wait outside. The nurse didn't know very much. She was a woman who did not know when it was time for the baby. She did nothing for me. When I asked her for a hot water bottle, she did not bring it to me. It was wintry and cold. When the head nurse came and saw that I was blue in the face, she told the nurse to get an electric heater. She did but never turned it on. I lay there until the doctor came. He gave me some ether and I remember absolutely nothing. When I woke up the next day, they brought the baby, Sarah, to me.

After the third day, I could feed the baby by breast, but she always needed bottle supplementing. She was breast fed for nine months. I had breast pains in the hospital because I had too much milk, and I think that's why we needed the bottle. But I think it was more the worries I had. I wanted to go home. One thing I didn't like was that they made me walk to the toilet after the third day. My husband visited me twice a day when he had time. My mother also came to visit but only during visiting hours. Through the day, I just lay around but couldn't sleep because there was too much noise. I went home on the sixth day, even though the doctor wanted to keep me longer. I had a semi-private room but the other bed was always empty.

The same mother described her second confinement at home as follows:

With this baby, our midwife of the neighboring colony came to attend me. I sat on a chair until it was time for the baby to come. My mother-in-law helped with the birth because my mother had to be with a sister who was also having a baby. I was much more comfortable because I was in my own home. The midwife had instruments. I had no worries that anything would go wrong. My husband was here and stayed with me during the labor. The midwife gave me ether—just a little; the pain was not bad. I was awake when the baby came and I helped the midwife when she delivered the baby, to make it easy. My husband was present all the time. My mother-in-law hit the baby after birth until it gave out with a birth cry. Then I watched them clean the baby. They dressed him in a diaper, shirt, and cap, just like he is dressed now. I was much more comfortable here. I didn't have to get up for anything for a whole week. I was with my own people. On the fourth day, I was able to sit up; everything was quiet. My husband and mother-in-law slept in the room as did my daughter Sarah. They took care of her. The midwife went home right after the baby was delivered. I didn't have many visitors, although anybody who wanted to come, could. We make no fuss about a birth.

Many husbands witness the birth and hold the wife's hand during her spasms of pain. Some break down and cry. The occasional woman who has feelings of resentment against her husband, of the privileges which males enjoy in this patriarchal society, can derive emotional satisfaction from the fact that the husband has to share the pain or breaks down emotionally, while she, the woman, shows so much strength.

The pains and physical dangers of birth are looked upon by some women as sacred. It is God's will that it be so. Did He not pronounce a curse on Eve, the mother of mankind, for her partaking of the forbidden fruit of paradise including the punishment: "In pain, thou shalt bring forth children?"[9] Many older women resist the use of drugs, although most midwives have now learned to administer chloroform, ether, nembutal, and demerol. Several Hutterites remarked about this practice as a sign of weakening of the present generation.

Hutterites believe that mothers should remain in bed for about two weeks after childbirth. The female relative who attends the mother, insists not only on taking complete charge of the newborn infant, but also makes the mother's bed, gives her sponge baths, and other nursing services. She also brings the mother her food, prepared by the community's special "sick cook" who specializes in meals that are considered to be nourishing and good tasting.

Relatives and neighbors in the colony will also help to take care of the older children and anything that might need attention. The mother has no duty beyond that of feeding her infant, who is brought to her whenever it is hungry. She is not expected to do any work for the community until eight weeks after confinement.

Post-partum women are considered ritually "unclean." They do not attend church during that period. During the fifth to eighth week, a woman generally announces her recovery to the community symbolically by attending church at night. This also signifies to the husband that she is ready to resume sex relations.

The environmental support, as well as psychic harmony of most mothers with their biological role, tend to make childbirth and confinement a relaxed period. The baby is born into the colony in which, particularly if it is a boy, he will live all his life. The Hutterite infant certainly experiences the emotional response and security claimed by proponents of the rooming-in type of maternity ward.[12, 22] The Hutterite culture and value system are conducive to many of the policies of the "Natural Childbirth" movement, without need of formal indoctrination or exercises.

Infant Feeding. It may be symbolic of the feeling of confidence of Hutterite mothers that they show little concern with feeding unless a baby is physically ill. Breast feeding is favored. Of the 94 babies on whom information was obtained by interviewing the mothers, more than half, 57 to be exact, received no supplementary bottle feeding. They were weaned directly and gradually from the breast to the cup and the spoon. Most women seem to find genuine enjoyment in the nursing process. Hutterite women nurse publicly, even in the presence of strange men. The strong general Hutterite taboo against exposure of the breasts is superseded by their acceptance of the nursing function. Some women explain their preference for breast feeding partly "because it reduces chances of becoming pregnant too quickly."

Most babies are breast fed on demand, although they usually acquire some sort of schedule after two months. This is the time when the mother resumes her normal work chores in the colony and is away from the home for several periods of each day, although usually within shouting distance.

When babies reach the age of six months, most of them eat some solid food. In early years, their cereals, mashed vegetables, fruit, and meats used to be cooked in the colony. In recent years, some canned baby foods are being purchased by a few colonies because "they involve no fussing." Other colonies still resist the use of commercial products because of their expense. About one third of the babies were given water or unpasturized milk from a cup at the age of six months, with the proportion increasing to three quarters of the children at the age of one year.

Most Hutterite informants thought that bottle feeding and breast feeding with bottle supplementation are rapidly increasing. Many women claimed that they had less milk now than they used to have with their earlier babies. A common remark was: "I guess our flesh is getting weaker, more like that of the rest of the world."

Feeding the baby is one of the major problems which preoccupies American pediatricians and worries the American mothers. Both fashion and "predominant scientific opinion" have shifted like a pendulum from extreme favoritism for breast feeding, to bottle feeding, and back to the breast again. Similar shifts have taken place with regard to the scheduled timing of feedings, from a primary emphasis on feeding when the mother thinks the baby demands it, to when the clock demands it, back to what mother thinks the baby thinks.[25] Some psychiatrists see in the manner of feeding a major determinant in the mental adjustment of the child's later life.

Feeding practices, and the same can be said to apply to other aspects of baby care, such as the timing of toilet training and discipline, are chosen by parents from a number of alternatives. Each have some support from tradition or pediatric experts. Correlations such as those observed by Amy R. Holway between breast feeding or permissive infant care with good adjustment[10] are not causal but spurious. They may be meaningful only to the extent to which they reflect a relatively high interest in children in comparison to alternate social and occupational opportunities for utilizing parental time and energy. The heat of the controversy is out of all proportion to the amount of valid scientific data available on the impact of a feeding practice on personality development.[19] Spock puts it well when he concludes:

Mothers who have read what psychologists and psychiatrists say about the importance of breast feeding sometimes get the idea that it has been shown that bottle fed babies turn out to be less happy than breast fed babies. Nobody has proved that.[24]

Perhaps the most justifiable case for suspecting a relationship of feeding to mental health can be made on the basis of an assumption that in the American culture, the manner of feeding her baby by a mother who is physically well, often reflects some of her unconscious feelings about the child. To breast feed a mother must be near her baby day and night. She must be ready to involve herself physically at every feeding. A bottle feeding mother can delegate her function easily to anyone capable of holding a bottle, including a mechanical bottle holder purchasable at any dime store.

The United States Children's Bureau's advice in its 1951 edition of *Infant Care* takes what is the most defensible position in the light of our current knowledge:

It matters much less, then, whether you feed your baby by breast or by bottle than that you feel easy and relaxed and confident in your ability to provide for him. . . . It is the spirit in which you feed your baby rather than the particular kind of milk he gets.[27]

Control of Elimination. Hutterite parents are generally conscious of the relationship of urination and defecation to health. While talk of sex is taboo, parents do inquire about the regularity of stools from the children. They view these functions as natural and necessary experiences of life. Few children were seen with complaints of constipation or diarrhea. Discussion of these subjects is relatively non-threatening, although uncommon between members of the opposite sex. There are no locks on Hutterite outhouses; taboos of modesty are thought to be sufficient to guarantee privacy.

The following ideas of a Hutterite teacher were typical:

Toilet training is started as soon as the child can sit up with a little help. Our seven month old baby is already on the pot. But not until the older boy, at the age of 1½ years defecated on the floor and then ran to get a pan, did his mother feel that he had enough of a mind to know that he had done something wrong. Then she spanked him.

Mothers indicated that they regarded toilet training primarily in the light of convenience for themselves. It was not viewed as a "problem" of child rearing. For 40 out of the 94 children, a little over 48%, bowel training was said by their mothers to have begun at the age of six months or before. For 80 out of 94, more than 85% of all the cases, mothers made it a practice before the end of the first year, to put the child on a pot at regular hours. Some parents guessed that their children became bowel trained within a few months, but admitted fairly regular "lapses" on more detailed questioning. They were particularly permissive towards urinary incontinence. Roughly 5% of the 94 children had bed wetting problems after the age of three. Parents expressed concern about them and sometimes consulted a doctor for advice if the children were older than six. They considered such incontinence to be a sickness and put no blame on the child.

The Hutterite approach to toilet functions is utilitarian. It is convenient to get children trained early, but parents show no anxiety to get the process accomplished quickly. They rarely arouse guilt feelings in their children for failures. Most parents know that control is a matter of bodily maturation and health. With due respect to the widespread belief concerning the damaging effects of early toilet training on personality, there is no evidence among Hutterite children that were seen that they showed anxiety related to these physiological functions. The fact that the training process tends to be relaxed may be more important than its timing. These observations seem to lend support to an opinion voiced by Margaret Mead:

> Early toilet training followed out for some causal reason of household arrangement will have a very different and possibly almost negligible effect, while toilet training at an age when it might be conceived to be less traumatic and more appropriate to the developmental stage may, because of the weight given to it by the adult, have far stronger effect.[17]

Swaddling. Immediately after birth, the baby is clothed. For reasons of modesty as well as to keep the infant warm, he begins life in a long dress reaching down to the ankles, and with a cap on his head. Boys and girls are attired alike, except that boys' caps are styled differently from girls'. Hutterite women attach great importance to having the cap fit tightly to insure that "the head will grow nice and round."

Most Hutterite infants are kept swaddled for from four to eight weeks in a soft down-feather quilt. Mothers say this will give their fragile infants the maximum protection from drafts and injury. The late Ruth Benedict, who compared such customs in four East European cultures, showed that certain fundamental values of the mothers could be seen to be symbolically expressed in the manner of infant swaddling.[2] In recent years Hutterite mothers have stopped binding the infant's arms. Only the legs and body are swaddled.

Culturally one could view this change as a reflection of the partial acceptance by the Hutterites of American values to accord "freedom" to the baby in his development. Girls, who as children and adults will be restricted by custom much more than boys, have the swaddling rope pulled more tightly. Many mothers do not seem to know why, although some explained that "boys need more freedom of movement for their legs so that they will not injure their genitals."

There are certain doctors, teachers, and nurses who express the belief that swaddling is experienced by infants as a restriction and will lead to deep-seated frustrations. But there is considerable question that the neurological development of young infants is sufficiently well developed to register the difference between being and not being "restricted" during the first weeks of life. Most infants seen by the study staff seemed to be relaxed. They gave no behavioral evidence of being restricted, no matter how restrictive they may seem by projection to adult observers brought up in modern middle-class American homes.

Permissiveness and the Onset of Discipline. During the first few months, Hutterite infants are cared for with considerable permissiveness. No social demands are made on the mother which might interfere with her devotion to the child. He is fed when he wants to be. He is often held and cuddled. The mother can usually arrange her work to fall into the baby's sleeping periods when she resumes her regular work routine in the colony. If the infant cries too much while his mother is at work in the kitchen, she will be called home by the baby-sitter. There are always women who will take her place at work. The entire process is very informal but it is not *compulsively permissive*[19] either. The rights of the infants come first most of the time, but the rights of parents are not abrogated.

Hutterites believe that children are born innocent, but develop the capacity to sin as they mature. Hutterites conceive of their culture as a *narrow path* on which it is hard to walk without straying. The child's "self-will must be broken early and decisively before physical and psychological impulses gain control of his personality; but in love, not in anger," as one teacher summarized the Hutterite approach to discipline.

Symbolic of this religiously supported disciplinary emphasis is the custom of teaching infants to pray. As soon as a baby can sit up and is fed a bit of pablum or allowed a drink of water from a cup, the mother will take his hands, hold them together, while she says the traditional prayer before and after the meal. Before the year is over, most babies will "pray" by conditioned response.

Around six months, when parents get clear indications of social response from their child, he is viewed as ready for corporal discipline. He will get a little spanking, which grows in length and intensity as the baby's body grows if he demands too much attention, knocks over a plate of food or throws a fit of temper.

Punishment of infants is rarely harsh or administered in anger. But the serious tone of voice and expression which accompanies the light slap on the posterior, condition the infant to the fact that his behavior is not socially approved. As children grow older disciplinary measures take several forms. The most common is a chiding—being given a "talking to," although it is naturally not very effective with the pre-nursery youngsters. After the parental patience wears thin, they will send a youngster to bed, pull his hair, or give him a mild thrashing. Some youngsters seem to view discipline as a sign of parental interest in them—an atonement for their impulsive behavior which clears the deck for another round of "mischief."

Hutterite adults rarely show any guilt feelings concerning the early use of punishments. They feel that they know what they are doing and that it is right. There is a good deal of consistency and predictability about discipline. It serves to impress children even before the age of one, that life will impose limitations on them, but it takes place within an emotional climate of love. Parents and at least some of the older siblings also serve as a dependable source of comfort and protection.

Family Relationships. Contemporary Hutterite parents are more affectionate and family centered with their own children than their parents used to be with them. The older generation was much more guided by the spirit embodied in the following written regulation of the early 18th century:

Women may not breast feed their children longer than one and a half years. After that, they must turn them over to a kindergarten (Schulnutter), who has a special room, where she looks after the children. When required, particularly at night, she has help from other women to undress them, put them to bed, and watch over them at night. They remain until the age of five, when they come under the supervision of the male teacher.[28]

Earlier in the 17th century in Moravia, infants were turned over to a communal nursery even earlier. As soon as the mother recovered from her confinement, she was supposed to leave the infant in a nursery, where she would come three times a day to nurse her baby. The communal emphasis in child rearing survives in the occasional instance when a woman who does not feel well or who has twins. She may then send one of the babies to her mother or a sister to reduce her "hard work." The baby usually returns after he gets to be two or three years old and ready for kindergarten. In at least two cases a sister was allowed to raise one of the twins until adulthood because she could not bear children of her own. The practice was explained by the mother with the remark: "We are community people. If one has too hard a lot, we try to help her out."

Family life patterns have changed in many ways in recent decades. Many a young parent was seen humoring the negative and disobedient action of a small tot, while saying verbally, "My father would never have let me be *that* fresh!" More and more fathers bring a toy or some candy home for each child when they go to town.

Children everywhere serve as an ego-extension of their parents. The first Hutterite boy is traditionally named after his father, the first girl after her mother. All children take their mother's maiden name as their middle name. Parents like to find a physical likeness in their children. But there is little room for competitiveness in expectations which are culturally and ideologically nurtured. Hutterites live in a non-competitive communal society, where it is not likely for anyone to develop strong thwarted ambitions. Few parents feel competitive about their infants. They derive satisfaction from the child's positive physical and mental development, but communal prestige does not require unusual achievement.

Being a good Hutterite is to live up to average expectations. Superior performance is recognized only provided it is concerned with traditional Hutterite practices of work or preaching, but it is not a compelling educational objective for most parents.

Pediatric Care. Pediatricians are not accepted as an authority in the emotional and psychic spheres. Most Hutterites have confidence that they know best how to look after infants. Only in what is considered a physical health emergency will a doctor be called. He is expected to administer medicine, give an injection, or take some other dramatic step to earn his fee. The Hutterites, by defining the role of the physician as that of an activist technician, protect their culture from much of what might well be a disorganizing influence of medical science on their traditions. Neither Gesell[11] nor Spock[24] are guide lines to Hutterite mothers. There is much prestige in tradition. For more routine infant ailments, colic, diarrhea, and eczema, the colonists use patent medicines which are in general use among farmers of the area. While this confident attiude of the parents discourages dependency on medical specialists, it does at times keep children from benefiting from timely professional treatment. There have been occasional cases of rickets or pneumonia which could have been prevented had the seriousness of incipient symptoms of the illness been understood by the parents.

By their own cultural, and by American medical standards, infants are generally given good care. No case of parental neglect of an infant's physical needs is known that would have justified the intervention of police authorities. But pampering is also uncommon. It is rare for any parent to become deeply involved emotionally in a particular baby. The type of parentally induced neurotic dependency and helplessness described in the case histories of Harry Bakwin[1] and Melitta Sperling[23] will not be likely in any Hutterite child. The demands of the community on the mother's time, together with the fact that most women have large families, usually preclude any extended pre-occupation with any single baby.

It is uncommon to find deep emotional involvement in a child. This fact becomes dramatically apparent in the event of a death. Typical was the comment of a Hutterite mother about the anxiety of a member of our staff because his child (an only child) was near the horse barn, "Sure, you got to be worried; you only have one!" Deaths are usually accepted with considerable fatalism. The conviction that there will be another baby to take his place, plus the belief that infants will automatically get into heaven as angels because they are too young to have sinned, support such an emotional adjustment.

Social Change. Hutterite infant care methods are in transition. The sect seems more ready to accept new ideas which affect physical health of babies than practices which would involve community moral values. The usual defensiveness of the community against innovations is smallest when they affect an "innocent baby" to whom it makes no difference. Doctors find it easier to prescribe a new feeding method for a baby and have it carried out than to affect changes in the diet of adults. A mother who has successfully repressed a desire for fashionable shoes or silk stockings can express these urges by going to the store and buying her baby "pretty" socks and shoes out of her annual cash allowance. More bottles are used in the colonies; pacifiers are bought; commercial strollers are copied by the colony carpenter.

Doctors are an important source of ideas in this process of culture change. They need to recognize that it can in time lead to a noticeable disruption of the existing cultural consistency. Medical advice given without understanding of its "fitness" for the total culture of the family can produce insecurity in previously self-confident parents. This has not happened so far to any great extent. The rate of influence of American practices which conflict with Hutterite tradition has been sufficiently slow and gradual so that many of these innovations have been integrated within the core of Hutterite traditions. But the seeds of change are firmly planted. They can be found in the following family planning ideas which are widespread among young parents:

1. Young girls freely express desires to postpone the time of their marriage age for a few years because, "you got to work so hard once you have children. You have less fun then." For women married during the period

1900–1910, the average age at marriage was 19. For women married between 1940–1950, the average age at marriage was 21. About a dozen
women are known to have made inquiries concerning birth control, although most commonly, their continued pregnancies indicate that they
do not practice it.

2. Breast feeding is thought of as a form of "birth control" which does not
   violate religious principles. Young women spoke of a preference for breast
   feeding partly because they believe that they would be less likely to conceive again right away.
3. The menopause, the age period so critical in the adjustment of many
   American women, seems to be welcomed by many Hutterite ladies. It
   provides a guarantee against further pregnancies. Hutterites have no guilt
   feelings when "nature" provides such birth-control relief.
4. Expressions of mild resentment against males who have so much less work
   than women with children are common. Everybody uses the proverb:
   "Men work from sun to sun, but woman's work is never done." There are
   many humorous jibes of what would happen to children if men had to look
   after them.

The cursory glances of curiosity of Hutterite women beyond the narrow
path of their culture are still insignificant in comparison to their deeply
rooted attachment to the cultural objectives of wanting children and finding
joy in rearing them. The community gives considerable recognition and support to the nurturance of these attitudes.

Conclusion. Why should a practitioner on *Mainstreet* view as relevant to his
work that West Bengal mothers rub an ointment of carbon and oil around
their baby's eyes to ward off the "evil eye,"[12] while Hutterites use red thread
or a copper bracelet around the right wrist? He is not likely to encounter
either of these groups in his work, but he can learn from them about the cultural factors in medicine. They are not only relevant, but central to practice.

"Primitive" superstitions about the evil eye have their counterparts or
functional equivalents in even the most sophisticated American milieu. Some
of our fellow citizens worry about thumb-sucking infants. Others have taboos
about allowing a neonate to sleep in the bedroom. Many families engage
in highly ritualistic activities in the preparation of *The Formula*. The Hutterites have none of these folk-beliefs.

Their family system shows many characteristics commonly found in
middle and lower-class American families with large numbers of children.
It is an extensive rather than intensive network of emotional relationships; it
tends to prepare children early to face the realities of life; there is much
stress on the welfare of the group rather than the individual and conformity
is valued more than self-expression. But unlike the families studied by James
H. S. Bossard and his collaborators, they are not "peculiarly vulnerable to
major crises, especially when children are young."[3] The Hutterite community
is organized to help in the child-rearing process. It provides medical care,
nursing service, and parental relief from the usual chores. No matter how
many children a family has, its standard of living does not change.

While children are generally loved, there is little deep emotional involvement with any particular child. Over-protection and spoiling are rare. Even death, particularly if the children are young, is accepted fatalistically and realistically.

Mothers and fathers are self-confident of being good parents. Guilt feelings over methods of handling their infants are rare, although from a "worldly" medical point of view, some of these practices are considered bad. This sense of security towards the infant may well be transmitted to him and give him security in turn.

There is much consistency of infant care practices from family to family, colony to colony, and generation to generation. In the major practices of parenthood, Hutterites get relatively clear guidance from their culture. They rarely need choose between a variety of greatly conflicting alternate practices.

The faddish shifts in culturally sanctioned practices which have occurred in America within the last sixty years, have left American parents and pediatricians alike, with many uncertainties regarding the propriety of many of their infant care methods. The integration of Hutterite individuals and communities with their system of values and traditions has insulated them to a considerable extent from this sense of uncertainty about the quality of their parental care.

The Hutterites are successful as parents in terms of what they expect of themselves. It is uncommon for their grown up children to leave the community way of life or to violate frequently major moral norms. Mental health conditions in the group are good despite the fact children rearing practices violate several psychoanalytic principles regarded as important for the adjustment of American children. The inadequate sex-education of parents, the early discipline of infants, the early start of toilet training, the delegation of much of baby care by their mothers to pre-adolescents, as well as the acceptance of some medically unsound traditions do not seem to be associated with personality difficulties in this culture.

A contrasting observation are the findings of Kluckhohn. He raises and answers the following question, after reporting on Navaho infant care practices:

How can the anxiety level be so high among people where infants are nursed whenever they want to be, where childhood disciplines are so permissive, where there is so much genuine affection for children? If the writing of certain psychoanalysts were literally true (and the whole truth), adult Navahos ought to have calm and beautiful personalities. However, this is certainly not the case. The high degree of tension observed among adult Navahos may be traced partly to the exceedingly grave pressures to which Navaho society is at present subject, and also to the conflicts caused by weaning, other experiences of later childhood and beliefs about supernatural forces.[15, 16]

The apparent "immunity" of Hutterites against theoretically expected ill-effects of their infant care practices when practiced by middle class Americans may disappear in time. At least the Hutterites think this. Leaders and members alike feel that there is a considerable weakening in the consistency and the integration of their way of life. Many have said somewhat sadly:

"Our flesh is getting weaker all the time, because we are going too much with the world." The lack of knowledge of Hutterites about certain sound obstetric and pediatric practices performs an identifiable function in their social system. As it is true with all folk-knowledge, such ignorance helps to maintain the power of elders and those within the group with a reputation for wisdom. It re-enforces their total network of traditions.[18] It is obviously more than a matter of giving sound *medical* advice when a doctor recommends something which goes contrary to existing cultural expectations. He becomes an agent of social change.

Contemporary Hutterites rear babies who would have died in earlier years because the group's greater reluctance to call for professional help early enough. But there are also more "problems" perceived by members of the sect in the area of child rearing in which they had once been more sure of themselves. So far, the changes in Hutterite practices are sufficiently slow and gradual to become well integrated in their general way of life. The vitality for growth and development of this group is sufficiently strong so far to absorb these changes through the process of *controlled acculturation*,[5] without major impairment of their total pattern of life, which makes their infant care practices generally "good" for them—good in terms of their moral values. As the sect continues to acculturate and ultimately assimilate more of the values of their sectarian environment, their confidence in themselves and their way of life may become severely impaired.

The social anthropological evidence that has been presented lends support to the theory that the effect of any particular infant care practice is not simply a consequence of what it does for (or against) the infant. It depends very much on its place in the total pattern of infant care, of which it is a part. A particular practice depends for its effectiveness on the re-enforcing support given it by other practices experienced by the growing child at every stage of his development.

It is methodologically impossible to single out any particular element of the parent-child relationship in a social system and an estimate of its specific effect on personality development independent of the continuity of influence of the total culture pattern. This relativistic hypothesis, which admits no absolute "rights" or "wrongs" in infant care, is in conformity with the observed fact that both in historical and contemporary times, men have learned to live in many different ways, each seemingly satisfactory to many of those who share a common cultural background.

This evidence does not imply that American pediatricians or child psychologists need abdicate in favor of untutored midwives or grandmothers; but it does emphasize that the psychological effect on infants and parents of any particular act is not a fixed quantum; it varies. Changes in infant care methods must be introduced with an understanding of the cultural matrix in which the change is expected to find acceptance. This fact makes pediatrics and child guidance something more than a science. It makes it an art, requiring the practitioner to match the approach to the multi-dimensional background of his patient.

23   PHYSICIANS' VIEWS ON THE LEVEL OF
          MEDICAL INFORMATION AMONG PATIENTS*

By Lois Pratt, Arthur Seligmann, and George Reader

In organizing medical services for ambulatory patients those planning them often forget the patient in the desire to provide all the personnel and equipment that is considered to be necessary for adequate scientific care. Likewise, they may overlook one of the primary purposes of any medical care activity: to provide an optimal environment for the development and continuance of the doctor-patient relationship. Essentially this relationship resolves itself into a give-and-take between two human beings, the nature of the interchange being determined by a number of factors, such as the previous experience and knowledge of the participants, expectations of each toward the other, ability to communicate, and ability to think and understand. The effectiveness of the doctor-patient relationship should be one of the fundamental considerations in evaluating adequacy of medical care.

In order to shed some light on the adequacy of patient care in the medical clinic of a large metropolitan medical center a number of studies have been made of this relationship. This paper will report findings that bear on the question of communication of information between physicians and clinic patients; more specifically, it will focus on the physician's attitudes and beliefs about patient information. In addition, to provide a context within which physicians' views may be interpreted, a summary of findings on some related questions will be presented.

Methods. 214 Medical Clinic patients were queried about etiology, symptoms, and treatment of ten common diseases, namely tuberculosis, diabetes, syphilis, arthritis, menopause, asthma, cerebro-vascular accident, stomach ulcer, leukemia, and coronary thrombosis. A 36-question multiple choice test was used. A sample question follows:

> Tuberculosis of the lungs is due to:
> 1. Prolonged exposure to the cold.
> 2. Infection with a germ.
> 3. Anemia and vitamin deficiency.
> 4. Don't know.

These same questions were then made part of a questionnaire administered to 89 physicians in the same clinic which was aimed at determining how much information these doctors thought laymen should know and how much they thought patients in the clinic did know.

The third part of this study consisted of an intensive longitudinal analysis of 50 patient-physician relationships, the 50 patients being randomly selected from among those making new appointments in the medical clinic. Each pa-

From *The American Journal of Public Health*, 47, (October, 1957), 1277–1283. Copyright 1957 by The American Public Health Association Inc.

tient visit to a physician in the clinic was observed and a record kept of the activity and conversation that took place; in addition, the patient was interviewed before making the first visit to the physician and after each visit with him. The observations of the patient-physician contacts provided data on how the patient's illness was discussed, while interviews with patients revealed their views of what they had been told.

Results. 1. The multiple choice test of knowledge about ten common diseases revealed that, on the average, the clinic patients could correctly answer 55 percent of these rather routine questions. The range was from one-third correct answers for patients with less than an eighth grade education to two-thirds for those with a high school education. It was also found that knowledge varied considerably by disease; knowledge of coronary thrombosis, for example, was particularly low, with only two-fifths of the information answered correctly.[1]

In addition a random group of fifty new patients were questioned on their arrival at the clinic about the condition they suspected they had. Some of these patients had received care for this suspected illness from another clinic or physician, but the majority had not. Most patients were found to have focused their concern on a particular disease possibility, and the findings pertain only to this group who suspected a particular disease.

No patients were found to have a thorough understanding about all three aspects about which they were questioned—the etiology or nature of the illness, the usual treatment, and the prognosis. Four patients were classified as having thorough understanding of the etiology or nature of the illness; but none had a thorough understanding of the treatment or prognosis. The majority—from $3/5$ to $3/4$—were classified as knowing almost nothing about the three aspects of the disease. The minority were classed as having some understanding of it.

On the basis of the findings it may be concluded that the patients studied were rather poorly informed about several common diseases and about their own suspected condition.

The next question to be considered, then, is what difference does this make?

2. How does the patient's knowledge of disease influence the way the patient interacts with the physician and the quality of care received from the physician. It was not possible to determine the effect of the patient's level of knowledge, because no patients in the sample were well enough informed about their disease.

What was observed, however, is that the patients in our sample participated with the physician at an extremely low level. They seldom requested information from the physician (one-third of the patients never asked a single question on any visit), they seldom requested the physician to do anything, and seldom even made a statement to direct the physician's attention to something. While it is assumed that the physician should direct the conversation and activity, complete lack of initiative by the patient may be dysfunctional for the physician as well as the patient. While it has been impossible to test whether this low level of participation by the patients was related to their low level of information and understanding of illness, the simultaneous presence of these two conditions is consistent with the notion that they are related.[2]

3. What are patients' attitudes about receiving and demanding information from physicians? Before attempting to modify existing patterns of communication, it would be wise to know what information patients want to obtain from physicians; for if patients expect more information than they are now receiving one would proceed differently than if they expect and want little information. On the basis of our study data it has been concluded that for the clinic patients studied, there was no demand for detailed and fundamental information among the patients; but there is apparently a certain amount of latent interest in receiving more information than they now receive. The findings on this point are summarized as follows:

a. Patients seldom make direct demands for information to the physician, particularly of the sort that would give basic understanding of the disease.

b. Patients' abstract notions about what constitutes a good doctor seldom include information-giving as a requisite characteristic.

c. Patients by and large evaluated their own clinic physicians as performing satisfactorily with regard to explanations and information giving.

d. In contrast to the above findings, which suggested little concern with information, it was found that a majority of patients indicated to the interviewer in some direct or indirect fashion that certain specific pieces of information about the disease process, implications of the test results, and so on, were of some importance to the patient.

In general, there was very little conscious demand for a thorough explanation of the illness on the part of the patients; but there was an unformulated, latent need.[3]

4. At least as important as the patients' views on this problem of communication are those of physicians. The attitudes of physicians determine, in part, what patients are now told. Furthermore, it would be necessary to take their attitudes into consideration in any future plan to change communication practices. This would be especially true if it seems desirable to encourage physicians to devote more attention to this problem, for, according to one study, 19 percent of the internist's time is now devoted to patient education.[4] What, then, are the attitudes of physicians about having patients know about medical matters?

The findings obtained on this question are based on a questionnaire administered to 89 physicians in the medical clinic. Each doctor was asked to indicate for each of 36 facts about disease whether or not he thought the fact should be part of the layman's fund of knowledge, from his own point of view as a doctor who has to deal with patients. For example, did he think laymen should know that tuberculosis is due to infection with a germ, or that treatment for stomach ulcer tries to cut down on acid stomach juices, or so on. These are the identical facts on which the clinic patients had been tested.

Here are the results. The doctors reported, on the average, that 82 percent of the facts included in the questionnaire should be known by laymen. Only 9 percent of the doctors thought patients needed to know no more than half the information; while 18 percent of the doctors thought patients should know it all. The types of information that doctors most unanimously thought laymen should know tended to be facts involving a favorable prognosis for a disease. Thus, the physician is a little more anxious that laymen be given hopeful information than that they be given facts on the etiology, symptoms and treatment of disease. Nonetheless, the preponderant opinion was that laymen should know most of the information in our test.

These findings must not be interpreted as indicating that physicians feel it desirable to tell a patient the full extent of his illness. On the contrary, when the clinical teaching faculty of the same institution were asked how they would feel if a physician in their specialty were to "always tell patients the full extent of their illness," almost three-fourths said they would disapprove.[5] When these two sets of findings are considered together, it suggests that physicians hold a general value that it is beneficial for laymen to have a rudimentary understanding of illness, but that in actual practice it is often unwise to give a sick patient all the facts.

5. Do patients now meet these standards of knowledge of the physician? It is clear from the foregoing figures that patients in general fall far short of physicians' standards of what laymen should know. The physicians thought 82 percent of the test information should be known by the ordinary layman, while patients knew only 55 percent of it, with even high school graduates knowing only two-thirds of the facts. This represents, then, one measure of the gap between physicians' standards of what patients ought to know, and the actual level of patients' knowledge. The fact that patients fall far short of physicians' standards underlines the suspicion, (reported earlier), that the patients may not be sufficiently informed to communicate with physicians with the highest degree of effectiveness.

6. The next question considered is: How do physicians preceive patients' level of knowledge about disease? Are they accurate in their evaluations, and do they overestimate or underestimate patients' knowledge? This question is thought to be significant in an investigation of communication problems, because physicians' judgements of patients' current knowledge undoubtedly influence what they discuss with patients and how they discuss it. Concerning the importance and direction of this influence, some limited findings will be presented later.

A first attempt to measure physicians' judgements about patients' level of knowledge was made by asking 89 clinic physicians to estimate the proportion of the clinic patient population who knew each of the 36 facts about disease. These estimates were then compared with the actual results on the knowledge test for the patient population. This is admittedly a gross measure of physicians' judgments because they were asked to evaluate an entire group rather than specific patients. Nonetheless, it provides an indication of how they perceive the clinic patients.

It was found that well over half the estimates made by doctors were in error by at least 20 percent, the median error for doctors being 23 percent. Eighty-one percent of all doctors had an overall tendency to underestimate patients' knowledge. This tendency to underestimate occurs in spite of the fact that patients' actual level of information is quite low.

7. What effect do these perceptions by physicians of the patients' knowl-

edge have on their discussions with patients about illness? The data available on this problem consist of a measure of the physician's tendency to underestimate, overestimate or accurately judge the knowledge of the patient population, and a rating of the amount of explanation given by the physician to one or two patients.[6] It was found that those physicians who seriously underestimated the knowledge of the patient population tended to have more limited discussions with the patient about his problem, than did the physicians who more accurately evaluated patients' knowledge or overestimated it.[7]

In addition to this statistical relationship, the intensive observation of 50 patient-physician relationships provided countless clues that the dynamics of the situation were somewhat like this: when a doctor perceives the patient as rather poorly informed, he considers the tremendous difficulties of translating his knowledge into language the patient can understand, along with the dangers of frightening the patient; and therefore avoids involving himself in an elaborate discussion with the patient; the patient, in turn, reacts dully to this limited information, either asking uninspired questions or refraining from questioning the doctor at all, thus reinforcing the doctor's view that the patient is ill equipped to comprehend his problem, and further reinforcing the doctor's tendency to skirt discussions of the problem. Lacking guidance by the doctor, the patient performs at a low level; hence the doctor rates his capacities as even lower than they are.

8. What are the actual practices of physicians now in giving explanations to patients about their illness? Our findings on this question are based on observations of 50 patient-physician relationships during the entire course of these relationships.[8] On the basis of examining all the conversation between patient and physician, an attempt was made to code the amount and type of information given by the physician to the patient as objectively as possible. Five types of information about the patient's illness were considered. They were:

1. Reasons for tests;
2. Test results;
3. Etiology of the illness or what the illness consists of;
4. Why treatment, or what is the treatment supposed to do;
5. Prognosis, possible complications, or other statements of what can be expected in the future.

It will not be possible at this time to report on how each of these areas were handled by physicians. The findings will be illustrated by discussing just one area—the reasons for tests:

—one-third of the patients were told nothing beyond the fact that tests x, y and z were to be done; that is, they were given no explanation of the tests on any level.

—one-half of the patients were told, with regard to at least one test, what organ or possible disease was being investigated by the test; for example, they might have been told they were to have an X-ray of their chest.

—the remaining 14 percent of the patients received an explanation, with regard to at least one test, of the type of evidence the tests would provide, or what the test means in terms of a possible disease.

The findings for the physicians' handling of the other information areas were similar. Physicians were significantly more likely to give some explanation rather than none at all. A small minority received what could be called a rounded explanation; while the majority received a limited number of isolated facts. It was further found that physicians were more likely to avoid completely discussion of the prognosis and etiology, than they were to bypass the more immediately practical issues of tests and treatment. It is strongly suspected that the limited explanations given by physicians in this sample is bound up with the low level of knowledge of the patients and the lack of overt interest shown by the patients in receiving information.

9. How much do patients learn about their illness from physicians? If a physician explains the problem carefully, does the patient always learn more than when the physician does not give a careful explanation? Are other factors—such as the patient's anxiety, interest, or education—such crucial determinants of what the patient learns from the physician, that undue emphasis should not be placed on the physician's giving elaborate explanations to all patients. The limited investigation made of this problem consisted of classifying patients in terms of how thorough an explanation their physicians gave them and then cross-classifying patients in terms of whether they improved in their understanding of their condition after interacting with the physician. It was found that the patients who received some explanation were more likely to increase their understanding of their problem than were those who did not receive explanations, but there was by no means a perfect relationship. While the measures are crude, it appears safe to conclude from the results that what the doctor tells the patient is certainly not the only factor determining how much the patient learns about his condition. Because of the small number of cases in the sample, it is not possible to trace what the most significant other factors are which intervene between what the doctor says and what the patient actually learns. Furthermore, it was not possible to ascertain definitely what patients can learn when they receive well-rounded explanations, for so few received systematic explanations.

10. The final consideration is what difference does it make if a doctor gives or does not give a thorough explanation to the patient about his illness? That is, does it affect the patient's health? It is not feasible at this stage of the research to attempt to determine whether patients who are informed by their physicians actually make better recovery from their illness than those who are not informed. It was thought more practical to attempt to specify some of the more direct and specific efforts that the doctors' explanations might have. First, were patients who received thorough explanations able to participate more effectively in the conversation and planning with the physician? It had been strongly suspected from the observations that the patients who were most confused about their condition and about what the doctor was doing or thinking, were the ones who participated least actively in discussions with the physician. Therefore, the number of requests for information made by the patient was used as a crude index of the extent of the

patient's participation. It was found that the patients who received some explanation from the physician tended to ask slightly more questions than did those who were given almost no explanation. This finding is far from conclusive, but is consistent with the notion that the patient is able to interact more productively when the physician provides at least a minimum framework of information within which the patient can arrange his thoughts and formulate his questions.

Another possible effect of the physician's explanations might be the extent to which patients accept the physician's diagnosis and plans for treatment. It was found that the patients who received some explanation of the problem from their physicians were slightly more apt to agree fully with the diagnosis and plans of the physician, than were those patients who received negligible information about their condition. The relationship is far from perfect, partly, perhaps, because refined measures have not yet been developed. However, the relationship found does suggest that the patient who receives regular explanations from the physician about what he is doing and what he is finding, may accept more fully the physician's plans and goals, and hence this patient may be better cared for. As reported in another paper, agreement with the physician's diagnosis and plans is apparently a crucial factor; for the patients who agreed with the physician's diagnosis and plans were found to complete their care in every case, while a significant number of those not agreeing completely with the doctor's formulation, left the physician.[9]

Summary and Conclusions. This paper has reported on findings from studies of problems of communication between patients and physicians in a medical outpatient clinic. It was found that:

Patients were quite poorly informed about their own condition when they came to the clinic and about ten common diseases. It was suggested that this might be partly responsible for the almost complete lack of initiative shown by the patients with the physicians.

The patients gave little evidence of conscious, aggressive demand for information about their condition from the physician; but there appeared to be an unformulated, latent desire for more information among the majority.

Physicians working in the clinic thought that basic facts on the symptoms, etiology and treatment of common diseases should be known by laymen. The fund of information that physicians indicated should be known by laymen was considerably more extensive than patients were actually found to have.

Physicians apparently cannot judge very accurately the level of medical knowledge in a patient population. The direction of their error was rather consistently to underestimate patients' knowledge, despite the low level of knowledge among patients. Physicians who seriously underestimated patients' knowledge were less likely to discuss the illness at any length with the patient, than were the physicians who did not seriously underestimate patients' knowledge.

A majority of patients were found to have been told a limited number of isolated facts about their condition; few were given a systematic explanation of either the etiology, prognosis, purpose of the tests, test results, or treatment.

Finally, patients who were given more thorough explanations were found to participate somewhat more effectively with the physician and were more likely to accept completely the doctor's formulation, than were patients who received very little explanation.

24   RITUAL AND MAGIC IN THE CONTROL OF CONTAGION

By Julius A. Roth

Tuberculosis is a contagious disease. But just how contagious is it? In what ways and under what circumstances is it likely to be transmitted from one person to another? And what procedures are most effective for preventing its transmission? The answers to these questions are quite uncertain and TB specialists show considerable disagreement in the details of the manner in which they deal with these problems. These uncertainties leave the way open for ritualized procedures that often depend more on convenience and ease of administration than on rationally deduced probabilities. They also leave the way open for irrational practices that can properly be called "magic."

Protecting the Outside World. In one Veterans Administration hospital, occupational therapy products are routinely sterilized by exposure to ultra-violet light before being sent out. (Patients sometimes by-pass this procedure by giving their OT products to their visitors to take out.) Books are sometimes sterilized before being sent out, sometimes not. Other articles mailed by patients may or may not be sterilized depending largely upon whether or not the patient requests it. Letters are never sterilized. The inconsistency of these procedures is not lost on the workers. One volunteer worker held up a package she was mailing for a patient, and said: "Now, I can mail this without sterilizing it, but if someone wants to send home some OT work, I have to sterilize it before I can mail it for him. It doesn't make any sense."

The fact that sterilization is carried out by volunteer workers under the direction of the Special Services Division is in itself an indication that it is regarded as an auxiliary rather than an essential activity of the hospital. The extent to which sterilization procedures are a matter of convenience is shown by the reply of a volunteer worker when questioned about sterilizing books to be returned to outside libraries: "Anytime you want a book sterilized before it's sent out, just let me know and we'll do it for you. Of course, we probably wouldn't be able to do it shortly before Christmas, because that lamp will be in constant use for sterilizing OT work that the men are sending out as presents."

Money regularly passes out of the hospital without sterilization. Patients give money to volunteer shoppers, the newsman, canteen, and postal workers. These people put the money into pocket, purse, or money box, and pass it on

From *American Sociological Review*, 22, (June, 1957), 310–314. Copyright 1957 by The American Sociological Society.

to others without raising any questions about the possibility of spreading the disease. Quite often money changes hands quickly after being taken from the patients. The volunteer shoppers, for example, take the patients' orders and money, go directly from the hospital to town to do the shopping so that the orders may be brought to the patients the same day. In the stores, the money passes into cash registers and pockets and is handed on to other customers as change—all within a period of a few hours. The danger of transmitting tubercule bacilli by money is probably very slight, but it is certainly many times greater than the chance of spreading the disease through books and OT products, which spend at least a day or two in transit through the mails.[1]

An even more striking example of inconsistency is shown in the policy toward visitors. Visitors are not required to wear any protective clothing, not even masks, and none of them ever do. The same is true of entertainers and members of service and veterans organizations who play games with the patients or bring them gifts. Some patients have positive sputum, so that a visitor probably runs a much greater risk of taking viable bacilli into his body than does the person who handles money, books, or OT products of a patient after a period of several hours or several days. However, TB hospitals have a tradition of permitting persons without protective clothing to visit patients, and to break such a tradition would almost certainly bring strong protests from patients and their families and would in any case be evaded by many people.

In Wisconsin the legislature prohibits public libraries and state-controlled institutions from lending books to patients in TB hospitals.[2] But the law says nothing about the protection of visitors or about other articles, which can be brought in and taken out by visitors, volunteer workers, members of service organizations, and patients themselves (when they go out on pass). The Chief of Special Services refused to guarantee the sterilization of books from outside libraries because he was afraid he might violate a law. This same man has direct control over entertainers and members of service organizations who come into the hospital, and he does not require these people to wear protective clothing nor does he try to control all the games, musical instruments, and other articles they bring into and carry out of the hospital.

In summary, the devices for protection against the spread of the disease outside the hospital are controlled largely by tradition, convenience, and adherence to legal technicalities rather than to rational estimates of the chances of transmission of tubercle bacilli. The limited efforts at preventing the transmission of the disease are concentrated chiefly in those areas where the chances of transmission are probably the least.

Rank and Protective Clothing. A number of procedures are designed to protect the employees and patients within the hospital from spreading TB. One method, which has come into prominence in recent years, is the use of protective clothing—masks, gowns, and hair coverings—which the hospital personnel are supposed to wear when they come into contact with the patients or their effects. However, this protective clothing is often not worn. There is a definite relationship between the degree to which it is worn and the rank of the employee.

I recorded the wearing of surgical cap, gown, and mask by the nursing personnel of a VA hospital when entering a patient's room over a four-day period. The results are shown in Table 1.

Table 1—Wearing of Protective Clothing by Nursing Personnel in Veterans Administration Hospital

	Times Entered Room	Percentages Wearing		
		Cap	Gown	Mask
Nurses	56	100	57	75
Attendants	200	100	72	90

More detailed records were made of the use of protective clothing when entering patients' rooms in a state hospital that had a more complex nursing hierarchy. The record was made on ten different days, plus additional days for doctors and professional nurses in order to increase their very small number. The records were made on three different wards with different sets of personnel and were always for complete days to avoid the selective influence of certain work shifts or kinds of ward duties. Results are given in Table 2. The two instances of a doctor wearing cap and mask on recorded days (Table 2) both involved the same doctor—an assistant surgeon on a temporary assignment. His successor does not wear protective clothing.

Table 2—Wearing of Protective Clothing by Doctors and Nursing Personnel in State Hospital

	Times Entered Room	Percentages Wearing		
		Cap	Gown	Mask
Doctors	47	5	0	5
Professional nurses	100	24	18	14
Practical nurses	121	86	45	46
Aides	142	94	80	72
Students	97	100	100	100

As both of these tables show, the use of protective clothing is inversely related to occupational status level. The people of higher rank seem to have the privilege of taking the greater risks, particularly in the case of masks. The cap and gown are intended in part to prevent the spread of the disease to others; the mask is almost exclusively for the protection of the wearer.

It might be argued that the lower status employees should wear protective clothing relatively more often because they perform tasks which require more intimate contact with the patients and their effects. Thus, the aides and students do most of the work of collecting food trays and trash, making beds, washing furniture, picking up soiled towels. Certainly, this factor makes a difference, but it is not sufficient to account for the whole difference.

When we examine overlapping functions (those carried out by two or more levels of nursing personnel), differences, if any, are almost always in the direction of more frequent wearing of protective clothing by the lower-status employees. Table 3 gives the figures for eleven overlapping functions in which such differences occurred.

Table 3—Wearing of Protective Clothing by State Hospital Nursing Personnel while carrying out Given Functions*

	Times Entered Room	Percentages Wearing		
		Cap	Gown	Mask
Take temperatures:				
Professional nurses	26	19	54	46
Practical nurses	24	79	63	71
Students	6	100	100	100
Dispense medications:				
Professional nurses	7	28	14	0
Practical nurses	15	87	40	40
Students	5	100	100	100
Talk to patients when not performing a duty:				
Professional nurses	11	18	0	0
Practical nurses	31	87	26	23
Aides	29	86	52	55
Students	5	100	100	100
Distribute towels or linens:				
Professional nurses	2	0	0	0
Practical nurses	6	100	67	67
Aides	12	100	100	83
Students	9	100	100	100
Adjust blinds or windows:				
Professional nurses	3	33	33	0
Practical nurses	4	75	25	25
Aides	14	93	72	72
Students	7	100	100	100
Collect food trays:				
Practical nurses	9	67	67	67
Aides	17	94	100	94
Students	14	100	100	100
Serve drinking water:				
Practical nurses	10	80	40	60
Aides	11	100	82	73
Students	3	100	100	100
Give out supplies (tissues, tissue bags, etc.):				
Practical nurses	11	82	73	91
Aides	9	100	89	100
Students	3	100	100	100
Collect soiled towels and linen:				
Practical nurses	7	43	29	57
Aides	14	93	50	43
Give out refreshments:				
Practical nurses	4	100	0	25
Aides	3	100	33	100
Collect trash:				
Practical nurses	13	85	85	77
Aides	27	93	85	78
Students	4	100	100	100

* Because the numbers of certain classes of personnel for some functions were very small, supplementary observations in addition to those given in Table 2 were made. These observations—which were always for complete days—have been included in this table. Doctors do not appear in this table because there was almost no overlap between their functions and those of the nursing personnel.

Why do persons with higher status wear protective clothing less often? For one thing, it is not considered necessary by people who know best. There is no good evidence that the systematic wearing of protective clothing makes any difference (even the person who planned and administered this program could cite no evidence showing its effectiveness) and people who know most about TB do not seem to consider it worth the trouble. Doctors, and to a lesser extent professional nurses, are, of course, most likely to recognize the probable futility of these procedures. The relative ignorance of the lower levels of ward employees makes it more likely that they will have doubts about whether it is safe to go without the protective clothing, especially on routine duties when they must enter patients' rooms repeatedly in a short interval. There are, of course, circumstances in which almost everyone would agree that the wearing of a mask and perhaps a gown was wise. It is the routine wearing of protective clothing for all contacts with patients that is generally rejected. Probably a more important factor is the likelihood that the employee can "get away with" a violation. A doctor need not worry about a "bawling out" for not protecting himself. A professional nurse might be criticized, but usually she is the highest authority on a ward. The chance of criticism increases down the scale. Students, who are new and unfamiliar with the situation (they put in four-week stints) and who worry about possible "demerits," wear protective clothing all the time in patients' rooms. Some ward employees, especially those of lower status, who are not "properly dressed" hurriedly don a mask and gown if they see the supervisor of the nursing education program on the floor.

Magic and the Tubercle Bacillus. Gauze or paper masks are rather difficult to breathe through. To make breathing easier patients and employees sometimes pull down the mask until their nostrils have a clear space. This, of course, destroys the point of wearing the mask and the mask then takes on the status of a charm necklace.

We can also find examples of institutional magic. In the state hospital patients are required to wear masks when they go to the first floor for a hair cut or for an x-ray and when they go to the eighth floor to see the social worker or the patient services director. They do not have to wear masks (and never do) when they go to the first floor for occupational therapy, to visit with their families, to attend socials or church services, or to see a movie, nor when they go to the eighth floor to the library and to play bingo. An examination of these two lists shows that patients must wear masks when they go somewhere on "business," but not when they go somewhere for "pleasure," even though they use the same parts of the building and come into contact with hospital personnel in both cases. The rules suggest that the tubercle bacillus works only during business hours.

The ward employee tends to wear protective clothing when carrying out her duties, but not when "socializing" with the patients. I kept a record over a short period of time on several practical nurses on the 3:00 to 11:00 P.M. shift. Table 4 shows the contrasts in their use of protective clothing. The nurses' contact with the patients was more prolonged and more intimate while socializing than while carrying out their duties. The average time spent in the room during this recorded period was less than half a minute for taking care of a duty and about three minutes for socializing. While giving out medicine or taking temperatures or bringing in food trays the nurses have very little close contact with the patients. While socializing, they often stand close to the patients, lean on their beds and other furniture, and handle their newspapers and other belongings. Logically, there is a greater need for the protective clothing—and especially the mask, which was hardly used at all—while socializing than while carrying out the routine duties.

Table 4—Wearing of Protective Clothing by Practical Nurses When Carrying Out Duties and When "Socializing" With Patients

	Times Entered Room	Percentages Wearing		
		Cap	Gown	Mask
Carrying out duties	39	97	75	80
"Socializing"	23	91	17	9

Apparently, these nurses believe they need protection only when working. They remark that the gown, and more especially the mask, is a barrier to friendly intercourse.

Man's Laws and Nature's Laws. Rationally considered, the controls and protections used to check the transmission of TB should depend on an estimate of the probability of such transmission occurring under given conditions and in given circumstances. The problem for persons responsible for controlling the transmission of TB is to set their controls and protections at a level where a "reasonable" risk is involved. Admittedly, this is not easy because of the uncertain knowledge about transmission and susceptibility and public anxieties about the disease. Even if one were able to establish general rules for a "reasonable" level of control on the basis of present knowledge about the disease, putting these rules into practice would still be a major problem. To deal with this problem realistically, the controlling agents need a good understanding of the social organization of the hospital, the disease concepts of the personnel, and the patterns of administrative thinking on the part of supervisory persons.

The practices surrounding contagion control in a TB hospital represent an effort to make man's laws approximate the laws of nature, and when nature's laws are not well understood, man's rules are likely to be more or less irrational and their observance vacillating and ritualistic.[3]

25   ILLNESS, THERAPY AND THE MODERN URBAN AMERICAN FAMILY

By Talcott Parsons and Renée Fox

The primary purpose of this paper is to show that the relations between illness and the family are to be understood only through combining sociological analysis of the structure of role-systems with psychodynamic analysis of

Reprinted from *The Journal of Social Issues*, Vol. VIII, No. 4, 1952, pp. 2–3; 31–44.

certain processes in personalities.[1] For we regard illness as both a psychological disturbance and a deviant social role.[2]

Doctor-Patient and Parent-Child: Some Analogies. We begin our analysis by suggesting that there are intimate psychodynamic relationships between the processes which occur in the normal system of family interaction, and those which obtain both in the doctor-patient relationship and in such more elaborately differentiated health-care institutions as the hospital. At the same time, we propose that the emergence of the medical profession and of the hospitals into their strategic position in contemporary society is not solely attributable to the accumulation of technical medical knowledge and its application in technological processes. Rather, it is our paramount thesis that the doctor and the hospital provide a set of institutionalized mechanisms for handling certain of the motivational problems of personality adjustment: mechanisms which, in certain respects, are functionally alternative to those of the family. Thus, the family and therapeutic institutions resemble each other; if this were not true, the kind of functional relationship between them which we wish to analyze could not exist. At the same time, they also differ in fundamental respects; if this were not the case, there would be far less reason either for the existence or for the effectiveness of these institutions.

The elements of correspondence are perhaps best approached in terms of two analogies: on the one hand, the similarity between illness and the status of the child in the family; on the other hand, the overlap between the physician's role and that of the parent. The common point of reference for the first analogy is the status of the non-sick adult member of society. Both child and sick person differ from this norm in two primary respects. The first is capacity to perform the usual functions of an adult in everyday life. The child is not yet able to do this; partly because biological maturation has not gone far enough, partly because his socialization is still incomplete. Similarly, one of our main criteria of illness is that the sick person is "incapacitated." In the usual case, he has been capable of normal functioning, but his illness, in some degree, makes him unable to carry on. The second respect in which the child and the sick actor are similar is that they are both dependent: needing and expecting to be taken care of by stronger, more "adequate" persons. Thus, in these two senses, illness is not unlike more or less complete reversion to childhood.

The analogy of physician (and other hospital personnel) and parents in part is simple and obvious. These are the stronger and more adequate persons on whom the child and the sick person, respectively, are made to rely; they are the ones to whom he must turn to have those of his needs fulfilled which he is incapable of meeting through his own resources. As we shall maintain, these analogies must not be pressed too far. But they do constitute a convenient jumping off place for our analysis.

Illness, so far as it is motivated, is a form of deviant behavior, and, as such, may be subjected to a standard sociological analysis of deviance. Compared with other types of non-conformist behavior, sickness characteristically entails passive withdrawal from normal activities and responsibilities. As such, it should be distinguished from active rebellion against the normal social expectations, and from the types of deviance characterized by compulsive conformity.[3] For it is an escape from the pressures of ordinary life. In a society such as our own, illness is a very strategic expression of deviance: first, because our culture enforces an unusually high level of activity, independence and responsibility on the average individual; and second, because it connects so closely with the residua of childhood dependency (which, we may suggest, are more intense in our society than in many others, because of the particular structure of our urban family).[4] From the point of view of the stability of the social system, therefore, too frequent resort to this avenue of escape presents a serious danger. This is the primary context in which we think of illness as an institutionalized role and its relation to therapy as an important mechanism of social control.

It should be pointed out that as a role the state of illness is partially and conditionally legitimized. That is, if a person is defined as sick, his failure to perform his normal functions is "not his fault," and he is accorded the right to exemption and to care. At one and the same time, however, the sick person is enjoined to accept the definition of his state as undesirable and the obligation to get well as expeditiously as possible.

Similarly, childhood is more than a condition. Like illness, it also is a conditionally legitimized social role. The child is permitted to be childish only temporarily. He accepts the obligation to grow up, even though at times it is very painful, and to cooperate with his parents in helping him to achieve maturity.

We feel it is largely *because* of this close correspondence between the status of the child and of the sick person that it is important to have the major part of illness in our society tended outside the family. However, since the family has been the principal refuge for the sick in most societies, the question arises as to why in our society we are so ready to send our sick outside the family to special medical institutions. The importance of the technological factors we grant; but, as already indicated, we feel that there is more to it than that.

Some Vulnerabilities of the American Family. The primary psychodynamically relevant reasons we find in the special character of the American urban family, which is extremely vulnerable to certain types of strain. Mechanisms have developed which relieve the family of the additional stresses which would be imposed upon it by making the care of the sick one of its principal functions. At the same time, most cases of illness with psychological components are probably more effectively cared for in the special circumstances of our society by professionalized agencies than they would be in families.

When ranged alongside the kinship groups of other social orders, the most striking features of our family system are: its small size; the isolation of the principal unit, the conjugal family, from other sectors of the kinship system; and the modern family's apparent functionlessness. With respect to its loss of function, the urban family has, above all, ceased to be an agency of economic production—by obvious contrast, for instance, with peasant families the world over. Furthermore, even in the close-knit setting of the immediate community, little political responsibility is taken by families as *units*.

We interpret this to mean that the influence of the family in our society has become highly *indirect*. In fact, as we see it, the contemporary American family derives its functional import almost exclusively from the effect it has upon its members as personalities. For us, the primary significance of this family type resides in the fact that it insures perpetuation of cultural patterns essential to the society (above all, its values) by motivating the actor to carry out these major patterns. With respect to adult family members this is primarily a "maintenance" or regulatory function: a matter of absorbing, easing and dealing with the consequences of various kinds of strain arising out of their life situations. For children, on the other hand, it involves the powerful process of socialization.[5]

The American family is well adapted to the exigencies of a modern industrial society. But it is also highly susceptible to many grave strains. For, though the wife-mother bears the major socio-emotional responsibilities within the family, she is largely excluded from those occupational roles which are the source of family status and socio-economic sustenance. Further, whatever her activities outside the home may be, they tend on the whole to be "representative" ones undertaken in the name of the family.

On the other hand, the husband-father as the provider and primary status bearer of the family is exposed during all the working hours of his existence to the distinctive rigors of the marketplace, wherein he carries the heavy load of responsibility *for* the family. In addition, he is classically a "scapegoat": the symbolic target at which the child primarily aims the hostile-aggressive impulses aroused in him as he undergoes the stressful process of socialization. It is the specialized function of the wife-mother to act as skillful mediator of the child-father relationship and thereby to assure both the perpetuation of family solidarity and the emotional security of the child.

The roles of the wife-mother and the husband-father, then, are characteristically subject to a complex of structural strains, as is the child in his role of socializee, particularly when sibling rivalry intervenes. Finally, in our society, the advent of old age brings still another set of problems in its wake: forced retirement from the occupational sphere so crucial to the male actor's sense of worth, and to the woman's status and security systems; and overwhelming socio-psychological isolation.

As a response to any one of these family-based or focused social pressures, illness could provide a tantalizingly attractive "solution." For the sick role is a semi-legitimate channel of withdrawal—exempting the social actor from adult responsibilities and enjoining him to allow himself to be taken care of by others. As we have already emphasized, illness is very often motivational in origin. Even in those instances where the *etiology* of the disorder is primarily physico-chemical, the nature and severity of symptoms and the rate of recuperation are almost invariably influenced by the attitudes of the patient.

It is easy to see, therefore, how the wife-mother, for example, might "choose" the sick role as an institutionalized way out of her heavy "human relations management" responsibilities in the family; or how she might seize upon illness as a compulsively feministic way of reacting to her exclusion from the life open to a man. Similarly, the passive-dependent role of illness offers the husband-father semi-institutionalized respite from the discipline and autonomy which his occupation demands of him.

As for the child, we have already indicated that he is being pushed and pulled along a tension-ridden path which points toward adulthood. It is almost a foregone conclusion, then, that at any point along this socialization continuum, illness can provide him with a method of escape from progressively more exacting obligations to behave in a mature fashion. For sickness not only allows the child to be nurtured and cared for as the infant that he still yearns, in part, to be; but, in becoming the central focus of family solicitude and concern, the sick child also achieves temporary victory in the competition with his siblings for a lion's share of parental attention. Coming around full circle in the family's life span, we can easily see how illness might serve not only the child, and the young and middle-aged adult, but the elderly person as well. The aged individual, occupationless, and with no traditionally assured place in the families established by his daughters and sons, through illness may once again become an integral member of a meaningful social group, cared for either by his grown children or by a medical community of some sort.

Family Care of the Sick: A Functional Analysis of Liabilities. We turn now to consider the problem of the resources available to the family for dealing with these tendencies to make psychological use of illness. What are the probable consequences of attempting to cope with the psychological impact of serious illness within the American family—both upon the sick person himself, and upon other members of the family?

First, we note the probability that handling sickness outside the family serves to discourage falling ill in the first place. It is a method of preventing a person from "eating his cake and having it, too." Care of the sick places upon those who assume the responsibility, the obligation to accept the sick person in his state of illness. If this component of acceptance, therefore, were *combined* with the supportive features of the normal familial role, there would be a double reinforcement of the motivation to illness. The sick person could then enjoy good standing in the family—in the psychological sense, "all the comforts of home"—without paying the normal price for such familial acceptance: the fulfillment of role-obligations. In this respect, then, the family has an inherent tendency to set a "vicious circle" kind of interaction into motion: driving the sick actor deeper and deeper into his illness, rather than reducing his psychological investment in his disorder.

Next, what of the position of the members of the family who are not sick: what resources do they have to meet the impact of illness? We suggest that these resources are relatively weak; that consequently, the inherent social control patterns of our family would be seriously jeopardized by the strain of caring for illness. In the first place, the American family apparently operates at high levels of emotional intensity—with relatively little margin for "shock-absorption." In the second place, the specific direction of pressures from the demands of the sick strike it as what appears to be a vulnerable point. We wish to discuss each of these aspects of the problem in turn.

What we have called the isolation of the conjugal family, combined with the impersonal character of so many of our social relationships outside the family, means that we place a very large proportion of our emotional eggs in the one basket of the family. Each relationship within this small group, then, becomes critically important, both to the stability of the family itself and to each of the participants as a personality. The focal problems, in turn, center at two points: the marriage relationship and the parent-child relationship, particularly that of the mother to her children.

The constitution of our family means that there are ordinarily only two adults to take the roles of major responsibility. Further, there are no clear-cut stipulations as to which of the two is really "boss." Rather, the husband-wife relationship in the American family is defined to a very high degree in terms of equality and spontaneous emotional mutual attraction.

There are many indications that the load placed upon the marriage relationship in our family system comes closer to the maximum it can stand than is true for most other systems. We have long felt, for example, that the high American divorce rate is not an index of the "withering away" or disorganization of the family, as it is sometimes supposed. Quite to the contrary, it is our conviction that the oft-cited increase of divorce derives from the unique intensity and emotional import of the husband-wife relationship in our society, and from the heavy burden that such heightened affectivity imposes upon marriage. Similar things can be said about the parent-child relationship. How, then, does illness play into this precariously balanced, emotionally highly-charged system? This question can best be answered by following out the consequences of the serious illness of family members, one by one.

Take first the case of the husband-father. Although the exemption from adult, masculine responsibilities granted him by the sick role worsens the position of the family and makes its adaptive problems more difficult, it is the husband-father's claim to be taken care of which has the more immediately disruptive impact on the family's internal situation. The wife, of course, is the primary sick-room attendant. The most obvious consequences of her ministrations is the withdrawal of her full quota of attention from the children. The presence of the husband-father in the home at unaccustomed times is relevant here; but far more important are his greatly enhanced physical and emotional needs. The intricately balanced way in which the wife-mother normally distributes her attention between husband and children is upset, for the children are called upon to sacrifice part of their maternal support to the father.[6]

The illness of a child, on the other hand, tends to disturb family equilibrium by making it more difficult for the mother to meet the needs of the father. What is more, the mother also runs the risk of making sibling rivalries more acute.

Finally, illness of the mother herself is clearly the most disturbing of all—and this may well be the nub of the whole matter. For, in the normal course of events, the mother is the primary agent of supportive strength for the entire family unit. Her illness, therefore, subjects husband and children alike to a condition of under-support, at a time when they are suddenly being asked to meet unexpected demands of major proportions. In the light of this, a mother-wife who is motivationally inclined to cast herself in the sick role may very well constitute the greatest single source of danger that illness can inflict on the family.

To all these foregoing considerations, a more general point should be appended: the insidious effects the claims of the sick person are liable to have on the healthy members of his family—regardless of whether the stricken actor is mother, father, or child. For, if we are justified in our supposition that latent dependency needs are present in almost all normal people in our society, it follows that most individuals will also have a tendency to develop defense mechanisms against those needs. As a result, there is a high probability that our families will be inclined to *over*-react to the passive-dependent nature of illness, in either of two ways. On the one hand, family members may tend to be *more* sympathetic and supportive of the sick person than they ought: bolstering their own defense against a desire to be taken care of by projecting this need onto the sick person. Through their indulgent attitude toward the ill actor (over-emphasis on the positive, supportive aspect of the treatment; under-emphasis on the disciplinary aspect) the family may invite him to perpetuate his illness. On the other hand, the family may display an excessive intolerance with respect to the debilitating features of illness— regarding them as a sign of weakness—and impose overly harsh disciplinary sanctions on the sick member. Such hyperseverity, of course, is as unfavorable to full and rapid recovery as over-permissiveness.[7]

In other words, what we are suggesting here is that the optimal balance between permissive-supportive and disciplinary facets of treating illness is peculiarly difficult to maintain in the kind of situation presented by the American family. Medico-technical advances notwithstanding, therefore, therapy is more easily effected in a professional milieu, where there is not the same order of intensive emotional involvement so characteristic of family relationships.

This, of course, is a functional argument, and as such does not explain how the segregation arose in the first place. Very broadly, however, we may suggest that technological developments provided the opportunity to treat illness outside the family, while the kinds of strains we have outlined have predisposed people to take advantage of the services of medical personnel. The further we have gone in our discussion of the American family, the more apparent have become the dynamic interdependence of illness, the family, the physician; deviance, socialization, and social control.

The Doctor-Patient Relationship and the Roles of the Ill. When the sick actor and his family join forces with the doctor, a therapeutic sub-system is established which, ideally speaking, should facilitate the actor's recovery from illness. At this meeting place, where the disabled individual contracts technically competent help with whom he agrees to cooperate in a concerted effort to get well, the sick role evolves into the patient role.

In spite of the fact that illness is often highly motivated, it should not be supposed that passage from health, to sickness, to the status of patient, is easily effected. From whatever socio-psychological baseline the actor enters the sick role, adherence to the institutionalized dictates of this role is attained only by virtue of a learning process: a socialization experience not without its special problems. In the words of one patient: "It sometimes takes a long time to learn the things we have to learn. . . ."

Even for a passive-dependent personality, the so-called exemptions of sickness usually present certain real difficulties. Since the sick individual is called upon to acknowledge the authority of medical personnages over himself, the obligations of the role of the patient imply temporary relinquishment of the *rights*, as well as the duties, of normal adulthood. For *any* socialized actor, then, acceptance of this child-like status, with its attributes of inferior status and its socio-emotional skewing, entails considerable adjustment; a sort of "*de*-socialization" process is necessary. In the light of the motivational challenge which this unlearning entails, it would seem that the structuring of the doctor's role serves a cushioning and delimiting kind of function. For, were the doctor to treat his patient exactly as the mother and father are enjoined to treat their child, in most instances, he would be *over*-taxing the adult actor's capacity to tolerate dependency.[8]

It is not merely on dependency grounds alone, however, that the sick patient role involves an affect-laden learning sequence. There is also the fact that an individual in our society, when befallen with a relatively acute or severe malady, is likely to be wrenched from the reassuring familiarity of his home, his job, and his friends, and placed in a totally strange hospital bed. Illness sets him down in a new, medical-scientific world to which he must become acclimatized. And this transplantation is by no means an easy one to undergo. Though the hospital community in which he finds himself is supposedly geared to returning the patient to his full participation in life outside, it is nevertheless true that the distance between this newly-inherited sick world and the well world which he has temporarily left behind is vast indeed. As one patient phrases the dichotomy between these two universes: "when you're outside on the sidewalk there, you know there's sick people in there in the hospital. But that's breezed right through your mind. You don't know what's going on in there. Furthermore, you don't really care. Because you're out. You're walking on the street. . . ."

The sharpness of this cleavage between sickness and wellness in our society, so problematic to the new patient, is a function of the physical and psychical separation of the hospital from the sites and activities of normal adult existence. We have already discussed some of the multiple reasons for which our society has seen fit to isolate the seriously ill patient from his family and the ranks of the non-sick in general. Most obvious among these is the phenomenal growth of scientific medicine in modern Western society— rendering the traditional home-remedy type of medical care obsolete by bringing in its wake teams of white-coated specialists, manifold test-tube procedures, an elaboration of machinery, and formal professionalized psychotherapy. Less apparent than these technological determinants, but fully as significant, are the socio-psychological reasons for which we have erected brick walls between the sick and the healthy: the special appropriateness of illness as a deviant expression in our society (hence, the dangers of exposing the non-sick to bio-psychical "infection"), and the unique defenselessness of the American urban family when faced with the illness of one of its members.

The insulation of the sick, however, not only serves passively to protect our family system and our society at large from "contamination." Rather, it is one of the potent mechanisms which launches the patient on his recovery-directed efforts, by involving him in a complementary role-relationship with therapeutic agents. If the therapy to which he becomes subject is truly successful, the getting well process which the patient undergoes will entail meaningful attitudinal changes as well as biochemical ones.

The Doctor's Role in the Therapeutic Process. Sociological analysis of the therapeutic process has brought out sharply certain broad conditions of effective therapy, yielding a list of its major components and the temporal order of their utilization. Looked at from the point of view of the attitudes and manipulations of the physician,[9] therapy involves four primary aspects.

In the first place, there must be *permissiveness:* allowing, even encouraging the patient to express deviant ideas, wishes, and fantasies. The mere privilege of being treated as sick belongs in this category, but presumably is not enough. In other words, the fact of deviant motivation must be accepted by the therapist, assuring the patient thereby that he is, in this sense, taken seriously.

The second therapeutic component is what psychiatrists often call *support:* a more holistic kind of acceptance. This is not so much a matter of respecting the details of the patient's troubles. Rather, it consists in valuing the sick actor as a person in his role: accepting him as a bonafide member of the therapeutic system because he is deemed worth helping. From one point of view, this is the sick person's immediate reward for trying to be a good patient.

In the light of the above analysis, it is clear that these features of the therapeutic role help to minimize inhibitions about giving way to dependency needs. In fact, through transference, the patient develops a powerful attachment to the therapist, the ingredients of which draw heavily on residua of unresolved childhood motivational structures. Thus, it becomes doubly necessary that the permissive-supportive aspects of the therapeutic process should not stand alone, if the leverage gained over the patient's motivational system is to transform, rather than confirm, his deviant motivational orientations.

The therapist applies this leverage in two primary ways. In the first place, the permissive-supportive aspect of the situation arouses the patient's expectations of positive deviant wish-fulfillment, and emboldens him to express them. The therapist must frustrate these desires by refusing the looked-for reciprocation. That is, though the patient will treat him as a parent-figure, a close friend, a lover (or, often, as a personal enemy), the therapist *will adhere scrupulously to a professional attitude.* Stated differently, he avoids reciprocating the patient's transference with countertransference of his own. This creates a conflict between the expectations of the patient which are encouraged in the permissive-supportive phases of therapy, and the disciplining of overt wishes that the therapist later demands of him. A secondary tension is thereby set up—which is easier for the patient to analyze than primary ones.

Concomitantly or increasingly the therapist *introduces conditional rewards* (of which his approval is probably the most important) for the patient's good work in the therapeutic situation. Above all, he approves the patient for gaining insight into the character and motives of his own behavior. Thus, through the therapist's denial of reciprocity and his wielding of conditional rewards, the patient is pushed out of his pathological dependency. At the same time, his dependency is positively utilized to sensitize him to the meaning of the refusal of the therapist to reciprocate, and to heighten the significance of rewards coming from that source. We may say, then, that a situation is created where conforming with the wishes of the therapist—gaining his approval for adult behavior—comes to outbalance the secondary gain of the pathological state itself. Ideally speaking, the patient gradually gives up his deviant orientation and comes to embrace maturity in its stead.

Though the basic components we have just reviewed for the case of psychotherapy are also the focus of child socialization, the *differences* between these two processes must be underscored. First, "classical" psychotherapy occurs in a two-person system, with one patient and one therapist. Socialization, on the other hand, entails two parents and a child, at the very least. Secondly, whereas the family milieu is a deeply affective one, the therapeutic setting is more neutrally-toned. Both these distinctions point up the fact that for all their striking similarity, the doctor-patient and parent-child relationships are not identical. Whereas the patient is a partially socialized adult who must be taught to *re-assume* his role-obligations, the child is learning his obligations for the first time. Because child socialization has much farther to go than the therapeutic process, rearing the child has been delegated to *two* adults: the primarily supportive mother, and the more disciplinary father. This division of labor lightens the parental load, and assures that both aspects of socialization will have balanced attention given them. The general protectiveness of the family, on the other hand, serves a bolstering function: endowing the child with the psychical fortitude he needs to cope autonomously with the outside world.

Family Care vs. Professional Care. These facts give us a baseline from which to point out some of the main reasons why too great a predominance of family-managed treatment might not only threaten the ongoing of the family itself but also impede the recovery of the sick person as well. First, in some cases, the power of a familial therapist (e.g. the wife-mother, when either the husband-father or the child falls ill) could easily overactivate the sick person's dependency, bringing about a regression to childhood level. Extra-familial therapeutic agents have better-developed safeguards against such an eventuality. For example, contact with the therapist is restricted to stated appointments under carefully regulated conditions; and the impersonal professional character of the hospital seems to have a similar function. Even so, evidence shows that particularly in cases of severe illness, it is relatively easy for the patient to acquire a very deep-seated investment in his sick role, either in the form of dependency on an individual therapist or in that of attachment to a hospital situation.[10] Though the process of desocialization in learning to become a good patient is an essential prerequisite of successful recovery in most cases, it is therefore equally important that it should not go too far;[11] and the condition under which it takes place should be carefully controlled. The American urban family, we suggest, has a strong tendency to permit desocialization excesses.[12]

Secondly, since our family is essentially non-authoritarian in nature, and the motivation to illness is so deep-rooted in our society, the American family is a relatively weak counteractant of sickness. The professional therapist, in contrast, derives his potency from two sources. For one thing, his role is integrated with the adult world in a way that the family member in his kin-ship status is not.[13]

If the sick person is to be healed, then, and the well-being of our kinship system is to be assured, the modern American family cannot undertake major responsibility for care of the sick. That the doctor may easily err in the direc-tion of *under*-support, however, if he too drastically extrudes the family from his sphere of operation, is cogently suggested by certain recent developments in the modern hospital. Of late, hospitals throughout the country have been experimenting with such plans as allowing the mother and her newborn infant to room together, permitting the mother to stay overnight with her hospitalized child, and extending visiting hours for all categories of patients. Since all these trial developments invite the more full-blown participation of family members in the hospital community, it appears to us that they may express a felt need for the greater inclusion of the family's permissive-sup-portive concern in current medical therapy.[14]

Our analysis of these particular empirical occurrences may be speculative. But the larger theoretical point it is intended to illustrate is much less challangeable: Making the sick individual better calls for the well-timed, well-chosen, well-balanced exercise of the supportive *and* the disciplinary com-ponents of the therapeutic process; and the ministrations of *both* the doctor and the family.

Illness and Recovery as a Learning Process. Our sick actor now stands poised on the threshold of recovery; and there is a deep motivational sense in which he may not be the "same" person who originally fell ill. Evidence for this hypo-thesis is the sizeable body of literature penned by former patients: subjective assertions of the fact that the sick role and successful emergence from it may effect a far-reaching socialization process in the recovering actor. For all the sociopsychological reasons we have been attempting to outline in this paper, it is highly probable that illness might bring an intensive learning experience in its wake. Incapacitated and emotionally disturbed; relieved of weighty responsibilities of the well world; removed in large part from the custodian-ship of his family and other significant actors who would be likely to reinforce or exacerbate his psychosomatic withdrawal—the ill individual comes to live for a while in a medical-dominated sphere. Here, he is granted nurture and sustenance; but never so much as to balance out the heavy impress of de-privation, subordination and loneliness to which he is also subject. These are the penalties which give impetus to the patient's desire to re-achieve wellness: the challenges to which he responds (ideally-speaking) by re-embracing the world of health.[15]

Conclusion. We have given evidence which, we feel, indicates that the devel-opment of specialized professional health-care agencies, and the consequent removal of much of the treatment of illness from the family, is attributable to something more than the technological developments of modern medicine. We have tried to show that it is highly probable that certain features of the American urban family, in their impact on the personalities of its members, have tended to push the sick person out of the home. And we have argued that, on the whole, extra-familial care of the sick is positively functional for American society in at least three respects. The first is protection of the family against the disruptive effects of the illness of its members. The second is the preservation of some of the positive functions of the sick role as a mechanism of social control—primarily, by directing the passive deviance of illness into closely supervised medical channels where it finds expression, but cannot easily spread. The third is facilitation of the therapeutic process—not only technologically, but in a *motivational* sense as well.

We wish to point out that such new insights as we have been able to gain into these matters are only possible because of certain rather recent developments in the sciences of human action: above all, the possibility of bringing sociological and psychological analysis to bear upon the same set of problems in a complementary way. A simple sociological analysis of family structure and of the therapeutic system would not have helped us very much; nor, we feel, would a purist personality theory approach have proven especially enlightening. And yet when the two are put together quite a new order of understanding emerges.

We have deliberately kept our discussion on a theoretical level, without attempting to work out its possible practical import; for, within the scope of a single article, it would not have been possible to do justice to both. In conclusion, however, we would like to suggest that the potential implications of our analysis for practice ramify in several directions. For example, we think that perhaps we can aid physicians and hospital administrators in their search for effective ways of dealing with the family members of their patients. Further, our material also seems relevant to the question of how visiting privileges and other forms of association with hospital patients accorded to families could be more optimally managed. It is our belief, however, that most important and far-reaching of all is the fact that both theoretically and empirically, the social and psychological sciences are now highly enough evolved to make "illness, therapy, and the family" a fruitful field of action research.

IV

The Patient:
A Person with an Illness

THE INDIVIDUAL who becomes sick is confronted with an entirely new set of expectations and assumes entirely different patterns of behavior in carrying out the role of the patient. His illness, his reactions to the experience of pain, to the physician and his ministrations, and to the others comprising the patient's milieu are included in this section. These studies restore the often forgotten fact that the patient is not only a sick biological organism but also a member of society with many duties, responsibilities, expectations, attitudes, and values of a social and personal nature. These latter components of the individual become especially significant in the management of the patient before, during and after the treatment-process.

Henry Lederer, M.D., analyzes the orientation of the sick person as he views his surroundings in the hospital during the process of medical treatment.

Some intriguing differences in response to the pain-experience by several sub-cultural groups are presented in a trail-blazing article by Mark Zborowski.

An analysis of some deep-seated problems of adjustment confronting persons treated for facial deformities is presented by Frances Cooke Macgregor.

The religious faith of the individual can quite feasibly influence his attitude toward medical treatment and his behavior as a patient. The Christian Scientist patient is analyzed by Lois Hoffman in focusing her study from the perspective of the practicing physician.

Beatrix Cobb offers some interesting case material in an effort to understand the conditions under which patients seek the help of quacks and other unauthorized practitioners.

26   HOW THE SICK VIEW THEIR WORLD

By Henry D. Lederer

The experience of illness is a complex psychological situation. To clarify the responses of the sick to this experience it is necessary to consider three main time periods, each of which has a characteristic orientation.[1] These stages of the experience of illness are: (1) the transition period from health to illness, (2) the period of "accepted" illness and, (3) convalescence.

The Orientations of the Sick in the Transition Period from Health to Illness. Upon falling ill most persons become aware of undesirable, unpleasant, and painful sensations; of a disturbing reduction in strength and stamina; of a diminution in ability to perform habitual acts. For example, at the onset of virus pneumonia, the patient experiences headaches, vague chest pains, tightness of the skin. He fatigues easily, desires more than usual rest, and "plays out" quickly on prolonged tasks. In addition, he finds the performance of his daily routine of work and play tiring and aggravating to his discomforts.

One finds certain definite patterns of response to these initial events. Some degree of apprehension or anxiety is felt as in any situation in which a painful, unpleasant, and threatening circumstance is encountered.[2] Consequently the pattern of response to the initial symptoms is often the characteristic mode of reaction to anxiety whenever it arises. Many persons attempt to ignore this threat and through such a denial of the frightening experience to allay their anxieties. This denial may be reinforced by a "plunge into health" through engaging in more than routine activity. In this manner the patient seems to be reassuring himself by saying, "If I can manage to be so very active there is nothing to fear—the whole affair is an illusion." Another form of denial is to minimize the importance of the symptoms by identifying them with symptoms of benign or trivial indispositions. Thus the "coronary vascular accident" symptoms are identified with "an upset stomach" and the chest pains of lobar pneumonia with a "touch of pleurisy."

Still further, one observes other patients who meet anxiety aggressively and such persons in the initial stages of illness are irascible, querulous, and ill-humored. Conversely, others allay anxiety by passivity and behave in a compliant, obsequious, and pitiable manner.

The ordinary day-to-day life routines of most persons constitute a source of satisfaction of various needs and defenses against anxiety. Since illness renders painful and tiring participation in such gratifying and reassuring activities, anxiety is compounded and frustration of many needs is felt.[3] Thomas Mann has written humorously and understandingly of this experience in "*The Magic Mountain.*" His hero, Hans Castorp, in the early febrile stage of an activated tuberculosis tries to preserve his daily rituals which have formerly proven gratifying and soothing. One of these practices is the smoking of the after dinner cigar, a luxury of great importance to Castorp; but now he finds an evil taste and light-headedness in the place of a delightful aroma and general feeling of well-being.[4]

From *The Journal of Social Issues*, 8, (1952), 4–15.

Certain men become especially anxious when they find themselves having to restrict their activities and to admit the existence of their discomforts.[5] To these persons, manliness depends on being active and never yielding to a physical discomfort; to them, passivity and any intolerance of pain are equated with femininity. Consequently, becoming ill is viewed as an emasculating process and, thereby, highly provocative of anxiety. There may be a dangerous denial of symptoms in such a person through his abortive attempts to reassert his masculinity in sports, late hours, heavy work, etc.

For many persons, parts of their bodies or certain bodily functions have been invested with intense emotion. The skin, the facial structures, the head, the genitals, the breasts are examples of bodily parts often intensely loved by the patient. Obviously great apprehension is experienced when symptoms seem to indicate dysfunction of these treasured parts.

There is a continuing folk tradition in some areas that suggests that illness is the just desert of the sinner. Persons holding to this misconception feel guilty when developing an illness and may even be impelled to malinger health rather than appear with the stigma of immorality.

Specific illnesses exhibiting a familial occurrence are particularly alarming since most persons do not want to discredit the purity of their families. This attitude has been one of the impedances to early diagnosis of such illnesses as carcinomata and tuberculosis. Often the afflicted person has great anxiety because of the unconscious fantasy of rejection and wrath by other members of the family. Most physicians have had contact with patients who are deeply shamed by symptoms which they interpret as a possible disgrace to their family lines.

Many persons, who, because of emotional immaturity and stressful living have been reduced to a psychoneurotic level of functioning, may react paradoxically to the advent of physical illness. Often there is an amelioration of the neurotic symptoms and the patient seems to welcome the concrete threat of physical illness which can divert his attention from his neurosis. With some neurotic persons, physical illness may actually bring emotional relief through its symbolic meaning as a penalty for unconscious guilt feelings. Moreover, the anticipated care and consideration as well as release from social responsibilities can be highly appealing to a neurotic patient. His feelings of guilt and shame for his withdrawing, dependent, and infantile wishes are relieved by the occurrence of physical sickness which "legitimizes" these claims. "The individual with a relatively weak ego may find an escape from his (neurotic) anxieties in the less demanding situation that illness provides."[6]

An example of this type of response to physical illness was observed in a young, single woman who was undergoing psychotherapy for severe phobias. Her neurosis developed in reaction to the stress of her approaching marriage for which her previous psychosocial growth had not prepared her. In the midst of this emotional distress, she developed visual and gait disturbances which were definitely diagnosed as symptoms of multiple sclerosis. At the onset of these grave symptoms and her entrance into the hospital, she announced with elation that her phobic obsessions had departed and that she was entirely rid of anxiety.

To recapitulate, in the initial symptom phase of many illnesses, one may encounter evidence of anxiety, guilt, and shame as well as the many personality defenses against these disagreeable affects. Moreover, in certain neurotic patients there may be a paradoxically positive acceptance of illness.

The continuing pressure, and often the increase, of symptoms forces the patient into another psychologically difficult set of experiences—those of diagnosis and the beginning of therapy. At this time the former habitual patterns of health still exert a powerful attraction on the patient whereas his submission to diagnostic and therapeutic procedures involves entering an unknown area. But in order to be rid of his discomforts and dysfunctions he must face this unknown situation.

(It is important to note that at this point another crucial factor is met which influences the orientation of the patient—this factor is the behavior of the medical personnel who are responsible for his diagnosis and therapy.)

Whenever one enters an unknown or partially understood situation, he exhibits fairly typical responses. Once again anxiety is aroused because of fantasied dangers and because of unfamiliarity with what one may expect. Under these circumstances there is much indecision reflected in vacillating behavior. For example, urgent requests for diagnostic examinations are rapidly alternated with failure to appear for examination. Physicians must learn to expect such vacillating and indecisive behavior and not to be angered or disgusted by it. The firm, patient, and understanding attitude of the physician will help in allaying the patient's anxiety.

The highly scientific nature of medical diagnosis places these affairs beyond the full understanding of the average layman. The physical paraphernalia of many diagnostic processes are awesome to many persons. In addition, the technical language of medicine is an unknown tongue to the layman who can only hope that what he overhears is an optimistic statement rather than a pronouncement of doom or further pain for him. When these mystifying matters are coupled to the impersonality of diagnostic activity in many modern hospitals and clinics, it is easy to empathize with the mounting anxiety of the patient and his problem of cooperating in diagnosis.

Much attention in recent years has been centered upon ways of cushioning the effects of these experiences by the attitude of the physician. The awe and fear of the cold, aseptic, impersonal atmosphere of the clinic can be considerably diminished by attitudes of personal interest in, and exhibitions of respect for, the patient in his contacts with medical personnel.[7] A concise but specific and clear-cut explanation of diagnostic procedures can undercut most of the mystery of diagnosis. Excluding all but the necessary equipment from the examination room is still another aid in this direction. Many clinics are now furnishing waiting rooms in styles which lessen their resemblance to operating rooms or laboratories and consequently are reassuring.

Unnecessary repetitions of diagnostic examinations and tests should be avoided because any signs of indecision or insecurity shown by the physician augment the patient's apprehension. When the doctor demonstrates his skill by his determination and decisiveness, the patient is usually grateful for such real reassurance; then he is sure he is in capable, trustworthy hands. There is much wisdom in the old medical dictum that "in any contact between doctor and patient there is room only for one anxious person—the patient."

The future course of the patient's behavior often depends upon the manner in which his diagnosis is presented to him. If the doctor speaks simply and forthrightly, in most instances anxiety is relieved. Clouding the issue in technical jargon or discussing equivocal findings usually increase the patient's emotionality. For example, nothing is gained and much may be lost by announcing "borderline" findings to a patient. It is easy to imagine the confusion aroused by informing a person: "I don't think you have much to worry about. Your heart seems O.K. but we want to watch your electrocardiogram because it was a little abnormal." After this report the patient is in a dilemma about understanding himself, his physical limits, and what, if any, dangers confront him.

Experienced physicians expect a possible distortion of facts when interviewing patients about their symptoms and the histories of their illnesses. These distortions stem from the patient's anxiety and his defenses and should be taken with a benevolent skepticism. Some of the art of interviewing rests on the doctor's recognition of these unconscious distortions. If the doctor behaves like a detective in pursuing facts, the patient is made even more tense [8]

Most persons view with conflicting, mixed feelings the start of therapy. Actually, some therapeutic maneuvers do cause discomfort and pain so that the patient has to accept a paradox—that is, to be relieved of discomfort, he must at times submit to a transitory increase in it. Usually a sick person anticipates far more discomfort than is involved in most treatments. This gloomy expectation is a reflection of his apprehensive state and calls for an unequivocal frankness from the doctor for correction. Again, a concise, unambiguous description of the therapy and the rationale for it alleviates anxiety and goes far toward gaining the patient's cooperation.[9] Vagueness about details of therapy must be avoided in order to reduce the opportunities for the patient to imagine the worst. Whenever possible, impersonal contact between the patient and his therapist should be reduced. For example, a visit by the anesthetist before an operation neutralizes some of the fear that most patients entertain about general anesthesia.

When treatment requires a hospital setting, the doctor and his aides have the responsibility for explaining hospital procedures to the patient. The patient is able to cooperate more easily when he knows about such routine matters as the duty hours of the floor nurses, when meals are served, visiting rules, the names of his internes, etc. Often antagonistic, belligerent behavior can be charged to negligence in clarifying the hospital situation when the patient was admitted—it is his way of aggressively resolving his anxiety. The rate of "sign-out against medical advice" is inversely related to the success of the medical personnel in their handling of these problems.

The Stage of "Accepted" Illness. When the patient has accepted diagnostic and initial therapeutic procedures, he enters another distinct time period in his experience of illness. Now, he views himself as ill and abandons pretenses of health. In our society, accepting illness includes accepting help from physicians and their aides. He temporarily withdraws from his adult responsible activities and, cooperating with his doctor, dedicates himself to the problem of getting well; he substitutes preoccupation with his symptoms and illness for the many concerns of mature life. Whereas in health he has made his own decisions, he now transfers this right to his physician, nurse and other attendants. These changes in orientation are reinforced by the doctor's prescription that he not pursue his work, his usual recreations, nor his responsibilities. Society as a whole also frees him for the duration of his illness from the discharge of ordinary duties and obligations.

All of these changes determine the structure of the patient's world which can be described as a simpler, more childish, constricted life. His illness has led him into a social setting which is similar to his childhood.[10] Therefore, one can refer to this arrangement as being very regressed and infantile.

To such a regressed social situation the patient now reacts with behavior used earlier during his childhood. His actions, thoughts, and feelings are regressive in response to the child-like world of illness. The main features of this behavior are: (1) egocentricity, (2) constriction of interests, (3) emotional dependency, (4) hypochondriasis.[11]

Charles Lamb, in his essay, "The Convalescent," accurately described the egocentricity of the sick when he wrote, "How sickness enlarges the dimensions of a man's self to himself! he is his own exclusive object. Supreme selfishness is inculcated upon him as his only duty."[12] Like a child the patient is concerned with the selfish matters of satisfying simple needs for rest, food, absence of pain, physical comfort, and relief of bodily tensions such as the urge to urinate, defecate, pass flatus, or to belch. Satisfaction of these needs assumes precedence over more social ones. The patient presumes that his attendants share in these preoccupations and he feels resentful or hurt if the doctor or nurse is distracted by other concerns.

His egocentricity renders him provincial and highly subjective, like a child, in his judging the events occurring around him. If the nurse frowns for a moment, he is worried that she has taken a dislike to him; if she does not respond to his ring, she is damned as lazy and uninterested in his welfare.

Often the patient becomes a sick-room tyrant, dominating others and intolerant or often unaware of their rights and needs. "If there be a regal solitude, it is a sick bed. How the patient lords it there"—"He keeps his sympathy, like some curious vintage, under trusty lock and key, for his own use only." This egocentric despotism frequently disturbs the friends and relatives of the patient who are accustomed to his former consideration and objectivity.

Dynamically related to his egocentricity is the constriction of interests of the sick person. The narrowing follows partially from the reduced scope of the patient's world and partly from his regressed narcissism. The ill person shows an often amazing disinterest or even apathy toward the impersonal events of the day. He has abandoned his concern for politics, business, social events and will not persist in discussion of these matters.

Lamb outlines this constriction of interest as follows: "A little while ago he was greatly concerned in the event of a lawsuit, which was to be the making or the marring of his dearest friend. He was to be seen trudging about upon this man's errand to fifty quarters of the town at once. The cause was to come on yesterday. He is absolutely as indifferent to the decision as if it were a question to be tried at Pekin . . . he picks up enough to make him understand that things went cross-grained in the court yesterday, and his friend is ruined. But the word 'friend' and the word 'ruin' disturb him no more than so much jargon. He is not to think of anything but how to get better."

The protection and devotion accorded the patient by his medical attendants relieve him of adapting himself to interests other than his own and thereby increase his provincialism. There is often little or no check to his regressive, constricted, and narcissistic behavior so that apathy appears.

Dependence on others is imposed by the physical helplessness stemming from illness and by the psychological inadequacy secondary to egocentricity and constricted interests. The patient's physical weakness, like that of the child, requires the strength of other persons to meet his needs. His regression into a self-centered, subjective world demands that healthier persons apply their more mature and objective judgment to his affairs—again paralleling the experience of the child whose parents assume responsibility for most important matters. With this dependency, one observes much ambivalence toward the benefactors. Like a child the patient often exhibits an uncritical "love" and admiration for his benefactors, but at the same time resentment toward them because of his weak and inferior relation to them. All persons working with the sick should anticipate and learn to recognize this ambivalent dependency and neither be flattered, nor offended, by it.

The unpleasant sensations of illness, in combination with the reduced regressive world and perceptions of the patient, lead to a great concern with the functioning of the body. There is usually much hypochondriacal worry over medical matters such as pulse rate, temperature, bowel movements, weight changes, etc., all of which may dominate the patient's thoughts and conversations. This hypochondriasis resembles in some ways the curiosity and exploration of the body and its functions undertaken normally by all children.

The attitudes and behavior of the medical personnel can limit or extend the emotional regression of the patient. The appearance of apathy as a response to over-protection has already been cited.[13] In recent years, many warnings have been sounded against unnecessary restriction of patient's activities.

The indiscriminate prescription of prolonged bed-rest has been demonstrated as a cause of invalidism out of proportion to actual physical incapacity. The current practice of encouraging patients to get on their feet as early as possible following operations has proven both physically and emotionally beneficial; it has prevented lengthy convalescence. It seems that the best course for the physician is to encourage the minimum amount of regression necessitated by the physical limitations of the patient and to avoid any unnecessary infantilizing.

This regression, during illness, is adaptive and often significant for survival. It is conceivable that through social and emotional regression the sick person re-distributes his energies to facilitate the healing process or possibly that the regressive integration is in itself an essential factor in the healing process. The biological task of the sick is to get well and this work is furthered by the focussing of personality energies on the self and withdrawing them from other uses and purposes.[14] Recognition of this utility in the regression of the sick should make medical attendants welcome it rather than deplore it.

In persons, whose general character development has led to elaborate behavior defenses against regression and the expression of dependency, there is little or no phase of "accepted illness." Denial of physical limits and symptoms continues to some extent; the advice and ministrations of medical personnel are challenged and not followed; hospital care may be refused. All in all the neurotic defenses of such a patient militate against the healing benefits of regression and the course of his illness may be worsened or fatal. His behavioral adjustment to his neurosis takes precedence over adaptive regression during physical illness.

To illustrate: A physician, in middle age, sustained an acute coronary heart attack. His professional colleagues, who diagnosed his illness, advised immediate and absolute bed rest, quiet, and heavy sedation, all of which the patient stoutly refused on the grounds of his heavy schedule of work with his own patients. He persisted in his medical work and died suddenly in his office twenty hours later. This patient's personality was structured largely to deny any dependent emotional trends. He was a "self-made" man who had labored hard to graduate from medical school. He steadfastly pursued his career, never permitting himself a vacation. In his personal life he lavished gifts on his family, but was Spartan in any self-indulgence. It can be conjectured that his neurotic character was a considerable factor in his early death.

Under those conditions, the total medical management must include measures to aid the patient in accepting regression and dependency. At times a psychiatrist or psychiatric social worker must be included in the therapeutic team to contribute their skills in meeting this neurotic complication of a physical illness.

The period of "accepted illness" gradually ends after optimal regression and medical therapy have reversed or arrested the pathogenic process. The patient then enters the convalescent period of his experience of illness.

The Stage of Convalescence. Convalescence is the time period of transition from illness back into a state of health. This recovery of health involves a return of physical strength and a re-integration of the personality of the patient who has been living, feeling, and thinking in a regressed, more or less infantile way.

The return of physical strength and health is usually an automatic process but it is not necessarily paralleled by a restoration of "healthy," adult behavior; getting well physically must be associated with the patient's relinquishing his dependent, egocentric and provincial reactions.[15]

Many students of convalescence have recognized its structural and dynamic similarities to adolescence. This analogy is instructive in understanding the problems of the convalescent and suggests many techniques for helping the convalescent "grow up" again into adult health.[16]

The convalescent, like the adolescent, has to leave a protected world in which responsibilities were minimal and the satisfaction of his self-centered needs the major concern of himself and those attending him. These pleasant aspects of illness attract the convalescent so that he wants to remain in his "regal home" of regression. It is hard for one to give up the attentions, protection, and kindnesses of doctors and nurses and to fend once more for oneself. "Farewell with him all that made sickness pompous—the spell that hushed the household—the mute attendance—the inquiry by looks—the still softer delicacies of self-attention—what a speck is he dwindled into (by his physical recuperation)."[17]

If the patient has suppressed his resentful hostility toward his medical attendants during the preceding phase, he frequently remains regressed because of a guilty over-dependence upon them. Recent studies on poliomyelitis patients who require respirators have shown that the patients who are slowly weaned from the "artificial lung" are those who have been unable to express openly any negative feelings toward their doctors and nurses.[18]

Convalescence is often prolonged in persons whose previous state of health did not provide them with sufficient gratifications and relief from anxiety. Examples of this situation are seen in military service where full recovery from illness means re-entering a hazardous and depriving existence.

Fortunately, for most convalescents, the broader scope of their "healthy" worlds is more attractive then the regressive pleasures of illness. In such persons the stronger motive is toward health but may be impeded by continuing feelings of inadequacy. Like adolescents who yearn for adult life but feel unsure of themselves, these convalescents wistfully long for health but are afraid to try it. These fears may be related to neurotic self-depreciation which was part of the original behavior pattern in childhood, reactivated during the period of regression.

Certain convalescents repeat their adolescent method of "growing up" by rebelliously wrenching themselves loose from dependency. These persons are in a tremendous hurry to get well, often prematurely dismiss their physicians, and over-step their physical strengths.

Again one realizes that the participation of the physician and his aides can profoundly affect the course of convalescence. Under these conditions the medical personnel occupy roles similar to those of the parents and counselors of adolescents; the successful medical management of convalescence is the analogue of proper parenthood during adolescence.

To illustrate: The parent who gradually and progressively relaxes his protection and instead offers guidance and advice is encouraging the adolescent toward adulthood. He quietly retires to the side-lines ready to reassure but willing to let his child experiment with new strengths, only stepping in when gross errors of judgment may arise. The adolescent senses the confidence of the parent and is reassured by it, especially when immediately perfect or ideal results are not demanded. Moreover, the helpful parent is not threatened by his child's interest in other persons or new activities.

Convalescence can be promoted and enhanced by similar attitudes on the part of the doctor. Physicians must have the courage to recommend more activity and to lift the restrictions on the patient's behavior. Some physicians, like parents, are unconsciously gratified by the dependency of others upon them; this narcissistic pleasure must be abandoned by no longer encouraging regressive dependency through protection. The physician sometimes is loath to risk his reputation through the possibility of a relapse and thereby continues to treat the convalescent with great caution; this is frequently the event when the patient is a person of some prominence in the community so that his illness has been under a public scrutiny which makes the physician uneasy.

The rehabilitation of the convalescent has become a matter of growing medical concern, research, and progress. During the war the military medical services were alert to these problems and contributed many important findings to this aspect of medical management.[19] Since the war some of the medical colleges have established departments of rehabilitation as integral basic training units.

Offering the convalescent stimulation for re-integration is stressed. Increasing visiting privileges, permitting the wearing of ordinary rather than hospital clothes, providing radio and television, permitting trial leaves overnight from the hospital are examples of opportunities which may stimulate the patient toward a state of health. Transfering the convalescent to a special rehabilitation center or ward has been recommended as an aid in helping him relinquish the regressive patterns of life followed on ordinary hospital wards.

The modern physician is urged to lead a team of therapists in the guidance and support of the convalescent just as the wise parent welcomes the contributions of the teacher, youth leader, student counselor, etc. who promote the growth of the adolescent. Social workers, occupational therapists, vocational counselors, recreational therapists, etc. can broaden the scope of the convalescent's world, encourage him and help reestablish his self-confidence and self-sufficiency.

While the patient is still in the state of "accepted illness," the caseworker may have discovered sources of tension and dissatisfaction in his family, home, work situations and can initiate changes which will make the return to health more attractive. In addition the cooperation of the family in the management of convalescence is often won by a skillful caseworker.

Much attention has been given to occupational therapy through which the patient is gently led into a more self-assertive, creative life. Moreover, he is given the opportunity to re-exercise rusty talents and techniques in an experimental setting. Here he can regain self-confidence through a series of progressive "successes."

Well-planned recreational therapies provide practice in socializing and in engaging in gradual competition. Here again the success in group living encourages the patient to re-enter the large arena of adult "healthy" society.

The expanding use of vocational counseling is an indication of its value to the convalescent. Many patients cling to regressed behavior because they cannot engage further in past occupations. For example, convalescent tuberculous patients frequently must find less strenuous jobs to protect them from relapses. In such a situation, hopeful and realistic planning can be constructed through consultations with a competent vocational counselor. The convalescent, like the adolescent, is less afraid of his future when his voca-tional potentialities are clear to him.

In addition to the special services each member of the therapeutic team has to offer, there is the over-all benefit of providing the patient contact with many mature, healthy persons with whom he can emotionally identify. This process is similar to the identification of the adolescent with key adult persons in his environment. Both the convalescent and adolescent find such identification a most positive aid in accepting an adult status. Conversely, emotionally immature persons serving on therapeutic teams can seriously retard the convalescent's recovery by not providing the bridge of a healthy identification.

All of these various services and stimuli can be offered to a patient but it is necessary to realize, no one can force him to use them constructively. For the majority of persons "health" is preferred to regression. With the few patients who cannot respond positively to planned convalescence, one usually finds that an earlier neurosis has been revived by the trauma of illness; these persons should be offered psychotherapy to resolve the neurotic difficulties prolonging their full recovery.

To summarize: the state of convalescence is structurally and dynamically similar to adolescence. The behavior of the convalescent is analogous to that of the adolescent. The success of helping the patient is dependent on the recognition of his "adolescent" emotional status which then should call forth from his medical attendants attitudes similar to those of the parent who encourages and aids the growth of his adolescent child. Opportunities must be provided for re-establishing self-confidence through graded "successes" in groups and in the exercise of one's returning physical strengths. The convalescent phase of illness terminates with the parallel recovery from physical limitations and psychological regression.

27   CULTURAL COMPONENTS IN RESPONSES TO PAIN

By Mark Zborowski

This paper reports on one aspect of a larger study: that concerned with discovering the role of cultural patterns in attitudes toward, and reactions to, pain which is caused by disease and injury—in other words, responses to spontaneous pain.

Some Basic Distinctions. In human societies biological processes vital for man's survival acquire social and cultural significance. Intake of food, sexual intercourse or elimination—physiological phenomena which are universal for the entire living world—become institutions regulated by cultural and social norms, thus fulfilling not only biological functions but social and cultural ones as well. Metabolic and endocrinal changes in the human organism may provoke hunger and sexual desire, but culture and society dictate to man the

Reprinted from Journal of Social Issues, 8, (1952), 16–30.

kind of food he may eat, the social setting for eating or the adequate partner for mating.

Moreover, the role of cultural and social patterns in human physiological activities is so great that they may in specific situations act against the direct biological needs of the individual, even to the point of endangering his survival. Only a human being may prefer starvation to the breaking of a religious dietary law or may abstain from sexual intercourse because of specific incest regulations. Voluntary fasting and celibacy exist only where food and sex fulfill more than strictly physiological functions.

Thus, the understanding of the significance and role of social and cultural patterns in human physiology is necessary to clarify those aspects of human experience which remain puzzling if studied only within the physiological frame of reference.

Pain is basically a physiological phenomenon and as such has been studied by physiologists and neurologists such as Harold Wolff, James Hardy, Helen Goodell, C. S. Lewis, W. K. Livingston and others. By using the most ingenious methods of investigation they have succeeded in clarifying complex problems of the physiology of pain. Many aspects of perception and reaction to pain were studied in experimental situations involving most careful preparation and complicated equipment. These investigators have come to the conclusion that "from the physiological point of view pain qualifies as a sensation of importance to the self-preservation of the individual."[2] The biological function of pain is to provoke special reactive patterns directed toward avoidance of the noxious stimulus which presents a threat to the individual. In this respect the function of pain is basically the same for man as for the rest of the animal world.

However, the physiology of pain and the understanding of the biological function of pain do not explain other aspects of what Wolff, Hardy and Goodell call the *pain experience*, which includes not only the pain sensation and certain automatic reactive responses but also certain "associated feeling states."[3] It would not explain, for example, the acceptance of intense pain in torture which is part of the initiation rites of many primitive societies, nor will it explain the strong emotional reactions of certain individuals to the slight sting of the hypodermic needle.

In human society pain, like so many other physiological phenomena, acquires specific social and cultural significance, and, accordingly, certain reactions to pain can be understood in the light of this significance. "A society in which a man finds himself becomes the conditioning influence in the formation of the individual reaction patterns to pain . . . A knowledge of group attitudes toward pain is extremely important to an understanding of the individual reaction."[4]

In analyzing pain it is useful to distinguish between self-inflicted, other-inflicted and spontaneous pain. Self-inflicted pain is defined as deliberately self-inflicted. It is experienced as a result of injuries performed voluntarily upon oneself, e.g., self-mutilation. Usually these injuries have a culturally defined purpose, such as achieving a special status in the society. It can be observed not only in primitive cultures but also in contemporary societies on a higher level of civilization. In Germany, for instance, members of certain student or military organizations would cut their faces with a razor in order to acquire scars which would identify them as members of a distinctive social group. By other-inflicted pain is meant pain inflicted upon the individual in the process of culturally accepted and expected activities (regardless of whether approved or disapproved), such as sports, fights, war, etc. To this category belongs also pain inflicted by the physician in the process of medical treatment. Spontaneous pain usually denotes the pain sensation which results from disease or injury. This term also covers pains of psychogenic nature.

Members of different cultures may assume differing attitudes towards these various types of pain. Two of these attitudes may be described as pain expectancy and pain acceptance. Pain expectancy is anticipation of pain as being unavoidable in a given situation, for instance, in childbirth, in sports activities or in battle. Pain acceptance is characterized by a willingness to experience pain. This attitude is manifested mostly as an inevitable component of culturally accepted experiences, for instance, as part of initiation rites or part of medical treatment. The following example will help to clarify the differences between pain expectancy and pain acceptance: Labor pain is expected as part of childbirth, but while in one culture, such as in the United States, it is not accepted and therefore various means are used to alleviate it; in some other cultures, for instance in Poland, it is not only expected but also accepted, and consequently nothing or little is done to relieve it. Similarly, cultures which emphasize military achievements expect and accept battle wounds, while cultures which emphasize pacificistic values may expect them but will not accept them.

In the process of investigating cultural attitudes toward pain it is also important to distinguish between pain apprehension and pain anxiety. Pain apprehension reflects the tendency to avoid the pain sensation as such, regardless of whether the pain is spontaneous or inflicted, whether it is accepted or not. Pain anxiety, on the other hand, is a state of anxiety provoked by the pain experience, focused upon various aspects of the causes of pain, the meaning of pain or its significance for the welfare of the individual.

Moreover, members of various cultures may react differently in terms of their manifest behavior toward various pain experiences, and this behavior is often dictated by the culture which provides specific norms according to the age, sex and social position of the individual.

The fact that other elements as well as cultural factors are involved in the response to a spontaneous pain should be taken into consideration. These other factors are the pathological aspect of pain, the specific physiological characteristics of the pain experience, such as the intensity, the duration and the quality of the pain sensation, and, finally, the personality of the individual. Nevertheless, it was felt that in the process of a careful investigation it would be possible to detect the role of the cultural components in the pain experience.

The Research Setting. In setting up the research we were interested not only in the purely theoretical aspects of the findings in terms of possible contribution to the understanding of the pain experience in general; we also had in mind the practical goal of a contribution to the field of medicine. In the relationship between the doctor and his patient the respective attitudes toward pain may play a crucial role, especially when the doctor feels that the patient exaggerates his pain while the patient feels that the doctor minimizes his suffering. The same may be true, for instance, in a hospital where the members of the medical and nursing staff may have attitudes toward pain different from those held by the patient, or when they expect a certain pattern of behavior according to their cultural background while the patient may manifest a behavior pattern which is acceptable in his culture. These differences may play an important part in the evaluation of the individual pain experience, in dealing with pain at home and in the hospital, in administration of analgesics, etc. Moreover, we expected that this study of pain would offer opportunities to gain insight into related attitudes toward health, disease, medication, hospitalization, medicine in general, etc.

With these aims in mind the project was set up at the Kingsbridge Veterans Hospital, Bronx, New York,[5] where four ethno-cultural groups were selected for an intensive study. These groups included patients of Jewish, Italian, Irish and "Old American" stock. Three groups—Jews, Italians and Irish—were selected because they were described by medical people as manifesting striking differences in their reaction to pain. Italians and Jews were described as tending to "exaggerate" their pain, while the Irish were often depicted as stoical individuals who are able to take a great deal of pain. The fourth group, the "Old Americans," were chosen because the values and attitudes of this group dominate in the country and are held by many members of the medical profession and by many descendants of the immigrants who, in the process of Americanization, tend to adopt American patterns of behavior. The members of this group can be defined as white, native-born individuals, usually Protestant, whose grandparents, at least, were born in the United States and who do not identify themselves with any foreign group, either nationally, socially or culturally.

The Kingsbridge Veterans Hospital was chosen because its population represents roughly the ethnic composition of New York City, thus offering access to a fair sample of the four selected groups, and also because various age groups were represented among the hospitalized veterans of World War I, World War II and the Korean War. In one major respect this hospital was not adequate, namely, in not offering the opportunity to investigate sex differences in attitude toward pain. This aspect of research will be carried out in a hospital with a large female population.

In setting up this project we were mainly interested in discovering certain regularities in reactions and attitudes toward pain characteristic of the four groups. Therefore, the study has a qualitative character, and the efforts of the researchers were not directed toward a collection of material suitable for quantitative analysis. The main techniques used in the collection of the material were interviews with patients of the selected groups, observation of their behavior when in pain and discussion of the individual cases with doctors, nurses and other people directly or indirectly involved in the pain experience of the individual. In addition to the interviews with patients, "healthy" members of the respective groups were interviewed on their attitudes toward pain, because in terms of the original hypothesis those attitudes and reactions which are displayed by the patients of the given cultural groups are held by all members of the group regardless of whether or not they are in pain although in pain these attitudes may come more sharply into focus. In certain cases the researchers have interviewed a member of the patient's immediate family in order to check the report of the patient on his pain experience and in order to find out what are the attitudes and reactions of the family toward the patient's experience.

These interviews, based on a series of open-ended questions, were focused upon the past and present pain experiences of the interviewee. However, many other areas were considered important for the understanding of this experience. For instance, it was felt that complaints of pain may play an important role in manipulating relationships in the family and the larger social environment. It was also felt that in order to understand the specific reactive patterns in controlling pain it is important to know certain aspects of child-rearing in the culture, relationships between parents and children, the role of infliction of pain in punishment, the attitudes of various members of the family toward specific expected, accepted pain experiences, and so on. The interviews were recorded on wire and transcribed verbatim for an ultimate detailed analysis. The interviews usually lasted for approximately two hours, the time being limited by the condition of the interviewee and by the amount and quality of his answers. When it was considered necessary an interview was repeated. In most cases the study of the interviewee was followed by informal conversations and by observation of his behavior in the hospital.

The information gathered from the interviews was discussed with members of the medical staff, especially in the areas related to the medical aspects of the problem, in order to get their evaluation of the pain experience of the patient. Information as to the personality of the patient was checked against results of psychological testing by members of the psychological staff of the hospital when these were available.

The discussion of the material presented in this paper is based on interviews with 103 respondents, including 87 hospital patients in pain and 16 healthy subjects. According to their ethno-cultural background the respondents are distributed as follows: "Old Americans," 26; Italians, 24; Jews, 31; Irish, 11; and others, 11.[6] In addition, there were the collateral interviews and conversations noted above with family members, doctors, nurses, and other members of the hospital staff.

With regard to the pathological causes of pain the majority of the interviewees fall into the group of patients suffering from neurological diseases, mainly herniated discs and spinal lesions. The focussing upon a group of patients suffering from a similar pathology offered the opportunity to investigate reactions and attitudes toward spontaneous pain which is symptomatic of one group of diseases. Nevertheless, a number of patients suffering from other diseases were also interviewed.

This paper is based upon the material collected during the first stage of study. The generalizations are to a great extent tentative formulations on a descriptive level. There has been no attempt as yet to integrate the results with the value system and the cultural pattern of the group, though here and there there will be indications to the effect that they are part of the culture pattern. The discussions will be limited to main regularities within three groups, namely, the Italians, the Jews and the "Old Americans." Factors related to variations within each group will be discussed after the main prevailing patterns have been presented.

Pain Among Patients of Jewish and Italian Origin. As already mentioned, the Jews and Italians were selected mainly because interviews with medical experts suggested that they display similar reactions to pain. The investigation of this similarity provided the opportunity to check a rather popular assumption that similar reactions reflect similar attitudes. The differences between the Italian and Jewish culture are great enough to suggest that if the attitudes are related to cultural pattern they will also be different despite the apparent similarity in manifest behavior.

Members of both groups were described as being very emotional in their responses to pain. They were described as tending to exaggerate their pain experience and being very sensitive to pain. Some of the doctors stated that in their opinion Jews and Italians have a lower threshold of pain than members of other ethnic groups, especially members of the so-called Nordic group. This statement seems to indicate a certain confusion as to the concept of the threshold of pain. According to the people who have studied the problem of the threshold of pain, for instance Harold Wolff and his associates, the threshold of pain is more or less the same for all human beings regardless of nationality, sex, or age.

In the course of the investigation the general impressions of doctors were confirmed to a great extent by the interview material and by the observation of the patients' behavior. However, even a superficial study of the interviews has revealed that though reactions to pain appear to be similar the underlying attitudes toward pain are different in the two groups. While the Italian patients seemed to be mainly concerned with the immediacy of the pain experience and were disturbed by the actual pain sensation which they experienced in a given situation, the concern of patients of Jewish origin was focused mainly upon the symptomatic meaning of pain and upon the significance of pain in relation to their health, welfare and, eventually, for the welfare of the families. The Italian patient expressed in his behavior and in his complaints the discomfort caused by pain as such, and he manifested his emotions with regard to the effects of this pain experience upon his immediate situation in terms of occupation, economic situation and so on; the Jewish patient expressed primarily his worries and anxieties as to the extent to which the pain indicated a threat to his health. In this connection it is worth mentioning that one of the Jewish words to describe strong pain is *yessurim,* a word which is also used to describe worries and anxieties.

Attitudes of Italian and Jewish patients toward pain-relieving drugs can serve as an indication of their attitude toward pain. When in pain the Italian calls for pain relief and is mainly concerned with the analgesic effects of the drugs which are administered to him. Once the pain is relieved the Italian patient easily forgets his sufferings and manifests a happy and joyful disposition. The Jewish patient, however, often is reluctant to accept the drug, and he explains this reluctance in terms of concern about the effects of the drug upon his health in general. He is apprehensive about the habit-forming aspects of the analgesic. Moreover, he feels that the drug relieves his pain only temporarily and does not cure him of the disease which may cause the pain. Nurses and doctors have reported cases in which patients would hide the pill which was given to them to relieve their pain and would prefer to suffer. These reports were confirmed in the interviews with the patients. It was also observed that many Jewish patients after being relieved from pain often continued to display the same depressed and worried behavior because they felt that though the pain was currently absent it may recur as long as the disease was not cured completely. From these observations it appears that when one deals with a Jewish and an Italian patient in pain, in the first case it is more important to relieve the anxieties with regard to the sources of pain, while in the second it is more important to relieve the actual pain.

Another indication as to the significance of pain for Jewish and Italian patients is their respective attitudes toward the doctor. The Italian patient seems to display a most confident attiitude toward the doctor which is usually reinforced after the doctor has succeeded in relieving pain, whereas the Jewish patient manifests a skeptical attitude, feeling that the fact that the doctor has relieved his pain by some drug does not mean at all that he is skillful enough to take care of the basic illness. Consequently, even when the pain is relieved, he tends to check the diagnosis and the treatment of one doctor against the opinions of other specialists in the field. Summarizing the difference between the Italian and Jewish attitudes, one can say that the Italian attitude is characterized by a present-oriented apprehension with regard to the actual sensation of pain, and the Jew tends to manifest a future-oriented anxiety as to the symptomatic and general meaning of the pain experience.

It has been stated that the Italians and Jews tend to manifest similar behavior in terms of their reactions to pain. As both cultures allow for free expression of feelings and emotions by words, sounds and gestures, both the Italians and Jews feel free to talk about their pain, complain about it and manifest their sufferings by groaning, moaning, crying, etc. They are not ashamed of this expression. They admit willingly that when they are in pain they do complain a great deal, call for help and expect sympathy and assistance from other members of their immediate social environment, especially from members of their family. When in pain they are reluctant to be alone and prefer the presence and attention of other people. This behavior, which is expected, accepted and approved by the Italian and Jewish cultures, often conflicts with the patterns of behavior expected from a patient by American or Americanized medical people. Thus they tend to describe the behavior of the Italian and Jewish patient as exaggerated and over-emotional. The material suggests that they do tend to minimize the actual pain experiences of the Italian and Jewish patient regardless of whether they have the objective criteria for evaluating the actual amount of pain which the patient experiences. It seems that the uninhibited display of reaction to pain as manifested by the Jewish and Italian patient provokes distrust in American culture instead of provoking sympathy.

Despite the close similarity between the manifest reactions among Jews and Italians, there seem to be differences in emphasis especially with regard to what the patient achieves by these reactions, and as to the specific manifestations of these reactions in the various social settings. For instance, they differ in their behavior at home and in the hospital. The Italian husband, who is aware of his role as an adult male, tends to avoid verbal complaining at home, leaving this type of behavior to the women. In the hospital, where he is less concerned with his role as a male, he tends to be more verbal and more emotional. The Jewish patient, on the contrary, seems to be more calm in the hospital than at home. Traditionally the Jewish male does not emphasize his masculinity through such traits as stoicism, and he does not equate verbal complaints with weakness. Moreover, the Jewish culture allows the patient to be demanding and complaining. Therefore, he tends more to use his pain in order to control interpersonal relationships within the family. Though similar use of pain to manipulate the relationships between members of the family may be present also in some other cultures it seems that in the Jewish culture this is not disapproved, while in others it is. In the hospital one can also distinguish variations in the reactive patterns among Jews and Italians. Upon his admission to the hospital and in the presence of the doctor the Jewish patient tends to complain, ask for help, be emotional even to the point of crying. However, as soon as he feels that adequate care is given to him he becomes more restrained. This suggests that the display of pain reaction serves less as an indication of the amount of pain experienced than as a means to create an atmosphere and setting in which the pathological causes of pain will be best taken care of. The Italian patient, on the other hand, seems to be less concerned with setting up a favorable situation for treatment. He takes for granted that adequate care will be given to him, and in the presence of the doctor he seems to be somewhat calmer than the Jewish patient. The mere presence of the doctor reassures the Italian patient, while the skepticism of the Jewish patient limits the reassuring role of the physician.

To summarize the description of the reactive patterns of the Jewish and Italian patients, the material suggests that on a semi-conscious level the Jewish patient tends to provoke worry and concern in his social environment as to the state of his health and the symptomatic character of his pain, while the Italian tends to provoke sympathy toward his suffering. In one case, the function of the pain reaction will be the mobilization of the efforts of the family and the doctors toward a complete cure, while in the second case the function of the reaction will be focused upon the mobilization of effort toward relieving the pain sensation.

On the basis of the discussion of the Jewish and Italian material two generalizations can be made: 1) *Similar reactions to pain manifested by members of different ethno-cultural groups do not necessarily reflect similar attitudes to pain.* 2) *Reactive patterns similar in terms of their manifestations may have different functions and serve different purposes in various cultures.*

Pain Among Patients of "Old American" Origin. There is little emphasis on emotional complaining about pain among "Old American" patients. Their complaints about pain can best be described as reporting on pain. In describing his pain, the "Old American" patient tries to find the most appropriate ways of defining the quality of pain, its localization, duration, etc. When examined by the doctor he gives the impression of trying to assume the detached role of an unemotional observer who gives the most efficient description of his state for a correct diagnosis and treatment. The interviewees repeatedly state that there is no point in complaining and groaning and moaning, etc., because "it won't help anybody." However, they readily admit that when pain is unbearable they may react strongly, even to the point of crying, but they tend to do it when they are alone. Withdrawal from society seems to be a frequent reaction to strong pain.

There seem to be different patterns in reacting to pain depending on the situation. One pattern, manifested in the presence of members of the family, friends, etc., consists of attempts to minimize pain, to avoid complaining and provoking pity; when pain becomes too strong there is a tendency to withdraw and express freely such reactions as groaning, moaning, etc. A different pattern is manifested in the presence of people who, on account of their profession, should know the character of pain experience because they are expected to make the appropriate diagnosis, advise the proper cure and give the adequate help. The tendency to avoid deviation from certain expected patterns of behavior plays an important role in the reaction to pain. This is also controlled by the desire to seek approval on the part of the social environment, especially in the hospital, where the "Old American" patient tries to avoid being a "nuisance" on the ward. He seems to be, more than any other patient, aware of an ideal pattern of behavior which is identified as "American," and he tends to conform to it. This was characteristically expressed by a patient who answered the question how he reacts to pain by saying, "I react like a good American."

An important element in controlling the pain reaction is the wish of the patient to cooperate with those who are expected to take care of him. The situation is often viewed as a team composed of the patient, the doctor, the nurse, the attendant, etc., and in this team everybody has a function and is supposed to do his share in order to achieve the most successful result. Emotionality is seen as a purposeless and hindering factor in a situation which calls for knowledge, skill, training and efficiency. It is important to note that this behavior is also expected by American or Americanized members of the medical or nursing staff, and the patients who do not fall into this pattern are viewed as deviants, hypochondriacs and neurotics.

As in the case of the Jewish patients, the American attitude toward pain can be best defined as a future-oriented anxiety. The "Old American" patient is also concerned with the symptomatic significance of pain which is correlated with a pronounced health-consciousness. It seems that the "Old American" is conscious of various threats to his health which are present in his environment and therefore feels vulnerable and is prone to interpret his pain sensation as a warning signal indicating that something is wrong with his health and therefore must be reported to the physician. With some exceptions, pain is considered bad and unnecessary and therefore must be immediately taken care of. In those situations where pain is expected and accepted, such as in the process of medical treatment or as a result of sports activities, there is less concern with the pain sensation. In general, however, there is a feeling that suffering pain is unnecessary when there are means of relieving it.

Though the attitudes of the Jewish and "Old American" patients can be defined as pain anxiety they differ greatly. The future-oriented anxiety of the Jewish interviewee is characterized by pessimism or, at best, by skepticism, while the "Old American" patient is rather optimistic in his future-orientation. This attitude is fostered by the mechanistic approach to the body and its functions and by the confidence in the skill of the expert which are so frequent in the American culture. The body is often viewed as a machine which has to be well taken care of, be periodically checked for disfunctioning and eventually, when out of order, be taken to an expert who will "fix" the defect. In the case of pain the expert is the medical man who has the "know-how" because of his training and experience and therefore is entitled to full confidence. An important element in the optimistic outlook is faith in the progress of science. Patients with intractable pain often stated that though at present moment the doctors do not have the "drug" they will eventually discover it, and they will give the examples of sulpha, penicillin, etc.

The anxieties of a pain-experiencing "Old American" patient are greatly relieved when he feels that something is being done about it in terms of specific activities involved in the treatment. It seems that his security and confidence increases in direct proportion to the number of tests, X-rays, examinations, injection, etc. that are given to him. Accordingly, "Old American" patients seem to have a positive attitude toward hospitalization, because the hospital is the adequate institution which is equipped for the necessary treatment. While a Jewish and an Italian patient seem to be disturbed by the impersonal character of the hospital and by the necessity of being treated there instead of at home, the "Old American" patient, on the contrary, prefers the hospital treatment to the home treatment, and neither he nor his family seems to be disturbed by hospitalization.

To summarize the attitude of the "Old American" toward pain, he is disturbed by the symptomatic aspect of pain and is concerned with its incapacitating aspects, but he tends to view the future in rather optimistic colors, having confidence in the science and skill of the professional people who treat his condition.

Some Sources of Intra-Group Variation. In the description of the reactive patterns and attitudes toward pain among patients of Jewish and "Old American" origin certain regularities have been observed for each particular group regardless of individual differences and variations. This does not mean that each individual in each group manifests the same reactions and attitudes. Individual variations are often due to specific aspects of pain experience, to the character of the disease which causes the pain or to elements in the personality of the patient. However, there are also other factors that are instrumental in provoking these differences and which can still be traced back to the cultural backgrounds of the individual patients. Such variables as the degree of Americanization of the patient, his socio-economic background, education and religiosity may play an important role in shaping individual variations in the reactive patterns. For instance, it was found that the patterns described are manifested most consistently among immigrants, while their descendants tend to differ in terms of adopting American forms of behavior and American attitudes toward the role of the medical expert, medical institutions and equipment in controlling pain. It is safe to say that the further is the individual from the immigrant generation the more American is his behavior. This is less true for the attitudes toward pain, which seem to persist to a great extent even among members of the third generation and even though the reactive patterns are radically changed. A Jewish or Italian patient born in this country of American-born parents tends to *behave* like an "Old American" but often expresses *attitudes* similar to those which are expressed by the Jewish or Italian people. They try to appear unemotional and efficient in situations where the immigrant would be excited and disturbed. However, in the process of the interview, if a patient is of Jewish origin he is likely to express attitudes of anxiety as to the meaning of his pain, and if he is an Italian he is likely to be rather unconcerned about the significance of his pain for his future.

The occupational factor plays an important role when pain affects a specific area of the body. For instance, manual workers with herniated discs are more disturbed by their pain than are professional or business people with a similar disease because of the immediate significance of this particular pain for their respective abilities to earn a living. It was also observed that headaches cause more concern among intellectuals than among manual workers.

The educational background of the patient also plays an important role in his attitude with regard to the symptomatic meaning of a pain sensation. The more educated patients are more health-conscious and more aware of pain as a possible symptom of a dangerous disease. However, this factor plays a less important role than might be expected. The less educated "Old American" or Jewish patient is still more health-conscious than the more educated Italian. On the other hand, the less educated Jew is as much worried about the significance of pain as the more educated one. The education of the patient seems to be an important factor in fostering specific reactive patterns. The more educated patient, who may have more anxiety with regard to illness, may be more reserved in specific reactions to pain than an unsophisticated individual, who feels free to express his feelings and emotions.

The Transmission of Cultural Attitudes Toward Pain. In interpreting the differences which may be attributed to different socio-economic and education backgrounds there is enough evidence to conclude that these differences appear mainly on the manifest and behavioral level, whereas attitudinal patterns toward pain tend to be more uniform and to be common to most of the members of the group regardless of their specific backgrounds.

These attitudes toward pain and the expected reactive patterns are acquired by the individual members of the society from the earliest childhood along with other cultural attitudes and values which are learned from the parents, parent-substitutes, siblings, peer groups, etc. Each culture offers to its members an ideal pattern of attitudes and reactions, which may differ for various sub-cultures in a given society, and each individual is expected to conform to this ideal pattern. Here, the role of the family environment affects the individual's ultimate response to pain. In each culture the parents teach the child how to react to pain, and by approval or disapproval they promote specific forms of behavior. This conclusion is amply supported by the interviews. Thus, the Jewish and Italian respondents are unanimous in relating how their parents, especially mothers, manifested over-protective and over-concerned attitudes toward the child's health, participation in sports, games, fights, etc. In these families the child is constantly reminded of the advisability of avoiding colds, injuries, fights and other threatening situations. Crying in complaint is responded to by the parents with sympathy-concern, and help. By their over-protective and worried attitude they foster complaining and tears. The child learns to pay attention to each painful experience and to look for help and sympathy which are readily given to him. In Jewish families, where not only a slight sensation of pain but also each deviation from the child's normal behavior is looked upon as a sign of illness, the child is prone to acquire anxieties with regard to the meaning and signifi-cance of these manifestations. The Italian parents do not seem to be con-cerned with the symptomatic meaning of the child's pains and aches, but instead there is a great deal of verbal expression of emotions and feelings of sympathy toward the "poor child" who happens to be in discomfort because of illness or because of an injury in play. In these families a child is praised when he avoids physical injuries and is scolded when he does not pay enough attention to bad weather, to drafts, or when he takes part in rough games and fights. The injury and pain are often interpreted to the child as punishment for the wrong behavior, and physical punishment is the usual consequence of misbehavior.

In the "Old American" family the parental attitude is quite different. The child is told not to "run to mother with every little thing." He is told to take pain "like a man," not to be a "sissy," and not to cry. The child's participation in physical sports and games is not only approved but is also strongly stimu-lated. Moreover, the child is taught to expect to be hurt in sports and games and is taught to fight back if he happens to be attacked by other boys. How-ever, it seems that the American parents are conscious of the threats to the child's health, and they teach the child to take immediate care of any injury. When hurt the right thing to do is not to cry and get emotional but to avoid unnecessary pain and prevent unpleasant consequences by applying the proper first aid medicine and by calling a doctor.

Often attitudes and behavior fostered in a family conflict with those pat-terns which are accepted by the larger social environment. This is especially true in the case of children of immigrants. The Italian or Jewish immigrant parents promote patterns which they consider correct, while the peer groups in the street and in the school criticize this behavior and foster a different one. In consequence, the child may acquire the attitudes which are part of his home-life but may also adopt behavior patterns which conform to those of his friends.

The direct promotion of certain behavior described as part of the child-rearing explains only in part the influence of the general family environment and the specific role of the parents in shaping responses to pain. They are also formed indirectly by observing the behavior of other members of the family and by imitating their responses to pain. Moreover, attitudes toward pain are also influenced by various aspects of parent-child relationship in a culture. The material suggests that differences in attitudes toward pain in Jewish, Italian and "Old American" families are closely related to the role and image of the father in the respective cultures in terms of his authority and masculinity. Often the father and mother assume different roles in promoting specific patterns of behavior and specific attitudes. For example, it seems that in the "Old American" family it is chiefly the mother who stimulates the child's ability to resist pain, thus emphasizing his masculinity. In the Italian family it seems that the mother is the one who inspires the child's emotionality, while in the Jewish family both parents express attitudes of worry and concern which are transmitted to the children.

Specific deviations from expected reactive and attitudinal patterns can often be understood in terms of a particular structure of the family. This became especially clear from the interviews of two Italian patients and one Jewish patient. All three subjects revealed reactions and attitudes diametrically opposite to those which the investigator would expect on the basis of his experience. In the process of the interview, however, it appeared that one of the Italian patients was adopted into an Italian family, found out about his adoption at the age of fourteen, created a phantasy of being of Anglo-Saxon origin because of his physical appearance and accordingly began to eradicate everything "Italian" in his personality and behavior. For instance, he denied knowledge of the Italian language despite the fact that he always spoke Italian in the family and even learned to abstain from smiling, because he felt that being happy and joyful is an indication of Italian origin. The other Italian patient lost his family at a very early age because of family disorganization and was brought up in an Irish foster home. The Jewish patient consciously adopted a "non-Jewish" pattern of behavior and attitude because of strong sibling rivalry. According to the respondent, his brother, a favored son in the immigrant Jewish family, always manifested "typical" Jewish reactions toward disease, and the patient, who strongly disliked the brother and was jealous of him, decided to be "completely different."

✻   ✻   ✻

This analysis of cultural factors in responses to pain is tentative and incomplete. It is based upon only one year of research which has been devoted exclusively to collection of raw material and formulation of working hypotheses. A detailed analysis of the interviews may call for revisions and reformulations of certain observations described in this paper. Nevertheless, the first objectives of our research have been attained in establishing the importance of the role of cultural factors in an area relatively little explored by the social sciences. We hope that in the course of further research we shall be able to expand our investigation into other areas of the pain problem, such as sex differences in attitudes toward pain, the role of age differences, and the role of religious beliefs in the pain experience. We hope also that the final findings of the study will contribute to the growing field of collaboration between the social sciences and medicine for the better understanding of human problems.

28   SOME PSYCHO-SOCIAL PROBLEMS ASSOCIATED WITH FACIAL DEFORMITIES

*By Frances Cooke Macgregor**

In recent years an increasing number of psycho-social studies[1] of the physically handicapped have been made. These investigations have been focused principally upon the problems of the crippled, the deaf and blind, the senile, those with diabetes and cardiac conditions, tuberculosis, etc.

However, there is another group of handicapped persons to whom less attention has been given, yet whose personal tragedy and problems may equal and indeed, often exceed, those with other body afflictions. These are the facially deformed or disfigured members of society.

Except when the disfigurement is accompanied by a functional impairment such as a harelip with cleft palate, these individuals do not necessarily suffer from organic or functional inability to perform the normal activities of daily living. Nevertheless, they are handicapped because of the way they look. The twisted mouth, the conspicuous port-wine stain or the peculiarly shaped nose may well be a barrier to the privileges and opportunities available to the non-handicapped. Such an affliction, therefore, is more of a social handicap than a physical one, for the individual's suffering results from the visibility of the defect and what it means to others as well as to himself. It is the aesthetic aspect alone which makes the problems of the facial cripple unique and quite different in some respects from those of other physically handicapped groups.

The victim of a rheumatic heart knows that his activities must be circumscribed because his heart is weak. The blind person realizes that his life must be quite different from that of the non-blind. The amputee is aware of his limitations because of his physical inability to perform certain tasks. The facially deformed, on the other hand, who is handicapped only because of his appearance, experiences a kind of resentment and frustration which differs in some respects from the feelings of the person who is physically incapacitated. The unsightly scar or the conspicuous defect may well be as severe a social and economic handicap as complete physical incapacity. This is due in large measure to the profound social significance of the face and the attitudes and prejudices of society toward one whose appearance is atypical.

Perhaps nothing is so eloquent and significant as the human face. Looking at one another is our most basic form of conversation, and wherever people meet in a primary or face-to-face relationship it is the face which is generally the center of attention. It is the source of vocal communication, the expressor of emotions, and the revealer of personality traits. The face is the person himself. By his face we feel we know him and tend to pass judgment upon him; for to the face and its separate features is attached a significance often weighted with unscientific concepts and folklore, which is strong and persistent. Visible physical characteristics evoke reactions, which, depending upon our particular cultural values, may be those of immediate repulsion or attraction. In-

From *American Sociological Review,* 16, (October, 1951), 629–638. Copyright 1951 by The American Sociological Society.

terpretation and misinterpretation of personality made on the basis of the appearance of another is a common occurrence. While evaluation of another may be formed by conscious interpretations, unconscious interpretations or misinterpretations play a predominant part in forming an image of the personality itself.[2] When we meet a new person, for example, we are prone to form a rapid impression of his character. A glance may be enough to tell us a good deal about him. Yet what we think we see often is determined by the assumptions we make at the time. If we do not like his looks, what may have begun with interest turns into social distance.

Many studies, particularly those dealing with racial differences and social distance, have shown that the symbolic significance of visible physical traits, such as skin color, shape of nose or eyes, which become meaningful according to a host of social and cultural definitions, plays no small part in determining the patterns of interaction between individuals and groups of individuals.[3] A man with black skin and kinky hair, one with a prominent hooked nose, or one with slant eyes and straight hair, is commonly judged in our society to be (1) a Negro, (2) a Jew, (3) an Oriental. The subsequent personality image of the individual, and thence our acceptance or rejection of him, is dependent upon manifold subjective factors which are influenced by our past experiences, social attitudes and prejudices. When prejudice exists, these visible traits which set an individual apart from the majority group, may serve as a barrier to further social interaction and prevent further knowledge of the man himself. If he looks different, he must, ipso facto, be different. And herein lies the tragedy of a facial deformity; for this same mechanism in the socio-sensory perception of differences in physical features tends to operate in the interactive processes between the facially disfigured and non-disfigured members of society, and results in biases or misunderstandings which frequently characterize minority and majority group relationships.

Myths and misconceptions regarding the man whose face is scarred or misshapen by disease, whose expression is distorted or who was born with a harelip or without an ear, are legion. He has been stereotyped in folklore, literature, and the movies. He is the "evil one" or the gangster; he is diseased or has led an "immoral" life; he is a "freak" paying for the sins of his father, or for the things his mother saw while she was pregnant. He is to be shunned, regarded with curiosity, or ridiculed and made a social outcast.

Even when a facial anomaly is slight, or the total configuration is only mildly atypical, negative judgments on the part of others are common. Most of us have heard such statements made even by those considered to be educated; for example: "I wouldn't trust a man with such a low forehead" or "With that receding chin, he must be a weak character."[4] Such value judgments or weighing processes in the social perception are seldom based on conscious rational thinking but are largely unconscious or "intuitive."[5]

That facially deformed persons are well aware of these social attitudes and fearful that they are being typed accordingly by others is reflected time and again in their own statements or doubts which are frequently reinforced by their experiences; it explains in part why their emotional reactions, which sometimes appear to others to be disproportionate to the specific defect itself, are so strong. The following statements by facially deformed patients are typical of what many such victims think others think or have been told that others think:

Patient with congenital facial malformation: "I won't eat in restaurants; people might think I have a contagious disease."

Patient with enlarged red nose due to an angioma: "A lot of people take me for a drunk."

Patient with facial paralysis: "People take me for a tough character or a 'wise guy' because I talk out of the side of my mouth."

Patient with saddle nose: "I've been asked if I had syphilis."

Patient with facial scars: "I always explain how I got these; I'm afraid people will think I'm an ex-convict."

Mother with child born without an ear: "People have asked me if it runs in the family, or if I were unfaithful to my husband."

Women with saddle nose: "People ask me if I'm a lady wrestler." After corrective surgery she said, "Now I look like a lady and I feel like one."

Mother with child born with harelip: "I've been asked if I touched a rabbit when I was pregnant."

Patient whose child was born with a hairy mole: "My mother claims it is because I bought two pet birds while I was pregnant."

Patient with facial deformity due to cancer: "I feel others shy away from me because they think it's contagious. I don't understand why I got it when I've always led a good, clean life."

The mother of a child with a harelip states that a Jewish woman informed her that "Somebody must have thrown a 'curse' or 'evil eye' on you."

Patient with facial deformity resulting from radical surgery: "People think I've changed because my face is changed."

In addition to existing attitudes and beliefs concerning those with facial deformities, there is a concomitant social force which also operates to their disfavor. This is the high social premium placed upon facial attractiveness. One need only look about for irrefutable evidence of this dominant cultural interest. Advertisements everywhere endeavor to persuade the public that their particular brand of toothpaste or automobile is the one to buy. Pictures of men, women and children—the idealized "American type"—with faces of perfect contour, fresh looking skin, shapely noses, mouths and chins, and two rows of straight, shining teeth, not only create a sensory and affective appeal designed to stimulate the interest and approval of potential purchasers, but aim to make them feel that by purchasing such articles they are somehow identified with the attractive people in the ads.

Advertisements in the press and radio inform, indeed threaten, us that we will never find a job, husband (wife), or friends with "that unsightly skin, those wrinkles or double chin." Such defects are considered insurmountable social and economic barriers to success. At all costs we must look attractive. The thousands of beauty parlors and barber shops, the movies with their emphasis and glamorization of external features, are further commentaries on our national mania for physical beauty.

With this generalized bias toward physical perfection, together with the profound social meaningfulness of the face, the plight of those whose expressions are distorted by burns or paralysis, who may lack an ear or have any other facial deviation which sets them apart from others, becomes obvious. That there may be serious socio-psychological consequences has been well established by the results of a study of 115 plastic surgery patients made by the author from 1946–49, upon which this paper is based. Both clinic and private patients[6] were interviewed during a three-year investigation of the psycho-social aspects of facial deformities. The number of interviews varied; some patients were seen for as many as fifteen hours, others for three. The majority were followed post-operatively for periods of two months to three years.

The facial defects of these patients ranged from gross to mild from the surgical standpoint and were classified according to origin of complaint as follows: congenital, traumatic, disease, surgical, familial and cultural.[7] There were those whose faces were so disfigured by trauma or disease that original appearance was almost obliterated, and there were greater numbers whose complaint was one conspicuous feature such as a scar, a malformed nose, or protuberant ears. However, it has been observed that the severity of the disfigurement had no direct proportional relationship to the degree of psychic distress it engendered nor the kinds of adjustment made to it. Each case was unique and such factors as personality configuration, family and social setting, not only differed in each instance, but played important roles in the attitude of the victim toward his affliction and the type of adjustment he made. Regardless of the differences, either of degree of deformity or personality structure and environmental factors, the group had many common problems. These centered mainly around society's attitude toward the atypical face, the negative value it places upon it, and around the concept of self, which is largely derived through social interaction with others.[8]

While the age range was from 1½ to 43 years, Table 1 shows that the majority of patients were between the ages of 15 and 40, a period in which the need to be physically attractive is particularly strong. The greatest number of patients were between 21 and 30, a time when jobs and marriage, if not already attained, became major concerns. With a facial defect, both of these goals become difficult and often impossible to achieve. The impact of this realization is one of the principal reasons for the greatest number of elective plastic surgery cases in this age group.

Table 1—115 Plastic Surgery Patients According to Age, Sex, and Marital Status*

Age Years	Male	Female	Single	Married	Divorced or Separated
Under 15	6	7	13	..	..
16–20	13	11	24	..	..
21–30	22	22	36	8	0
31–40	12	11	12	8	3
Over 40	1	10	4	6	1
Total	54	61	89	22	4

* 74 patients were clinic cases; 41 private.

The complaints of the majority of patients with reference to their appearance centered around the patterns of interaction between themselves and others. Not only were they daily dismayed by the reflection of their own mirrors, but, more damaging to their ego esteem, they saw their handicaps reflected in the reaction of others toward them. These reactions, as noticed by patients, which they stated caused them to feel self-conscious and unhappy, were: staring, remarks, curiosity, questioning, pity, rejection, ridicule, whispering, nicknames, and discrimination.

In addition to the humiliation caused by the foregoing manifestations of disapproval, there were major problems confronting patients in their attempts to obtain jobs, attract members of the opposite sex, or make friends. Set apart as different from others and even regarded as social outcasts, they frequently developed psychological disturbances which often became more grave than the physical impairment. The majority of patients suffered from behavior difficulties which ranged from feelings of inferiority, self-consciousness, frustration, preoccupation with the deformity, hypersensitivity, anxiety, hostility, paranoid complaints and withdrawal from social activities that varied from partial to complete, to anti-social behavior and psychotic states.

The following cases demonstrate the nature of some of the characteristic psychosocial problems associated with facial deformities.

Case 1. Tom M., 31, had incurred a birth injury which resulted in a complete paralysis of the right side of his face. When in repose, his defect, though noticeable, was not dramatically disfiguring. The lid of his left eye drooped slightly and did not open or close completely when he blinked. When Tom spoke, however, his handicap became most conspicuous. He literally talked "out of the side of his mouth."

If he had not had a facial paralysis, he would have been a rather good-looking man, for his features were most acceptable. He was slim and well built, had nice eyes, good skin and hair. He was neatly dressed, soft spoken, well-mannered, sensitive and intelligent.

Tom came from a middle class family of Irish American descent, and was the eldest of five children. His father, a policeman, managed to support his family fairly comfortably. They lived in their own house in a suburban area and the children, until the death of their mother, were well taken care of. When Tom was an infant, his parents noticed when he cried or laughed that he "screwed up" one side of his face. But not until he began to talk did they realize the seriousness of his affliction. They took him to many doctors, all of whom said nothing could be done as the facial nerves and muscles had atrophied.

Upon entering school he soon learned that something was "wrong" with his face. "It was my teachers who first made me self-conscious," Tom said. "They would stop me in the middle of a recitation and ask me what was the matter with my face. They would say, 'try and control it and don't talk on one side of your mouth like that.' This embarrassed me because I couldn't help talking the way I did. In trying to help me they crossed me up by mentioning it in front of the other children. If they had only waited until after the class was over."

Tom came home from school every day and did not linger on the streets with other children who had begun to taunt him. "I became self-conscious and shied away from everything and everybody. I hung around my mother in the kitchen. She taught me to cook and did everything she could think of to keep my mind off myself." The only children he occasionally played with were the "fireman's kids." "I liked them because they had a brother who had a club foot and they never mentioned his deformity or mine."

In high school, his life was similar to days in grammar school. He preferred poor grades to the ridicule and staring of other students. He did not try to make friends nor did he participate in school dances or other social activities.

Out of school Tom said he was "driven" into sports in order to prove that he was a good ball player, "so the fellows in the neighborhood would overlook my face." However, when they played other teams, their opponents would try to upset Tom by calling him "crooked mouth" or admonishing the batter to "hit it (the ball) back at him and straighten out his crooked face." This upset him so much that he would leave the game.

When he was in high school his mother died, and Tom decided to leave home and school and go to work. "But I was always given jobs where I wouldn't meet people . . . so it didn't help much." His ambition was to be a policeman like his father and grandfather. But when he applied to the department, he was turned down. "They gave no reason, just said I failed the physical." Later, a friend told him the physician refused to pass him because of his facial deformity.

Tom then endeavored to get a job in a large department store. Six times he was turned down, but eventually, through the intervention of a friend, was given work in the packing department where he would not be seen by the public. This job, like all subsequent ones, presented difficulties. "The fellows made my life miserable. They would tell jokes and make faces the way I do when I talk. Or they would say 'are you trying to be tough, talking out of the side of your face?' "

Though only eighteen and earning a small salary, Tom married the only girl he had ever dated. She lived in the same neighborhood and he had known her since he was ten. While in high school they went together, "usually to the movies, where I wouldn't be seen or stared at." She was the only girl who did not make him feel uncomfortable about the way he looked and he was devoted to her. He wanted to get married and "have responsibilities so that I would not feel that life was not worth anything." At first he was opposed to having children, afraid they too might be deformed. Nevertheless, there are now three children. As each was born, Tom anxiously watched them for signs of the defect with which he is afflicted. Meanwhile he has worked hard at odd jobs to keep his family together on the small salaries he is able to make. "I always have to go for jobs where they'll take anybody."

In 1948, when seen at the clinic, he had lost his last job because "business was slow." There had been an opening in the company, however, for the position of salesman which he wanted, but didn't apply for as he knew he'd be "turned down." "My handicap has made me feel so inferior and afraid to compete with others that I don't dare try. Besides, I can't express myself to the boss or fight for something because when I get nervous my face gets twisted more than usual and I can't be myself." Instead, he accepted a job as superintendent of an apartment house in order to obtain an apartment for his family.

When Tom is not working, he spends his time at home with his children. He avoids all outside contacts because he can't endure the staring of others or the quick furtive glances toward and away from his face. This self-imposed isolation has resulted in some "serious arguments" with his wife who is very sociable. Tom said, "I just can't enjoy myself when I go anywhere, even with my wife's relatives. If I laugh my mouth goes sideways. It dampens everything for me. I get embarrassed when I talk and so I don't say anything. Other people seem repulsed by my appearance or embarrassed when they talk to me. It seems like they want to get away. If I do go anywhere I always hear people off in a corner saying, 'What's the matter with him?' If they asked me outright it wouldn't hurt so much." In addition, he notices the way they unconsciously draw up their mouths and mimic him while watching him talk.[9] "They don't seem to realize that it's not my fault that I look this way, and one crack about my face stops me cold. I will go home and brood for two months and draw into a shell. I get cross and snap at the kids and my wife and won't talk to any of them."

In 1947, Tom went to an eye clinic because his eye became irritated due to his inability to close it completely. He was referred to the plastic surgery division with the suggestion that he might receive further help. His hopes, suddenly raised, were as rapidly shattered when he was informed there was no hope for corrective surgery. "For the first time in my life, I went out and got drunk," he said. The following summer he drove 2,000 miles mainly in Canada, to visit St. Anne de Beaupré and other shrines "hoping for a miracle."

At the time of our initial interview, a year later, Tom had again returned to the hospital clinic. He had heard of a new surgical technique for facial paralysis and hoped there would be some chance for him. "My relatives said the doctors might use me for a guinea pig and I'd only be worse off than I am now. But I'd rather take a chance. I can't be worse off than I am and even if it fails, if by having the operation I can help someone who comes after me, I'm glad to do it. I'm filled with pent-up emotion; I can't laugh or smile or do anything. I have long periods of depression and resentment. I'm terribly sensitive. Even in the movies if I see another handicapped person I get tears in my eyes faster than a woman. I've been so handicapped all my life, so ridiculed and humiliated, that anything is worth trying." He was told again by the doctors that in his particular case surgery would be of no avail.

Tom said even though there seemed no hope for him to be relieved of his deformity, he was going to have his son's lop ears corrected. "The kids are beginning to call my son 'rabbit ears.' I don't want him to go through what I have."

Discussion. While this young man has made a fair adjustment to his life situation, has been able to marry and support a family, he has been crippled psychologically. His feelings of inadequacy and hostility, his periods of depression, are due less to his deformity than to his reactions to the actual and anticipated reactions of others towards his appearance. We see here the influential role the group may play in determining the kind of interpretation an individual makes toward his own deformity. Given derogatory nicknames by his contemporaries, offered jobs where he would have a minimum of social contact, and characterized as being "tough," seemed to accentuate behavior patterns of a negative nature. Not only have his own feelings of frustration, anxiety and deep hostility prevented him from developing more positive aspects of emotional living, but his personality distortions have in turn been inflicted on his environment. By his periods of depression and short temper, his refusal to enter into social activities, both his wife and children are affected and the family harmony considerably damaged.

Case 2. Charlotte B., age 36 and divorced, had suffered for a prolonged period from frontal headaches. It was discovered that she had chronic suppurative frontal sinusitis; a radical operation was performed involving the removal of a large portion of the frontal bone. The operation resulted in a deep, conspicuous depression in the mid-portion of her forehead, immediately above the bridge of her nose, and a scar across her nose. When Charlotte saw herself in the mirror, she was so distressed that she cried for two days. She would not let any of her friends come to visit her. "I felt I would look so repulsive to others," she said. At the end of two weeks, the attendant swelling and inflammation had subsided and the wound looked less disfiguring. Her courage somewhat restored, she returned to her job as stenographer which she had held for 17 years. Before two weeks had passed, her self-confidence was severely undermined. "People continually asked me questions and stared at me—in the office, in elevators. Even in buses and public dressing rooms, strangers would look at me and ask what had happened to my face." When she resumed her work in a hospital as a nurse's aid after office hours, an activity she had thoroughly enjoyed, the patients questioned her so much about her disfigurement that she felt unable to continue her work. "My friends tried to cheer me up by saying, 'It's not very nice to look at, but someday you can have it fixed.' "

Until her operation, Charlotte had been a very social and outgoing person. She enjoyed other people, loved to dance and play bridge with friends. Now she refused to go anywhere. "I couldn't stand the staring." She had a "steady boy friend" but would no longer go anywhere in public with him. She refused to meet new people because "it made me so nervous and self-conscious." She learned to avoid the eyes of others by turning her head or keeping it down. She bought dark glasses to cover the incision over her nose. She stopped going into restaurants to eat. Her depression and preoccupation with her appearance increased. She refused to see anyone after office hours, preferring to remain alone in her room and listen to the radio. Many hours were spent weeping. Unable to sleep as her anxiety increased, she began taking sleeping pills, and a number of times had considered taking "the whole bottle."

Her doctor had told her that in a few months plastic surgery could be performed. To earn enough money she tried to get a job in a restaurant after her regular office hours. "But I was always turned down. They would look at my face and say they had no position available."

Eight months later when seen at the clinic, Charlotte was filled with anxiety, self-pity, and was in a semi-hysterical state. She appeared to have lost all interest in the way she looked. "If I had known the results of this operation," she wept, "I would not have had it. I have wished many times my headaches were back and not this awful disfigurement. It's nerve-wracking to be stared at and asked questions all the time and it makes me want to slap people in the face." She felt she could "go on no longer" unless something were done to correct her appearance. She was afraid she would lose her job because of the way she looked. She was also frightened by the thought that she would no longer attract men. "I want to marry again some day and this defect would certainly interfere."

Charlotte underwent an operation for the reconstruction of her frontal bone by bone grafts removed from the ilium. The results were highly successful. At the end of three weeks, except for a slight and inconspicuous scar, her face appeared to be normal. The patient herself was remarkably changed. In contrast to her drab and untidy appearance when first seen, she was now well groomed and her expression radiant. No longer emotional and nervous, she seemed extremely happy. "I've been a different person since this operation. It's as though I had gone to sleep and awakened as somebody else. I look in the mirror and grin from ear to ear and spend hours looking at myself. Before, I couldn't bear to see myself. Everyone is amazed at the physical and mental change in me and I feel relieved of a great weight. I have gone out with my boy friends and to parties and restaurants almost every night since I got home from the hospital. I'm not shy now and don't try to hide my face. I don't cry anymore, or feel depressed and inferior. Now I'm glad to get up in the mornings."

Discussion. The case is cited to illustrate the rapidity with which social and psychological conflicts may develop when a facial deformity is acquired. It resulted in a complete alteration of the patient's inter-personal relationships with consequent severe damage to her self-esteem. She had changed from a social, outgoing person to one who preferred to remain isolated rather than endure the humiliation of others' reactions toward her. That deep-seated personality distortions were not incurred, which might not as easily have been removed as the physical deformity, was due to the short time she was forced to live with it.

Conclusions and Recommendations. The two cases cited illustrate the social situation with which a facially disfigured individual may be confronted. Not only does the social prejudice toward one with a conspicuous or unesthetic defect tend to operate to his social and economic disadvantage, but such prejudice can play a powerful role in determining the attitude of the handicapped person toward himself and his own mental health.

If the impact with his family, who reflect the social and cultural attitudes of society, his school and other social experiences, has been one of disapproval or rejection, either overt or covert, opportunity for full and healthy personality development is denied him.

If the facial cripple must endure years of being shunned, regarded as a curiosity, or diseased, or if he is stereotyped as a tough character or ex-pugilist, he is deprived of the social security one derives from group acceptance and belongingness. Regarded as different, he may view himself as different or inadequate and behave in accordance with others' evaluation of him. Conflict between social opportunity and inner desires may arouse undue frustration and anxiety. Enforced awareness of his social handicap may demand the expenditure of much energy and time to the handling of the difficulty. To relieve anxiety, to compensate, to build up defense mechanisms require efforts which might otherwise be channeled into more positive aspects of living.

While there are many additional psycho-social problems associated with facial deformities, those discussed in this paper are intended to point out the need for broader understanding of this particular group of handicapped persons, whose numbers are increasing every day due to war and mounting numbers of civilian accidents.

Wherever plastic surgery can correct or improve the facial injury or congenital malformation, it should be undertaken as early as possible in order to avoid not only the obvious disadvantages, but to prevent deep psychological wounds which may be incurred but not so easily eliminated. When surgery can accomplish only partial correction or none at all, techniques for psychotherapy and psychological rehabilitation should be developed to aid the person to adjust to his situation. Furthermore, even when satisfactory surgical correction can be achieved, psychological help is frequently indicated for those who have endured prolonged periods of facial disfigurement with resulting personality disturbances. In such cases, surgery alone is seldom enough to complete psychological rehabilitation.

Finally, it should be recognized that the problems associated with facial deformities and the problems of adjustment are not those of the handicapped individuals alone, but are of equal importance for the non-handicapped, who by their negative attitudes and prejudices help to create or perpetuate the difficulties. To remove deep-seated social prejudice is difficult but not impossible. We have seen in the past two decades a radical change in society's attitude toward those with venereal disease, cancer, cerebral palsy, and other physical disabilities, and we have witnessed the gradual acceptance in industry of the deaf, the amputee and the paralytic. It is to be hoped that the time is not too distant when the public, through education, will understand more fully the plight of one who has a marred or atypical face, and will not add to his difficulties either by rejection or by unsought sympathy.

29   PROBLEM PATIENT: THE CHRISTIAN SCIENTIST

By Lois Hoffman

He didn't want to consult you. He isn't entirely sure you can help him. But there he is: that paradoxical, once-in-a-while patient, the Christian Scientist.
    What do you do about him?

From Medical Economics, 33, (December, 1956), 265–283. Copyright 1956 by Medical Economics, Inc.

You treat him, of course, to the best of your ability. And, if you practice the art as well as the science of medicine, you persuade him to follow your advice.

A *Medical Economics* survey of several hundred U.S. physicians shows that they're seeing more Christian Scientists than they did a few years ago. Probably you are, too. So let's examine some of the special problems that Christian Science patients present. Let's look, too, at the tactful, sometimes ingenious ways in which such patients are being helped in spite of themselves.

Whenever a Christian Scientist visits you, he's bound to feel guilty about it. For Mary Baker Eddy, who founded the Christian Science church in 1866, taught that "materialist" healing was unnecessary for true believers. Only the action of the divine mind on the human mind can cure disease, she held. So when one of her followers is "in error"—i.e., ill—the recommended therapy is "earnest, silent prayer."

It's only when prayer doesn't relieve his symptoms that the Scientist visits a doctor. But he seldom blames his religion for its failure to work a cure. He blames his own inadequacy.

A California G.P. illustrates this by quoting a woman patient of his. She had an ovarian cancer that had metastasized through her abdomen. She came to the doctor after trying prayer for five months. "I'm seeing you," she explained, "because I've failed Christian Science."

Actually, Christian Scientists *needn't* feel guilty about consulting a doctor in some situations. Though many Scientists don't realize it, the ban on medical care isn't absolute. According to a church spokesman: "A doctor of medicine is called only in unusual circumstances, and then more in a surgical capacity, such as for childbirth, fractured bones, severe lacerations, etc."

Fractures, lacerations, and the like are thus considered mechanical difficulties rather than spiritual errors. One Christian Scientist reflected this point of view when he asked a West Coast doctor to remove a splinter that had caused his son's foot to fester:

"While I'm a Christian Scientist and you're a medical man," he said, "taking out a splinter is essentially a carpenter's job. So don't wonder at my having come to you for aid."

This man had waited much too long before seeking medical help. Like him, many Scientists rely solely on prayer until the case gets desperate.

Another typical case report:

"On and off for years, I've been treating a woman for severe bronchial asthma. When the asthma's bad, she calls me. When it isn't bad, she calls a Christian Science practitioner."

By the time the Christian Science patient reaches your door, it may be too late to help him. Even when you *can* help, he often puts stumbling blocks in your way. He may have fixed ideas about what services he will and won't accept. For example:

A New Jersey physician tells of a patient with operable carcinoma of the lung who calmly agreed to all necessary diagnostic procedures—and then refused surgery. A West Coast M.D. reports that he was called in by a Scientist who hadn't had a bowel movement for two weeks—but who still resisted medication and even an enema.

Even if he agrees to follow the doctor's orders, the Christian Scientist sometimes follows them only as long as *he* thinks best. A Georgia physician says: "I told a Scientist who had pneumonia to take an antibiotic for four days. He felt better after one day, so he stopped."

Preventive Medicine? Christian Science frowns on compulsory vaccination, inoculation, patch tests, chest X-rays, and quarantine. In states where such procedures are required by law, Scientists usually submit to them. But the church carries on an unremitting fight—and has won quite a few battles—to get members exempted.

Despite the church's fight against compulsion, some of its younger members accept preventive medicine voluntarily. A Syracuse G.P. reports that one Christian Scientist brings her entire family to his office every year for complete physicals. And one Chicago physician says he had "quite an influx of Christian Scientists coming in for check-ups right after Ike had his coronary." [From the church's viewpoint, of course, such people "aren't really Christian Scientists," since they're obviously not following the teachings of Mary Baker Eddy.]

WHAT DO CHRISTIAN SCIENTISTS DIE FROM?

Christian Scientists get less medical care than the average person. How does this affect their death rate and their life expectancy? Partial answers come from a recent Forensic Medicine article by Dr. Gale E. Wilson, autopsy surgeon in King County, Washington. During the period 1935–1955, he noted 1,041 deaths of known Christian Scientists. His analysis of those deaths provides the following statistics:

Average age at death was about 70—slightly below the latest figure for the state's population as a whole.

In twenty-one years, there were only three deaths from trauma, none at all from homicide or suicide.

The proportion of deaths from coronary artery disease was far below the national average.

The proportion of deaths from pneumonia, diabetes, and tuberculosis was higher than average.

The proportion of deaths from malignancy was nearly double the national average. But the incidence of carcinoma of the lung was very low. (Christian Scientists don't as a rule use tobacco or alcohol).

Dr. Wilson estimates that 6 per cent of Scientist deaths could be prevented by surgery—which is condoned by the church, although many don't realize it.

Such Scientists are likely to be as cooperative as any of your other patients. But watch out for their more orthodox relatives. Consider this story told by a Pittsburgh G.P.:

"A Christian Scientist with cardiac failure was brought to my office. Her husband was out of town, so I drove her home in my car and made arrangements to have her taken care of. After several days' treatment she was making a nice recovery.

"Then her husband returned. He decided that she needed exercise. So he induced her to get out of bed and take a hike with him. Next morning at 5 o'clock, I received a frantic summons to the house. She died a few minutes after my arrival."

The Science Practitioner. Like the Christian Scientist's relatives, the Christian Science practitioner is a force to be reckoned with.

Such practitioners go through years of self-instruction in the Bible and in the works of Mary Baker Eddy. Then they take about two weeks' intensive training from an authorized teacher. Those who can show their ability by demonstrating actual "cures" may apply for formal listing as practitioners.

Most of the practitioners are women. By church rule, they must devote all their time to healing. How do they do it? By praying in their own homes for ill Scientists who engaged them. Or—less frequently—by praying at the sick person's bedside.

The physician who isn't used to the practitioners' methods may be in for a shock when he first encounters one. A West Coast doctor tells of the following incident:

"A man came in with a long laceration of the forearm. I told him I'd have to sew it up, but he insisted I call his Christian Science practitioner first. I got the practitioner on the phone and explained the situation. 'You go right ahead,' she told me. 'I'll be working on it here.'"

Christian Science practitioners often charge $3 for a single "absent treatment" and $5 for a house call. So the church member who visits a doctor usually has double bills to pay.

A Midwestern surgeon tells of the time he charged a patient $200 for removing his gall bladder. The man's Christian Science practitioner also sent a bill: $225 for a ten-day course of absent treatments.

This surgeon doesn't say whether the church practitioner claimed full credit for the cure. But a Pennsylvania G.P. knows one who did:

"Some years ago," he says, "I was called out to a farm to attend a Christian Scientist in labor. I found her in severe pain, with her baby in the occipitoposterior position. The fetel heart sounds were faint and irregular.

"I told her husband I'd have to use instruments. He and the church practitioner, who was sitting by the patient's bed, protested vehemently. It wasn't until the husband saw his wife approaching the limit of her endurance that he finally agreed to let me go ahead.

"I promptly did a Scanzoni operation and delivered a very blue baby that refused to breathe. The husband dashed up and down stairs with tubs of hot and cold water, while I worked with the baby and the practitioner paced the floor.

"After twenty minutes, the child uttered a cry. Immediately the Christian Science practitioner stepped up to me. 'Now, Doctor,' she said, 'you'll have to admit my prayers saved the baby's life.'

" 'I don't know about that,' I answered. 'I prayed too—but I also worked like hell!' "

If you get little thanks for treating a Christian Scientist—well, maybe that isn't too important. What you chiefly want is cooperation during treatment rather than gratitude afterward.

How can you best get such a patient to pull with you instead of against you? Here are three practical suggestions drawn from the surveyed doctors: **How to Work with Him.** 1. *Go along with the Scientist's request if he asks you to help him conceal the visit.* One doctor with a sizable Christian Scientist following says he's often asked to wait until evening to make a house call. Another physician always parks his car at some distance from the house of a bedridden Scientist patient. Still a third doctor lets Scientists visit him at his home rather than at his office.

There seems no reason why doctors shouldn't go along with such harmless subterfuges. But this sort of thing can be carried too far. Witness the following almost farcial tale from a Massachusetts M.D.:

"I was called to a hotel to see a middle-aged woman who had a cold. While I was examining her, there was a sudden rap on the door. My patient gasped and turned white.

" 'What's the matter?' I asked.

" 'I'm a Christian Science practitioner,' she whispered. 'I'll be ruined if you're discovered in my room. Get in the closet, quick!'

"This idea had little appeal to me, so I went to the door instead. Luckily, it was only the bellboy bringing her the evening paper."

2. *Use indirect ways to suggest treatment without offending the patient's religious sensibilities.* One respondent makes a point of avoiding medical terminology. "I describe digitalis as a food for the heart rather than as a drug," he explains. "And I refer to an X-ray as a picture."

Sometimes it's best to be even more devious. A New Englander recalls this case:

"A Christian Science practitioner who was high up in the church came to me to ask what I though of his chance of getting life insurance. He apparently had angina pectoris. After answering his direct question about the insurance, I went on to explain in detail what medical advice I'd give him if he weren't a Christian Scientist. I don't know whether he followed the advice. But he certainly listened with rapt attention."

Occasionally, of course, there's no time for tact. Says an Eastern G.P.: "I once got a call from the husband of a Scientist who was in labor. When I got there, I found three church members with the patient. One of them kept patting the struggling woman and repeating, 'God will relieve you.'

"Seeing that it was a breech presentation, I said firmly, 'I'm going to help God a little. He won't mind.' Maybe they were put out. Or maybe they were secretly relieved. Anyway, I just couldn't worry about their feelings at that point."

Practitioner Can Help. 3. *Cooperate with the Christian Science practitioner.* Most of the surveyed doctors say they've found it best not to object to the church practitioner's giving absent treatments or even standing by in person. "I not only don't object, I actively encourage it," says an Arizona M.D. "I've found that a Science practitioner can often do a good job of relieving the patient's fears. For the sincere believer, Christian Science provides excellent psychotherapy."

You may find that a Christian Scientist resists even the surgical care condoned by the church. In such cases, the church practitioner can become a valuable ally.

"A Scientist I knew had a large cutaneous horn protruding above her eyebrow," says one doctor. "It interfered with her glasses, but she refused to have it removed. So I got in touch with her church practitioner. He persuaded her the horn could be removed within the laws of her faith."

Mental Struggle. All the above suggestions are summed up in this comment from a West Coast G.P.: "It always bothers me to see the mental struggle these patients are having—their rational selves conflicting with their spiritual selves. I find that a tactful, understanding approach is always best, except when I'm faced with an active obstructionist in a real emergency. And that doesn't happen often these days."

30   WHY DO PEOPLE DETOUR TO QUACKS?

By Beatrix Cobb

One of the most frustrating problems confronting physicians working in the cancer field is the patient who detours to nonmedical practitioners. When the detour occurs during the early stages of the disease, it often becomes the deciding factor between control and a fatality.

Who detours to quacks? Why do they detour? What determines the unswerving loyalty of such patients which makes it almost impossible to secure testimony against the quack? What is the key to the success of the nonmedical practitioner? These questions formed the basis for a preliminary investigation of a sample of 20 patients who had detoured to nonmedical sources for treatment when cancer was suspected.

Who detours and when. An analysis of the psychological factors involved in the detouring behavior of this sample indicates that there are four categories of patients who seek nonmedical treatment. There are the miracle seekers, the uninformed, the restless ones, and the straw-graspers. People of these four groups may detour prior to, during, or following orthodox treatment. The stage during which the patient chooses to detour is of utmost importance in light of the urgency for early and adequate treatment.

The miracle seekers and the uninformed. The two groups most likely to seek help from the quack during the pre-orthodox period of treatment are the miracle seekers and the uninformed. The miracle seeker is the person who is in search of a sure-cure over night. This is the woman who sends for a prayer cloth when she realizes she has cancer of the breast. Just last year one Negro woman depended upon her prayer cloth for six months before presenting herself for medical help. She confided that she fully expected each

From *The Psychiatric Bulletin*, 3, (Summer, 1954), 66–69.

morning to wake to find the fungating mass in her breast gone. In the six months, the disease had progressed to uncontrollable stages. She now is terminal; she still believes that the failure of the prayer cloth was due to her sins. The prayer cloth was much more intelligible to her than the mysterious x-ray machines to which she was subjected during orthodox treatment. Being left alone in a room, strapped to a table, and prey to the fears aroused by the clicking mechanism was an experience of great trauma to her.

The uninformed group was the largest in the sample studied. Although the people with little or no education form the bulk of this group, this is not always the case. For instance, an intelligent man of 42, who had completed high school and a business course, explained his detour as follows: "Well, to tell the truth, I went to a nonmedical practitioner without really knowing what the difference in a M.D. and other people who call themselves doctors is. The only time I remember going to a doctor was when I had my tonsils out. I didn't think too much about doctors. Someone told me this man was good with cancers, and I went."

Many people unversed in medical areas are unaware of the difference between specialists and clinics specializing in cancer. The daughter of a 78-year-old-man, who had been under treatment in a cancer clinic operating without benefit of medical approval, expressed the following idea: "When any of us is sick, we go to a doctor right away. That is the reason when daddy got his skin cancer, we took him to ——— Clinic. They specialize in cancer you know, and we didn't want no experimenting on my daddy."

The restless ones. Those seeking help from the quacks during intra-orthodox medical treatment fell completely within the "restless" category in the sample studied. The moot question becomes: what made them restless under medical care? Several psychological factors seem to be operating. One man of 46, who had completed the seventh grade, went to a quack because the physician to whom he had presented himself recommended surgery. He preferred to take his chance with the cancer rather than the surgeon's knife! When some friend recommended a non-medical practitioner who gave "pills and ointment," he promptly sought his help.

Another man of 53 became impatient during the two-week diagnostic period required for adequate medical workup and laboratory analysis before initiation of treatment. He withdrew from the clinic and went to a quack, who gave him treatment within the hour. Several months later, he returned somewhat shamefaced to confess: "It just took so long to get anything done here, that I got 'antsy'. You know, when you've got cancer, every minute counts. And when you just sit around waiting for two whole weeks, and all they do is examine you once or twice, and then just stick you every day for a blood test . . . well, us people who don't understand why you don't get something done right now, like your home doctor does when you go to him . . . well, we don't know, and we get impatient, and then just plain mad, and do things we wouldn't do, if we understood."

The straw-graspers. Finally, there are the graspers at straws. These are the people the doctors have told, "We have done all we can. There is nothing more medical science can do." Few people can accept such an ultimatum.

Many are so constituted that for their own peace of mind, they must continue to try to do something about it.

Often, this group contains people of high intelligence and professional training. An accomplished young oral surgeon explained his detour logically: "The report was malignant melanoma. The final decision was to take off the left arm and shoulder. I thought it over and decided against it . . . I had studied melanoma, and I knew there was no real hope in that kind of tumor, that there was no adequate control. Surgery was the only hope . . . so, in trying to evaluate my position when my arm and shoulder had to come off, I had to evaluate my family, my profession, and myself. If I consented to surgery, it would mean financial difficulties for the family, and turning to another means of livelihood for me, with all chances against me at my age . . . so looking at it all around, I thought it best to continue as long as I could, get a man partner who could be trained, and who would continue to operate the shop when I was ill, or after I was gone. The family would still have some means of support. This has now been accomplished. Since that time, I have been just marking time. And, well, I heard about this biochemist down in Florida. He was giving pituitary extracts and insulin and a strict diet. I knew he could do me no harm. So I went."

The mother of a three-year-old girl in terminal stages took her to a non-medical practitioner. She explained: "I just couldn't just sit down and watch her die. The doctors told me they could do nothing more. I kept hearing about this new shot this man was giving and the success he had with it. I just had to try it. For my own peace of mind, I had to know that I had done everything humanly possible to save her."

Why the patient is loyal to the quack. Whether the patient goes to the nonmedical practitioner searching for miracles, grasping at straws, seeking action, or just because he simply does not know the difference between the medical authority and the quack, it is seldom that he will speak disparagingly of the quack. But the patient has no such scruples against voicing his disapproval of the physician. This loyalty to the quack, even in face of failure of treatment, is astonishing.

A 56-year-old woman, with one year of college to her credit, explained her loyalty eloquently: "They was all so courteous to me, I am going to stay with them no matter what else I do. The last doctor I went to was abrupt to me. He said I was in some stage of cancer and the way he said it scared me to death. Now these ——— people said, 'Look on the bright side and enjoy life all you can.' This doctor took all the joy out of living because he scared me to death. Now with these ——— people, I feel safe and happy. I went to the ——— Clinic because I wasn't getting no satisfaction from my doctors. And well, like I said, I'll stick by them if it is the last thing I do. They helped me more than anybody. I feel better when I take that medicine, and when you start to hurting they give you something for it. They don't say, 'Well, that is just part of your illness, so we can't help it if you are sick at your stomach.' Or they don't say, 'You imagine you are hurting.' They give you medicine for anything that ails you."

A lovely young mother of 23, a high school graduate, was approached by a quack-follower while waiting for an appointment in a medical clinic. She verbalized the appeal to her meaningfully: "I get a little nervous sometimes. I really got nervous before I came down here because none of the doctors would hold out any real hope; they just kept saying that they would keep me alive with blood transfusions and then maybe a cure would be found. I don't want to be just kept alive . . . I want to live . . . I want to live normally . . . I want to get well. That is the reason we were pretty tempted by the quacks. They are really interested and seem to want to help so much. And the people who take the treatments are really sold on it. They won't let you take the treatment unless you really have faith in them. You know, sometimes I think maybe it operates sort of like hypnotizing people . . . they sell them so thoroughly. This man I know who is going to a quack . . . everytime he goes up there he comes back all fired up to preach about it for the rest of his life. I know the treatments aren't responsible, but he does actually look and feel better every time he takes one. I know, too, that faith and hope can make you feel better, and sometimes I think that is what they do that perhaps the medical profession doesn't do . . . make you feel completely hopeful and have faith in the treatment you are given."

A business man of 65 somewhat violently expressed his feeling for the quack who had treated him. Learning of his being treated, his daughter called him long distance. He reported his reaction as follows: "I know the medical profession is fighting Mrs. ———. I was sitting at her desk when the call came through. My daughter was real mad and demanded that I get right out of there that moment, that the doctor had told her that Mrs. ——— was just a 'quack.' It made me plenty mad, for Mrs. ——— had given me more useful information than my daughter's doctor had, and I really told her off."

Still another man who was treated for ten months by a quack, and then came for orthodox care, said that his sister was currently under treatment with the quack. When questioned as to whether he had discussed the failure of the quack to help him with the sister, he responded: "Nope, I thought about it, but I just couldn't do it. I don't want to do them no harm. They was nice to me. I wouldn't want to hurt them none. I know lots of people are agin them, but they was nice to me. They didn't do me no good, but . . . well, I don't think she would listen to me nohow. She's awful sold on them. I don't know, I just can't tell her."

How the quack operates. The psychological techniques of management utilized by the quack make it almost impossible to secure evidence against them. The foregoing excerpts are eloquent reminders of the potency of kindness, consideration, and recognition of the patient as a person. The approach of the quack is a positive one. "I can cure cancer; all I ask is the opportunity to prove it!" This they shout through the press and by word-of-mouth. "I challenge any medical man in the world and prove it beyond the shadow of a doubt that cancer is not hereditary, but that it is infectious." To the miracle seeker, the quack says, "Don't look for a mortician if your doctor diagnoses your illness as cancer. Get a round-trip ticket to ———." To the strawgrasper they say, "you have to do your part mentally, physically, spiritually; it is a three-fold process requiring cooperation of yourself, your doctors and your Creator. With this team of workers, you can look forward to a happy life."

To the man grown impatient with the doctor and his medical terminology which has no meaning for him, the quack sounds particularly logical. "Tumors result from the loss of control by the innate intelligence of certain parts and functions of the body," they maintain. "Just as crime often results from the loss of control by parents of the activities and characters of their children." This sort of explanation sounds much more logical to the layman than the medical jargon given him by the physician who does not take time to communicate.

To the practical man who questions, "How can one form of treatment be so beneficial for so many types of ailments?" the answer is simple. "These catalysts have no special affinity for certain types of tissues or form of disease. When injected into the body, they enable the body to produce its own defense mechanism and thus bring about a curative action." When the practical man questions further: "But, how does the same shot cure so many diseases?" the answer is still a ready one. The shot is likened to a starter button on an automobile—once the engine is started, it is not necessary to keep stepping on the starter. So, through simple logic and positive thinking the quack sways many to his support.

To this biased logic and positive approach, the quack then adds the potent ingredient of courteous and gracious treatment as a person at all times. In this way he ties the patient to him through the bonds of grateful appreciation. Finally, when he links his treatment with the Deity, success or failure becomes a part and parcel of the religious faith of the patient. And the quack has placed himself above reproach in the heart of the patient.

The physician can prevent the detour. This brief resume of the psychological factors underlying the "detouring" behavior highlights the importance of the emotional responses of the patients to the physician and to treatment. The medical world has long been aware of the role of improper diagnosis and padded statistics in the success of the quack with cancer. The words of the patients in this sample group emphasize the fact that often they were searching for reassurance, for hope, for recovery, for kindness, consideration, and for communication with the doctor so they might understand what was being done for them when they detoured to the quack. The physician, then, must give proper consideration to the panic psychology which drives a person to the quack when the doctor tells him he has done all that is medically possible, and sends him home to die. The physician must understand the impatience engendered through professional reticence to discuss the disease with the patient. The role of the doctor in prevention of detouring behavior, then, seems to be a dual one. The cancer patient seeks not only adequate medical care, but sympathetic emotional support as well.

V

Becoming a Physician:

Medical Education

THE PROCESS of becoming a physician has been investigated by sociologists in particular who are interested in the social process of medical education and its impact upon the student-physician. Changes in the art and science of medicine as reflected in the changing medical curriculum and the problems of teaching medicine are included in this section. In addition, the process of professionalization of the physician in the shifting of roles from medical student to practitioner through the channel of medical schools is being studied. Some problems involved in teaching behavioral science concepts to medical students are now being investigated.

Oswald Hall, one of the first sociologists to study physicians' careers, presents a penetrating analysis of the various phases of development confronting the physician as he passes from his pre-medical training to establishing his practice.

Some transformations of certain personal characteristics of medical students are described in a medical school study by Howard Becker and Blanche Geer.

Some similarities and differences between the clergy and the medical profession as they effect medical education are presented by Granger Westberg.

Samuel Bloom presents some new trends in medical education, which indicate a return to the patient as well as to the medical student as a whole person, in analyzing the process of the professionalization of the physician.

Patricia Kendall and Robert Merton condense the extensive findings of a large-scale study of several major medical schools of the United States, as reported in their recent volume on *The Student-Physician,* in their analysis of medical education as a distinct social process.

31   THE STAGES OF A MEDICAL CAREER

By Oswald Hall

Medicine, like other professions, is practiced in a network of institutions, formal organizations, and informal relationships. The medical career may be conceived as a set of more or less successful adjustments to these institutions and to the formal and informal organizations. In this paper I trace the stages of the medical career, so conceived, as I observed them in the study of the medical profession in an eastern American city.[1]

For purposes of discussion four stages may be singled out as follows: (1) the generating of an ambition; (2) gaining admittance to the various medical institutions (noting among other things the ethnic, class, and religious character of such institutions, the points at which various types of recruits enter them, and the steps by which one climbs within or among these institutions); (3) acquiring a clientele, retaining and improving it, and perhaps eventually transferring it to a successor; and (4) developing a set of informal relationships with colleagues which facilitate the above in some fashion.

The stages of a career, so conceived, are by no means unique to the medical profession. Presumably one could investigate similar phenomena in the academic field, in law, in the ministry, in engineering, and so forth. Although the content of each of the above differs substantially, for purposes of analysis they are fundamentally alike.

The materials have been drawn from interviews centered around the circumstances involved in success and failure in the practice of medicine. Almost without exception the subjects interviewed were enthusiastically interested in the problems raised and were eager to discuss their hunches and observations with an outsider. In reporting on them ordinary care has been taken to conceal the identity of the subjects, but this in no way detracts from the relevance of the documents.

I. Generating an Ambition. One function of an ambition is to discipline present conduct in the interest of a future goal. An ambition is usually conceived to be a highly subjective matter, generated in private fashion and internalized as a drive. Some careers are presumed to require more of it than others do. The medical career is supposed to require a great deal of ambition of the tough type. The fewer the day-to-day rewards in the early stages of a career and the longer delayed the substantial rewards, the more ambition is needed. The medical career is characterized by long periods of training and probation.

In the case of the doctors studied it appeared that the ambitions were largely social in character. They had their genesis in social groups and were nourished by such groups which in turn provided constant re-definition and redirection of the ambition. In most cases family or friends played a significant role by envisaging the career line and reinforcing the efforts of the recruit. They accomplished the latter by giving encouragement, helping establish the

From *The American Journal of Sociology,* 53, (March, 1948), 327–336. Copyright 1948 by The University of Chicago Press.

appropriate routines, arranging the necessary privacy, discouraging anomalous behavior, and defining the day-to-day rewards.

From this point of view one can see why doctors tend to be recruited from the families of professional workers. The latter possess the mechanisms for generating and nurturing the medical ambition. Only the member of a profession can translate the public protestations of the profession into the vernacular of useful advice. By contrast, families of nonprofessional background may generate the initial urge or itch in their members but fail to nourish the ambition. Such a family may endow a member with the anxiety to achieve a professional career but fail to provide the means for implementing that ambition. Much of the aggressiveness ascribed to new groups invading the medical field may be attributed to their individual (and often misguided) efforts to achieve those things which are usually managed by an informal group. Excluded from the subtle nuances of meaning which are involved in communicating the steps in a career, the newcomer and his individual efforts strike the initiated as singularly uncouth.

Excerpts from interviews with two doctors who stand at opposite poles as far as professional success is concerned throw light on the ways in which professional ambitions are generated and nourished. The first is a young general practitioner at a disadvantage because of his Armenian origin. He is an introverted person who seems to suffer from self-consciousness when meeting his patients.

My parents were too poor to help me through medical school. An aunt had promised that if I did well in school she would help. She did until the depression came along, and after that I had to scrape along as best I could.

I had a lot of trouble getting a good internship; of course that is the important thing in success in medicine. I went to a big medical school in Philadelphia, but the large hospital there was very choosy. My roommate was much more brilliant than I, but they turned him down too. So I came back to my home town for an interview and left feeling confident that I would get an appointment. But none came. Finally I had to take one in a small Philadelphia hospital. When I came back here I got a chance at X Hospital, and stayed there for seven months.

The hospital is the place where I really come alive. Every moment there is thrilling. My internships from beginning to end were thoroughly enjoyable. The saddest day of my life was the day I left X Hospital and started practice. One of the other interns lent me a hundred and fifty dollars, and promised to let me have forty or fifty a month.

The medical world is a hard one to start up in. It is a terrific change to come from the medical world to the practice of medicine. I thought that when I graduated my troubles would be over. But this part of medicine was just the opposite of what I had anticipated. I thought that when I opened my office all these sick people needing help would come in. But it isn't so. You wait for days and days and no one comes. Then you become frantic and wonder if you have gotten into the wrong kind of work. Sometimes I stayed in the office for six days and no one came. The first calls were those that no one else would take, ones that came late at night. For a while I stayed up nights, and slept in the daytime, in case I missed any of the night calls. I was sure that I was going to be a doctor—my mother had impressed that on me since I was three years old.

The second of these doctors is a successful specialist. He belongs to the Yankee elite of the community. He has a very substantial practice and does considerable consultant work. His office, which is part of a large structure shared by a group of co-operating specialists, is in the best residential area. He has posts in the most important hospitals of the community. In addition he plays an active part in the administration of the hospitals with which he is connected and he has a leading role in the medical organization of his city and state.

I guess I pretty well took it for granted that I was going to be a doctor. My family was a medical family, and there was always lots of interesting reading matter lying around. At college my teachers in biology were connected with the hospital and they had a way of making me feel that I would go to medical school. They seemed to feel that I should go to Harvard Medical after I finished University.

When I came back from medical school I got an internship in the large hospital here. One of my old college teachers was acting as superintendent of the hospital, and he seemed glad to have me send in an application.

Of course it takes a while to get started in a medical practice. My father bought my instruments for me and paid my office rent for the first couple of years.

When the specialty board was set up in this field, I was invited in as one of fifty charter members. My friends say that if I had had to try the examinations that I would never have passed them. Being a charter member gives a person a real sense of belonging.

The second doctor is conspicuously successful by whatever standards success in medicine is judged. By comparison the first will remain moderately unsuccessful. The initial drive was presumably greater in the first than in the second, but the latter was continuously assisted by groups who had an inside knowledge of the profession. These groups were able to redefine the career at its various stages in such a way that the young doctor made a minimum of false steps. He was left free to devote his energy to achieving relatively clear-cut goals. The other doctor received aid and advice but it lacked a realistic touch.

II. Incorporation Into the Institutions of Medicine. Medical services in the urban community are mediated through a multiplicity of institutions, such as doctors' offices, hospitals, clinics, laboratories, nursing homes, dispensaries and drugstores, various medical associations, and so forth. Although each institution has significance in the doctor's career, only the hospital is considered here.

The first point for discussion concerns the hierarchical nature of hospitals. The doctors of a given department, the various departments of the hospital, and the range of hospitals in the community form a hierarchy in each case. The doctors in a specific department are arranged in strata, such as intern, extern, staff member, staff association member, and the like. Within these strata there are finer gradations. For example, the staff members (those doctors who have full access to the facilities of the hospital) may be organized into many distinct levels which indicate clearly the prerogatives and prestige of the men concerned. Such a hierarchical pattern provides an exceedingly large number of steps for the new member of the profession. His progress through them symbolizes achievement in his personal career. For the administrator the hospital is a finely articulated status structure; the various positions represent a wide range of rewards to be conferred on the doctors attached to the hospital. The number and variety of these rewards function to keep a large staff reasonably satisfied by providing neat packages of advancement at relatively short intervals.

Within the departments competition goes on among the doctors. This competition is tempered by the established set of authority relations and the code of ethics which discourages individualistic striving for position. Between departments there is practically no competition because of the rigid nature of the specialization concerned. There is, however, a jealous struggle for prestige between different lines of specialization.

The various hospitals of the community studied form a status hierarchy. The Yankee Protestant hospitals have the most adequate facilities, those organized by the Catholics follow, while those organized by the Jewish group or by medical sects are the least adequate. The prestige of identical positions in the various hospitals would vary in the same way. There is very little moving between these institutions. Actually there are serious barriers hindering the doctor who has become associated with one hospital from moving up in another. Hence, the acceptance of an appointment in any of these hospitals represents a crucial point in his career. This is particularly the case with initial appointments. The internship that a doctor has served is a distinctive badge; it is one of the most enduring criteria in the evaluation of his status.

The second point to be borne in mind concerns the linkages between the various medical institutions. Hospitals, for example, are linked with the medical and the preprofessional schools. These provide typical chains in which each institution aids the newcomer to move along to the next level. The religious cleavages in medicine provide the most conspicuous illustrations. The major hospitals are organized along religious lines within which class and ethnic differentiation are discernible. Thus, in the community studied the upper-class Yankee generally goes to an undergraduate school where fees are high, proceeds to Harvard Medical school, interns at the dominant Yankee hospital, and enters the competitive practice of medicine from that vantage point. The Italian lad aspiring to a medical career would find these avenues almost completely blocked. However, there are other chains of institutions (in this case Catholic) which provide an alternative route, and not only open a road to a medical career for him, but also shelter him in some degree from the competition of those whose advantages are indicated above. This second set of institutions was originally organized for the Irish Catholic group, but other Catholics can use them in the manner indicated. It is worth noting that the marginal men in medicine are largely those who have forsaken the shelter of these enabling institutions and are seeking their fortunes in the wider competitive field of medical practice. Such cases lie outside the purview of this paper.

Hospital appointments are crucial for successful medical practice. The more important hospital posts are associated with the highly specialized practices and usually with the most lucrative types. The two form an interrelated system. Success in one's private practice may lead to advancement in the hospital system. Such advancement becomes an outward symbol of achievement and enhances the doctor's status in his own eyes and in the eyes of colleagues. His new position is likely to bring him into a new set of relationships with other doctors and permit him to participate more extensively in the co-operative system in which medicine is practiced. This again may influence his private practice. The linkage is discussed below in connection with gaining a clientele.

The gist of the foregoing is that the successful practice of medicine involves participation in the hospital system. This system is integrated with a series of other institutions. These constitute a sifting device which functions to establish the status of the various doctors in the community. In this sense they influence markedly the careers of medical men.

To illustrate the above points, materials are presented from interviews with key figures in the administrations of the big hospital and the Catholic hospital. Dr. S is Irish Catholic, a specialist, and heads one of the departments in the Catholic hospital.

One of our most important problems here is picking interns. The main qualification as far as I can see is "personality." Now that is an intangible sort of thing. It means partly the ability to mix well, to be humble to older doctors to the correct degree, and to be able to assume the proper degree of superiority toward the patient. Since all medical schools now are Grade A there is no point in holding competitive examinations. So the main problem confronting the selection committee is that of getting interns who will fit well into the pattern of the hospital.

Not all interns can fit in well here. There are trouble makers who just can't help being that way. You know the kind. Just like labor agitators in industry. If they get in they disrupt hospital efficiency no end. Another reason for not holding competitive examinations for internships is that there are a lot of Jews in medicine. Did you know that? Now there is something about the Jew. Of course there is prejudice against him, but there is also something else. He seems to lack a sense of balance. He finds too many things wrong and too many symptoms. He tends to overtreat his patients.

Now for the ideal type of internship the young doctor should come to the city where he intends to practice. This probably means taking a general type of training and getting little of the specialized kinds of things that he wants to do. However, it is more important to get to know the doctors with whom one is going to associate. After he gets established in this fashion, he should go away to a larger hospital for the specialized kind of internship that fits his interests.

In my own case I made the mistake of going to New York to a large hospital and getting to see a large number of the kinds of cases I was interested in. That was a blunder. I received only an alternative appointment at the big hospital so the New York plan was second choice. They had competitive examinations here then. Three other young fellows besides myself tried them. But none of us secured an appointment. One of the others was so disgusted that he omitted interning and went straight off to practice in New Hampshire. The next year he came back and secured a very handsome internship in the very field he was interested in. I asked him if he knew more a year later, and he said that he knew less medicine but more people. All such appointments can be manipulated if one knows powerful friends.

The significance of the above is not the refreshingly frank discussion of the manipulation of appointments; one would expect that personal factors would enter into the selections. The main point is the importance of such appointments—especially initial appointments—for the later careers of the beginners. Moreover, the likelihood of being appointed depends much less on superior technical competence than on one's acceptability by an established institution with its defined policies.

Dr. R is one of the main administrators of the large hospital in the community. He discussed at length the recruitment of personnel into the hospital.

We have a formal policy here with respect to internships. Applications must be in by a specified date, and then a committee goes to work to judge the applicants. They are judged on a variety of bases with a personal interview in some cases. In the earlier days we had competitive examinations, but we had to discontinue these. The person who did best on an examination might not show up well in the intern situation. He might lack tact; he might not show presence of mind in crises; or he might not be able to take orders. And more than likely the persons who did best on the written examinations would be Jewish.

The externs are usually chosen from the intern group. This is not always the case, but the interns are usually offered the privilege when an opening occurs in the Outpatient Department. Similarly the members of the Outpatient Department are brought back into the house if and when openings occur. There is a continuous selecting process at work; the judgment of the head of the department plays a large part in determining the speed of promotion for a given person.

The biggest change going on here concerns the setting up of the specialty boards in each of the specialized fields. They set examinations to establish membership in the various specialized fields. These tend to raise the standards and they simplify the problems of the hospital administrator. The older doctors on the staff recognize this but are slow at falling in line. Of course it is a bit unfair to expect these older men to go off and write examinations, especially in competition with young fellows. Besides there are good specialists among the older doctors who cannot pass examinations but they still deserve to be protected in their positions in the hospitals.

These things have lengthened the period it takes the person to become a practitioner. The surgeons are the ones most affected. It lengthens the time that the student must be subsidized, and pretty well prohibits the student from working his way through in medicine. In this way it raises the ethics of the profession. It means that the specialists are selected from the old established families in the community, and family and community bonds are pretty important in making a person abide by a code.

The doctors on the active staff here carry a very heavy load of charitable work. This of course, is part of the code, but at times it gets very arduous. There are a lot of people who never pay their bills and make suckers of every new doctor who comes to town until they get wise. Also there are a lot of low-income people who like to live like the upper group and who contract for better medical services than they can afford. Doctors have had to get better at bookkeeping and better at collecting. Most doctors go into medicine because of their humanitarian impulses and for the love of the game.

From the above statements some generalizations emerge. Appointments are not made on the basis of technical *superiority*. The appointee must be technically *proficient,* but after that level of competence is reached other factors take precedence over sheer proficiency. At this level personal factors play a part in determining who will be accepted. However, the question is not whether the applicant possesses a specific trait, such as dark skin, or is of the wrong sex, but whether these traits can be assimilated by the specific institution. Hence, personal traits are not nearly so important in determining admission as is institutional acceptability. To the extent that hospitals have distinctive policies and unique histories they tend to exclude doctors with specified backgrounds and to encourage others.

III. Acquiring a Clientele. Acquiring a clientele is an enterprise as far as the doctor is concerned—an enterprise in which he plays the role of promoter. It is not sufficient for the doctor merely to attract patients; he must adopt the type of strategy which will enable him to retain them. Success in medicine also involves improving the practice. The doctor must carry on an intelligent campaign to attract the desired type of patient, and he must discourage those who do not fit well into the pattern of his practice. The practice of medicine goes on in a competitive milieu; freedom of choice for the patient requires the doctor to exercise constant vigilance or see his patients gravitate to competitors with more power of attraction. In this competitive struggle intelligent enterprise may be more important than medical knowledge and skill.

As stated earlier, the good practices of the city are the specialized practices. The statistics on income differentials[2] between specialists and nonspecialists and the data on trends toward specialization are equally convincing on this point. The specialists are highly conscious of their superior status and refer to the general practitioners by unflattering terms such as "signposts" and "information booths." In discussing below the ways in which clienteles are acquired, attention has been directed to the specialized practices. In order to provide perspective two facts should be kept in mind. A specialized practice cannot be achieved without the active assistance of a group of colleagues. These must refer cases to the specialist; and he must have some corresponding way of repaying them for their favors. A specialized practice is a hospital practice and requires access to hospital facilities. Moreover, hospital connections facilitate the development of referral relationships between doctors.

As noted earlier such practices are carried on in a competitive milieu. This competition is never of the cutthroat variety. A profession connotes a code of ethics. The code of the medical profession specifically defines the degree of advertising that a doctor may indulge in. However, in a community in which the profession is well organized the code is practically superseded by a set of expectations and understandings deeply imbedded in the personalities of the doctors concerned. These understandings may go so far as to control the entry of new practitioners into the community, allocate them to posts in the various medical institutions, and incorporate them into the established office practices.

The extent to which these expectations control the conduct of the established doctors can be seen in the following comments by an old obstetrician.

A ticklish problem arises when a doctor has left the city for a while and turned his practice over to other doctors temporarily. Recently a young woman came to me whose chosen obstetrician was out of the city. I took care of her confinement and everything went smoothly. The next time she became pregnant she came to me and said that she had been so pleased with her former treatment at my hands that she wanted me to take her on as a patient. I had to tell her that she could go to any other obstetrician in town in preference to her old one, but that she couldn't have me. A person just can't be too meticulous in such cases.

There is another difficult question in dealing with the mother and child. As long as the child gets along satisfactorily in the hospital all is well. But if the child develops some illness, what should the obstetrician do? He has the responsibility for the mother and child while they are in the hospital. Should he refer the matter back to the family doctor who may think that he (the family doctor) can handle the case? Or should he safeguard the interests of the mother and child by calling in a qualified pediatrician? And if he does the latter, how many more patients will that family doctor send him? Doctors are jealous and shortsighted about such things. One must be scrupulously honest about such things or he will get labeled by his colleagues.

One has to be careful at the Maternity Hospital not to antagonize the pediatricians. It would be dangerous to play favorites. I make the patient take the initiative in choosing her own. Of course I may have to help her to remember the names of the pediatricians and help her eliminate some. I just wouldn't feel justified in helping her choose her pediatrician. They are all equally good as far as I am concerned.

This doctor seems to recognize that the hospital pediatricians comprise an established unit and that he should not discriminate among them. However, he would be equally solicitous not to deflect patients to an intruder trying to establish himself.

Dr. P is a surgeon who is well liked by the most influential leaders of the medical community but whose relations with his fellow specialists are far from congenial.

How does one get ahead? There are just two things to keep in mind. First, do good work and your reputation will get around. Second, keep your mouth shut. It does no good to talk about your achievements. Doctors are a jealous group.

In medicine one has to build a practice. And in medicine there is no structural steel. With steel one can go straight up like a skyscraper. Medicine is like building with stones. One has to build on a solid foundation. This goes for the kind of training one gets and the type of clientele he gathers. My practice is largely a personal kind. One person is pleased and he tells another. There is very little referred work. I refuse to give any *quid pro quo* for the cases that other men send me. One or two men do send me a few. My practice would be a lot bigger if I did otherwise. However, I never allow the doctor who sends the patient to act as assistant at the operation (and hence receive the assistant's fee). Operating is teamwork and only my anesthetist and my own assistant can work together satisfactorily.

Although his own is not of that type, this doctor recognizes the existence of practices based on referrals. Some, but not all, of these turn out to be convenient arrangements for sharing fees. Although this doctor protests that surgery is an open competitive field he gives the impression that his surgical colleagues, the older medical men in the community, and the closed hospital system not only control entry to the field but also delay the age at which an accepted entrant can start practicing. Finally, the discussion of these aspects of a career arouses emotion at an early stage of the interview.

The materials which follow are from interviews with one of the prominent heart specialists of the community. His Irish Catholic allegiance is largely nominal, making him acceptable to the Yankee Protestant segment of the community. His comments indicate that in a community there is usually a preeminent hospital, and that the prestige of being associated with that hospital is sufficient recompense for undergoing a long probationary period and assuming onerous duties into the bargain.

The goal of every good doctor here is to get on the staff of X Hospital. I spent twelve years on the outpatient staff and then twelve years on the active staff, working up to be head of that department. When I came here I got an appointment on the staff of a small hospital. At one of the meetings of the local medical society I met one of the doctors on the staff of X Hospital, and he asked me about my training and whether I would like a position over there. I didn't tell him that I would give my eye teeth for a chance, and you can bet I was over there in plenty of time the next day.

Over there a person rises by merit. Of course there may be some personal factors involved. For instance when questions of promotions come up I was always approached privately by the administration and asked who should go ahead. It's true that the Italians and Jews don't seem to catch on there. Many of them get tired of waiting, especially when they see themselves get jumped over in the course of promotions. And in the meantime they are building up private practices and feel that they can no longer spare the time. And some of them try to go ahead too fast. A Jew has just opened up an office across the way with a lot of that ornate furniture. I had him as an intern once. After two days he asked me to let him operate. I told him his chances were pretty slim for a while yet. He complained to the Mother Superior and resigned later on. Do you think the other doctors are going to do much for him?

In the above, one can discern a rigorous system of selection, and a system of prolonged apprenticeship. The participants in the system must be prepared to expect long delays before being rewarded for their loyalty to such a system. The doctor interviewed seemed to think his twelve-year apprenticeship eminently fair. In his eyes a satisfactory clientele is one which he can treat in the best hospital in town. Hence it is selected as to social class and income level. His ability to offer it the desired hospital facilities required a long, intelligent campaign.

Dr. G was ready to volunteer information on how much aid he gives to his colleagues. He is an outstanding physician and heads the department of medicine in the big hospital.

A doctor's career consists of an upgrade, a plateau, and a downgrade. Doctors don't usually discuss the reasons for the downgrade. Partly it is the competition of the young men coming in. Partly it is a matter of patients retiring the doctor. Many doctors end up with a shriveled practice. In a way their colleagues help retire them. In the old days I sent a lot of surgery to Dr. R. He was one of the big men in surgery —a fifty-thousand-dollar-a-year man. He was the owner of the building as well as being my landlord, so there was an added reason for sending cases to him.

But every doctor has one or two young doctors in whom he is interested and he needs to send them all the work that he can in order to get them launched. Because of this I have had to withdraw almost all my support from Dr. R.

When a person gets up to a position like mine there are a lot of kinds of help you can give your staff. I can always give a good fellow a couple of kicks in the right direction. I can always get an internship for a good boy if I really want to. I did that for M. I met him at a medical banquet while he was a student. I found out that he was a local boy and wanted an internship here. He was a nice sort with a good character. Now I've got him on the staff, and in a year or two I'm going to bring him into this office to share my practice. Then there was young Y. He was a nephew of the mayor. I got him an internship and the position of resident physician. Young D was another fine lad. I helped him the same way but then he was drafted. But I've arranged things so that when he comes back there will be a good position waiting for him.

Dr. B represents still a different type of doctor. He is a heart specialist who had spent some time teaching and then, as a stranger, decided to take up practice in this community. Having a private income, he is willing to break in to the local situation slowly.

One of the ways that a person can start up is to split fees with the person who refers the case. I don't think that is common here. It may occur to some extent in surgery, but I wouldn't know about that. In some newer towns the surgery is practically offered for sale.

I don't need to try anything of that sort. I expect to do sufficiently good work so that my name will get around, and in the meantime I can afford to wait. The first two years I was here my practice was pretty slim. Now I'm going into the forces, but when I come back a lot of the older men here will be through.

Fee-splitting must be a different thing for the young fellow who needs money to feed his family and cover his overhead. In that case the temptation must be almost unbearable. The usual manner in which these things develop is for a general practitioner to send a case to the specialist as a gesture. If the latter reciprocates then an association develops without anything overt being said.

A new man who tries to start in a community like this has to be very good and very careful. The other men watch him like hawks. One error would be too much and would jeopardize his reputation. News spreads fast.

Dr. B lacks completely the several kinds of assistance enjoyed by the doctors who are sponsored by one of the established practitioners. Only a doctor with substantial financial resources could assume the risks involved in trying to build up a practice in this fashion.

Further light on the problems of the unsponsored doctor is supplied by Dr. B who is an outstanding physician and an able administrator.

How would a new specialist get into the setup here? Well, there is a case in point now. A new heart specialist came here, practically unknown. He had very good recommendations from the medical school where he had been teaching. Naturally there is a considerable waiting period. A person may have to wait a couple of years before he finds things coming his way. This man was reputed to be one of the best in his field. Doctors waited to see. Some of them rate his work very high. Others have been a bit disappointed in what he can do. The local medical association had investigated when it heard that he was coming. However, there had been no overt attempts to keep him out.

Of course local conditions differ in such cases. In some cases the local doctors would advise a man not to come in. For example, a man came here very well trained in psychiatry, intending to settle. He met some of the local men in medicine and they advised him not to come. The reason was that the field was pre-empted by a man not nearly as well trained, but who would be hard on the newcomer. He would be tough on him and the new man would have a disagreeable time here, and might never catch on. The man coming had decided to go to another place and was eminently happy there.

IV. The Inner Fraternity. The interviews indicate that as far as recruiting new members, allocating them to positions in the various medical institutions, and securing clienteles are concerned there exists a set of controls exercised by a central core of the profession. This gives the main clue to the structure of the profession. It comprises four major groups of practitioners. The inner core is made up of the specialists who have access to, and dominate, the main hospital posts. Below these there are a number of recruits at various stages in their careers who will in the future inherit the positions of the central core. Around the core are men who practice medicine in a general fashion (as opposed to specialization) and who are bound to it in the sense that they refer their complicated cases to those specialists. Outside the core are doctors who are attempting by their individual efforts to break into the central core. However, as the core has its own specific mechanisms for recruiting and legitimating its members, the would-be intruders gain admittance only with the greatest difficulty.

The inner core has three distinctive features. In the first place, it represents a technical division of labor. Given the present range of knowledge and techniques in modern medicine, it is impossible for one person to master the whole. The specializations represent the manageable segments of present-day medicine. The inner core represents the integration of these distinctive lines of specialization.

Second, this inner core represents a method of organizing the market. It is a system for seeing that the patient eventually gets to the specialist most likely to be able to help him. This implies that the various specialists have access to the various hospital facilities necessary for carrying on specialized medicine. It also implies that there is a sort of machinery which directs patients from the general practitioner to the specialist and from one specialist to another. In general this involves the localization and concentration of the specialists in a specific part of the community; actually, many of them cluster in the same building to afford a closer integration of their services.

The third point is that the members of the inner core comprise a social group. Because of their technical interdependence, their spatial proximity, and their daily working relationships, they become a fraternity. They have roughly similar educational and social-economic backgrounds. They are tied by common professional bonds and participate in the same specialized professional associations. The group is sufficiently small to become a democracy of first names. Taken together, these factors explain why the group can develop an extremely high level of consensus. Because it shows so many of the characteristics of the primary group and of the secret society it has been labeled here "the inner fraternity."[3]

From this perspective one of the major stages of a medical career involves acceptance by the inner fraternity. The interviews show that there are specific accepted mechanisms for both incorporating the newcomer and repelling the unwanted intruder. The mechanisms operate at all levels, from that of intern to that of practicing specialist. Thus they tend to minimize mobility and control competition in such a way as to stabilize the provision of medical services in a community. The mechanisms include such phenomena as the institutional investigation of the newcomer, informal discussion and advice by high-ranking medical personnel, casual neglect in granting promotion in the hospital system, specific acts of encouragement and reward by the established practitioners, and direct sponsorship of a new recruit by one of the inner fraternity.

On balance the system operates more by rewarding the accepted recruit than by punishing the intruder. By and large, one rejection is sufficient to repel the intruder. On the other hand the sponsored protege must be assisted and vouched for at each step in his career. This involves active intervention in his career by the established practitioner who has sponsored him. In some of the cases studied the encouragement originated long before the person went to medical school, then, later, in the form of aiding him over the crisis of securing a superior appointment as intern; it continued as the young doctor climbed up in the hierarchy of institutional positions, and was evidenced by the referral of patients by the sponsoring doctor.

If the inner fraternity is the central core of the social organization of the profession, then sponsorship is the major social facet of a medical career. It is the positive means by which the inner fraternity controls its members. The function of the inner fraternity is to organize the provision of medical services. In doing so it appears to control the induction of new recruits, to exclude the intruder, to allocate positions in the hospital system, to control competition, to enforce a set of rules, to reward effort, to distribute patients, and to perpetuate the practices of its members. Because it is a going concern dealing with the day-to-day problems of the profession, and because it is a persisting organization which must recruit new members as old ones drop out, it exercises an extremely pervasive influence on the careers of doctors.

It is worth remarking that sponsorship has very few of the characteristics of nepotism. The protege must live up to the expectations of his sponsor, he must "deliver the goods." Failure on his part would be more than personal failure—it would involve the prestige of his sponsor. The protege is bound to go through the institutional apprenticeship. He must necessarily accept the discipline of being a functionary in an institution. Progressively he must accept the responsibilities of leadership. Sponsorship is by no means a one-sided set of favors.

In conclusion, it would appear that specialized medicine is no longer an independent profession—a free-lance occupation. It has become highly interdependent rather than independent, and it is carried on within the framework of elaborate social machinery rather than within a freely competitive milieu. The main contingencies of a medical career hinges on the role which the doctor plays in a very complex, informal organization. Within such a frame of reference there is room for much more research on careers and institutions.

32   THE FATE OF IDEALISM IN MEDICAL SCHOOL

By Howard S. Becker and Blanche Geer

It makes some difference in a man's performance of his work whether he believes wholeheartedly in what he is doing or feels that in important respects it is a fraud, whether he feels wholeheartedly that it is a good thing or be-

From American Sociological Review, 23, (February, 1958), 50–56. Copyright 1958 by The American Sociological Society.

lieves that it is not really of much use after all. The distinction we are making is that one people have in mind when they refer, for example, to their calling as a "noble profession" on the one hand or a "racket" on the other. In the one case they idealistically proclaim that their work is all that it claims on the surface to be; in the other they cynically concede that it is first and foremost a way of making a living and that its surface pretensions are just that and nothing more. Presumably, different modes of behavior are associated with these perspectives when wholeheartedly embraced. The cynic cuts corners with a feeling of inevitability while the idealist goes down fighting. *The Blackboard Jungle* and *Not As A Stranger* are only the most recent in a long tradition of fictional portrayals of the importance of this aspect of a man's adjustment to his work.

Professional schools often get a major share of the blame for producing this kind of cynicism and none more than the medical school. The idealistic young freshman changes into a tough, hardened, unfeeling doctor; or so the popular view has it. Teachers of medicine often rephrase the distinction between the clinical and pre-clinical years into one between the "cynical" and "pre-cynical" years. Psychological research supports this view, presenting attitude surveys which show medical students year by year scoring lower on "idealism" and higher on "cynicism."[1] Typically, this cynicism is seen as developing in response to the shattering of ideals consequent on coming face-to-face with the realities of professional practice.

In this paper, we want to describe the kind of idealism that characterizes the medical freshmen and trace both the development of cynicism and the vicissitudes of that idealism in the course of the four years of medical training. Our main themes will be: though they develop cynical feelings in specific situations directly connected with their medical school experience, the medical students never lose their original idealism about the practice of medicine; that the growth of both cynicism and idealism are not simple developments, but are instead complex transformations; and that the very notions "idealism" and "cynicism" need further analysis, and must be seen as situational in their expressions rather than as stable traits possessed by individuals in greater or lesser degree. Finally, we see the greater portion of these feelings as being collective rather than individual phenomena.

Our discussion is based on the study we are now conducting at a state medical school,[2] in which we have carried on participant observation with students of all four years in all of the courses and clinical work to which they are exposed. We joined the students in their activities in school and after school and watched them at work in labs, on the hospital wards, and in the clinic. Often spending as much as a month with a small group of from five to fifteen students assigned to a particular activity, we came to know them well and were able to gather information in informal interviews and by overhearing the ordinary daily conversation of the group.[3] In the course of our observation and interviewing we have gathered much information on the subject of idealism. Of necessity, we shall have to present the very briefest statement of our findings with little or no supporting evidence.[4] The problem of idealism is, of course, many-faceted and complex and we have dealt with it in a very simplified way, pointing only to some of its grosser features.[5]

The Freshmen. The medical students enter school with what we may think of as the idealistic notion, implicit in lay culture, that the practice of medicine is a wonderful thing and that they are going to devote their lives to service to mankind. They believe that medicine is made up of a great body of well-established facts that they will be taught from the first day on and that these facts will be of immediate practical use to them as physicians. They enter school expecting to work very hard and expecting that if they work hard enough they will be able to master this body of fact and thus become good doctors.

In several ways the first year of medical school does not live up to their expectations. They are disillusioned when they find that they will not get near patients at all, that the first year will be just like another year of college. In fact, some feel that it is not even as good as college because their work in some areas is not as thorough as courses in the same fields in undergraduate school. They come to think that their courses (with the exception of anatomy) are not worth much because, in the first place, the faculty (being Ph.D.'s) know nothing about the practice of medicine, and, in the second place, the subject matter itself is irrelevant, or as the students say, "ancient history."

The freshmen are further disillusioned when the faculty tells them in a variety of ways that there is more to medicine than they can possibly learn. They realize it may be impossible for them to learn all they need to know in order to practice medicine properly. Their disillusionment becomes more profound when they discover that this statement of the faculty is literally true.[6] Experience in trying to master the detail of the anatomy of the extremities convinces them that they cannot do it in the time they have. Their expectation of hard work is not disappointed; they put in an eight hour day of classes and laboratories, and study four or five hours a night and most of the weekend as well.

Some of the students, the brightest ones, continue to attempt to learn it all, but succeed only in getting more and more worried about their work. The majority decide that, since they can't learn it all, they must select from among all the facts presented to them those they will attempt to learn. There are two ways of making this selection. On the one hand, the student may decide on the basis of his own uninformed notions about what constitutes medical practice that many facts are not important, since they relate to things which seldom come up in the actual practice of medicine; therefore, he reasons, it is useless to learn them. On the other hand, the student can decide that the important thing is to pass his examinations and, therefore, that the important facts are those which are likely to be asked on an examination; he uses this as a basis for selecting both facts to memorize and courses for intensive study. For example, the work in physiology is dismissed on both of these grounds, being considered neither relevant to the facts of medical life nor important in terms of the amount of time the faculty devotes to it and the number of examinations given in it.

A student may use either or both of these bases of selection at the beginning of the year, before many tests have been given. But after a few tests have been taken, the student makes "what the faculty wants" the chief basis of his selection of what to learn, for he now has a better idea of what this is and also has become aware that it is possible to fail examinations and that he therefore must learn what the faculty wants if he wants to stay in school. The fact that one group of students, that with the highest prestige in the class, took this view early and did well on examinations was decisive in swinging the whole class around to this position. The students were equally influenced to become "test-wise" by the fact that, although they had all been in the upper range in their college class, the class average on the first examination was frighteningly low.

In becoming test-wise, the students begin to develop systems for finding out what it is the faculty wants and learning these things. These systems are both methods for studying their texts and short-cuts that can be taken in laboratory work. For instance, they begin to select facts for memorization by looking over the files of old examinations maintained in each of the medical fraternity houses. They share tip-offs from the lectures and offhand remarks of the faculty as to what will be on the examinations. In anatomy, they agree not to bother to dissect out subcutaneous nerves, reasoning that it is both difficult and time-consuming and the material can be gotten out of books with less effort. The interaction involved in the development of such systems and short-cuts is one of the things that makes a group out of a class which had previously been only an aggregation of smaller and less organized groups.

So the students learn to separate what they do in the first year from the original feelings they had that everything that happens to them in medical school will be important. Thus, they become cynical about the value of their activities in the first year. They feel that the real thing—that learning which will help them to help mankind—has been postponed, perhaps until the second year, or perhaps even farther, at which time they will be again able to act on idealistic premises. They believe that what they do in their later years in school under supervision will be the same thing they will do, as physicians, on their own; the first year had disappointed this expectation.

There is one thing, however, in which the students are not disappointed during the first year. This is the so-called trauma of dealing with the cadaver. But this experience, rather than producing cynicism, reinforces the student's attachment to his idealistic view of medicine by making him feel that he is enduring at least some of the necessary unpleasantness a doctor goes through. Such difficulties, however, do not loom as large for the student as those of solving the problem of just what the faculty wants.

On this and other points, a working consensus develops in the new consolidated group about how to interpret their experience in medical school and how to behave in it. This consensus, which we call *student culture*,[7] focuses their attention almost completely on their day-to-day activities in school and points them away from their earlier idealistic preoccupations. Cynicism, griping, and minor cheating become endemic, but the cynicism is specific to the educational situation, to the first year, and then only to parts of that. Thus, the students keep their cynicism separate from their idealistic

feelings and by postponement protect their belief that medicine is a wonderful thing, that their school is a good one, and that they will become good doctors.

Later Years. The sophomore year does not differ much from the freshman
year. The work load probably increases as does the anxiety over examinations. Though they begin some medical activities, as in their attendance at
autopsies and particularly in their beginning course in physical diagnosis,
most of what they do continues to repeat the pattern of the college science
course. Their attention still centers on the problem of getting through school
by doing well in examinations.

During the third and fourth, or clinical years, teaching takes a new form.
Instead of lectures and laboratories, the students' work now consists of the
study of actual patients admitted to the hospital or seen in the clinic. Each
patient who enters the hospital is assigned to a student who interviews him
about his illnesses, past and present, and performs a physical examination.
He writes this up for the patient's chart, and appends his diagnosis and the
treatment he would use were he actually allowed to treat the patient instead
of simply observing the treatment given by the staff. During conferences with
faculty physicians, often held at the patient's bedside, the student is quizzed
about items of his report and called on to defend them or explain their significance. Most of the teaching in the clinical years is of this kind.

This contact with patients brings a new set of circumstances for the student to deal with. He no longer has any great pressure created by tests, for
he is told by the faculty, and this is confirmed by his daily experience, that
examinations are no longer so important. Instead his problem now becomes
one of dealing with a steady stream of patients in a way that will please the
staff man he is working under, and of handling what can be the tremendous
load of clinical work so as to allow himself time for studying diseases and
treatments that interest him and for play and family life.

The students have expected that once they arrive in the clinical years
they will be able to realize the idealistic ambitions they had to help people
and to learn those things immediately useful in helping people who are ill.
But they find themselves working to understand cases as medical problems
rather than working to help the sick and memorizing all the relevant available facts so that these can be produced immediately for a questioning staff
man. When they make ward rounds with a faculty member they are likely
to be quizzed about any of the million and one facts possibly related to the
condition of the patient they are taking care of.

Observers speak of the cynicism that overtakes the student and the lack
of concern for his patients as human beings. This change does take place, but
it is not produced by "the anxiety brought about by the presence of death
and suffering."[8] The student becomes preoccupied with the technical aspects
of the cases he deals with because the faculty requires him to. He is asked
about enough technical details that he must spend most of his time learning
them.

The frustrations created by his position in the teaching hospital further
divert the student from idealistic concerns. He finds himself low man in a
hierarchy based on clinical experience, so that he is allowed very little of

the medical responsibility he would like to take. Because he has no experience, he cannot write orders, and he gets permission to perform medical and
surgical procedures (if at all) at a rate he considers far too slow. He usually
must content himself with mere vicarious participation in the drama of
danger, life, and death that he sees as the core of medical practice. The student culture concentrates attention on these difficulties so that events (and
especially those involving patients) are interpreted and reacted to as they
push him toward or hold him back from further participation in this drama.
He does not think in terms the layman might use.

As a result of the increasingly technical emphasis of his thinking the student appears cynical to the non-medical outsider, though from his own point
of view he is simply seeing what is "really important." Instead of reacting
with the layman's horror and sympathy for the patient to the sight of a cancerous organ that has been surgically removed, the student thinks only that
he did not get to close the incision when the operation was completed and of
the hours he will have to spend searching in the fatty flesh for the lymph
nodes that will reveal how far the disease has spread. Just as in any other
line of work, he drops the lay attitude for that relevant to the way the event
affects someone in his position.

This is not to say that the students lose their original idealism, for they
do not. When such issues are openly raised in a situation defined as proper
for raising them, they respond as they might have when they were freshmen. But the influence of the student culture is such that questions which
might bring forth this idealism are not brought up. Students have patients
assigned to them for examination and follow-up who might, thought of in
one way, provoke idealistic crises. But they tend not to think about such patients in this way. Rather, they discuss them with reference to the problems
they create for the student. Patients with terminal diseases who are a long
time dying, or patients with chronic diseases who show little change from
week to week, are more likely to be talked about as creating extra work without extra compensation in knowledge or the opportunity to practice new
skills than as cases which raise questions about euthanasia. Such cases require the students to spend time every day checking on the progress which
he feels will probably not take place, and to write long "progress" notes in the
patient's chart although little progress has occurred.

This apparent cynicism is a collective matter. Group activities are built
around this kind of workaday perspective, constraining the students in two
ways. First, they do not openly express the lay idealistic notions they may
hold, for their culture does not sanction this; second, they are less likely to
think such thoughts when they are engaged in group activity. The collective
nature of this "cynicism" is indicated by the fact that students become more
openly idealistic whenever they are removed from the influence of student
culture: when they are alone with a sociologist as they near the end of school
and sense the approaching end of student life, or when they are isolated
from the rest of the class and thus less influenced by this culture.[9]

They still feel, though much less so than before, that school is irrelevant
to actual medical practice. Much of what they do, like running laboratory
tests on patients newly admitted to the hospital or examining surgical speci-

mens in the pathology laboratory, seems to them to have nothing to do with what they envision as their future activity as doctors. They still feel, as they did as freshmen, that perhaps they may have to get the knowledge they will need in spite of the school. They still conceive of medicine as a huge body of proven facts, but no longer believe that they will ever be able to master it all. They now say that they are going to try to apply the solution of the practicing M.D. to their own dilemma: learn a few things that they are interested in very well and know enough about other things to get through examinations while in school and, later on in practice to know which specialist to send these difficult patients to.

Their original medical idealism reasserts itself as the end of school approaches. Seniors show more interest than students in earlier years in serious ethical dilemmas of the kind they expect to be presented with in practice. They have become aware of the kind of dilemmas laymen often see as crucial for the physician—whether it is right to keep patients with fatal diseases alive as long as possible, or what they will do if an influential patient demands that they perform an abortion—and worry about them. As they near graduation and student culture begins to break down as the students begin to go their separate ways, these questions are more and more openly discussed.

While in school, they have added to this lay idealism a new and peculiarly professional idealism. Even though they know that few doctors live up to the standards they have been taught, they intend always to examine their patients thoroughly and to give treatment based on a firm diagnosis rather than just to relieve symptoms. This transformation of their idealism appears most explicitly in their consideration of alternative career plans, with regard to both specialization and the kind of arrangements they will make for setting up in practice. Many of their hypothetical choices aim at making it possible for them to be the kind of doctors their original idealism pictured. Thus, many seniors consider taking specialty training so that they will be able to work in a limited field in which it will be more nearly true that they know all there is to know, thus avoiding the necessity of dealing in a more ignorant way with the wider range of problems general practice would present. In the same way, they try to think of ways of setting up partnerships or other arrangements making it easier to avoid a work load which would prevent them from giving each patient the thorough examination and care they now see as ideal.

In other words, as school comes to an end, the cynicism specific to the school situation also comes to an end and their original and more general idealism about medicine comes to the fore again, directing choices within a framework they have picked up since it went underground. Their idealism is now more informed although no less selfless.

Discussion. We have used the word "idealism" and its opposite "cynicism" loosely in our description of the changeable state of mind of the medical student, playing on ambiguities we can now attempt to clear up. Retaining a core of common meaning, that of the dictionary definition, in our reference to the person's belief in the worth of his activity and the claims made for it, we have seen that this is not a generalized trait of the students we studied but rather an attitude which varies greatly, depending on the particular activity whose worth is questioned and the situation in which the attitude is expressed.

This variability of the idealistic attitude suggests that in using such an element of personal perspective in sociological analysis one should not treat it as homogenous but should make a determined search for subtypes which may arise under different conditions and have differing consequences. Such subtypes can presumably be constructed along many dimensions. There might, for instance, be consistent variations in the medical students' idealism through the four years of school that were related to their social-class background. We have stressed in this report the subtypes that can be constructed according to variations in the object of the idealistic attitude and variations in the audience the person has in mind when he adopts the attitude. The medical students can be viewed as both idealistic and cynical depending on whether one has in mind their view of their school activities or the futures they envision for themselves as doctors. Further, they might take one or another of these positions depending on whether their implied audience was made up of other students, their instructors, or the lay public.

A final complication arises because cynicism and idealism are not merely attributes of the person, but are as dependent on the person doing the attributing as they are on the qualities of the person to whom they are attributed.[10] Though the student may see his own disregard of the unique personal troubles of a particular patient as proper scientific objectivity, the layman may view this objectivity as heartless cynicism.[11]

Having made these necessary analytic distinctions, we can now summarize the transformations of these characteristics as we have seen them occuring among medical students. Some of the students' determined idealism when they enter is reaction against the lay notion, of which they are uncomfortably aware, that doctors are money-hungry cynics; they counter this with an idealism of similarly lay origin stressing the doctor's devotion to service. But this idealism soon meets a setback, as students find that it will not be relevant for awhile, since medical school has little relation to the practice of medicine they envision. As it has not been refuted, but only shown to be temporarily beside the point, the students agree to set this idealism aside in favor of a realistic approach to the problem of getting through school. This realistic approach, which we have labeled as the cynicism specific to the school experience, serves as protection for the earlier grandiose feelings about medicine, by postponing their exposure to reality to a distant future. As that distant future approaches again at the end of the four years and its possible mistreatment of their ideals moves closer, the students again worry about maintaining their integrity, this time in the situation of actual medical practice. They use some of the knowledge they have gained to plan possible careers which can best do this for them.

We can put this in propositional form by saying that when a man's ideals are challenged by outsiders and then further strained by reality, he may salvage them by postponing their application to a future time when conditions are expected to be more propitious.

33   **RELIGIOUS ASPECTS OF MEDICAL TEACHING**

By Granger Westberg

During the past 10 or 15 years some rather unexpected things have happened in the relationship between medicine and religion. Ministers and physicians who previously have had only a speaking acquaintance are now discovering that they have quite a bit in common—the patient—and so they are
beginning to converse on a professional level. We cannot at this time trace
the history of that change to show the many events of the past 50 years which
contributed materially to it. Suffice it to say that there has been a growing
interest in the patient as a person, a whole person, with physical, mental and
spiritual needs which somehow do not respond well to piecemeal treatment.
A great many physicians, seeing the needs of the whole patient, are seeking
new ways to minister more effectively to all these needs.

More than Sermons. The clergyman also has become aware that there is
more to his job than merely preaching sermons. He knows that only about 10
percent of his week is spent preparing or delivering lectures and sermons. He
has come to see that his theological education has not prepared him adequately for the 90 percent of his week which is spent primarily in working
personally with individuals. He knows he cannot remain aloof to personal
problems, or handle them with pious platitudes. His parishioners demand
that he get down out of his pulpit and work with them and their problems
down where they are.

This demand that religion be made relevant to life has shaken the foundations of theological education. Within the short span of approximately five
years almost every seminary in the United States has added a chair in pastoral care which in one way of describing the pastor's ministry to the individual. More than that, because it has been demonstrated that pastoral care
can best be taught by the clinical method, seminaries which long enjoyed a
picturesque location high on a hill outside the city walls, have suddenly
realized that this is precisely where they should *not* be. At this moment a
number of seminary boards are discussing how to move into the center of
great cities close to laboratories such as medical centers, social agencies, industrial plants, community houses, etc. which will provide students with
clinical material. In this way students will be able to test the validity of religious faith in actual contact with fellow humans in crisis situations.

It is no secret that theological educators are indebted to medical education for demonstrating how theory may be made relevant to practice, by
daily moving back and forth between classroom and clinic. In addition to
this, theologians, recognizing that they never minister to a soul apart from a
body, have invited physicians during the past 5 or 10 years, to participate
in the instruction of theological students. We are convinced that such teaching by men of science has enriched our theological curriculum.

Physicians' Blind Spots. But it is at this point we must speak frankly to

From *Journal of Medical Education*, 32, (March, 1957), 204–209. Copyright 1957 by
The Association of American Medical Colleges of Evanston, Illinois.

medical education. As we in theology have been working more closely with physicians on a professional level, and have included them on our faculties and in frequent discussion groups we have discovered that just as clergymen have blind spots in regard to physical and psychological needs of people, so physicians have blind spots in terms of the philosophical or theological dimensions of the lives of their patients. So obvious has this become that we must select physicians who lecture to theological students with the greatest care lest the students lose respect for them and dub them, as they have, "mechanics."

Clergymen on the faculty? Now that theological schools profit by the presence of mature physicians in their classrooms and clinics could it be that medical students might profit from having qualified clergymen related in some way to their educational program? If so how could this be begun and what would be the content of such teaching?

In simplest outline form the steps might be something like the following:

a. Begin the program by appointing a clinically trained chaplain to the medical center or hospital used by the medical school. (Chaplains who are approved by the American Hospital Chaplain's Association have had four years of college, three or four years of seminary, two to five years in a parish followed by a two year residency in designated clinical training centers.)

b. As the chaplain develops a teamwork relationship with individual physicians they will gradually use him in informal discussions with medical students on the wards.

c. Encourage the chaplain to have joint seminars on religion and medicine in which cases of mutual interest are presented.

d. When, after a year or two, the medical faculty is assured of the quality of the chaplain's work he might be invited to be a participating observer in certain courses, (psychiatry, gastro-intestinal diseases) he also may become an instructor, give a series of lectures, or lead discussion seminars in a more structured setting. The subjects of joint interest to religion and medicine are too numerous to discuss here in any other way than to list them.

Subjects of joint interest

1. *The role of the parish pastor in the hospital.*

(This would include actual case presentations describing vividly how clergymen of various faiths go about their work and also at what points the physician might assist them.)

2. The unique aspects of the hospital chaplain's role as he works in a special way both with medical personnel and parish clergy.

3. A brief history of the relationship of religion and medicine in both Christian and non-Christian cultures.

4. The art of professional conversation with normal individuals under stress. (This discussion would draw upon the resources both of Christian pastoral care through the centuries together with modern insights based on newer psychological discoveries.) (A method of presenting this material will include recorded interviews, studied with reference to religious concepts which color human behavior.)

5. Sex education and the family, or the doctor's role in such educational

programs with youth groups, and married couples' clubs on a community wide scale.

6. The role of the physician in pre-marital counseling—developing the theme of physical, emotional and spiritual factors in the marriage relationship. The church's new interest in this field is significant because of its previous mishandling of the subject and its need now for a joint approach with medicine.

7. Functional illness as it is related to attitudinal factors which are often intertwined with religious concepts.

8. Faith healing, its philosophy, its exponents, its problems and relationship or lack of relationship to the Christian churches.

9. The broad area of morals and medicine—with special reference to birth control, sterilization, artificial insemination, eugenics, abortion, and euthanasia.

10. The handling of grief—as related to terminal illness; involving problems of "to tell or not to tell," the ministry to close relatives and the Eric Lindemann theory of the "grief work" necessary for those who are bereaved.

11. When to call a minister or priest or rabbi and—when *not* to call a clergyman. (A discussion of when the physician may be of more help religiously than the clergyman.)

12. The Church's attitude toward psychiatry.

These 12 subjects could obviously fill more than 12 discussions or lecture hours.

Religion and medicine are so intertwined that the medical student who graduates without having an opportunity to confront most or all of these issues under a qualified instructor will be at a serious disadvantage out in practice. In almost all these areas listed he is considered to be some sort of expert. If he is expected just to pick up this information in dormitory bull sessions, his information will probably not be very accurate. It is incongruous that his medical knowledge should be so accurate and up-to-date while his knowledge on religious matters which are so closely involved in his practice of medicine often stamp him as being quite *un*informed.

What exactly do we suggest should be the content of these lectures and semi-formal discussion groups with medical students? One way to find out would be to sit in on these classes, and this we strongly urge medical deans to do. As a sort of sample of what is said I should like to quote snatches of a lecture given a week or so ago to the University of Chicago freshman medical students. This is a voluntary series of five lectures attended by approximately 85 percent of the class. This particular discussion is on "The Church and Psychiatry" and attempts to bring medical students up-to-date on the attitude of the Church toward psychiatry as of today, with the hope that it will stimulate him to keep abreast of new developments of which a medical student should be aware.

The Church's Attitude Toward Psychiatry. The Church has been both irritated and intrigued by the developments in the field of dynamic psychiatry. It was irritated particularly in the 1930's and 40's because some of the representatives of this new field made such extravagant claims for it and gave the impression that all their findings about the nature of man were unknown prior to Freud. But the Church was intrigued by psychiatry's almost uncanny ability to get behind the facade of man to the real person inside. The analytical approach has helped religion to understand more scientifically what it had previously perceived intuitively.

In the 1930's a typical parish clergyman was quite naturally irritated by psychiatry when a church member who was being treated by a psychiatrist would say, "Since I have gone into analysis I have come to see that my religious beliefs are very superficial." When he went on to describe his beliefs as having been "superimposed" upon him by his parents and other religious people it took a very secure pastor to be able to admit that this was in some degree true. It was true that this patient, and many others like him, *had* merely parroted religious statements which he had never been helped to examine. The doctrines of the church had never "spoken" to him personally. As distilled wisdom of the ages they should have added meaning to his life but instead they were kept in a separate compartment unrelated to the rest of his life experiences.

When the thoughtful pastor got around to reflecting on what this parishioner was saying, he began to examine his own teaching and preaching and realized that they were not related to life as they could be. Many of his present church members were merely parroting what he told them was true. This experience was typical of the kind that jolted him and many of his fellow pastors in a way that over a period of 25 years has brought about a rethinking on the church's total educational program, beginning with the very young child right on through the theological seminary. The rethinking process has sought to devise new ways to make the Christian faith relevant.

Psychiatrists have broken away from the established pattern of medical practice in order that they might wrestle with some of the basic causes of illness. By this revolt they have called attention to the fact that the average minister is spending far too much time making the wheels of an organization go around to the neglect of his pastoral care responsibilities. Of course, the clergy were at first outraged at this attack upon their faithlessness, later they were chagrined as they recognized their own lethargy in matters of personal concern for individuals, and finally in humility, they expressed willingness to be taught by this renegade group. The next logical step in the process of helping people is to combine the insights of both psychiatry and religion.

The Church, says the late David Roberts of Union Seminary, appreciates that psychiatry is "documenting and widening our awareness of what the human race is up against in its attempt to reach inner freedom. It offers clinical details on some matters on which the Church fathers were either completely ignorant or only vaguely aware in their descriptions of human ills and perversities. Yet, strikingly enough, the means which have been employed in exploring the seriousness of the situation have at the same time been instruments of healing. If psychotherapy has widened our acquaintance with the ramifications of 'sin,' it has at the same time widened our conceptions of how this bondage can be overcome. It is as though a full awareness of what is involved in being in psychological fetters were a key that opens the lock."[1]

Psychiatry has given us tools to help distinguish between a faith that is genuine and one that is false. We see what a tremendous role inner security plays in changing people's attitudes—how difficult it is for one who is insecure to allow his present system of values to be questioned lest the foundation on which he now stands be knocked from under him.

The Church has been smoked out by psychiatry regarding its stand on sex. While in 1930 there were almost no books available describing the Church's attitude toward sex, by 1956 a score of excellent works by serious theologians help us to understand the Church's position.[2]

Sex means more than merely physical relations. It is in a sense a mystery because it is always pointing beyond itself. While it may appear to be mere biology, it actually contains at all times, even when least expected, a spiritual ingredient. When it fulfills its function we know it has somehow gone beyond what we anticipated.

Because a follower of Christ has been taught to love himself and his neighbor as himself he will try to resist the temptation to exploit any other fellow human for purposes which would degrade either of them.

The Christian knows about the problem of lust from personal experience. He is not proud of this but is grateful for the continuing forgiveness of God which he receives in his daily strivings against these temptations. The fact that he is never wholly free of these temptations or of the daily grace of God helps him to be more humble, understanding and forgiving in his relationships with his fellows.

To this end he strives to understand the peculiar problems of the sexual "deviate" which he sees as having their origin perhaps in deeper problems of interpersonal human relations.

The Christian person must never take sexual union lightly. It is always a serious and radical matter to the persons involved, to their relation and attitude toward God and the meaning of life. Whenever such union is entered into casually, or with animality, or spiritualized out of existence, then its true value cannot be appreciated. There is revealed in sexual union more of the other person's true self than in perhaps any other joint human act.

Sex is too often equated with sin. But sex is no more nor less sinful than other areas of human activity. However, because it impinges on so many aspects of the human personality it may appear to be more sinful than most other realms of human activity. When sex plays too important a role in the life of a person, it always stands in danger of becoming an idolatrous thing and eventually a substitute for God.

The hope is that sex will be looked upon as a gracious gift which is given us to use as an open channel for mature and serious love. When used in the service of such a high goal it has a tremendous potential for bringing about an unusual sense of happiness and even a sense of partnership with the Creator. Our Hebrew heritage with its down-to-earth conviction about the goodness of God's creation could never permit a categorical separation between spirit and matter in man's life.

These are some of the things we are saying to the medical students at the University of Chicago. We think they will help clergymen and physicians to understand each other better and thereby to serve the patient in a way which would otherwise be impossible.

34   SOME IMPLICATIONS OF STUDIES IN THE
PROFESSIONALIZATION OF THE PHYSICIAN

By Samuel W. Bloom

It is strange but true that this is a closed society with ideals and Gods of its own. The world about is the "other" world and one in which prestige is gained by being a member of the medical world. Within the medical world one can re-define, relive and work out a completely or almost so, satisfactory life on the principles, ethics and demands set up by this group. . . . There is no reason to believe that medicine is the only occupation which might lead to similar feelings of attachment. However, it does give one all the things that one looks for in finding an in-group. Tradition, prestige, purpose, esotericness, challenge, human associations, a means to financial security, personal satisfaction in achievement, strength in a strong association, . . .[1]

The above statement, written by a second year medical student, expresses vividly something about medicine which even the visitor to its institutions cannot fail to notice. The medical school and the hospital comprise a unique and highly distinctive world within itself. Its members possess a special identity and culture which are reserved for medical initiates.

For many years, sociologists and social psychologists have been fascinated by the problem of how various cultures provide for the indoctrination of its new members, its children, into the codes of behavior which will control their behavior as adults. The name "socialization" has been used as the technical term to describe this general process of social maturation. *Professionalization,* as I will use it here, is a process of socialization, which involves a matrix of social relations in which the (medical) student internalizes and makes his own the attitudes and values which will largely determine his future professional role.[2]

The institution which has evolved within the profession of medicine for the purpose of professionalizing its recruits is the medical school. It has been said that, "achieving any high occupational status usually involves a probationary ordeal which inculcates the requisite technical skills sometimes, and the necessary social attitudes and behavior patterns always."[3] Medical education is just such a probationary ordeal. The medical school provides the social environment in which this process of social maturation takes place.

Recent events in the history of medical education have directed particular attention to the medical school as a complex social environment and as the context of *education as maturation* rather than *education as technical training.* The events I refer to are those program changes such as the Western Reserve curriculum revision, the Cornell Comprehensive Care and Teaching Program, and the Pennsylvania Family Health Advisor Service, which Dr. Berry refers to as "provocative experiments aimed at making such revisions in our teaching programs as are consistent with a growing understanding of the whole patient rather than just a part of the patient. . . ."[4]

Not since the events surrounding the "Flexner Report," has medical education responded so profoundly to the question: is modern medical education preparing adequately and appropriately the physicians of tomorrow?

Quoting again from Dr. Berry:

Today's generation of doctors as they enter medical practice find a very different environment from that prevailing 50 years ago. The whole atmosphere has changed, yet the medical curriculum has not evolved to meet these changes. On the contrary, the curriculum continues to adhere to a pattern that was designed in different times and under different circumstances.[5]

Today, barely five years after Dr. Berry offered this challenge in his presidential address to the Association of American Medical Colleges, one finds that the medical curriculum is yielding rapidly to the pressures for change. The six "provocative experiments" which he was able to refer to then have been multiplied several times. It was in association with some of these programs that the studies of professionalization which I know best were started. When for example, "the faculty of the School of Medicine of Cornell University construed its Comprehensive Care and Teaching Program as an 'experiment in medical education,' they set about almost at once to collaborate with sociologists in a study of the operation and educational results of that program."[6] Similar procedures were followed at Colorado, Western Reserve and Pennsylvania. This brings me to the first fact which I would like to emphasize:

(1) The current outstanding experiments in medical education are genuinely experimental in principle. As Dietrick and Berson pointed out, looking back over a half-century of medical education, it is not unusual for medical educators to try out new courses and pedagogical methods. It is highly unique, however, for them to subject such programs to intensive evaluation, bringing in skilled investigators trained in the best available methods for this purpose.[7]

The application of this principle is complicated by the nature of the basic educational problem involved, which focuses on the *doctor-patient relationship*. According to the stated aims of the various teaching experiments, their main purpose is to teach students to see patients as *whole persons* rather than as disease entities, and also to be able to give *comprehensive care* to patients.

Fifty years ago, the problem of medical education was primarily involved with the relationship between the medical profession and what might be called the community of science. Indirectly, but in a very real sense, the relationship between medicine and the lay society at large was concerned. As Flexner documented so unsparingly, *the medical profession, by condoning and actually sponsoring the proprietary school, was contributing to the neglect of the public health*. It was not that medical education in this country was poor in all instances, but, as Flexner stated it, ". . . there is probably no other country in the world in which there is so great a distance and so fatal a difference between the best, the average, and the worst."[8] The solution which was accepted and put into operation was to incorporate the medical school in the university, applying the standards of excellence traditional to the graduate study of the scientific disciplines to the education of doctors.

Today, the problem if I have interpreted it correctly, is of a very different quality than that of fifty years ago. It is also more difficult to solve. This is not to say that the revolution which Flexner triggered was an easy one to accomplish. A plan of social organization had to be forged which would give laboratory science a place of high status in the medical school. This involved enormous financial burdens which the professional school was not accustomed to assuming. To motivate the university and the medical profession in this direction must have been a considerable task. Nevertheless, the speed of the events which followed Flexner's report is remarkable. Within ten years, half of the schools which he surveyed had gone out of existence. The remainder were well on the way toward firm alliances with universities. The selection criteria for the recruiting of medical students were corrected. No longer was it possible for virtually anybody, as President Eliot had remarked just a few years earlier, to "walk into a medical school from the street, . . . and of those who did walk in, many could barely read and write."[9] Nor is there any question that the physician who emerged from the new university-affiliated schools was far better able to do his job than the doctors of the previous medical era.

In a curiously paradoxical way, the problem of medical education now may be interpreted as the product of the success of the reforms of fifty years ago. The chain reaction set off by Flexner dealt more than a swift death-blow to the proprietary school. There was also a dramatic effect on the health of the nation.

During the past half-century the average life-expectancy in America has increased by one-third. The consequences for medical practice, are vividly expressed in these words from a physician who experienced it:

Medical practice has changed from concern for problems of serious disease and death to problems in which the threat of death is small. Now, patient feelings about their own symptoms are as significant as the actual disease itself.[10]

Or, as stated by another physician:

We are faced with the fact that perhaps one half of all patients or more have nothing very serious wrong with them in terms of prospective death. But can we say that there is nothing very serious wrong with them in terms of prospective life?[11]

The course of medical training, vis-a-vis the patient, may be said to be rounding its full cycle: (1) as an apprentice, the medical trainee saw patients in their home environment, and studied disease first-hand at the bedside; (2) in the proprietary school, with its didactic method, the lecture and the book replaced direct observation as the primary method of learning, and the medical student was removed from the living patient; (3) he then returned to the patient, but, as Flexner stated so well, "relying no longer altogether on the senses with which nature endowed him, but with those senses made infinitely more acute, more accurate, and more helpful by the processes and instruments which the . . . (previous) half century's progress . . . placed at his disposal."[12] The return to the patient, however, took a special turn. It was not to the whole patient, but to the patient's disease. The *new methods for diagnosis and treatment, instead of taking a place only as a means for achieving the goals of medicine,* the cure and prevention of disease, *tended to become ends in themselves.*

I will now make an assertion, based upon the foregoing, but hypothetical in character:

(2) The prime challenge to medical education today is to prepare future physicians for a deeper understanding and skill with the interpersonal

part of the doctor-patient relationship. In other words, the art of medicine is striving for the discipline of a social science of medicine. This is a reflection of a shift in the requirements of medical practice. The emphasis has shifted from questions of *what* and *how* to *whom;* that is, *from* the knowledge and techniques of biological science as they apply to disease *to* the patient, his feelings and potential reactions to the whole complex of factors involved in his illness, including the physician and the way the physician acts in the doctor-patient relationship.

As L. J. Henderson has said, the physician can do harm to the patient with words just as surely as he can do harm by prescribing the wrong drug or making a false cut with a scalpel.[13] The present challenge to medical education is to help prepare future physicians to deal with the reactions of his patients in the emotional and social aspects of behavior as well as with the biological.

The programmatic changes which have evolved to deal with this problem may be classified in the following categories:

(1) *Integrated* teaching. This may be sub-divided into two types:

   (a) the *horizontal,* cutting across the traditional departmental lines in pre-clinical subjects, or across the lines of clinical subjects, but remaining within so-called preclinical or clinical boundaries. Harvard's small-scale experiment with integration of the pre-clinical subjects, for example, now is being applied to the whole of entering medical classes. At Cornell, a limited integration of clinical subjects is being tried in the fourth year in the Comprehensive Care and Teaching Program.

   (b) the *vertical,* cutting across the boundary between the clinical and the preclinical. Western Reserve offers an example of both horizontal and vertical integration, and, in the latter, outdistances similar efforts elsewhere.

(2) The elimination of a full two year period between the student and patient contact. At Western Reserve, all students have a significant amount of patient-contact from the beginning of the four years. At Syracuse, contact is provided through a course in behavioral science in the first year. Pennsylvania, on a volunteer basis, offers opportunity to act as a Family Health Adviser from the first year. Second year courses in clinical medicine, including opportunity to see patients, are now common.

(3) New types of courses, designed specifically to teach in some formally organized way, about *psycho-social aspects of medicine.* The most ambitious program of this type is at Syracuse, where a de facto department of behavioral science teaches over one hundred hours in the first year. This is still an exceptional example. By and large, this trend is exemplified by an expanded responsibility for departments of psychiatry to teach in the preclinical years.

What I would like to do in the remainder of this paper is explore the deep underlying assumptions of these curriculum changes and then discuss them in terms of the professionalization process.

Without referring for the moment to specific programs, I believe one may describe three general assumptions which are widely prevalent, either singly or together among medical educators today:

(1) there is a *de-humanization effect* implicit in the preclinical curriculum;

(2) there is a *compartmentalization* or *segmentation* effect implicit in the whole of the medical curriculum;

(3) there is an *institutionalization effect* implicit in the training of the modern hospitals.

The impact of any one or more of these three kinds of educational experiences upon attitudes toward the patient is considered harmful to the doctor-patient relationship.

The first assumption, de-humanization, refers to the "arbitrary segregation of the student in laboratory, library, and lecture hall for the first two years of the medical course. . . ." As I understand it, the belief is that the intensive experience of medical students with cadaver, specimen, and elaborate pathology, unrelieved by contact with the whole living patient for two years, can and often does produce an "emotional callous" which blights the development of attitudes toward the patient. The de-humanization hypothesis has been stated as follows:

The desire to be of service to persons suffering from pain and stress represents a major motivation for undertaking the study of medicine. It deserves careful nurture from the first moment of the medical student's career and should not be dampened by two years of work in which human contact with patients is absent or minimal and the emphasis is on science for science's sake.[14]

The origins of the compartmentalization hypothesis have been described by Dr. Harper of Western Reserve:

From a historical perspective one can readily see how modern medicine has been fettered by its own tradition. It was less than one hundred years ago that medicine was a tyro among the natural sciences. . . . From Virchow's brilliant observation sprang the new era of scientific medicine. . . . With the rapid expansion and development of the new disciplines of biochemistry, physiology, pathology, and microbiology, modern scientific medicine erected its new structure on the firm conviction that all functions of the living organism could be explained on a physiochemical basis. . . . To be really scientific, it became necessary for the doctor to impose an instrument of some sort between himself and the patient. *The patient was ignored in order to obtain a coned down view of a single part.* . . .[15]

The line of argument associated with the compartmentalization hypothesis follows: (a) the pre-clinical phase of medical education tends to be a recapitulation of the evolution of medicine as biological science, and the highly developed knowledge about localized pathology is the climax of this evolution; (b) the emphasis in the laboratory is on dissection and other forms of reduction of the whole into component parts; (c) this reductive process is reinforced by didactic presentations by experts who dramatize the extent to which knowledge about each part has been developed, and reinforced by patient demonstrations for illustration of the disease entity; (c) the effect is to overwhelm students with the scope of knowledge about disease processes and heighten their sense of the need for specialization. Moreover, the student's image of the patient is fractionated and a frame of reference is learned for the perception of a "segmented" rather than a "whole" patient.

Finally, *"institutionalization effect"* describes a learned tendency to see patients as isolated individuals, as *hospital cases* rather than as human beings in the fullness of life's natural contexts. Again, the assumption is that a latent danger has grown in medical training, this time in the clinical phase. This implicit harmful effect on student attitudes represents an *un*anticipated consequence of what were otherwise advances in both science and education. If, it is argued, a student learns his clinical skills in the hospital only, his perception of the patient is limited to an institutional context which is not indigenous to the patient's basic problem. Thus, he lacks first-hand experience with the social and emotional background of the patient.

I would like to call your attention to the fact that these are all assertions which are *negative*. They interpret harmful or toxic potentials in a situation, and, as would be expected, are usually followed by recommendations concerning the types of experience needed to neutralize or antidote these attitudinal effects.

In general, these assumptions are connected with programs which expand the range, in time and space, of contact between the student and the patient. Quite obviously, these are underlying in at least a large portion of the Western Reserve reforms. They are also present in the thinking of those programs of home care, or family health advisors which are brought into the preclinical years.

One also finds positive assumptions. These are evident in a program like the Comprehensive Care and Teaching Program at Cornell, where an effort is being made to introduce formal instruction in comprehensive care without the underlying assumption that student attitudes are harmed by other aspects of their training. This is also true of the Syracuse program of behavioral science. The assumption underlying the latter is that new developments in anthropology, sociology, and social psychology have significant contributions to add to medical instruction. The program is offered as a valuable added element, *not* as a corrective for something else.[16]

The three negative hypotheses—dehumanization, compartmentalization, and institutionalization—describe a process of *attitude impact*. In other words, they assert that a type of educational environment is likely to provide an experience which effects student attitudes. The impact of the basic science curriculum upon student attitudes toward patients causes the attitudes to change.

It is my belief that the form of these impact hypotheses is inaccurate. The process is *not* one in which B (the educational environment) acting upon A (student attitudes toward patients) results in A (changed attitudes). My belief is that A (student attitudes toward patients prior to the preclinical experience) encounters B (the preclinical environment) with C (a frame of reference related to the anticipated experience) *intervening*. In other words, the interaction between prior attitudes and the educational environment is selective according to the attitudinal frame of reference. For illustration, I would like to examine briefly the opinions of a class of medical students who were questioned concerning their expectations about the experiences in medical school which they were just about to begin.[17]

It was found that students, just prior to the beginning of medical school, expect the year to come will contrast sharply with the years just passed. They expect the scholastic demands will be much greater than those of pre-medical studies. However, they also anticipate that the first two years of medical school will be more demanding, more difficult and less pleasant than later years of medical study. It appears that the preclinical years are thought of as an impending *ordeal*, a *rite de passage*, which must be undergone in order to qualify for future rewards. Rogoff has called this an expectation of "*delayed gratification*," whereby the preclinical years are perceived as a "price to pay" for the rewards and gratifications of the clinical years of study and, ultimately, doctorhood.[18]

I would like to construct for you a picture of a typical medical student's experience in the preclinical years, requesting that you be indulgent about the necessarily over-simplified portrait that results:

(a) Students anticipate a generally difficult, unpleasant "ordeal" in the preclinical years.

(b) This ordeal is a "necessary evil" before "real" medical training in the clinic can begin.

(c) The result is an orientation which *overvalues* the clinical and *undervalues* the preclinical.

(d) Filtered through this frame of reference, the preclinical studies are *not* valued for their own "whole" intrinsic merit, *but* for their *practical medical utility*. Thus, the student, early in the preclinical years, seeks for all the bits of information which he can spot as useful later on.[19]

(e) The resulting utilitarian view of preclinical study serves to channel the student's perception toward the *parts* as opposed to the *whole*. It reinforces the funneling effect which is already implicit in his studies. The disease-entity point of view thereby is promoted and nurtured.

The most important conclusion to this analysis is that student and physician attitudes toward the patient as a dehumanized, segmentalized, institutionalized entity are *not* conceived as the direct result of a given kind of environment which is interpreted as the single primary cause of the attitude. Instead, the prior expectations which students bring with them to the preclinical years are shown as selective determinants which contribute to attitudinal learning.

Before concluding, I would like to introduce one more thought concerning the professionalization of the physician. Growth, however one conceives it, is usually described in terms of stages through which the organism develops. Professionalization is a growth concept which pictures the development in human individuals of a professional self, an identity in the role of doctor. In the development from studenthood to physicianhood, at one stage, it appears to be important for the student to perceive the patient as a disease entity. In this way, he masters and gains control of an important area of knowledge (pathology), and adapts to significant requirements of his future role as a physician. However, this is only a stage of growth. If he fixates on this stage, if he is unable to develop beyond it to a perception of the patient in his whole unity as a person and in the fullness of his environment, then the student's development toward physician is handicapped. His "social maturation" is incomplete. If this view of professionalization as growth is correct, the disease entity concept may be seen *not as an evil in itself*, but as an important step in the development of medical scientific thought. As the preclinical curriculum (ontogeny) recapitulates the history of medical science (phylogeny), a disease entity view of the patient has a proper place within it. Perhaps the most important objective in medical education is to provide students with enough freedom to experience deeply and fully each step in his professional growth. Thought of in this way, excessive integration in teaching may be just as inhibiting as an excessive specialization.

Summary and Conclusions:

In this discussion, I tried to show first that new trends in medical education which emphasize the patient as a whole person have been accompanied by an increase of attention to the student as a whole person. Implicit is the proposition:

(1) in the attempt to train future physicians for better doctor-patient relationships, one cannot teach only about the *other* (the whole patient) but must also know about the self (the student). Only thus can this self-other interaction be improved.

Studies in the professionalization process, consequently, are appropriate adjuncts to the experimental programs which, in recent years, have appeared in medical education.

In important examples of the current reforms in medical education, one finds gratifying evidence that the most basic principle of scientific method —the principle of self-correction—has been included.

An intrinsic danger in any reform program is that the program itself solidifies into an *end* rather than a *means to an end*. In current trends of medical education, the end, broadly stated, is to train physicians for the problems which are most salient in their professional lives. In this paper, I have tried to show how the increased importance of psycho-social aspects of medical practice has led to the increased importance in medical education of training in the human relations skills and the whole view of the patient. On the other hand, I raised some questions about the validity of certain assumptions which have determined the structure of some educational experiments.

My purpose in raising these questions is to emphasize the necessity of continuous inquiry concerning all the elements which are part of these educational experiments. *What* is taught, *how, to whom*, for *what purpose* and with *what* effect? All five particular questions command attention.

In conclusion, I would like to quote from a statement which is dated 1766. It presents a model spirit for the guidance of all scientific endeavor, whether it be an educational experiment or a study of the effects of such experiments. Thomas Bond, this nation's first professor of clinical medicine, wrote, arguing in behalf of bedside training for medical students:

There the Clinical professor comes in to the Aid of Speculation and demonstrates the Truth of Theory by Facts. He meets his pupils at stated times in the Hospital, and when a case presents adapted to his purpose, he asks all those Questions which lead to a certain knowledge of the Disease and parts Affected; and if the Disease baffles the power of Art and the Patient falls a Sacrifice to it, he then brings his Knowledge to the Test, and fixes Honour or discredit on his Reputation by exposing all the Morbid parts to View, and Demonstrates by what means it produced Death, and if perchance he finds something unexpected, which Betrays an Error in Judgment, he like a great and good man immediately acknowledges the mistake, and, for the benefit of survivors, points out other methods by which it might have been more happily treated.[20]

35   MEDICAL EDUCATION AS SOCIAL PROCESS

By Patricia L. Kendall and Robert K. Merton

In basic science as in applied science, in sociology as in medicine, specialties are multiplied through subdivision. So it is that the fast growing specialty of the sociology of medicine has itself divided into at least four distinct though connected subspecialties.

Perhaps the first of these to become established, though it too has only lately come of age, centers on the social etiology and ecology of disease (and, by implication, of health). This branch systematically examines social variations in the definition and conception of illness, the incidence of particular diseases among people variously located in the social structure and the ways in which their position in the social structure tends to make them more vulnerable, or less, to particular diseases (for example, by putting them under different degrees of stress). The importance of this subdivision of the sociology of medicine has been widely acknowledged by medical scientists possibly because it deals with classes of problems neighboring upon epidemiology with its latterday focus on sex, class, ethnic and other status differences in the frequency and character of endemic as well as epidemic conditions of morbidity.

Of more recent vintage, but maturing rapidly, is the subspecialty dealing with sociological components in therapy and rehabilitation. It begins with the premise that sick people are engaged in networks of social relations that can advance or curb their recovery and rehabilitation, that is, the re-storing of once sick people to their social statuses and roles. The concept of the 'therapeutic environment' largely emerging from the treatment of mental illness, has evident implications for other kinds of sickness as well. The concept of 'secondary gains' from illness must also come to be recognized as more than psychological in nature, this having been only its first formulation; it is plainly sociological as well, if only because social structures differ in the extent to which they provide opportunities for the occurrence of such secondary gains; it is possible to stipulate the rudiments of a "sociology of 'malingering'" on the basis of numerous studies of the social environments of failure and success in social rehabilitation.

A third division studies medicine and health care as a social institution, with its various structures of interlocking statuses and roles. In contemporary Western society, at least, the organizations directly concerned with the prevention of illness, the care of the sick, and the maintenance of health form a vast institutional complex, bringing together into one interdependent whole a great variety of personnel, organizations, and facilities—patients and physicians, nurses, dentists and pharmacists, proliferating numbers and varieties of health technicians, all kinds of hospitals and centers for medical research, agencies designed to protect the public health, philanthropic organizations aiding medical research and practice, large drug houses, associations to provide health insurance, and professional schools, in and out of universities, to educate health personnel. Sociologists have begun to work on the formidable task of analyzing the components and organization of this great institutional complex; in particular, by intensive study of hospitals as social systems.

These three subdivisions are interwoven with a fourth that has most recently become the object of systematic inquiry: the sociology of medical education. This field of inquiry variously connects with each of the others. First, it searches out unwitting as well as planned differences in those values and technical skills acquired by students in diverse programs of medical education that go far to affect the motivated sensitivity to social factors in the *etiology and ecology* of sickness. Second, it departs from the sociological premise that *therapy* is greatly affected by the relationship between patient and physician; that this can provide an optimum setting for the care and cure of the sick. But the optimum relationship cannot be assumed to occur automatically; as Alan Gregg once observed, too often, the educational experience of the physician is such as to invite a spirit of easy compromise with the exigencies of difficult situations; too often, the letters M.D. stand for "Make Do." It therefore becomes necessary to discover the ways in which medical students acquire a trained capacity to elicit the deserved confidence of patients, so that the patient-physician relationship becomes a therapeutic resource.

Finally, the concept of medicine and health care as a social institution implies that physicians, as one of the chief actors in that institution, have somehow learned the requirements of that status and the many roles they are called upon to perform when they are assigned that status. This concept of medicine thereby enlarges the scope of the sociological study of medical education. The medical student is seen as engaged in a complex array of social relations; in the first instance, of course, with fellow-students and the faculty, but beyond this, with all manner of other health professionals and technicians, with patients, and with a changing relation to his own family once he is launched upon the beginnings of a career in medicine. Willy-nilly, and entirely irrespective of whether he is aware that this is so, he must come to terms with these diverse social relations, each with its distinctive and partly overlapping complement of expectations of what he should do and each entailing the distinctive responses of others, contingent upon what he actually does. In the language of sociology, the medical student occupies a particular status and this involves him in a particular role-set: the organized array of role-relationships characteristic of that status. This is a sociological fact. It is a sociological problem to discover how the structure of the medical school helps him to learn, or keeps him from learning, how to relate himself effectively to these diverse others so that he may perform his many roles as healer, director of a health-team, clinical or laboratory investigator, educator, member of a professional society and distinctively prepared member of his local community. This requires the sociologist to trace out the patterned reciprocities between the medical student and the others with whom he develops sustained social relations, for it is through these relations that he comes to know and to act in terms of the mores of medicine.

The sociology of medical education can thus be identified as a specialty that connects the sociology of medicine with the sociology of the professions.

Some five years ago, the Bureau of Applied Social Research of Columbia University began its investigations in this field with an intensive and continuing study of three schools of medicine, at Cornell University, the University of Pennsylvania, and the Western Reserve University. This paper condenses some findings of these studies: It divides into four main parts:

First, a short essay in the sociology of science examines the developments in medicine and in sociology that have converged to produce the new specialty of the sociology of medical education;

Second, a sample of findings on the processes of electing to enter the field of medicine and how these affect the orientations of entrants into the field;

Third, a sample of findings on the changing values and attitudes of medical students as they move through successive phases of a status-sequence from novice, through undergraduate training, toward the status of junior-physician. This deals with the processes of socialization and of career-choice (such as the choice of one or another type of internship and subsequent medical practice), with attention to the structurally induced stresses upon acquiring the value-orientations and behavior patterns defined as appropriate for each of the successive statuses.

Fourth, a summary of studies now in progress that are designed to find out how the medical student is affected in his professional development by members of his role-set: faculty, student-peers, paramedical personnel, patients, and his own family.

CONVERGENCE TOWARD THE SOCIOLOGY OF MEDICAL EDUCATION

[Condensed from "Some Preliminaries to a Sociology of Medical Education," by Robert K. Merton]

Medical educators have long taken note of what they were teaching students, but only lately have they begun to examine the social processes involved in their teaching and the educational environment they were creating for students. This recently emerging interest in medical education as a social and psychological process appears to be the result of a convergence of forces at work in medicine and of others at work in sociology.

Sources of Convergence in Medicine. *Advancement of medical knowledge.* As has often been said, the growth of science itself provides an important source of continuing and periodically intensified scrutiny of the current content and organization of medical education. Every considerable advance in medical knowledge, or in the sciences upon which medicine draws for a large part of its intellectual sustenance, brings in its wake the pressing question of how this new knowledge can be most effectively taught to the student. Moreover, science advances at an increasing rate. Although the scientists responsible for these advances in knowledge do not of course have this impact upon going systems of medical education as their immediate objective, it is nevertheless an observable result. Most sciences have some bearing upon one or another part of medicine and, as these develop, they generally have some repercussions on medical education. At the very least, these increments in medical knowledge press for reexamination of the methods, content, and organization of medical instruction. Such reexamination, as we shall soon see, has distinctively sociological aspects which are beginning to gain recognition.

Stresses on time-budget of the curriculum. The time-bound character of the curriculum also exerts pressure upon medical educators for an unending series of institutional decisions about the nature of the education they are providing. As everyone connected with it is acutely aware, the timetable of a medical school is fixed within fairly narrow limits: although the time set aside for instruction has been steadily increasing during the past half-century, it is not indefinitely expansible.

This means, of course, that departments and faculty members of the medical school in effect compete for the scarce time of the student just as patients compete for the scarce time of the physician. Hours of instruction are carefully computed and parceled out. The introduction of new teaching materials and courses must often be at the expense of other materials and courses. The relatively fixed number of hours available for instruction means continued competition between departments for their due share of time. In this sense, and without any disparaging implications of the word "competition," some degree of competition among faculty members for time in the curriculum is built into the structure of medical education, with its numerous branches of knowledge and application.

The prevailing organization of medical schools as a federation of departments contributes further to this form of competition. Departmental loyalities develop, and it requires a strong sense of loyalty to the school as a whole and an appreciable consensus on the nature and purposes of medical education for departments to relinquish willingly, rather than under the duress of their colleagues, long-established or newly-emerging claims to a particular share of time in the curriculum.

This process of competition for time, as well as the more intensely personal conflicts which sometimes develop between departments and between their members serve, whatever their other outcomes, to keep many medical educators alerted to new problems and potentialities of medical instruction. It is difficult for them, even if they were so inclined, to rest comfortably on their oars.

Rediscovery of the patient as person. Contributing further to an emerging interest in the sociological study of medical education is the renewed emphasis, within medicine, upon the concept of "the patient as a whole person." Although this conception of the patient is long established and generally acknowledged in medical circles, it is also said to be a conception often not carried into practice. Many physicians, it is said, continue to regard the patient as a case of sickness rather than as a person. This suggests that certain forces in the situation make it difficult for some physicians to live up to this conception. It is therefore held essential that these forces be counteracted by methods of education designed for the purpose.

In an earlier day, the structure of the society and the organization of medical practice were such that many practitioners would intuitively and almost automatically take into account both the stresses and the potentials for therapeutic support which the environment afforded the patient. With the growing complexity of the social environment, the increasing specialization of medical practice, and the often diminished association of physicians with their patients outside the sphere of medical care, the problem of taking the social context of the patient into account becomes greatly enlarged. Faced with such exigencies, physicians may find themselves backsliding from what they acknowledge to be the appropriate conception of the patient. The patient, in turn, often confronting a physician whom he knows only slightly or not at all, is more apt to experience difficulty in communicating a sense of his daily life—his relationships within the family and outside, the stresses of his work situation, his difficulties in coping with the demands of his multiple roles in society.

These social changes have evidently induced a newly-emphasized concern with the old problem of having the patient regarded as a whole person. Increasingly, medical educators believe that the attainment of this objective can be facilitated by the introduction of a sociological orientation into medicine.

Reduction of empiricism. Medicine, in company with most of the other sciences, is engaged in a continuing effort to reduce the degree of empiricism in its body of knowledge by increasing the systematic empirical verification of logically connected sets of ideas. For a long time, it was tacitly assumed that this outlook is appropriate for medicine but not for the study of medical education. More recently, the same scientific outlook is being transferred to this latter sphere. Committed to a belief in the eventual superiority of systematic inquiry over casual empiricism, some medical educators, together with associates in psychology and sociology, are turning to methodical study of the educational process, rather than relying upon casual impressions.

Innovations in medical education. This interest in finding out as methodically as present methods of inquiry permit the actual course and outcome of differing forms of medical education is, understandably enough, particularly marked in those schools which have initiated programs of instruction aimed at increasing appreciation of the patient as a whole person. To be sure, most medical schools are constantly engaged in revising their curricula. But especially when these involve changes of some considerable magnitude, there develops a marked interest in systematic observation of how these changes are actually working out. Naturally enough, the faculties of these medical schools seek, so far as is now possible, to apply scientific method to the study of the workings and consequences of these new arrangements, if only because they have been committed to that method in the development of medical knowledge itself.

Sources of Convergence in Sociology. Independent developments in the field of sociology have also been leading to a substantial interest in the study of medical education.

The sociology of the professions. First among these is the marked growth of the sociology of occupations.[2] Studies of the social organization of occupations and of occupational roles, sporadically undertaken during the last generation,[3] have more recently accumulated into a steady and growing stream. Occupations in general and the professions in particular have come to be recognized as one of the more significant nuclei in the organization of society. A great share of men's waking hours is devoted to their occupational activities; the economic supports for group survival are provided through the pooled work of socially interrelated occupations; men's aspirations, interests, and sentiments are largely organized and stamped with the mark of their occupations.

As part of the newly-emphasized focus on this field of inquiry, a Columbia University Seminar on the Professions was established in 1950.[4] This group reached the conclusion, among other findings, that, although the professional school plainly constitutes the major formative influence upon the development of the professional man, we have little systematic knowledge about the social and psychological environments provided by schools in the various professions and about the ways in which the processes and results of learning are related to these environments.

It was felt that sociological study of the medical school might afford a prototype for comparable studies in the other professions. For one thing, all inquiries into the comparative prestige of the professions in American society have uniformly found that medicine commands the greatest measure of public esteem. For another, many of the professions look to medicine as a model for the directions their own development might effectively take. If systematic studies of the medical school should prove their worth, other professions might follow suit.

Lending further sociological interest to the study of medical schools is the relative complexity of the social structure of these schools. Medical students must relate themselves to many and diverse groups in the course of their training; more so than students in any of the other professions (except, possibly, for social workers and nurses). Such networks of relationships, it is assumed, constitute important parts of the social environment of learning by the medical student, and therefore call for systematic study.

Collaboration of social science and health professions. As we have noted, modern medicine has developed a distinct interest in examining the actual and potential connections between the medical and the social sciences. A very considerable growth of interest in such collaboration has also become evident among social scientists.[5] A recent census[6] has identified more than 200 individuals at work in medical sociology; even a decade ago, a comparable census would have probably found only a small fraction of this number.

Just as laboratory and clinical research has had and continues to have an essential part in radically reshaping medical practice and teaching throughout the first part of the century, so the social and psychological sciences, in their own necessarily limited fashion, bid fair to provide perspectives and knowledge during the second part of the century. As disciplined inquiry moves forward on the social, and not only the economic, contexts of illness and medical care, there is a developing body of knowledge to be drawn upon in the clinical training of medical students. Even now, sociologists and psychologists have here and there been attached to the staffs of medical schools to advance the use of social science in helping to prepare the physician for his role in society.

The sociological study of organization. It is a short step from this interest in the sociological study of illness and medical care to an interest in the sociological study of illness and medical care to an interest in the sociological study of the medical school itself, for this links up with a long-standing sociological tradition of studying social institutions and formal organization. During the past generation, this tradition has taken on a new vitality as empirical research based on systematic field observations rather than only on available documentary evidence has begun to be developed.[7] In large part, these have been studies of industrial and business organizations, government departments, trade unions, and hospitals.[8] But the methods of inquiry and some of the fundamental concepts are equally appropriate for study of the social organization of the medical school in its bearing upon the behavior and learning of those involved in it.

The process of socialization. Social scientists have long had an enduring interest in studying the process of "socialization."[9] By this is meant the process through which individuals are inducted into their culture. It involves the acquisition of attitudes and values, of skills and behavior patterns making up social roles established in the social structure. For a considerable time, studies of socialization were largely confined to the early years in the life cycle of the individual; more recently increasing attention has been directed to the process as it continues, at varying rates, throughout the life cycle. This has given rise to theoretical and empirical analyses of "adult socialization."[10]

Adult socialization includes more than what is ordinarily described as education and training. Medical students learn not only from precept, or even from deliberate example; they also learn—and it may often be, most enduringly learn—from sustained involvement in the society of professional staff, fellow-students, and patients that comprises the medical school as a social organization. Our on-going studies have therefore assumed that in the course of their social interaction with others in the school and of observing and evaluating the behavior of their instructors (rather than merely listening to their precepts), students acquire the values which will be basic to their professional way of life. The ways in which these students are shaped, both by intent and by unplanned circumstances of their school environment, constitute a major part of the process of socialization.

Methods of social research. Substantively, then, newly-developing attention to the sociology of medical education derives from interest in the sociology of the professions, in the application of social science knowledge to the health field, in the sociology of formal and informal organization, and in the processes of adult socialization. Had these substantive interests existed a generation ago, it would not have been possible to pursue them with any rigor. The appropriate methods of investigation and analysis were not then part of the social scientist's equipment. But the past few decades have witnessed distinct advances in the methods of collecting and analyzing sociological facts that have made empirical studies of organization possible. Detailed accounts of these methods of sociology are available in several recent books.[11] We need therefore only list the principal methods adopted in our studies: first-hand observation, sociological diaries and focused interviews, the panel technique based on repeated interviews with the same individuals, sociometric procedures, and documentary records.

From these various sources, in medicine as well as in sociology, is gradually beginning to emerge a new field of inquiry: the sociology of medical education. In the rest of this paper, we shall summarize some results of our on-going studies.

Career Decisions. A first problem requires us to identify the characteristics of students making different sorts of decisions about their professional careers. Obviously, medical students are faced with many important decisions during the course of their training. Before even setting foot in the medical school they have already made the far-reaching decision to study medicine, and have prepared themselves accordingly. Once in medical school, they are faced with the need for making many more decisions. Some of these are seemingly limited: how much and what to study; how to spend whatever free time is allowed by the schedule of classes, laboratories and clinics; what electives to choose; what research project to undertake; and so on. Others are more enduringly consequential; for example, the type of internship he decides to apply for will greatly affect his later career. It is such basic decisions that we now consider.

"YOUTHFUL DECIDERS" AMONG MEDICAL STUDENTS[12]
[Condensed from "The Decision to Study Medicine," by Natalie Rogoff]

Students who committed themselves to a medical career long before they reached college are in the minority—fewer than 20 percent of those under study had reached this decision before they were sixteen. The youthful deciders are in some respects distinct from the rest. Having made up their minds before they could express their choice in action (e.g., by selecting one college course rather than another), these students, it is tentatively assumed, had a greater sense of a "calling" for medicine. To this extent, they would more readily decide that medicine was the one career for them. It is assumed, further, that the process of decision is not the same at all stages of the life cycle: for example, those who decide on a career in medicine at 14 and at 18 may differ not only in the ease with which they made up their minds, but in being subject to differing influences, owing to differences in their age-status.

To discover whether an early decision was in fact reached with less difficulty, we consider students at three different points in time: first as they selected the one career rather than others; then as they waited to put their decision into substantial effect by starting medical school; and finally as they actually "crossed the threshold" into medical school and reflected on their choice. At all three points, those who made a relatively early decision appear to be more certain that they made the right choice.

Among those who ultimately abided by their decision, and the sample of medical students of course includes only these,[13] the younger the age at decision, the less frequently had other occupations been seriously considered. Some 83 percent of those having decided on a medical career before they were 14 never gave serious thought to any other occupation—in contrast to a bare 9 percent of those at the other extreme who postponed their final decision until they were 21 or older.

There is nothing very surprising about this marked divergence, of course. After all, making a commitment to a particular profession implies the exclusion of alternatives; a 21-year-old who has not yet settled upon an occupation will presumably have given serious thought to some occupation, even if it is not the one which he finally selects. At the same time, the marked lack of interest in other occupations among youthful deciders indicates that a career in medicine seemed so attractive to them that it never really had any serious competitors.

An early commitment to medicine meant a long waiting period before embarking upon professional training, sometimes as long as a decade. But during this interval, these students were less likely than the others who had a shorter "waiting time" to have experienced doubts about their career decision. Their enthusiasm for medicine apparently led them to choose this career sooner and to maintain the choice with assurance throughout the extended period before they could put their choice into action. The probability of having experienced doubts relates directly to age at time of decision, except for the most recent deciders, who had very little time during which uncertainties might have occurred (Table 1).

Table 1—Doubts about Selecting Medicine as a Career, According to Age at Decision

Age at decision	Percentage who had had no doubts since deciding*	No. of students
Younger than 14	55	(29)
14 or 15	56	(39)
16 or 17	32	(106)
18–20	28	(152)
21 or older	41	(46)

* The question was worded as follows: "Once you made up your mind to become a doctor, did you ever have any doubts that this was the right decision for you?"

Table 2—Satisfaction with a Medical Career, According to Age at Decision

Age at decision	Percentage who feel medicine is "only career that could really satisfy" them*	No. of students
Younger than 14	86	(29)
14 or 15	87	(39)
16 or 17	62	(106)
18–20	57	(152)
21 or older	50	(46)

* Most students who did not endorse this statement said they felt that medicine is "one of several careers which (they) could find almost equally satisfying."

When they begin their studies, the early deciders tend, more than the others, to feel that medicine is "the only career than can really satisfy" them. Their initial enthusiasm, which made the decision itself easier to reach, is largely maintained through the intervening years. Later deciders, for whom the process of choosing a career was more often a matter of selecting one among several considered alternatives, less often think of medicine as uniquely gratifying (Table 2).

In certain respects, then, time of decision denotes ease in reaching the decision. Youthful deciders differ from their future classmates in other respects as well; for example, in the influence exerted upon their choice by family and friends. It is suggested that the varying frequencies of such influences result from differences in the social relations typical of people in disparate age statuses, and have relatively little to do with facilitating the decision itself.

As one instance of this: the father of the youthful decider was more likely to have played an important part in the decision and to have encouraged the youngster, once the decision was made. These tendencies might signify that strong paternal support facilitated the choice; again, they might signify that father-son ties are in general closer in early adolescence than they are after the sons go off to college; or they might signify both. Further evidence suggests that the changing character of relations between father and son at different times in the life cycle of the two more nearly accounts for the observed differences.

Several bits of evidence suggest that paternal advice and encouragement did not uniformly facilitate the choice of a career in medicine. No matter how much reinforcement was provided by the father, the early decider tends to be less ambivalent toward his decision than the later decider. Furthermore, if the strong support by the father had made the son's decision easier to reach, it would presumably have shortened the interval between the "beginning" and the "end" of the process. For example, the father might be able to provide information, or access to information, for his son which he could not as readily obtain for himself. But the data do not support an inference such as this. The interval between first thinking about a career in medicine and finally deciding upon it is not consistently less the more important the reported role of the father in the decision.[14]

Other evidence bears out the general conception that different people ("significant others") affect the decision at different phases of the life cycle. The fathers of younger deciders, for example, play a greater part in the career decisions of their children just as age-peers more often affect the decision of older deciders. Waiting until the college years to choose a career implies greater emancipation from the family and the acquisition of friends of like age with whom information and evaluative judgments on various occupations are exchanged. It is in this context that we take note of the double fact that a sizeable number of late deciders attributed an important role in the decision to friends who were already in medical school, whereas, in view of the pattern of age-graded friendships, this course was, of course, almost completely inaccessible to the very youthful deciders at the time they made their commitment.

Thus it is that the influence of the parental generation decreases with the age of making the career decision, while that of contemporaries increases. The difference between the relative influence of the generations may prove to have a bearing on students' perspectives on the medical profession. Youthful and older deciders may form different images of their professional training and future career, if it is true that students' images of the profession are affected by the interests of, and information held by, the people who influence their decision. Young adolescents and their families may more often look upon medicine from the "outside," and see it primarily as an occupation in which one helps sick people, with emphasis on the face-to-face dealings between doctor and patient. College students, and, all the more, medical students, may be more closely aware of the intellectual challenge of medicine, for they are in a position to relate the substance of the doctor's role to the scientific studies they are pursuing.

It is at least consistent with this idea that youthful deciders, as late as a few weeks before arriving at medical school, show a propensity for the interpersonal rather than the intellectual side of medicine (Table 3).

Table 3—Patient vs. Technical Orientation, According to Age at Decision

Age of decision	Percentages who would prefer appreciative patient*	No. of students
Younger than 14	41	(29)
14 or 15	36	(39)
16 or 17	41	(106)
18–20	32	(152)
21 or older	22	(46)

* The question was posed in the form of a dilemma: "Do you think you would get more personal satisfaction from successfully solving a relatively simple medical problem for a patient who expresses great appreciation, or from successfully solving a very complicated problem for a patient who expresses no appreciation whatever?"

In all this, it should be recognized that in the interim between selecting a medical career and entering medical school, youthful deciders were exposed to much the same environment as later deciders. During their years at college, they too acquired friends among those already in professional training. Nevertheless, they, more than their classmates, begin their studies with a greater tendency to prefer the reward of working with an appreciative patient rather than the reward of solving a challenging medical problem.

CAREER DECISIONS OF MEDICAL STUDENTS AND LAW STUDENTS[15]

[Condensed from "Some Comparisons of Entrants to Medical and Law School," by Wagner Thielens, Jr.]

Medical students not only include a substantial minority of youthful deciders but, it turns out, they tend to make their decisions to enter professional school earlier than do law students. As Table 4 shows, about three-quarters of the medical students included in our study had decided to enter medical school at least two years before they actually did so, while only about one-third of the law students had made their decisions by that time.[16]

Table 4—Time of Final Decision to Enter Professional School

Time of decision	Medical students, per cent	Law students, per cent
Less than 2 years before entry	27	66
2–4 years before	29	19
More than 4 years before	44	15
No. of students	(496)	(248)

At least three factors seem to operate together to make for an earlier commitment to professional school by medical students: more extensive pre-medical course requirements; greater contact of medical entrants with their chosen profession; and the higher standing in the community and larger incomes of physicians as compared with lawyers.

Entrance requirements. Because of the differing nature of the entrance requirements laid down by the two types of professional schools, it is often possible for a college junior or senior who has had other plans to make a belated decision to enter law school, while a similarly late decision to enter medical school is more difficult. With rare exceptions, entrants to the School of Medicine at the University of Pennsylvania are required as undergraduates to take at least 52 semester hours of specified courses in biology, chemistry, physics, mathmetics, and English. Generally, at least two years of study are needed to cover these requirements; an undergraduate making a late decision to study medicine would seldom have taken the often highly specialized courses and would need to devote extra time to them. The law school requirements are neither so extensive nor so detailed. According to the school catalogue, the prospective law student must have studied "satisfactory courses in English, in economics, and in English and United States history or the equivalent." At most, such courses might require a year of undergraduate study; moreover, many upperclassmen pursuing a liberal arts program will already have taken these courses, whether planning to enter law school or not. Thus, institutional contexts affect the time of decision.

Possible family influences. It is generally known that sons of professional families are more apt to become professionals themselves than are sons of families in other occupations, especially the lesser white-collar and manual occupations. It may be, therefore, that differences in social origin might account for the observed differences in time of decision. If more medical students come from medical families than law students from law families, and if, as we might expect, the decision to enter a profession is made earlier by individuals who have relatives in the profession, this might help explain the earlier decisions of medical students. Table 5 shows, however, that nearly identical proportions of the two groups under study have at least one relative in their own profession[17]—51 percent of the law students have relatives who are lawyers and 50 percent of the medical students have relatives who are doctors. This similarity holds also within the immediate family: 15 percent of the law entrants have fathers or mothers who are lawyers, while 17 percent of the medical entrants have a physician parent. We note further that 35 percent of the law students have relatives who are doctors, just as 34 percent of the medical students have relatives who are lawyers. The figures show that the medical students are somewhat more likely to have clergymen and teachers as relatives, but on the whole the two groups are similarly affiliated with the professions by family relationship.

Table 5—Students with Relatives in Each of Five Professions

Profession	Percentage of students with at least one relative in the profession	
	Medical students	Law students
Lawyers	34	51
Doctors	50	35
Dentists	16	14
Clergymen	21	15
Teachers	53	44
No. of students	(498)	(248)

Medical students have not had more contact than law students with relatives in their respective professions, and apparently have not been more influenced by them. Both groups report about equal contact with relatives in their professions: 31 percent of the medical students have had "a great

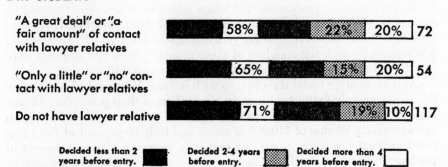

MEDICAL STUDENTS

"A great deal" or "a fair amount" of contact with M.D. relatives	28%	26%	46%	145
"Only a little" or "no" contact with M.D. relatives	28%	29%	43%	102
Do not have M.D. relatives	25%	31%	44%	245

LAW STUDENTS

"A great deal" or "a fair amount" of contact with lawyer relatives	58%	22%	20%	72
"Only a little" or "no" contact with lawyer relatives	65%	15%	20%	54
Do not have lawyer relative	71%	19%	10%	117

Decided less than 2 years before entry.   Decided 2-4 years before entry.   Decided more than 4 years before entry.

Note: Numbers to right of bars indicate students.

deal" or "a fair amount" of contact with physician relatives before entering medical school, while 29 percent of the law entrants report like contacts with lawyer relatives. And the data in Figure 1 suggest that relatives in the profession, even for students who had been in close contact with them, exert less influence than we might expect. Contact with lawyer relatives apparently leads a few law students to somewhat earlier decisions, but contact with doctor relatives has, in general, no effect on the timing of the final decision to study medicine.

Other contacts with the professions. Nevertheless, medical students may more often have experienced contact with their profession than law students with theirs. Common observation attests, for example, that a larger proportion of people have at one time or another been the patient of a physician than have been the client of a lawyer. Almost every child and adolescent in our society has at some point required the services of a doctor, whether for a case of measles, a broken bone, or swollen tonsils. Fewer, we suppose, have been the client of a lawyer, perhaps as beneficiary of a will, participant in a divorce suit—or as juvenile delinquent. Replying to a question on this matter, 87 percent of the medical entrants can recall at least some contact with doctors as a patient. Law entrants, presumably more likely than other young adults to be related to lawyers, are doubtless also more familiar with lawyers' skills and more inclined to turn to lawyers for help; but only 19 percent report having been the client of a lawyer. Again, both groups may have had considerable opportunity to observe or to hear about doctors treating relatives and friends, but fewer may know of similar contacts with lawyers. After all, the professional services of lawyers are less often provided in the homes of clients where impressionable youngsters may witness them. In these respects, the role of a doctor is more often than the role of a lawyer a matter of direct experience and knowledge.[18]

Social standing and income. Sociological studies have repeatedly shown that doctors as a group have higher social standing in the community than lawyers. For instance, North and Hatt[19] found that 67 percent of the participants in a nation-wide survey gave doctors the highest of five possible ratings of an occupation's "general standing", while 44 percent gave this rating to lawyers. It is possible, of course, that law students would assign higher standing to their chosen profession. Yet when asked to assess the community's ranking of seven occupations, fully 50 percent of them gave first ranking to doctors and only 3 percent put lawyers first. Even when asked, "How would *you personally* rank the standing of these groups?" more law students gave first place to physicians (24 percent) than to lawyers (19 percent).

As with relative social standing, so with income. When asked to estimate the average yearly (after-tax) income of members of their profession, 42 percent of the medical students pictured general practitioners as having an average yearly income of $10,000 or more, and fully 90 percent of them pictured medical specialists as earning that sum. In contrast, only 9 percent of the law students estimated this amount as the average income of lawyers.

Medical practice, then, tends to be conceived of by students as accompanied by both higher prestige and higher income than is law practice.

Insofar as these factors induce students to make career decisions, such perceptions may contribute to the earlier decisions of the medical students.

SPECIAL INTERESTS AND FACULTY INFLUENCE[20]
[*Condensed from "Tendencies toward Specialization in Medical Training,"
by Patricia L. Kendall and Hanan C. Selvin*]

From general decisions to enter the field of medicine (and, by way of comparison, the field of law), we turn to the more particular decisions about the kind of medical practice in which the student hopes to engage. How do some come to prefer general practice and others, specialized practice?

The trend toward specialization. We start with a finding that seems to obtain quite generally in American medical colleges. Most students enter medical school with intentions *not* to specialize, and only modify these intentions gradually during the course of their training.[21]

This trend could be identified in any of several ways. We could choose as our indicator the intentions of students to enter either general practice or specialty practice. Or we could use the internship preferences expressed by students, assuming, as do Deitrick and Berson in their survey of medical education,[22] that the student's intention to serve a rotating internship, in which he divides his time between three or four fields of medicine, signifies a more general interest than does the intention to serve a specialized internship in a particular field of medicine. Because we shall want later on to consider the actual internship assignments received by two classes of Cornell seniors, we find it more convenient to document the trend toward specialization by reference to internship preferences.

Table 6 contrasts the internship choices of students in the first, second, and third years of medical school.[23] Although no other type of internship is as often sought, the number of students expressing a preference for rotating internships decreases from year to year. Correlatively, the number choosing internships in medicine, surgery, pediatrics, and other specialized fields increases from year to year.[24] In short, as students proceed through Cornell Medical College, they exhibit a growing interest in specialized training.

Table 6—Internship Choices, According to Class in Medical School

| | Percentage in each class | | |
Type of internship	First year	Second year	Third year
Rotating	72	59	49
Straight medical	10	17	18
Straight surgical	5	1	10
Straight pathology	..	3	1
Mixed medical and surgical	11	11	13
Obstetrics and gynecology	..	1	2
Straight pediatrics	1	3	5
Other	1	5	2
No. of students	(79)	(76)	(83)

Many beginning medical students may prefer the most general, all-encompassing kind of internship because they do not yet want to commit themselves to any particular field of medicine. Not having enough experience to judge whether they are more interested in internal medicine than in pediatrics, or more skilled in surgery than in psychiatry, they can avoid a premature decision by planning to obtain an internship which will give them some training in most or all of these fields. As one first-year student put it, "I won't really be qualified to judge [what field of medicine I'm interested in] until we get into the specialties in the third and fourth years."

Furthermore, first-year students probably do not have a clear idea of what is actually done during the fifth year of training, or of the actual differences among alternative types of internships. Beginning students, in short, know relatively little about their own interests and talents, and relatively little about the specialized training available to develop their interests.

What leads so many of these medical students to abandon their early interest in general, comprehensive training, and to turn instead to specialized fields? A partial answer seems to be their growing appreciation of the complexity of modern medicine, and increased awareness of their inability to master all of these complexities personally.

Medical students may genuinely want to receive as broad and general training as possible, and they may preserve this aspiration throughout their stay in medical school. But as they are introduced successively to internal medicine, to surgery, to psychiatry and to other specialized fields, they may become aware of the virtual impossibility of achieving equal competence in all fields, and may therefore feel compelled to select one branch of medicine in which to concentrate.

Consider the following entry in the journal of a first-year student, made after he had visited an exhibit of clinical projects in the medical school,

The exhibit did point out in a striking fashion how completely variegated the field of medicine is, and how absolutely impossible it would be for one person to be a specialist in everything. That old axiom of 'the more you know, the more you don't know' holds quite true here.

And a more advanced student, appraising what he had learned in his third-year course in pediatrics, decided that it was not very much. He wrote in his journal:

We feel very inadequate in Pediatrics even at the termination of the course. I can see why specialization is the rage today. Medicine is so large now that a doctor doesn't feel confident unless he knows at least one field extremely well, rather than just a little about all subjects.

Up to this point, our provisional hypotheses about the sources of growing interest in specialization have been stated largely in terms of the individual student's maturation and development. But, as we shall see, the internship assignments which graduating students receive seem to be determined, to a degree not true of earlier internship preferences, by influences from faculty members in the medical school.

Specialized internships and faculty influence. If the trend discernible in internship choices continued through the period in which actual assignments are made, a considerable majority of the graduating students at Cornell would seek and receive specialized internships. But this is not the case. Although most fourth-year students do end up with specialized internships of one kind or another, it is a somewhat smaller number than had expressed preferences for such internships at the end of their third year in school. In line with the trend noted earlier, we find in Table 7 that 20 of the 71 students who had expressed a preference for rotating internships at the close of their third year ended up the following March with specialized assignments. But the trend in this direction is counterbalanced—even slightly outweighed— by a trend in the opposite direction. Of the 91 students who had originally said that they hoped to obtain specialized internships, 27 ended up with rotating assignments.

Table 7—Internship Assignments Compared with Third-Year Preferences of Same Students

Actual assignments in fourth year	Third-year preferences		
	Rotating	Specialized	Total
Rotating	51	27	78
Specialized	20	64	84
Total	71	91	162

The reason for this is that the trend toward specialized interests is not, as the evidence up to this point would suggest, a simple one. When the final commitment must be made, when students must make calculations about where their best prospects lie and the faculty must decide which students to recommend for what kinds of internships, a selective process is set in motion. Some students who have already developed an interest in specialized internships reverse the trend and end up with an assignment to a rotating internship. To find out how this selectivity operates, we begin by noting the absence of any relationship between performance in medical school, as graded by the faculty, and the internship preferences that are expressed. For example, at the end of their third year, high-ranking students were almost as likely as low-ranking students to say that they hoped to obtain rotating internships.[25]

Table 8—Actual Internship Assignments, According to Cumulative Grades

Internship assignments	Percentage in each quartile			
	Top quartile	Second quartile	Third quartile	Bottom quartile
Rotating	32	43	51	71
Straight medicine	41	33	18	7
Straight surgery	12	14	18	12
Other specialized (pathology, pediatrics, obstetrics and gynecology, etc.)	15	10	13	10
No. of students	(41)	(42)	(39)	(42)

All this changes, a year later, when these same students actually receive their internship assignments. As Table 8 shows, there is then a consistent and marked relationship between class standing and internship assignment. About one-third of the top-ranking students received rotating internships in contrast to substantially more than two-thirds of the lowest-ranking students. The results for specialized medical internships are just the opposite: fewer than one in ten of the fourth-quartile students and nearly six times as many of those in the first quartile, had received internships in internal medicine. The relationship is consistent throughout. From the top to the bottom quartiles, there is a steady increase in the proportion of students assigned to rotating internships, and a steady decline in the percentage assigned to internships in internal medicine. The absence of a relationship between internship preferences and grades was consistent with the conclusion that, through the first three years of medical school, the trend toward specialization equally affects students on all academic levels; in contrast, the marked relationship between internship assignments and class standing is consistent with the notion that, after that point, actual internship assignments are highly selective.

The full picture is obtained when these three variables—third-year internship preferences, actual internship assignments, and cumulative grades—are considered simultaneously. This results in a panel finding, and reveals the changes which took place for *individuals* rather than for quartile groups in composite.

As Figure 2 shows, high-ranking students, those in the upper half of the class, were most likely to end up with the kind of internship they wanted when, at the end of their third year, they had expressed a preference for *specialized* internships. Among these good students, over 75 percent of those who had chosen specialized internships, but fewer than 60 percent of those who had chosen rotating internships, received the kind of assignment they wanted. Exactly the reverse was true of the lower-ranking students. Those in the bottom half of their class were most likely to end up with the kind of

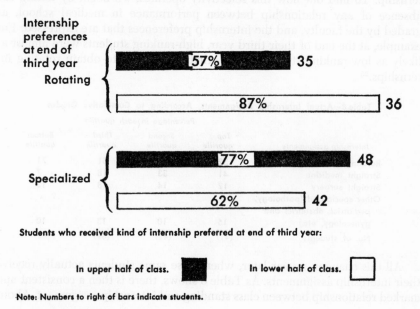

Internship preferences at end of third year

Rotating {
57%   35
87%   36
}

Specialized {
77%   48
62%   42
}

Students who received kind of internship preferred at end of third year:

In upper half of class. ■   In lower half of class. ☐

Note: Numbers to right of bars indicate students.

assignment they wanted when they had expressed a preference, at the end of their third year, for rotating internships. Within that group, 87 percent of those who had chosen rotating internships, but only 62 percent of those who had expressed a preference for specialized training, received assignments which coincided with their earlier preferences.

To explain why it is that the low-ranking students are less likely than the high-ranking students to end up with specialized internships, we must remind ourselves that there is considerable competition for the best internships —particularly the specialized internships in large, prestigeful hospitals. Now, although the students in Cornell Medical College do not know their exact standing in their class, they do know in which quartile they rank. They can therefore estimate their chances of obtaining a desirable internship. Those in the upper half of the class can generally count on getting good recommendations from the dean and faculty of the medical college, and favorable comparison with graduates of other medical schools; those in the bottom half of the class cannot be as sure of either of these advantages.

Nor need the students rely only on their own estimates of their prospects. It is customary at Cornell that, before submitting their formal internship application, fourth-year students discuss their plans with a member of the faculty or with an administrative officer. During the course of these discussions, students may be discouraged from some of the plans which they have developed, and encouraged in others. For example, a low-ranking student may be advised not to apply to a hospital which normally receives so many applications that it can select only top-ranking students.

As a result of these self-estimates, corrected or reinforced by discussions with faculty members, when the day of crucial decision approaches, low-ranking students seem to scale down their intentions to meet the probable reality; and, as we saw in Table 8, the reality for most of the students in the bottom half of the class is a rotating internship.

High-ranking students presumably engage in the same process of appraising their prospects. If they are realistic, they know that there is a good probability that they will end up with the kind of internship they want. Why, then, do so few receive rotating internships, even among those who several months previously had said that they wanted this type of internship? The answer seems to be that they are given strong encouragement by the faculty to apply for specialized internships.

Even though the Cornell student may not be taught, in so many words, to develop specialized interests, diverse tendencies turn him in that direction.[26] Indeed, the student's development of a specialized orientation may be as much a part of his indoctrination in medical school as is his acquisition of certain technical skills and knowledge. He may start out with a strong interest in a rotating internship but he may learn later that New York Hospital, the teaching hospital associated with his medical college, considers such internships relatively poor preparation for a residency, and therefore does not offer them. He may have come to medical school with the firm conviction that he will work as a general practitioner; in medical school, however, he probably has little opportunity to see, at first hand, what general practice is like; his clinical instructors and the other physicians with whom he comes in contact are specialists. As a result of these experiences, he may gradually revise his original plans and intentions.

It appears that high-ranking students are particularly sensitized to this general atmosphere in the medical school, for they, especially, are encouraged to recognize the positive values of specialization in modern medicine. In some cases, members of the staff express their values in the judgment that a rotating internship is less desirable than a specialized one, and they may respond in terms of these values when they learn of the plans of a high-ranking student to apply for a rotating assignment. In contrast, the high-ranking student who expresses a preference for a specialized internship will, of occasion, receive support and encouragement from the faculty. The social process of interaction with prestigious and significant others seem to bring about the trend observed among medical students in this school toward a correlation of demonstrated ability and specialization.

Processes of Attitudinal Learning. Students learn more than medical facts, techniques, and concepts; they develop particular ways of thinking about themselves, their patients, and their profession. As can be seen from the three studies to be reported, the acquisition of these is not fortuitous. Patterned situations provided by the medical school are found to lead, not always intentionally, to the student's acquisition of attitudes, images, and values.

PROFESSIONAL SELF-IMAGE OF FIRST-YEAR STUDENTS[27]
[Condensed from "The Development of a Professional Self-Image," by Mary Jean Huntington]

As students move through medical school they of course tend to develop an image of themselves as doctors rather than as mere students. What is less readily understandable is that, as early as the end of their first year, some students have already adopted this professional self-image.

The special circumstances of the first-year student at Western Reserve School of Medicine offer a unique occasion for examining some of the processes by which this comes about. At that school, every student is provided with the opportunity of having contact with patients early in his first year. All students are assigned a family to follow during this year and preferably throughout the four years of medical schooling. This serves to introduce them to the patient-physician relationship, and allows them to act in a role approximating that of physician, although they have only limited responsibility for helping a family cope with health problems. In the assigned families, the wife is pregnant, but there is no serious or longstanding history of medical, emotional, or social pathology. Students are expected to *observe* their patients periodically during the course of pregnancy, the delivery, and the early growth and development of the child. These repeated observations in the hospital and in the home of the family provide students with early clinical experience that is correlated with didactic instruction by clinical preceptors.

Nearly a third—31 percent—of the students reported at the end of their first year that they thought of themselves as doctors in their contacts with patients.[28] In part, these self-images seem to reflect the views that patients have

of the student-physicians with whom they come in contact. Thirty-nine percent of the 117 first-year students who thought that their patients regarded
them primarily as doctors also saw themselves primarily as doctors, whereas
only 6 percent of the 35 first-year students who thought that their patients
regarded them primarily as students saw themselves as doctors.

It would seem, then, that as students are defined by their patients, so
they tend to define themselves. But we are on less than firm footing with this
inference, because it is not based on reports from patients. The data can be
quite otherwise interpreted: as students define themselves so do *they tend to
assume* that patients define them. It may be a matter of a self-image *projected*
onto patients rather than the patient's image *reflected* in their self-image.
Other data in hand permit a rough test of this interpretation. The same students had been asked a year earlier, before they had actually entered medical
school, whether they *expected* to think of themselves primarily as students
or as doctors when they came to work with patients. This information provides a clue to the antecedent "definition of the situation"[29] with which students began their dealings with patients.

These earlier definitions of the social situation appear not to have colored
students' impressions of the image which patients have of them. To be sure,
of those who had expected to play the role of doctor, 78 percent felt, a year
later, that they had been so defined by patients. But almost exactly the same
proportion, 77 percent, of those who had expected to play the role of student
felt that they had been defined by patients as doctors.

What elements in the student's relationships with patients promote the
development of one or another self-image? Since each student follows only
one family, this allows fairly wide variation in the objective situation that
students meet. Aside from providing students with the opportunity to observe
the medically instructive processes of pregnancy and birth and early development of an infant, certain families do not present further health problems requiring medical attention. In such cases, students have less occasion to establish ongoing relationships with their patients, and consequently, to perform
their assigned role. This, in turn, seems to affect the formation of self-images.
Thus, 30 percent of the 129 first- and second-year students whose families had
definite medical problems came to see themselves primarily as doctors, in
comparison with a bare 5 percent of the 22 students whose families did not
present such problems.

The amount of difficulty students experience in handling patients further
affects the formation of their self-image. For some students, the requirements
of the assigned task outrun their still very limited capacities, both to handle
technical problems and interpersonal relations with patients. These experiences apparently impede their developing an early sense of doctorhood. But
where the task and their abilities seem to the students to be matched, they
come to feel they have handled the situation well—not very differently from
the way a doctor would. Even in the first year, 45 percent of the 29 students
who reported having had no difficulty in handling patients indicated that they
felt more like doctors than students; this compares with 29 percent of the 91
who had little difficulty, and with 25 percent of the 32 who had a fair or

considerable amount of difficulty in handling patients. Differing self-images result from different patterned situations.

SELF-CONFIDENCE, AFFECT, AND PREFERENCES FOR PATIENTS[30]
[Condensed from "Preferences for Types of Patients," by William Martin]

Medical students not only acquire distinctive self-images but also particular attitudes toward patients during the course of their training. Some of these attitudes may enlarge their effectiveness as junior physicians, others reduce it. Consider, for example, the professional obligation to accord interest and care to all patients and how this might be affected by the student developing preferences for certain kinds of patients. If he feels less favorably disposed to some types of patients, rather than uniformly detached, he will either accord them less than effective care or will experience stress in trying to provide them with the care they require. This leads to the question of the types of students who prove most vulnerable to this loss of professional detachment and the types of patients, the so-called "uncooperative" ones, most likely to evoke this response.

The concept of the "uncooperative patient" is deeply embedded in medical practice. In a study conducted in the outpatient clinic of a teaching hospital for example, it was found that students, faculty and other medical personnel could readily describe "the uncooperative patient." As they formulated it, a patient is uncooperative "when he is stubborn," "when he won't recognize that help is being given to him," "when he refuses to accept his condition" or when he fails to appreciate the effort being expended on his behalf.[31]

Excerpts from the diary of a fourth-year student, describing a sequence of clinic visits by a patient whom he came to define as uncooperative, exemplify the process of losing a sense of professional detachment. (The italics are supplied.)

Monday, Dec. 7. [My patient] is a woman who has been followed for several months with globus hystericus. She *is still bothered* by this, but has noted some improvement in the frequency of attacks and feels that she is improving. This was only a brief interview most of which was devoted to learning her problem, and a little of her home and family life. She is a very pleasant person, tending toward hyperactivity. . . . I have hopes that *I may be able to continue her progress, give her a little more insight* into her problem and make her adjust to this entire situation.

Monday, Dec. 14. My usual patient visit for the morning with a 38-year old woman with globus hystericus. This woman is very unhappy about husband's lack of interest in her, etc. and wonders if she loves him. . . . I think that *if I can relieve this doubt* of her love for her husband, much of her anxiety may be relieved and in turn, her globus should improve.

Monday, Jan. 4. My other patient, the woman with the unhappy home situation and difficulty in swallowing returned. We talked about her home situation, nothing new! *I don't know how successful this therapy is going to be* with this girl. By that I mean I'm not too certain whether we will ever get this woman over some of her anxious moments. I mean I don't think she'll be cured completely.

Monday, Jan. 18. At 11:00 A.M. I had my weekly appointment with Mrs. B and her problems. This woman is beginning to get on my nerves. She is a chronic complainer and in some instances shows very poor judgment in her relationships with her husband. I have tried to point out how she may show more interest in him, etc. but she's always not feeling well, or has some difficulty which prevents her doing as she knows she should. However, I realize that by letting her come weekly and ventilate, she seems to have achieved some measure of improvement.

Monday, Jan. 25. The other patient was my weekly revisit, who came in with a new raft of symptoms, worrying about what's going to happen next, etc. I really have difficulty at times restraining myself from telling this woman that she's far too concerned with herself, and in no uncertain terms. I shouldn't react like this and I would like very much to think that I have helped this woman but as soon as she is assured that one symptom has no organic basis she immediately digs up some new ones.

Monday, Feb. 15. Also saw my weekly revisit. . . . She still is over-reactive to any form of symptom and I think she'll continue to be. . . . I look forward to the end of this period of treatment.

By the time ten weeks had elapsed, this student was motivated to end the relationship with his patient. In the interim, he had become increasingly pessimistic about the prospect of bringing about marked improvement in the patient, he had been confronted by what seemed to him a never-ending stream of bodily complaints, and he had found himself faced with the serious problem of controlling his own affect. The student's detachment and confidence seem to have been closely interrelated in the gradual unfolding of this case; as the patient failed to conform to the normative expectations of the student-physician, both detachment and confidence diminished.

Some statistical evidence also suggests this connection between detachment and confidence in handling some kinds of uncooperative patients. Students who feel relatively unable to control the emotional outbursts of patients more often report irritation with some of the patients they have seen. (Table 9).[32]

Table 9—Irritation with Uncooperative Patients, According to Confidence in Ability to Deal with Patients Who Have Emotional Outbursts

Degree of confidence	Percentage reporting irritation	No. of students
Complete	56	(48)
Moderate	62	(213)
Little	69	(39)

Lack of confidence and lack of detachment seem to develop when students work with patients whom they define as uncooperative, that is, patients who do not conform to their expectations. Each of these reactions, in turn, motivates students to avoid working with particular patients. It also appears that when both reactions are present, they reinforce each other. Students lacking self-confidence with patients *and* having difficulty in maintaining detachment are most likely to prefer certain kinds of patients to others (Figure 3). Students who were able to carry out their work with the least strain, both confidently and without undue affective involvement, also have the fewest preferences.

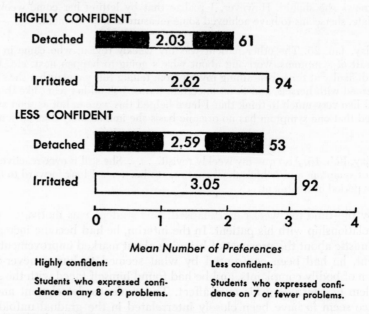

HIGHLY CONFIDENT

Detached — 2.03 — 61

Irritated — 2.62 — 94

LESS CONFIDENT

Detached — 2.59 — 53

Irritated — 3.05 — 92

0   1   2   3   4

Mean Number of Preferences

Highly confident:
Students who expressed confidence on any 8 or 9 problems.

Less confident:
Students who expressed confidence on 7 or fewer problems.

Note: Numbers to right of bars indicate students.

This abbreviated report on the formation of attitudes toward patients and the consequences for performance of the professional role is only the prelude to a detailed study now in progress.

TRAINING FOR UNCERTAINTY IN THE PRECLINICAL YEARS[33]
[Condensed from "Training for Uncertainty," by Renée C. Fox]

As we have seen, students develop new self-images and attitudes toward patients as they pursue their medical studies; as we shall now see, they also acquire attitudes toward the field of medicine as a whole. The processes through which this occurs are exemplified in the developing orientation of students toward uncertainties in medicine.

To the layman it may seem that the primary purpose of medical training is to replace the uncertainties of the acknowledged novice with the certainties of a mature physician. But this is only partly so. Despite unprecedented scientific advances, the professional life of the physician remains full of uncertainties.

Two basic types of uncertainty can be identified. The first results from incomplete or imperfect mastery of available knowledge. No one can have at his command all the skills and knowledge comprising the lore of medicine.

The second depends upon limitations in current medical knowledge. There are many questions to which no physician, however well trained, can as yet provide answers. A third kind of uncertainty derives from these two basic types. This consists of difficulty in distinguishing between personal ignorance or ineptitude and the limitations of present medical knowledge. Every doctor must constantly cope with these forms of uncertainty and grave consequences may result if he is not able to do so. It is for this reason that training for uncertainty in a medical curriculum and in early professional life is an important part of becoming a physician.[34]

Learning to acknowledge uncertainty. The first kind of uncertainty encountered by the student has its source in his role as student. It derives from the policy of avoiding "spoon-feeding," a philosophy of the pre-clinical years at Cornell Medical College (as at many other medical schools). From the first, the student is told that he will be "given the major responsibility for learning"; that information is not presented "in neat packets"; and that no precise boundaries are set on the amount of work expected of him. Under these conditions, the beginning student faces the uncertainty of not knowing how much he "should" know, exactly what he "should" learn, and how he "should" go about his studies.

Great as it is, this uncertainty is reinforced for the beginner by the absence of grades, so that he does not have the familiar kind of evidence by which to gauge the quality of his work.

The same teaching philosophy also leads to a beginning awareness of the second type of uncertainty: by making the student conscious of how vast medicine is, the absence of spoon-feeding readies him for the fact that even as a mature physician he will not always experience the certainty that comes with knowing "all there is to know" about the medical problems with which he is faced. He begins to realize that no matter how skilled and well-informed he may gradually become, his mastery of all that is known in medicine will never be complete.

It is perhaps during the course of studying Gross Anatomy that the student experiences this type of uncertainty most intensely. As a result of his struggle to master a "huge body of facts," the student comes to see more clearly that medicine is such an "enormous proposition" he can never hope to command it in a way both encompassing and sure. The student's own sense of personal inadequacy may be further reinforced by the contrast he draws between his knowledge and that which he attributes to his instructors. Believing that "when it comes to the gross anatomy, they know just about all there is to know," he is made increasingly aware of how imperfect his own mastery really is.

Other courses and situations in the preclinical years acquaint the Cornell student with uncertainties that result, not from his own inadequacies, but from the limitations in the current state of medical knowledge. For example, the tentativeness of Pharmacology as a science, the fact that only in recent years has it begun to emerge from a trial-and-error state of experimentation, advance the student's recognition that not all gaps in his knowledge indicate deficiencies on his part. In effect, Pharmacology helps teach medical students that because "there are so many voids" in medical knowledge, the practice of medicine is sometimes largely "a matter of conjuring . . . possibilities and probabilities."

The "experimental point of view" pervading much of the early training at Cornell Medical College also promotes the idea that an irreducible minimum of uncertainty is inherent in medicine, in spite of the promise of further scientific advance. The preclinical instructors presenting this point of view adopt the basic premise that medical knowledge thus far attained must be regarded as no more than tentative, and must be continually subjected to further inquiry. They assume that few absolutes exist. In this way, the student is encouraged to acknowledge uncertainty, and, more than this, to tolerate it. He is made aware that it is possible to act in spite of uncertainties and that some of his teachers make such uncertainties the basis of their experimental work.

The student has other experiences during the early years of medical school which present him with the problem of distinguishing between these two types of uncertainty—that is, at times he is unsure where his limitations leave off and the limitation of medical science begin. The difficulty is particularly evident in situations where he is called upon to make observations.

Whether he is trying to visualize an anatomical entity, studying gross or microscopic specimens in pathology, utilizing the method of percussion in physical diagnosis, or taking a personal history in psychiatry, the preclinical student is being asked to glean whatever information he can from the processes of looking, feeling, and listening. In all these situations, students are often expected to see before they know what to look for or how to look for it. And yet, the ability to "see what you ought to see," "feel what you ought to feel," and "hear what you ought to hear," students assure us, is based upon "a knowledge of what you're supposed to observe," an ordered method for making these observations, and a great deal of practice in medical ways of perceiving.

The uncertainty for a student lies in trying to determine how much of his own "trouble in . . . hearing, feeling, or seeing is personal," and how much of it "has to do with factors outside of himself." (Or, as another student phrases the problem: "How do you make the distinction between yourself and objectivity?") Generically, the student's uncertainty in this respect is no different from that to which every responsible, self-critical doctor is often subject. But because he has not yet developed the discrimination and judgment of a skilled diagnostician, a student is usually less sure than a mature physician about where to draw the line between his own limitations and those of medical science. When in doubt, a student seems more likely than an experienced practitioner to question and "blame" himself.

Learning to cope with uncertainty. In describing the various kinds of uncertainty to which a student is exposed during his preclinical years at Cornell, we do not mean to portray him as groping helplessly around in the midst of uncertainty. As time goes on, a student begins to develop effective ways of dealing with these forms of uncertainty, so that, gradually, he comes more capable of meeting them with the competence and equipoise of a mature physician.

To begin with, some of his uncertainty gives way as he acquires medical knowledge and skill. "A more complete and satisfying picture of the organism takes shape" in his mind. He feels more at home looking in a microscope; he finds it easier to draw slides; he begins to have more confidence in what he sees and hears in Physical Diagnosis; and he becomes more adept at talking with patients. In these and other respects, cognitive learning and a greater sense of certainty go hand in hand.

With the growth of his knowledge and skill, moreover, a student's perspective on his own uncertainty changes. Now that he "knows a little more" and is a "little more sure of himself," a student says, he realizes that although some of his uncertainty is attributable to his ignorance," some of it is "really well-justified." By this he means that he is better able to distinguish between those components of his uncertainty that derive from his own lack of knowledge and those that are inherent in medicine. He is therefore less apt to think of his uncertainty as largely personal and now considers it more appropriate to give voice to the doubts he feels.

This more "affirmative attitude" of the student toward doubting is only in part a product of book knowledge and skill in the techniques of physical diagnosis. In part it results also from what he learns about the uncertainties of medicine through his daily contact with members of the faculty. From time to time in the classroom, for example, a student will ask what he considers a "well-chosen question" only to discover that his teacher "does not have immediate command of the known medical facts on that point" or to be told that the problem into which he is inquiring "represents one of the big gaps in medical knowledge at present." In the autopsy room,[35] the student is struck by the fact that the pathologist cannot always explain the causes of death and that, although the "doctors' diagnoses are often right, they can also be wrong." Examining patients under the supervision of clinical faculty, he discovers that when "different instructors listen to (or feel or see) the exact same thing, they frequently come up with different impressions . . . and have to consult one another before they reach a final conclusion."

In short, observing his teachers in various classroom and clinical situations makes a student more aware of the fact that they are subject to the same kinds of uncertainty that he himself is experiencing. Furthermore, he notes that in confronting these uncertainties, his instructors usually deal with them in a forthright manner, acknowledging them with the consistency of what one student has termed a "philosophy of doubting." Thus, a student's relationship to the faculty, like his advances in knowledge and skill, encourages him to accept some of his uncertainty as "inevitable" and thoroughly "legitimate" and to handle that uncertainty by openly conceding that he is unsure.

Another process by which the student learns to face up to uncertainty in an unequivocal manner is connected with his membership in the "little society" of medical students, for a medical school class is a closely-knit, self-regulating community, with its own method of "tackling a big problem" like that of uncertainty. Through a process of "feeling each other out," the group first establishes the fact that uncertainty is experienced by "everyone," thereby reassuring a student that his own difficulties in this regard are not peculiar to him.

Out of the more than "casual joking, asking around and talking to others" that constantly go on among students, a set of standards for dealing with uncertainty gradually evolves—standards that tend to coincide with those of the faculty. If he acts presumptuous about his knowledge a student will be reproached by his classmates, whereas an admission of ignorance on his part will evoke their approval. From the positive and negative reactions of his peers, a student learns that they, like his teachers, often expect him to be uncertain about what he knows and candid about his uncertainty. (As one student puts it, "It really isn't fashionable to believe much or to be overly sure.")

This short account may indicate the complex processes of social interaction that result in learning an orientation which is only in small degree taught didactically.

Studies of the Role-Set of the Medical Student. As we have noted, the medical student is involved in a network of social relations that are taken to be consequential for his professional socialization: relationships with fellow-students, with the faculty of the school, with patients, with his family, and with the paramedical staff of the teaching hospital. The foregoing report has only touched upon some of these, for each sector of this array of relationships is the subject of intensive study to be reported in separate monographs. In view of the basic importance of these relationships for the developing competences and value-orientations of medical students, this report would be seriously deficient if it did not include at least a *precis* of some problems under review in each of these monographs.

SOCIAL RELATIONS AMONG MEDICAL STUDENTS
AND ATTITUDINAL LEARNING
[William Nicholls, II]

From numerous indications, it appears that the interaction betwen students importantly affects their socialization. Is it the case here, as Roy Harrod says of English universities, that students learn more of value from their fellow-students than in any other way? Since this unorganized and unplanned aspect of the educative process has tended to be a matter of anecdote and conjecture it, in particular, should profit from methodical inquiry.

Nicholls is investigating the ways in which friendship and alienation among medical students come about and the consequences of changing peer-relations for maintaining or modifying professional interests and values. For example, do students with friends farther along in medical school acquire professional attitudes earlier? Are the friendships carried over from earlier days an aid or a hindrance to attitudinal learning? Unlike the asymmetrical relation of student and teacher, the potentially symmetrical relation between friends affords no antecedent basis for deciding which member of the pair will be more influential. Does the academic standing or the relative popularity determine the direction that influence will take within the pair? What are the consequences of turnover in friendships for the morale and socialization of students? Intensive inquiry into questions such as these will begin to supply an understanding of the significance of peer-relations for professional learning.

RECIPROCAL RELATIONS OF MEDICAL STUDENTS
AND FACULTY MEMBERS
[David Caplovitz]

The effects upon students of the social environment constituted by faculty can be understood only if there are systematic data about the values held by the faculty and their relations with students, data of the kind that Caplovitz has collected from nearly 500 members of the clinical faculty at one medical school. Having data about both students and faculty, he is able to compare the values held by students and the members of the faculty whom they most admire in their roles as teachers, researchers, and physicians. How does the selection of role models differ with the capacity or interests of the student or with the relative position of the faculty member in the school hierarchy? What, in turn, are the images of the promising student held by faculty members in different departments and of different rank? Does the student tend to absorb the values of the men he most admires? The design of this kind of inquiry, with its parallel information about students and faculty, promises to extend our knowledge of the ways in which this important sector of the student's role-set affects his socialization.

MEDICAL STUDENTS AND PATIENTS: THE FORMATION
OF A PROFESSIONAL ROLE
[William Martin]

This study deals primarily with the patterned situations in medical school that facilitate or hinder the efforts of students to conform to the norms governing professional relations with patients. It begins with the traditional formulation of the problem of social conformity and deviation by examining the conditions that make for overt conformity to the requirements of a role and those that make for overt departures from them. But it goes further to distinguish, among those who overtly conform to these requirements, those who find it possible to do so with relative ease from those, who though still outwardly conforming, do so only with difficulty. In this way, this inquiry has implications, beyond the immediate scope of the medical school, for a theory of social conformity and deviation.

In substance, this study examines (1) the orientations of students toward patients, (2) the norms governing professional behavior and attitudes toward patients, (3) the conditions making for greater or less ease of conformity to these norms, and (4) the consequences of conformity or nonconformity for effective learning of the therapeutic role of the physician. These are examined at several stages of the student's training.

SOCIAL ORIGINS OF MEDICAL STUDENTS AND THEIR
PROFESSIONALIZATION
[E. David Nasatir]

This study compares the development of students who are the children of physicians and of students coming from other kinds of occupational origins. In its broadest implications, it opens up a line of inquiry that is only now beginning to be developed by sociologists engaged in the study of social mobility. These studies have commonly dwelt upon the social origins of those in broad occupational strata: the professions at large, business executives, lesser white-collar and manual occupations. This study focuses on the disparate origins of those entering a particular profession; moreover, it seeks to find out the ways in which the diverse origins of students affect their professional development. It also considers students as involved in the two social systems of the family and the medical school, examining sources of compatibility and incompatibility between the two and tracing out their consequences for adaptations and learning by students.

SELF-IMAGES AND SELF-APPRAISALS OF MEDICAL STUDENTS
[Mary Jean Huntington]

As the short extract from this empirical study may have suggested, it examines the sources and consequences of the self-images and self-appraisals of medical students, drawing upon and seeking to extend the theory introduced by G. H. Mead and others a generation ago. It begins with the theoretically strategic observation that students of the same degree of ability in selected respects rate themselves differently depending upon their choice of reference groups, that is, whether they compare themselves with classmates, faculty members, practicing physicians, or interns and residents. What kinds of students, then, choose these different reference groups for self-appraisal and how do these cumulatively affect their self-images? The data make it possible also to trace the implications of the idea that self-images are formed in the course of social interaction—specifically, that medical students tend, in particular situations, to live up to the expectations they infer that designated others have of them. The consequences for the professional development of students of discrepancies between their abilities, as judged by objective measures, and their self-images remain to be examined.

Even this short summary of five monographs in preparation may be enough to bring out an implication pervading studies in this field: although investigations in the sociology of medical education are of course centered upon particular subject-matters, they, like other specialized inquiries, can contribute to the advancement of sociological theory.

VI

Healing Practices and

Practitioners

THIS SECTION is concerned with the practice of medicine and the physician. In addition, the functioning of non-medical healers in contemporary society is analyzed. Trends in the specialization of medical practice, alterations in physicians' careers, problems of medical ethics and malpractice, the interpersonal relationships of medical specialists in their own field and others are included. This section primarily deals with the physician-patient relationship and how it is affected by the social and personal milieu of the physician and his patients.

One of the earliest and most penetrating analyses of specialization in medical practice is offered by the late Bernhard J. Stern. The impact of time after graduation from medical school upon changes in the careers of physicians toward increasing specialization is reported in a recent study of medical graduates by Milton Terris, M.D. and Mary Monk.

Results of a recent effort to evaluate the factors that develop good doctors is summarized in the article by Lois Hoffman.

An analysis of factors involved in malpractice lawsuits is presented in a recent survey conducted by the staff of *Medical Economics*.

One of the first social psychological investigations of the interrelationship between surgeons and their patients in a teaching hospital is presented in a penetrating paper by Bernard Kutner.

The significance of the cultural environment of patients for the practicing pediatrician is vividly demonstrated in the contribution of D. B. Jelliffe, M.D.

One of the newest medical specialties, anesthesiology, is analyzed in terms of its relationship to other medical specialties in a pioneering study by Dan Lortie.

Some of the problems of the osteopath, particularly in his relationship toward the medical profession, are discussed by Peter New from the standpoint of the osteopathic student.

The marginality of another type of non-medical healer, the chiropractor, is analyzed extensively in the article by Walter Wardwell.

Some of the consequences of socialized medicine, as now practiced in England, for the doctor-patient relationship, and the increase in "functional illness" are presented in a most stimulating and thoughtful paper by R. S. Ferguson, M.D.

Robert Straus discusses some of the problems confronting the physician in coping with the alcoholic patient.

36 THE SPECIALIST AND THE
GENERAL PRACTITIONER

By Bernhard J. Stern

Specialization in the United States is to a considerable degree dependent upon the invention of instruments which are indispensable to physical diagnosis of diseases and of the organs which they involve. As long as these were unavailable, knowledge of morbid anatomy and pathology, however well defined theoretically, remained in a crude and undeveloped state. When appropriate instruments were invented, medical science expanded to such an extent that specialists became a necessity, for no man could master the field of medicine in its entirety. Progress in medicine has been accelerated by specialization which facilitates conceptional refinements and develops the manipulative accuracy, speed, and skill which are impossible when the energies of the physician are diffused.

There had been in the English tradition and law the distinction between the apothecary, the physician, and the surgeon, which caused Smollett in the eighteenth century to complain, in the tenor of complaints against specialism today, that the patient was being "parcelled out into small enclosures."[1] But the medical exigencies in frontier United States with its scattered population required every doctor to do everything, and the cleavages and distinctions, especially between physicians and surgeons, did not prevail as in Europe. The Marquis de Chastellux in his *Travels Through North America* in 1781 observed:

I make use of the English word doctor, because the distinction of surgeon and physicians is as little known in the army of Washington as in that of Agamemnon. We read in Homer, that the physician Macaon himself dressed the wounds. . . . The Americans conform to the ancient custom and it answers very well.[2]

There was little opportunity for specialists even in the larger towns, although as cities increased in size, some doctors became identified by their mastery of skills in fields such as internal medicine or surgery, and there were sufficient patients to sustain their practice along the lines they had mastered.

While subdivisions of medical practice according to organs and disease developed slowly, any considerable degree of successful specialization awaited advances in medical technology, as well as an increase in the size and wealth of the population. The field of ophthalmology may be used as an example. The ophthalmoscope was invented in 1851. In 1855, Elkanah Williams of Cincinnati introduced the instrument to this country and was the first American physician to limit his practice exclusively to ophthalmology and otology. The medical schools gradually established independent departments of ophthalmology and otology, Cincinnati in 1860, Bellevue in 1868, Rush in 1869, Northwestern in 1870, Harvard in 1871, and Pennsylvania

From *American Medical Practice In The Perspectives Of A Century*, (New York: The Commonwealth Fund, 1945), 45–61. Copyright 1945 by Harvard University Press and The Commonwealth Fund.

in 1872.[3] The American Ophthalmological Society was organized in 1864, and the section on ophthalmology of the American Medical Association was organized in 1879. In 1866, when Joseph S. Hildreth was appointed oculist and aurist on the staff of Cook County Hospital, it is reported that great indignation was felt because "it was thought that an eye specialist was out of place in a general hospital, and that every good all-around surgeon was quite competent to treat such cases."[4] The ophthalmologist encountered difficulties in other parts of the country as well. In 1891, S. Weir Mitchell declared that he could remember the day in Philadelphia when "older physicians refused to recognize socially a man who devoted himself to the eye alone."[5]

After ophthalmology had become established as a specialty in spite of this attitude, many doctors designated themselves as ophthalmologists who did not meet the standards advocated by leaders in the medical profession. William H. Wilder, Chairman of the Section of Ophthalmology of the American Medical Association in 1908, urged that some standards be set so that "it should no longer be possible to be called an oculist after a month or six weeks in a post-graduate school."[6] Eight years later, the American Board of Ophthalmology was established to certify doctors as specialists in this field and in the twenty-six-year period ending January 1, 1942, 1,971 physicians have met the Board's increasingly stringent requirements.

In this brief telescoped account of the development of ophthalmology, there is revealed the general pattern of growth of the other specialties. Special competence is needed to master instruments. More important, the interpretation of the findings requires special knowledge. If a physician is to become expert in one field, he must focus upon it to the neglect of others, and the division of labor that results promotes progress in all fields. The innovator in a specialty risks finding an inadequate paying market for his skills. He risks, moreover, the resentment of the other physicians who feel that their competence is being challenged and their sources of income curtailed. In 1869, the Committee on Specialties of the American Medical Association, which resolved that "this Association recognizes specialties as proper and legitimate fields of practice," acknowledged that: "The chief objection brought against specialties is that they operate unfairly against the general practitioner in implying that he is incompetent to properly treat certain classes of diseases and narrowing his field of practice."[7]

A considerable volume of polemical literature relating to specialization continued to appear during the decades in which this field of medical practice would be looked upon "as the recourse of the mediocre and unambitious" or "as a sort of purgatory for the abandoned in medicine."[8] While the bulk of the literature reflected the fear of the non-specialist that he would be unable to compete with the specialist, certain real fundamental dangers were incidentally underscored, which will be discussed later.

Step by step in the face of persistent opposition,[9] a specialty comes to be recognized, the medical schools establish first courses and then departments in the subject, thereby making the specialized findings the common possession of the younger practitioners, and these findings in turn serve as the foundation for ever narrower specialities. When a field that once disparaged or regarded with suspicion wins professional standing, an increasing number of physicians designate themselves as specialists in the field in the Directory of the American Medical Association. It becomes necessary to identify and qualify a specialist by other means than his own statement. Certifying boards are then instituted to impose standards that have no legal sanction but which must be met before the physicians are recognized as specialists by their professional colleagues and patients. Fourteen of such certifying boards have followed the lead of the opthalmologists: the board for otolaryngology was established in 1924, obstetrics and gynecology in 1930, dermatology and syphilology in 1932, pediatrics in 1933, orthopedic surgery, psychiatry and neurology, and radiology in 1934, urology in 1935, pathology and internal medicine in 1936, surgery in 1937, anesthesiology and plastic surgery in 1938, neurological surgery and proctology in 1940. The total number of specialists certified by the boards by 1942 was 18,000. Since 1933 there has been an Advisory Board for Medical Specialists whose function is to coordinate the work of the certifying boards and to advance the standards and improve the methods of graduate education and training in the medical specialities. These certifying boards are evidence that specialization has finally been recognized as an inherent and essential characteristic of modern medicine. They are efforts to prevent abuses lest the state intervene and make a license to practice a specialty mandatory as is advocated in some circles.

There has been a striking increase in specialization among physicians during the last fifteen years, coincidental with specialization in other aspects of American economic and scientific life. In 1928, 74 per cent of the nation's physicians reported themselves engaged in general practice; the remaining 26 per cent were almost equally divided between those who regarded themselves as full-time or part-time specialists.[10] By 1942 general practitioners decreased in number from 112,200 to 86,000, and in percentage of the profession from 74 to 49 per cent. The number of physicians devoting their entire time to specialties was 36,000, more than double the corresponding number fourteen years before, and the partial specialists had increased even more. According to the *American Medical Directory* for 1942, the distribution of specialists was as follows: surgery, obstetrics, gynecology, neurological surgery, orthopedic surgery, plastic surgery, proctology, and anesthesia, 12,866; pediatrics and internal medicine, 8,325; ophthalmology, otology, laryngology and rhinology, 5,021; psychiatry and neurology 3,118; dermatology and urology, 2,355; roentgenology and radiology, 2,126; pathology, bacteriology and anatomy, 1,827.[11]

Specialists require funded economic resources and hospital facilities for their practice even more than do general practitioners and so they are even more highly concentrated in the cities than are the latter. Of the 1,754 ophthalmologists certified by the American Board of Ophthalmology in 1941, one-half practiced in five states; 87 per cent were in cities of over 25,000 population, and only 376 counties had certified ophthalmologists. Of the 1,717 certified pediatricians in 1941, 71 per cent were in cities of 100,000 or more, while 2,762 out of 3,073 counties in the United States had no certified pediatricians. Of the five surgeons in Vermont certified by the American Board of Surgery, all were in the city of Burlington, and Utah's five were in Salt Lake City. All of Kentucky's certified surgeons were in Louisville and Lexington and twelve of Colorado's fifteen practiced in Denver. Idaho and Nevada had but one certified surgeon each, and there were only three in Montana.[12] Advanced medical practice involving the utilization of specialists may be said, therefore, to be restricted to urban, and in some fields to metropolitan areas, and the full benefits of scientific medicine are not available to the less populated areas.

Data on the patient load of specialists are limited, but those which are available reveal little regularity of pattern[13] (see Table I). The specialists of the District of Columbia and Baltimore, with the exception of the pediatricians and the ophthalmologists and otorhinolaryngologists, carry a somewhat lower patient load on the average than do general practitioners. Specialists in Georgia, however, have consistently a higher patient load, indicating that in relation to demand there are fewer specialists in Georgia than in the other areas studied. In all three localities, the ratio of home to office visits is lower for all specialists, except pediatricians, than for general practitioners.

Table 1—Average weekly patient load of white male specialists, by specialty and place of practice, 1942

Specialty and place of practice	Number of physicians giving information	AVERAGE WEEKLY PATIENT LOAD			
		Office	Hospital	Home of patient	Total
Internal medicine		111	8	5	124
District of Columbia	50				
Baltimore, Md.	81	71	10	14	95
Georgia	42	49	10	17	76
Surgery		84	19	17	120
District of Columbia	37				
Baltimore, Md.	55	66	21	8	95
Georgia	39	74	25	11	110
Obstetrics & Gynecology		87	28	9	124
District of Columbia	31				
Baltimore, Md.	47	75	16	8	99
Georgia	16	56	22	7	85
Pediatrics		88	21	8	117
District of Columbia	27				
Baltimore, Md.	19	62	10	23	95
Georgia	28	51	15	50	116
Ophthalmology and otorhinolaryngology		91	12	36	139
District of Columbia	40				
Baltimore, Md.	51	89	7	3	99
Georgia	48	100	19	3	122
Neurology and psychiatry					
District of Columbia	13	20	10	1	31
Baltimore, Md.	12	20	7	4	31

Source: Antonio Ciocco and Isidore Altman, "The Patient Load of Physicians in Private Practice, a Comparative Statistical Study of Three Areas," Public Health Reports (September 3, 1943), vol. 58, no. 36, p. 1336.

The specialists are not only largely located in the cities and in the wealthy areas of the country, but their clientele is concentrated in the upper income brackets. Of 9,000 families surveyed for twelve successive months during the period 1928–1931, ten times as many specialists were consulted by families with incomes over $5,000 as by those whose incomes were under $1,200, while the frequency with which general practitioners were employed by the two groups differed within a range of only about 15 percent.[14] Although the investment of the specialists is greater, this is more than compensated for by the fact that they averaged twice the income of general practitioners, largely because their paying practice is concentrated among groups that can afford substantial fees.[15]

Larger incomes and wider opportunities to advance the scientific frontiers of medicine and to obtain public and professional recognition have increased the number of specialists. These inducements have also led medical students to attempt to go into specialties immediately after graduation, before they have had the opportunity to acquire the experience in general practice which would give them more intimate contacts with patients, and a broader medical setting for their specialties.[16]

Considered from the viewpoint of the patient, specialization has complicated medical care in manifold ways, and increased costs tremendously. Not long ago, a patient complaining of indigestion and pain in his stomach would go to a physician and be diagnosed and treated in one or two office visits. Today, to have his condition diagnosed by scientific standards, he must have a gastrointestinal x-ray series, a chemical analysis of his gastric secretions and possibly one or more gall bladder studies. Should the diagnosis be duodenal ulcer, the treatment is likely to involve hospitalization of the patient from one to three months, with the additional costs of all the routines prior to and during surgery or medication. In the case of many patients, diagnostic procedures may be employed, not only to obtain affirmative diagnoses which aim to establish or confirm the existence of a suspected condition, but to exclude the possible existence of other conditions. In this way, the number of specialists who may be involved in a single case may be increased considerably.[17]

With such increased specializations, the danger has become apparent that a situation might develop in which there would be "fifty-seven varieties of diseases and lesions but no physician to take care of the patient."[18] There is little doubt but that the specialist tends to confine his observation of the causes of illness to the narrow field of vision with which he is most familiar. His special training and experience bring certain symptoms into focus, while his lack of experience in other fields dims his appreciation of the meaning of equally important symptoms. He fails as a rule to consider the patient as a whole, either physiologically or psychologically. Moreover, inasmuch as patients, for the most part, come to the specialist only after their diseases are well advanced, the specialist's approach tends to be almost exclusively curative and only incidentally preventive.

The hazards of specialization were expressed very bluntly by Lewellys F. Barker when he wrote:

Specialists, as a class, are exposed to a particular set of dangers, including those of the narrowness and the monotony of the "piece worker," those of loss of adaptability, those of objectionable aggressiveness, those of stubborn opinionatedness, those of boastful self-sufficiency, those of selfish materialism, and those of vanity and arrogance. . . . Special workers should take pains to neutralize as far as possible the evils that tend to accompany concentrated interests and narrow ranges of operation.[19]

There are scientific and socioeconomic factors conducive to the development of these undesirable behavior patterns in specialist-patient relationships, which require special effort on the part of the enlightened specialist to overcome. It is one of the disparities of modern medicine that while developments in the field of the deficiency diseases, endocrinology, psychiatry, and psychosomatic medicine have led to the consideration of the patient in the context of his life history, the trend of diagnostic specialties is to ignore as irrelevant anything but the particular matter under scrutiny. The criticism that specialists tend to develop a more impersonal physician-patient relationship than in the days of the family doctor is often grounded in fact, and this is to the detriment of medical practice.[20]

Although the increase in specialization has changed somewhat the structure of medical practice, basically the social-psychological nexus of the relationship between physician and patient remains the same as it has been throughout history. The patient is a person who is ill, or who thinks himself ill, or in danger of illness or death. He consults the physician as the authoritative expert whose technical competence can relieve his pain, restore his health, or prevent the disease or disorder which threatens his security. He comes to him, however, not merely as a person whose body is diseased or threatened with disease, and who is seeking diagnosis and cure by the use of the instruments, procedures, and drugs which the science of medicine has at its command; he comes also as a personality with moods, insights, prejudices, conceits, opinions, and attitudes that are a basic part of the medical culture. He craves health, security, and self-esteem, yet illness or fear of illness has made him anxious and dependent. In the medical interview with the physician, whether specialist or practitioner, he wants release from psychological tension as much as from physical pain. He resents being considered merely a body to be examined in a laboratory situation. He seeks the time and opportunity to gain the sympathetic ear of the physician to relate his troubles, and to receive satisfying assurance as well as medical ministrations from an understanding person.

The physician has thus always been not only a scientist but a practitioner, and his maturity as a scientist is in no wise irreconcilable with corresponding maturity as a practitioner. The traditional emphasis on the "bedside manner" is acknowledgement that the way in which doctors handle their patients as personalities has an important effect upon the functioning of their physiological systems. Much of the "art" of medicine has consisted in this type of psychotherapy which is a necessary accompaniment of all other therapy. The education of the physician not merely as a technician, but as a cultured person equipped with insights into human relationships and sensitized by an appreciation of the social sciences and the liberal arts, will do much to humanize the patient-doctor relationship, whatever other factors may tend to formalize such a relationship.

The problem of personal relationship between the physician and the patient is not so simple as it formerly was. In small homogeneous communities, it is possible for the family backgrounds of patients, both medical and social, to be well known to the physician over a long period of years. The situation is very different in larger socially and economically heterogeneous communities. Here patients are for the most part strangers who come to an office for medical care without any social contact whatsoever with the physician, and remain strangers over the years, their association with the doctor being limited to visits to his office for medical attention.

Patient-doctor relationships have also changed because the physical background of the professional relationship has changed. The doctor formerly met his patients in a room set aside in his home, and the neighbors, when ill, came to see him and were received somewhat in the manner of guests. When his office is removed from the neighborhood to the center of town, the contact is more impersonal and it is further formalized when receptionists and nurses take records. The further shift of diagnosis and treatment from the home to the hospital also reduces the physician's opportunity to acquire first-hand knowledge of the family setting and economic background of his patients. It is because pediatricians have intimate contacts with families in their homes that they have more affectionate relations with their patients than do other specialists whose home visits are relatively infrequent.

The danger of formalism in the medical interview is inherent in the nature of the specialist's work. When diagnoses involved fewer instruments and procedures, the patient thought himself familiar with what was being done to him and knew the implications of the questions he was asked. Now he is being put through routines which are darkly mysterious to him and which the physician has usually neither the time nor the inclination to clarify. The specialist, equipped with his diagnostic instruments and laboratory aids, is no longer as dependent upon the patient's recital of his complaints as he once was. He tends therefore to be abrupt and indifferent as the patient relates what the physician feels to be irrelevancies. Moreover, formerly no matter what the ailment, the patient, at the end of the visit, invariably had the satisfaction of getting a prescription, and this made him feel that something concrete was being done, that some progress was assured as soon as the directions of the prescription were fulfilled. Even when the formidable use of drugs gave way to less heroic prescriptions, the potions, pills, and plasters, scrupulously administered, were regarded as the formulae of recovery. If the recipe failed, another would have to be tried. If it succeeded, it was kept by the patient to be used again when a similar ailment developed, and often handed on to another member of the family or to a neighbor.

Many honorable physicians have confessed in their autobiographies that they knowingly prescribed worthless drugs to patients because they could not cope with the case medically but saw the need for action of some sort to circumvent despair on the part of the patient. As medicine matured scientifically and especially during the decisive period of "therapeutic nihilism" when the older drugs were being repudiated and new reliable ones had not yet been discovered, prescriptions were issued less often. There was hence-forth less dependence on one of the procedures by which the physician had given concrete evidence of his attentiveness to the immediate needs of the patient.

Many physicians, in their desire to give security to the patient, have developed pat terms by which they seek to evade full clarification of the pa-tient's illness, and yet to give him some satisfaction that would perhaps relieve tension. Alvarez describes this process as follows:

Partly because most patients so demand a diagnosis of organic disease, partly because they are inclined to be resentful against the physician who tells them the truth, and partly because it takes as much time and skill and tact to explain the real situation to them, we physicians will always be tempted to dismiss them quickly with some placebo of diagnosis—some pleasant-sounding name such as colitis, ptosis, spastic colon, low blood sugar, or low blood pressure. Unfortunately, such placebos seldom have any curative effect, and often they have a very bad effect because they concentrate all the patient's fears on one organ.[21]

The need to consider the patient as a whole and the value of recogniz-ing diseases in their early stages to prevent serious developments, increase the importance of the competently trained general practitioner in modern medicine. His function is to have an intimate knowledge of the patient and an over-all responsibility for his health, no matter how many specialists serve him over the years. Contrary to the fears of the early critics of specialization, the general practitioners, although they are declining in number, have not been eclipsed by the development of specialties. The standards of the younger general practitioner have in fact been raised and his skill developed by the work of the specialists. The clinical and laboratory methods which were once used only by the specialists, such as the x-ray, the fluoroscope, the electro-cardiograph, the basal metabolism test, and other mechanical and chemical tests, have become simpler and more readily handled. They are now part of the equipment of the general practitioner or are at his disposal through special service laboratories set up for that purpose. Each year finds the general practitioner adding new weapons to his arsenal, aids in the attack on disease which had previously been the prerogative of the specialists, while the specialists move on to new, previously unexplored fields. It is important that this should be so, not only because the general practitioner must be able to correlate the work of specialists where and when they are available, but because, as already noted, the services of specialists are now largely con-fined to persons in the large cities and in the upper income brackets. It is therefore left to general practitioners to bring the resources of modern science as far as possible to persons in smaller towns and rural areas and to those in the lower income groups who do not have access to hospitals with outpatient departments. The standards attained by the general practitioner determine the quality of medical care which the rural and lower income groups will receive.

The recognition of the great importance of the general practitioner in modern medical practice does not imply a glorification of the older type of family physician. As early as 1913 Charles L. Dana wrote aptly of the old-fashioned family physician: "He was a splendid person and useful person in his day; but he was badly trained, he was often ignorant, he made many mistakes, for one cannot by force of character and geniality of person make a diagnosis of appendicitis, or recognize streptococcus infection."[22]

While it is clearly desirable that a family should have the services of the same general practitioner over a period of time, such a long association is by no means the general pattern of medical practice today, especially in urban communities. In earlier periods of American history, when people lived for many years in one place, when neighborhoods were social units, and when personal contacts were more intimate, the family doctor had a better social situation in which to operate. Then the patient attached himself to a physician to whom he was loyally devoted, and if he deserted him for another practitioner an explanation was in order. But today, irrespective of the effects of medical specialization, the impersonal human relations of urban life have made the family-doctor relationship, however ideal it may be as an institution, less possible in practice. For example, in a study of 365 households in New York City, more than four-fifths of which had incomes of less than $2,000, it was found that two-thirds of the families had no family doctor. Moreover, in the case of the one-third who testified that they had a family doctor, the continuity of relationship upon which the concept of the family doctor is based was largely nonexistent.[23] Likewise in a study of about 1,200 medical and surgical cases in various communities in New York State outside of New York City, it was found that about 50 percent had no regular family physician, and that fewer patients with long-standing ailments had family physicians than patients with acute and recurrent ailments.[24]

The most effective diagnosis, therapy, and prevention of disease are attained through the comprehensive funding, coordination, and integration of the knowledge and skills of different specialists working with general practitioners, an important role in the distribution of such medical services being assigned to the hospital. While formerly physicians were accustomed to work primarily as individuals, specialization has required collaboration. Every specialty requires, for its own proper functioning, a close interdependence with all other aspects of medicine. This pooling of the judgments of experts has become the general practice in the consultation procedures of large hospitals and medical schools and such clinics as the Mayo Clinic. In addition to improving the quality of service, collaboration by the physician with the hospital offers opportunities to reduce capital investment in expensive medical technologies by avoiding duplication by the individual physician, and to lower unit costs by increasing the number of patients using each instrument or machine.

Specialization in medical practice, an imperative concomitant of developments in medical science and technology, has then after a period of considerable opposition, become one of the marked characteristics of modern medicine. This has raised problems of certification, of the relation of the specialists to one another and to the general practitioner, of the relation of physicians to patients, and of the marketing of medical services—problems the solutions of which are basic to the future efficacy of medicine.

37   **CHANGES IN PHYSICIANS' CAREERS:**
        RELATION OF TIME AFTER GRADUATION
        TO SPECIALIZATION

        By Milton Terris and Mary Monk

The physician's career is far from static; a considerable number of physicians move from one location to another and from one type of practice to another. For example, Mountin[1] found that during the period 1923 to 1938 more than one-fourth of the practicing physicians in the United States changed their place of practice one or more times, for a total of 87,000 moves. (These figures do not include changes of location within cities, towns, or villages.) Of the rural physicians who moved during this period, more than two-fifths set up practice in other rural areas, a third went to small cities, and a quarter moved to larger cities. Similarly, half of the migrating large-city physicians went to other large cities, a third moved to small cities, and a fifth moved to rural areas.

This present study is concerned with another significant phenomenon, which is the shift from general practice to specialization during the physician's career in active practice. Much of the current discussion of general practice and specialization is focused on medical students' attitudes and career plans. Attitudes and plans change, however, and it is therefore important to determine the actual choices made by medical graduates and the changes that occur in those choices during the course of their professional careers.

Weiskotten and Altenderfer[2] studied the choices of physicians at one point in their careers through the use of questionnaires sent to all graduates of American and Canadian medical colleges of the class of 1915, 1920, 1925, 1930, 1935, and 1940. They found a sharp increase in limitation to a specialty among the 1935 and 1940 graduates, but point out that: In comparing the data for the graduates of the various classes, it should be noted that the time elapsed between graduation and the date of the study amounted to 11 years for the graduates of 1915; six years for the graduates of 1920, 1925, and 1930; 15 years for the graduates of 1935, and 10 years for the graduates of 1940. Nevertheless, the data may be interpreted as indicating a markedly increasing trend toward limitation to a specialty. . . . The high percentage of the 1930 graduates in general practice may possibly be explained by the fact that the class was graduated in a period of economic depression.

The present study was undertaken in an attempt to answer the following questions: 1. To what extent do physicians change from general practice to full specialization during the course of their careers in active practice? 2. How are such changes related to the amount of time that has elapsed since graduation? 3. If time after graduation is a significant factor in the extent

From *The Journal Of The American Medical Association*, 160, (1956), 653–655. Copyright 1956 by The American Medical Association.

of specialization, what quantitative adjustments of the Weiskotten-Altenderfer data can be made to take this into account?

Methods and Results. The graduates of the University of Buffalo School of Medicine for the years 1915, 1920, 1925, 1930 and 1935 were chosen for study of career changes from time of graduation up to 1950. The 1940 class was not included because of the short period that had elapsed from graduation to 1950. Information on the graduates' careers was obtained from the American Medical Association directories as follows: 1915 class—1921, 1930, 1940, and 1950 directories; 1920 class—1927, 1931, 1940, and 1950 directories; 1925 class—1931, 1940, and 1950 directories; 1930 class—1936, 1940, and 1950 directories; and 1935 class—1940 and 1950 directories. Physicians were classified as specialists only if the directory designated them as limiting their practice to a specialty; part-time specialists were classified as general practitioners. In general, limitation to a specialty was designated by a distinctive symbol in the directory. In addition to the physicians so designated, hospital and public health administrators, pathologists, and residents in specialties were also classified as full-time specialists.

Since the designations were self-assigned, however, it was decided to check the possibility of error from this source. Accordingly, the 1940 and 1950 American Medical Association directories were checked with the corresponding New York state medical directories (1939–1940 and 1951) in which workmen's compensation ratings are available. These ratings are given by local medical society committees and, although there are some differences in the definitions used, they provide a rough check on self-assigned ratings. Information was obtained in the 1939–1940 New York state directory for 78% of the physicians studied and in the 1951 directory for 84%. For both years, the agreement between the New York state and American Medical Association directories on the ratings given was 90%. This high degree of agreement appears to indicate that the designations in the American Medical Association Directory are fairly accurate.

Table 1 shows the number of graduates who were newly listed as full-time specialists in the American Medical Association directories at varying intervals after graduation. It is clear that for each class there is a considerable and continued increment of full-time specialists with the passage of time. In order to determine for each class the probability of becoming a specialist in different periods of time after graduation, a life table method was used. This method[3] takes into account the possibility that some of those withdrawn from observation because of death or retirement had become full-time specialists in the interval between directories. The results, shown in table 2, clearly demonstrate that the percentage of graduates becoming full-time specialists increases markedly with the lapse of time after graduation. Thus, only 4% of the class of 1915 had become full-time specialists during the first 6 years after graduation, as compared with 27% during 16 years after graduation and 54% during 35 years after graduation. Similarly, while 16% of the class of 1935 had become specialists in the first five years after graduation, this had increased to 46% in 15 years after graduation.

Table 1—Number of New Full-Time Specialists Found in Different Years, University of Buffalo Classes

Class	No. in Class at Time of Graduation	No. of New Full-Time Specialists, Yr. of Directory						Total Full-Time Specialists
		1921	1927	1931	1936	1940	1950	
1915	53	2	..	12	..	5	7	26
1920	57	..	7	6	..	7	9	29
1925	51	..	..	4	..	9	5	18
1930	66	..	..	..	7	9	11	27
1935	66	..	..	..	..	10	19	29

Table 2—Percentage of Full-Time Specialists, University of Buffalo Classes (Life Table Method)

Class	Years After Graduation	Percentage Full-Time Specialists
1915	6	3.8
1915	16	27.0
1915	25	37.4
1915	35	53.8
1920	7	12.6
1920	11	24.0
1920	20	37.3
1920	30	56.1
1925	6	7.9
1925	15	26.5
1925	25	38.0
1930	6	10.9
1930	10	25.5
1930	20	44.2
1935	5	15.5
1935	15	46.0

If we now estimate for each class the proportion becoming full-time specialists during an equal period after graduation, we can obtain a corrected estimate of the trend toward specialization in the different classes. In table 3, such data are presented for a 15-year period after graduation and are compared with the Weiskotten data based on varying time periods. It will be noted that the highest proportion of full-time specialists in the Weiskotten study occurred in the classes of 1915 and 1935, which were questioned after a longer interval than the other classes. When the classes are compared after identical time periods following graduation, there is a strikingly different picture, with the lowest proportion of full-time specialists in the class of 1915 and the highest in the classes of 1930 and 1935. That Weiskotten's percentages are higher than the 15-year estimated percentages for the 1915 and 1935 classes, despite a shorter or equal time interval, is due chiefly to the different methods employed, i.e., questionnaire as against directory. Although full-time specialists were self-designated in both studies, in the Weiskotten study percentages were based on the number of questionnaires returned, which somewhat overrepresented the full-time specialists.[2] These results confirm Weiskotten and Altenderfer's previously quoted warning that their data for the various classes, based on varying time periods following graduation, are not truly comparable. The decline in specialization that they obtained for the 1920, 1925, and 1930 classes is an artefact caused by the short time period used for these classes.

Table 3—Estimated Percentages of University of Buffalo Graduates Becoming Full-Time Specialists in Fifteen Years After Graduation*

Class	Estimated Percentage of Full-Time Specialists, 15 Years After Graduation	WEISKOTTEN DATA Percentage of Full-Time Specialists:	Years After Graduation
1915	25	35.7	11
1920	30	23.8	6
1925	27	18.4	6
1930	35	17.5	6
1935	46	52.2	15

* Compared with Weiskotten data based on varying time periods.

Comment. It is significant that the trend toward greater specialization did not decline for the medical graduates of 1920, 1925, and 1930 and then increase sharply for the 1935 and 1940 graduates. On the contrary, the trend toward specialization generally increased throughout this period. Even a major cataclysm like the economic depression of the 1930's did not appear to halt this trend; the depression class of 1930 produced more specialists than the classes of 1920 and 1925. The phenomenon of specialization of medical graduates must therefore be considered to be more than a temporary trend among recent graduates, which can easily be replaced by a new trend toward general practice. We are dealing instead with a long-term trend toward specialization of physicians, the roots of which are to be sought in long-term developments in medical science and practice. The most important finding of this study is that specialization among the members of each graduating class continued to increase throughout the active professional lives of the graduates. For the class of 1915, 37% specialized in the first 25 years after graduation but 10 years later the proportion had increased to 54%. Similarly, for the class of 1930, 26% specialized in the first 10 years, but in another 10 years the proportion was 44%. The fact that physicians have continued to change from general practice to full-time specialization many years after graduation indicates that the determining causes of increased specialization are to be found more in the conditions of professional life in which the medical graduate finds himself than in the orientation he receives in medical school. While the latter undoubtedly affects the graduate's attitudes, it also is conditioned by and essentially secondary to the changing character of medical practice in the community.

Summary and Conclusions. A study of the 1915, 1920, 1925, 1930, and 1935 graduates of the University of Buffalo School of Medicine demonstrates that physicians continue to change from general practice to full-time specialization during their active professional careers. The degree of specialization among medical graduates increases markedly with the passage of time after graduation. For identical time periods following graduation, succeeding classes generally show an increasing trend toward specialization throughout the period studied. It is suggested that this increased specialization is a long-term phenomenon, the causes of which are to be found primarily in developments in medical science and changing conditions of medical practice in the community.

38   HOW DO GOOD DOCTORS GET THAT WAY?
By Lois Hoffman

I. A Look at Practice Methods. If you were to peer over a colleague's shoulder while he treated a full month's roster of patients, you'd get a good idea of his competence. Since you can't do this, you judge his skill—at least in part—by the kind of medical school he went to, his hospital and medical society affiliations, his diligence in graduate work, and his apparent prosperity or lack of it.

How accurate are such valuations? Not very, if we can draw conclusions from a limited but intensive study made by a research team from the University of North Carolina medical school. ("In the case of some schools, a large percentage of graduates remain in medical education or enter specialist practice," says the study report, published in December, 1956, by the Association of American Medical Colleges. "It is possible that general practitioners graduating from such schools are not representative of their schools' graduates.")

Members of the team spent months in a detailed on-the-spot examination of the practices of eighty-eight family doctors scattered through the state. One team member (and sometimes two) followed each G.P. through three or four days of office, hospital, and house calls, noting what he did and how well he did it.

Each doctor was graded on six activities: history taking; physical examination; use of laboratory aids for diagnosis; therapy; preventive medicine; and keeping of clinical records. Then his clinical skill, as rated by the researchers, was stacked against his medical school record, internship, patient load, medical society and hospital affiliations, family background, office facilities, and so on.

Chief aim of this study was to discover what it takes to make a really competent G.P. Its most striking conclusion: Many common assumptions about what makes a good doctor are false.

The researchers found, for instance, that a Harvard man may be no better—and no worse—a family doctor than an alumnus of Podunk U. The G.P. with hospital connections may do no better by his patients than the man who has none. (But the physician who sticks to an appointment schedule is very likely to outshine his "come-in-any-time" colleague.)

The findings have interesting implications for you, whether you happen to be a specialist or a G.P.

From *Medical Economics*, 34, (May, 1957), 164–173; 34, (June, 1957), 124–129; 34, (July, 1957), 222–234; and 34, (August, 1957), 144–153. Copyright 1957 by Medical Economics, Inc.

They may confirm your impression that you've done everything possible to become an efficient, skillful doctor—and your determination to stay that way. On the other hand, they may suggest some desirable changes in your postgraduate study habits, your office routine, or some other aspect of your practice.

First of all, though, they can give you a new slant on yourself *as a doctor*. If you—rather than one of the eighty-eight North Carolina G.P.s—had opened your office to an observer, how would he have rated your competence? What aspects of your medical practice would he have considered most important?

In the North Carolina study, the researchers assigned the following "values" or points to the six medical activities studied:

Medical history	30 points
Physical examination	34
Use of laboratory aids	26
Therapy	9
Preventive medicine	6
Clinical records	2

Thus, diagnostic procedures accounted for 90 points out of a possible 107. Reason: The research team considered the family doctor's primary role to be that of "first-line diagnostician."

It's true, of course, that the G.P. sees many more "unsorted, unclassified" cases than the man with a large referral practice. But *no* doctor can prescribe the right therapy (or call in the right consultant) until he has a good idea what ails the patient. So the study findings should be applicable to almost any type of practice.

This is so even if you'd be inclined to place entirely different values on the ingredients of your own practice. For example, you may consider therapy more important than the medical history. Yet a comparison of your methods with those of the North Carolina G.P.s may still be revealing to you.

The study shows that a given doctor is likely to display much the same degree of competence in everything he does: The North Carolina man who took a careful history was almost certain to do a thorough physical, and so on (see Table 2). So no matter what point value had been attached to each activity, the same men would have come out on top. No doctor was given a high rating because his brilliant performance in one field overshadowed his inferior performance in another.

It so happens that comparatively few of the North Carolina G.P.s *were* given a high rating: In the researchers' opinion the substandard clinicians outnumbered the budding Oslers by almost two to one. The observers found twenty-two men to be better than so-called average, thirty-nine worse. Here's the method they used for ranking the G.P.s:

After completing his study of a man's practice, the observer summed up his impressions by assigning the G.P. to one of five ranks designated by Roman numerals. Numeral V stood for an excellent clinical performance, I for a very poor one, with III "average" or fair. Ranks II and IV represented intermediate grades. The number of G.P.s finally assigned to each rank was as follows:

V....7   IV....15   III....27   II....23   I....16

In other words, only seven of the doctors received the highest grade. Why? Because, the report says, only they knew exactly what they were doing and did it thoroughly and systematically. Even more important, they showed real interest in patients and their problems. They seemed to enjoy the intellectual challenge of medicine.

At the other extreme, the report states, Rank I doctors did a sketchy, haphazard job. Sometimes the researchers simply couldn't figure out *why* these men did certain things. Some of them had evidently never had the basic training needed for the practice of good medicine. Others knew better, but didn't seem to care enough.

Some of the research team's standards of judging competence may seem overly stringent. But the significant question isn't really whether or not the grades were too low. It's whether the ratings were *relatively* sound. This they probably were. The observers' painstaking methods of systematizing their judgments left little room for erratic or hasty conclusions.

Chances are, you can't be quite so systematic or impartial in measuring your own performance. But, from the examples given here, you *can* get an idea of how your practice methods would appear to an outsider. First of all, then, let's consider:

The Medical History. You belong with the minority—a very small but elite group—if you customarily take a thorough history.

Something under 10 percent of the North Carolina G.P.s showed up well on history-taking. They were the men who asked their patients questions that showed they had thought of all the diseases and complications that might possibly relate to a specific complaint. In addition, they asked methodically about symptoms in all the major organ systems and delved into the medical history of the patient and his family. The observers also felt these doctors showed considerable clinical knowledge and interviewing skill.

Thirty percent of the G.P.s turned in adequate but not outstanding performances. Though they did almost everything the first group did, they seemed to be less painstaking. They asked fewer questions, took less complete histories, showed less skill at interviewing.

Finally, low ratings were assigned to 61 percent of the men. Some of them took no history at all. Others asked only about the patient's complaint or about the part of the body involved. They tended to ask rambling, unrelated questions that showed little thought or clinical knowledge.

None of the eighty-eight G.P.s took a planned psychiatric history. Many of them complained to an observer that their schooling had given them no groundwork for dealing with emotional problems. While most of the doctors recognized such problems in an occasional patient, few tried to do anything about them.

Physical Examination. If you do head-to-toe physicals on new patients and on old patients you haven't seen in some time, apparently you're again among the select few. The observers found that such physicals were the exception rather than the rule among the North Carolina G.P.s.

So the doctors had to be graded chiefly on how carefully they examined a patient's ear, elbow, or epidermis—and on whether such examination seemed indicated by the patient's complaint. (As it turned out, the North Carolina doctors who examined individual organs or regions most thoroughly were also likely to do the greatest number of complete physical examinations.)

The research check-list included twenty-odd examining-room procedures. A doctor's handling of each procedure was given one of two or three possible point values, thus:

Examination of Chest by Percussion

	Point Value
Not done	0
Chest thumped perfunctorily	1
Percussion over all major lobes, determination of diaphragmatic level, diaphragmatic movements	2

Similar point values were given to examinations of the eyes, ears, nose, mouth, neck, lymph nodes, heart, etc. Only 2 percent of the G.P.s got top scores for their eye examinations (which were supposed ideally, to include conjunctivae, visual fields, pupillary reactions, and extra-ocular movements). But, at the other extreme, 62 percent got top scores for their mouth examinations (including tonsils, throat, teeth, gums, and tongue).

In the researchers' opinion, 45 percent of the doctors didn't have their patients take off enough clothes to allow easy access to the part being examined. Some of them tried to perform auscultation of the heart or lungs through several layers of clothing. Others might drop the stethoscope chest piece down through the neck of the patient's blouse. A number of men did abdominal examinations with the full dressed patient sitting or standing.

Though the state had a mild polio epidemic at the time of the study, 71 percent of the doctors did no neurological examinations. Another 20 percent tested only knee and ankle jerks. No more than 9 percent "tested the reflexes in all extremities and made other neurological tests where indicated."

Many of the men apparently figured that he who pays Dr. Piper should call the tune: Eighty-three percent of them omitted an indicated rectal exam, 64 percent a vaginal exam, because of the patient's "implied or expressed disapproval." It was so unusual for any man to use a protoscope that the six G.P.s who did so were given extra credit. Only one of the G.P.s routinely examined the breasts of female patients during general check-ups.

While their vaginal specula gathered dust, the doctors seemed determined to wear out their sphygmomanometers. "Measurement of the blood pressure is probably the most frequently executed and least understood examination in general practice," says the report.

Every one of the G.P.s took routine blood pressure readings, probably because he thought patients expected him to. But only 17 percent of the men took careful systolic and diastolic measurements and examined the peripheral pulses when indicated.

Laboratory Tests. Here, it may not be too easy for you to compare your performance with that of the typical North Carolina G.P.: The touchstone was whether the doctor chose a laboratory procedure that—in the *observer's* opinion—seemed to fit the complaint. But you may still want to consider whether you routinely omit or include certain tests through force of habit rather than because of clinical indications.

The research check-list of laboratory tests comprised seventeen entries, ranging from urinalysis to blood chemistry and bacteriological tests. The tests most consistently ordered were urinalyses (used by 89 percent of the G.P.s when they seemed indicated), examinations of cerebrospinal fluid (85 percent), and diagnostic X-rays (82 percent). Only about half the men called for red or white blood cell counts, biopsies or smears for cancer, and ECGs or BMRs.

Forty-three percent of the doctors were judged to be careless about sterile technique. They used unsterilized syringes, forgot to wipe the patient's skin before a shot, and forgot to wash their own hands after contamination.

Therapeutic Measures. The observers didn't attempt to judge the G.P.'s treatment of every sort of case. Instead, they concentrated on his handling of potentially dangerous drugs and on six complaints that, in their view, come up frequently in general practice, are fairly easy to diagnose, and call for a wide but representative range of therapeutic measures. If some of these complaints don't fall within the scope of your own practice, perhaps you can use comparable examples.

Among the thought-provoking findings in the seven surveyed categories:

Sixty-seven percent of the men received low ratings because they routinely gave antibiotics for all *upper respiratory infections.* They reportedly made no attempt to find out whether such infections were viral or bacterial in origin. Many of them thought penicillin was good for the common cold, while others argued that it was harmless or might prevent complications.

Eighty-five percent prescribed "shot-gun" preparations of vitamins, minerals, iron, etc. for *anemia* without trying to track down its cause.

Fifty-seven percent prescribed some drug or other for *hypertension* without probing into its possible causes. They didn't advise the patient to take off weight, throw away his saltcellar, get more rest, etc.

Eighty-three percent seemed either indifferent or uneasy when faced with *psychological problems.* They often spoke of "malingering," "hypochondriacs," "problem patients," or of "getting them out of the office quickly."

Some of the men made half-hearted attempts to treat disturbed patients with vitamins, antacids, iron preparations, sex hormones, or antispasmodics. And a few of them set aside special times when such patients could talk out their troubles. But the doctor's willingness to *listen* wasn't always evident.

Only one-third of the G.P.s apparently recognized *obesity* as a clinical problem with psychological overtones. These men gave their overweight patients detailed diet list, explained the rationale of weight reduction, and provided "needed emotional support." The other G.P.s completely ignored the problem unless the patient himself mentioned it. Then these doctors were likely to prescribe an appetite depressant, along with some general advice about cutting down on starches and fat.

Perhaps because they were rarely called on to treat *congestive heart fail-*

ure, few of the G.P.s reportedly handled the condition with skill. The report says only one out of four "individualized the dosage of drugs," recommended low salt diets, and "utilized the patient's weight, determination of circulation time, and respiratory vital capacity as aids to diagnosis and management."

When prescribing potentially dangerous drugs, only about half the doctors kept an eye out for possible complications—by asking about previous reactions to penicillin shots, for instance, or by giving "proper supervision and advice" to patients who were taking propylthiouracil, ACTH, cortisone, and other such drugs.

Preventive Medicine. Are you educating your patients to the need for regular check-ups, immunizations, etc.? If so, you're right in step with most of your colleagues. As a group, the eighty-eight North Carolina G.P.s scored much higher in this category than in any other. They were judged on two counts only: antenatal care and well-child care.

Over two-thirds of the men gave careful initial and follow-up examinations in pregnancy. And 87 percent followed a schedule of prenatal and postpartum visits similar to that recommended by the American Committee on Maternal Welfare.

In addition, 93 percent of them followed a set schedule of immunizations for the very young children. One-fifth gave periodic well-baby check-ups as well.

Clinical Records. You may well argue that there isn't necessarily any connection between the scope of a man's records and his professional skill. Some doctors just happen to keep meticulous records. Others don't.

Though inclined to agree, the researchers included this activity because it "should provide some indication of the physician's thoroughness and attention to details which add up to good patient care." They found that the average man's performance in this category was on a par with his performance in the other five.

Seventeen percent of the North Carolina men kept thorough records. They wrote down everything the clinical history, physical exam, and laboratory tests revealed. They noted the treatment prescribed and the results of hospital visits.

A middle group, comprising about half the G.P.s, made brief notes on positive findings and medications prescribed.

The rest—some 36 percent—set down only scraps of information or none at all. Eleven men simply recorded the patient's name and the fee.

Table 1—Average Clinical Performance Scores of 88 G.P.s

Rank	No. of G.P.s	% of G.P.s	Medical History	Physical Exam.	Lab Aids	Therapy	Preven- tive Med.	Clinical Records	Av. Total Score
				ACTIVITY					
V	7	8%	77%	81%	80%	72%	76%	62%	73%
IV	15	17	57	87	75	58	53	53	66
III	27	31	40	62	35	38	29	34	47
II	23	26	24	49	30	25	18	19	39
I	16	18	12	49	15	21	16	16	28

At first glance, the survey findings are anything but encouraging. Yet the North Carolina observers themselves point out that a doctor may well give better care than his score on a test of this sort indicates. For example:

Judged by academic standards, the typical surveyed G.P. didn't handle emotional problems well. But this doesn't necessarily mean he muffed his traditional role as family friend and counselor. "Generally," say the researchers, "patients were very satisfied with their doctor and praised him openly. . . . The sympathetic physician probably provides more emotional support than he realizes."

The study team was left with a high regard for the "selflessness" of many doctors. Says the report: "The irregularity and frequency of the demands made upon the physician's time are greater than in most professions. He is pictured in the minds of many as being ever available, never too fatigued to see one more patient, and having little personal need for rest or recreation. Many of the general practitioners participating in this study fit this picture."

II. The Influence Of Medical Education. In asking its alumni for contributions, your alma mater probably plays variations on the old theme song, "We Made You What You Are Today." But does your medical school really deserve credit for the level of practice you maintain? The answer seems to be an almost unqualified "No."

The study team went all the way back to medical school admissions records. Medical College Apitude Test scores for thirty of the men (and medical school grades for all of them) were obtained from their medical school deans. A comparison of these figures with the doctors' clinical ranking at the time of the study produced the researchers' first finding:

A man's score on the Medical College Aptitude Test doesn't indicate how good a medical student—or doctor—he's likely to be. So if admissions committees rely too heavily on such scores, they may not always choose the most promising students.

Admissions committees are popularly supposed to be partial to doctors' sons. So the study team next had a look at the G.P.s' family backgrounds. Their fathers had been professional men, business executives, teachers, ministers, accountants, merchants and small entrepreneurs, farmers, skilled and unskilled workmen. Finding:

Doctors' sons aren't any more likely to become good doctors than anyone else. The only group that ranked slightly better than average in the North Carolina study were the sons of executives. The sons of merchants and small entrepreneurs ranked slightly below average. Conclusion: "The father's occupation is of little importance" in the making of a good general practitioner.

How important was the choice of medical school? Thirty-two different medical schools were attended by the North Carolina men. Did it make any difference that some schools graduated an unusually high percentage of teachers and researchers, while other schools put more emphasis on practical medicine? Did the twenty privately supported schools turn out better qualified G.P.s than the twelve state universities? The study group's finding:

The type of medical school a doctor attended seems to have no bearing on his clinical performance—at least as far as general practice is concerned.[1]

This may be because "present-day medical schools in this country are all very good and (offer) almost identical curricula," the study team adds.

Presumably, then, a man who got high grades at one medical school might have done just as well anywhere else. But do those high grades indicate he's likely to be a good doctor? Finding:

The best medical school students tend to become slightly better than average doctors. Among the North Carolina G.P.s who'd been in the top third of their class, 44 per cent were rated in the two top ranks (Ranks V and IV) as clinicians. Only 20 percent of the "middle third" men and 23 percent of the "bottom third" men were rated that high.

But the *average* rank of all the "top third" men was only a trifle higher than that of the other two groups. "The difference is not striking," say the researchers, "and the range of performance, even among the top group of students, was wide."

Table 2—G.P.s' Medical School Standing Compared With Later Clinical Performance, by Age Groups

How Doctors Ranked as Medical Students	How Doctors Ranked Later as Clinicians		
	Average at age 28–35	Average at age 36–45	Average at age 46–65
Top third of class (21%)	4.2	3.0	2.8
Middle third of class (48%)	3.3	2.5	2.0
Bottom third of class (31%)	1.5	3.7	2.3

In other words, good grades don't guarantee a good doctor—any more than they do a good lawyer, a good general, or a good playwright.

This may mean that medical schools emphasize some subjects that don't help their graduates in daily practice. It may also mean that many good students gradually relax their standards after leaving school.

The latter point seems to be borne out by the researchers' next finding:

Up to the age of 35 or so, men who did well as medical students do an outstanding clinical job. After that, they let their standards slip somewhat, judging from Table 2. At the same time, some of the poorer students acquire skills they weren't taught in college. But after reaching 45 most doctors—whether they were good or poor students—seem to be less careful about keeping their clinical standards high.

Residency Evaluated. What about the effect of hospital training? The North Carolina men had had anywhere from sixty months of hospital training to none at all. After matching these figures against the doctors' clinical rankings, the researchers concluded:

The length of time spent in internships and residencies has little relation to clinical performance. True, the five North Carolina doctors with more than thirty months of hospital training all ranked average or better. And three-fourths of the men who'd had no internship at all were ranked at the bottom as clinicians. But between these two extremes, the researchers couldn't find any link between length of training and clinical skill.

In fact, the "average" clinicians had almost twice as much hospital training as the top-rated clinicians in Rank V. The average length of hospital training, in months, for each of the five ranks was as follows:

V..14.4   IV..17.8   III..21.4   II..15.3   I..12.2

If the length of hospital training isn't very significant, what about its quality? If a man spent all his training time in a teaching hospital, is he likely to be a better doctor than the next man? Finding:

There's no clear relation between quality of hospital training and clinical performance. And at this point the researchers began to wonder: *Something in the G.P.s' hospital training must have influenced their clinical performance. What was it?*

The researchers set off on a new statistical hunt. After much calculation and correlation, they came up with their most significant finding:

The longer the hospital training IN MEDICINE, *the better the doctor.* This emerges clearly from the following table, in which Roman-numeral rankings have been averaged in Arabic figures (the higher, the better);

Months of Hospital Training in Medicine	Doctors' Average Rank as Clinicians
More than 8	3.60
5–8	3.31
4	2.81
3	2.63
Less than 3	2.53

By contrast, there seemed to be *no* connection between clinical skill and the length of internship and residency training in surgery, pediatrics, or obstetrics and gynecology.

Is it possible that this finding was influenced by the make-up and methods of the research team? Were the observers biased in favor of their own specialty, internal medicine? Did they put undue emphasis on diagnostic procedures?

These challenges were anticipated by the researchers themselves. They point out that a given doctor tended to perform each of the six clinical activities studied with about the same degree of competence. Presumably, then, if his skill in delivering babies had been graded, the score would have been similar to the score he made on history taking, for example.

The researchers *did evaluate* the G.P.s' skill in prenatal care. And they found that the quality of such care "increased directly with the amount of (the doctor's) training in internal medicine." Curiously, length and type of *obstetrical* training had no apparent effect.

Like all conclusions based on statistical averages, those reported in this article probably aren't entirely true of any individual doctor. A few of the North Carolina men had been good students and had received good training— but they were still mediocre practitioners. Others had become outstanding doctors despite poor scholastic records and poor training. In addition, though most of the older doctors were rated relatively low, some of them "showed every evidence of continuing improvement."

These variations can be explained only by "the individual's interest in medicine," the study group concludes.

III. The Effect of Refresher Work. If you're really interested in your work, you're likely to do well at it. And because you want to do well, you probably attend a good many medical society and hospital meetings, take periodic refresher courses, and read a number of professional journals.

Your diligence is commendable—but it may do you less good than you think.

The study team concludes that the typical doctor isn't likely to gain much from the post-graduate courses available to him. What's more, medical society and hospital meetings don't seem to improve his clinical skill. Only the number of journals he reads regularly appears to bear a direct relation to how good a doctor he is.

Some more time-honored medical beliefs are shattered when we compare the North Carolina G.P.s' post-graduate study habits with their clinical rankings. The researchers' first finding:

There's no consistent relationship between the quantity of refresher work a man does and the quality of his clinical performance.

The G.P.s studied took anywhere from 110 hours of refresher training annually to none at all. Such training included hospital and medical society clinical sessions as well as formal courses.

The top-rated clinicians in Rank V averaged forty-seven hours a year—a higher average than in any other rank. But when all surveyed doctors are classified according to the number of hours of refresher work they put in annually, we find that the men who take a moderate amount of such work (forty to fifty-nine hours) have a better average rank as clinicians than those who take sixty or more. (In the table that follows, Roman-numeral rankings have been converted to Arabic numerals—the higher, the better.)

Hours of Refresher Work Annually	Average Clinical Rank
60 and over	2.61
40–59	3.21
20–39	2.58
0–19	2.43

The researchers conclude that "doctors who do more than sixty hours . . . annually may be doing more than is necessary for their purposes, or . . . interest in medicine or study may not be their primary motivation in attending medical meetings."

They're inclined to think, too, that many courses simply aren't fitted to the family doctor's needs. P.G. courses, they say, are often too theoretical, too advanced, or too complex to be covered in the allotted time.

Is it a waste of time, then, to sign up for such courses? The researchers don't go so far as to say that.

Formal Courses Better. They found that doctors who attended only medical society and hospital meetings were considerably less skillful, on the average, than the men who took formal courses. But the doctors who took from one to nine hours of formal work actually ranked slightly *higher* as clinicians than the men who took forty or more hours.

Without drawing any hard-and-fast conclusions on this point, the researchers say: "Either good doctors tend to do formal post-graduate study or doctors are made better by doing it."

The grades a man got in medical school bear almost no relation to his later study habits, the research team found. Neither does the length, type, or quality of internship and residency training.

What about the effects of medical society affiliations? The researchers report that the North Carolina men had almost 400 society memberships among them, with an average of 4.2 per doctor. Finding:

There's no measurable relationship between the quality of a doctor's work and the number of medical societies he belongs to.

Similarly, the type of medical society seems to have little effect on the physician's competence—with one exception:

Members of the American Academy of General Practice tend to be better-than-average clinicians. The A.A.G.P. is the only national medical organization that requires its members to take regular refresher training. That training must average at least fifty hours a year—roughly the amount that the North Carolina researchers hit on as ideal.

But the study team isn't convinced that it's the A.A.G.P. refresher requirement that accounts for the clinical superiority of its members. The Academy has been in existence for just ten years—perhaps not long enough for the effects of such training to show up. The researchers suspect that members may be better because of "self-selection." That is, the G.P.s most interested in improving their work are the ones most interested in joining.

If the average medical society doesn't do much to make better doctors of its members, what about the average hospital? Most hospitals conduct educational programs for their staff men; and presumably it does a man good to be able to observe his colleagues at work and swap ideas with them. Yet here is the researchers' finding.

Doctors on an active hospital staff don't rank higher as clinicians than men who either have no hospital connections or don't use them. Staff doctors did score somewhat higher in the use of laboratory aids for diagnosis. But not on other counts, including over-all clinical skill. The researchers conclude:

"It seems . . . that the physicians and the citizens of a community determine the level of care which will be extended by their hospital . . . (It doesn't seem) that the hospital specifically influences the level of care rendered by the physicians comprising its staff."

Incidentally, though some of the North Carolina men didn't have hospital connections, this was entirely a matter of their own choice. Every doctor who wanted a hospital appointment had one. (It's true, though, that some of the men had been turned down by certain hospitals and that others were restricted in their obstetrical and surgical work.)

A final check-point in evaluating the G.P.s' refresher training was the number of medical journals they subscribed to. The average man took a fraction over four such publications. The researchers' finding:

The more medical journals a man takes, the better doctor he's likely to be. This shows up clearly in the following tabulation of the average number of journals subscribed to by men in each clinical rank:

V...5.7   IV...5.1   III...4.2   II...3.8   I...3.1

Naturally, none of the findings reported here necessarily reflects what any individual physician is like. Some of the best doctors surveyed took almost no post-graduate work and read very few journals; some of the poorest clinicians put in a lot of time on such things.

IV. The Importance of the Office Set-Up. The ghost of Old Doc still walks in the minds of many medical men. Old Doc sat at his cluttered roll-top desk taking care of an endless stream of patients with the aid of nothing but a stethoscope, a thermometer, and a bottle of pink pills. He never sent a bill. When he died, half the town owed him money. By his lights, that was the way to practice medicine.

Though today's medical man doesn't want to be like Old Doc, he may have the uneasy feeling that he ought to be. He knows it's more convenient to have a well-equipped office and efficient business routines. But he's heard it implied time and again that the doctor who pays attention to business efficiency must not be paying enough attention to his patients.

If you're one of the physicians who have been troubled by such thoughts, you can throw away your guilt complex. The study reveals that the doctor who organizes his office most efficiently is generally the one who gives his patients the best medical care.

This isn't really too surprising. For businesslike methods bespeak a man who's self-disciplined and orderly—qualities that are just as important in arriving at a diagnosis as in arriving at a fee schedule.

A good doctor is likely to have a spacious and attractive office. About half the G.P.s studied had only one examining room, next to (or combined with) a consultation room. Some of their offices were dirty, cluttered, and in a bad state of repair, showing little regard for the patient's comfort.

But the top-rated clinicians in Ranks V and IV tended to have well-planned offices with a special room for the secretary; special treatment, operating, and laboratory space; and a number of examining rooms. "In these practices," the study report says, "the nurse conducted patients to the examining rooms in rotation and had them undressed for the doctor. He could then see patients without losing time while they were ushered in or out or while they were disrobing."

An arrangement of this sort was taken to indicate that the doctor "had given some thought to his own time as well as to that of the patients." (But just to show that exceptions still prove the rule, one or two doctors with such facilities were evidently a little *too* concerned with saving their own time, since they appeared to give their patients very superficial care.)

A good doctor is likely to invest in some specialized medical equipment. After listing the major pieces of diagnostic equipment that each of the eighty-eight men used, the researchers found that five items seemed significant in judging the physician's skill: microscope, clinical centrifuge, electrocardiograph, BMR machine, and photoelectric colorimeter. The more of these a man had, the higher his clinical ranking was likely to be:

Amount of Lab Equipment Doctors Own:	Doctor's Average Rank as Clinicians
None	1.8
Microscope only	1.9
Microscope plus 1 item	2.7
Microscope plus 2 items	2.9
Microscope plus 3 items	3.2
Microscope plus 4 items	3.3

The men who owned special pieces of equipment didn't generally use them as money-makers, the study team reports. For instance, they charged such low BMR fees that they weren't likely ever to recoup their investment. These doctors had apparently bought equipment in "an attempt to broaden the scope of practice," rather than to increase their profits.

Over half the doctors did some radiology, and they generally felt it was "of vital help in meeting the problems of general practice." But the researchers couldn't discover any definite relation between clinical skill and ownership of X-ray machines.

A good doctor is likely to employ two or more aides. It's obvious that the physician who delegates routine tasks has more time to practice medicine. And sometimes by hiring, say, a lab technician, he's able to provide services that wouldn't otherwise be available in his community. For these reasons, the researchers say, a doctor is apt to invest in extra help if he wants to give his patients extra-good care.

A good doctor is likely to run his practice "by appointment only." The majority of the North Carolina general practitioners said they couldn't possibly attempt to follow an appointment schedule. In some rural areas, for example, it would be difficult for patients to telephone the office before a visit.

But the researchers conclude that such arguments were often an excuse for "the physician's own reluctance to discipline himself." Some men (including a few in even the most sparsely settled regions) did have appointment systems—and they were generally better doctors:

Doctors' Appointment System	Doctors' Average Rank as Clinicians
Appointments only	3.4
Some appointments	3.1
Office hours only	2.4

A good doctor does not necessarily work longer hours, spend more time with each patient, or earn more money than the less skillful man. The eighty-eight G.P.s worked anywhere from three to sixteen hours a day. The average was a little over nine hours, or about fifty-one hours in a five-and-a-half-day week (not counting Sundays, night calls, and night deliveries).

The researchers couldn't find any connection between the amount of time a man devoted to practice and the quality of care he gave. Their conclusion: "The popular idea that a busy doctor is a very good doctor does not appear to be entirely justified. The fact that the best doctors spend no more time in their practices tends to refute the idea expressed by some that 'I could do a better job if I had more time.' "

Average Patient Load. Four of the North Carolina family doctors saw fewer than fifty patients a week, while one man saw well over 500. The average, based on a five-and-a-half-day week, was about 170, or just over thirty patients a day.

A comparison of patient load with clinical rank convinced the researchers that "a large practice does not necessarily depress the quality of work done, and in more careful, methodical histories or physical examinations." In fact, generally speaking, the better the doctor, the more patients he was likely to see.

The top-rate clinicians in Rank V were an exception to this general rule. They averaged only 138 patients a week, as compared with 193 for the Rank IV men. This fact, says the study report, "may possibly (provide) an explanation for the difference between these two groups both as to quality (of practice) and (as to) net income."

The very best doctors had a much lower average income than those ranked just below them:

Clinical Rank	Average Net Income for 1952–1953
V	$14,500
IV	18,900
III	17,300
II	14,600
I	13,400

The study group didn't find any evidence that the best medical school students are likely to have extra-high incomes from practice. But it did find a direct relation between the doctor's income and both the length of his work day and the number of aides he employed.

"It seems probably that a higher income simply enables the physician to employ more help," the researchers say; "it is unlikely that more employees contribute significantly to the physician's income." (But other studies have shown that the doctor who adds another girl to his staff tends to net several thousand dollars more each year as a result.)

Office-Call Fees. Most of the survey general practitioners' fees were quite low. The usual charge for an office visit (sometimes including an injection or a laboratory test) was $3.

"Only one or two instances of patient-overcharging were seen," the researchers say. "Most physicians manifested little preoccupation with fees or collections . . . The usual practice was not to send monthly statements, the attitude being that those who could pay would do so of their own volition."

A good doctor is likely to practice in a group or partnership. Group and partnership doctors in North Carolina had an average clinical rank of 3.4, as compared with 2.5 for the average solo practitioner. They also had better academic records, on the average, and more training in medicine. They read more medical journals, took a little more post-graduate work, worked slightly longer hours, owned more laboratory equipment, and earned more money.

The researchers aren't sure whether the better doctor is more likely to go into group practice, or whether group practice is likely to make for a better doctor. But they're inclined to think that the former is true: "The better physician recognizes the advantages of the group practice arrangement and sets out to provide himself with these advantages in order to render a higher quality of medical care to his patients."

The way a man sets up and runs his practice seems to be a good indication of his feeling about medicine. A handsome office and gleaming equipment can't make him a good doctor. But the fact that he invests in such things usually shows that he wants to give his patients the best possible care.

This theme recurs again and again in the research report: The most important—and intangible—ingredient of clinical skill seems to be a sincere interest in medicine. The man who has that interest can often overcome a poor record in medical school, inadequate training, and the lack of opportunity to do much post-graduate work. Because he wants to be a careful, skillful, and conscientious physician, he probably will be.

Maybe Old Doc—who puts his patients' welfare above everything else —was a pretty good doctor after all. But he was good despite his office set-up, not because of it.

Discussion: Critical Sidelights on the North Carolina Study. A careful reader is bound to challenge certain aspects of the North Carolina study. The researchers themselves did some challenging: In the study report they dissect their methods and findings, to show up weaknesses where they exist and to justify conclusions that seem justifiable. Here are the main criticisms of the project, along with clarifying comment based on the North Carolina researchers' report:

The eighty-eight G.P.s may not have been typical. In type and length of hospital training, at least, they were much like G.P.s everywhere. And they had come from fifteen different states and had attended thirty-two different medical schools. Included among them were good students and poor ones. Some of the men had done no post-graduate work, others had done over sixty hours a year. They practiced in cities, small towns, and rural areas. Their ages ranged from 28 to 65.

To draw any sweeping conclusions from a study of only eighty-eight men is unwarranted. The researchers agree. That's why they're now planning further studies which they hope will shed more light on some of their initial findings.

A test based on personal observations can't be completely impartial. True. Even though the researchers used a rigorously detailed check-list, they found that one of them gave consistently higher ratings for the physical examination. All ratings *were* standardized in the final accounting. But in a test of this sort no mathematical computation can completely overcome the effect of personal bias.

Daily practice can't be judged by textbook standards. These are probably the only standards most doctors would agree on *in principle.* Besides, one purpose of the study was to compare the G.P.s' skill as practitioners with their medical school grades. This wouldn't have been possible unless much the same criteria had been used in both instances.

When a doctor gets too busy, he HAS *to lower his standards.* Not so, according to the North Carolina study: Generally speaking, the G.P. with an above-average patient load also practiced above-average medicine.

Doctors in rural areas may have scored low because they didn't have access to proper medical facilities. To quote the report: "A physician presumably enters practice with all that is required for taking a good history and performing a careful physical examination." And he doesn't need a roomful of expensive equipment to run a few basic screening tests. The fact appears to be that many of the surveyed doctors did not make full use of such diagnostic equipment as they had.

Maybe some of the surveyed men jacked up their usual performance because they were being observed. It's possible. Yet, as the researchers say, "It is difficult abruptly to change established habits and reaction patterns and even less likely that alterations could be consistently maintained for the three or four-day period during which observations were carried out." Incidentally, no one told the men their clinical performance was being graded; but some of them guessed it.

Usually, the family doctor doesn't need to take an involved history: He's already well acquainted with most of his patients and their families. When a G.P. sees an average of thirty patients a day, as these men did, he can't possibly remember everything about everybody. Unfortunately, he's sometimes more likely to remember that Mr. Smith's brother-in-law is a carpenter than that Mr. Smith once had shingles. An example of such medical forgetfulness: One surveyed doctor's patient had a large surgical scar on his abdomen. The doctor knew he'd referred the man to a medical center a few months before. But he couldn't remember what for—and he had no idea what operation had been done.

If a G.P. IS *inclined to forget, he should keep better records rather than go over the same ground every time a given patient comes in.* True enough. But the men who scored badly on history taking were generally the very ones who kept skimpy records.

You can't judge a physical examination by overt acts alone. That's admittedly a weakness in any study of this sort. The observers tried to compensate for it by asking questions about the G.P.'s thinking and observations. But there wasn't always time for either question or answer.

The typical G.P. does a lot of surgery and obstetrics. Yet these weren't included in the study. They weren't included because the research team (composed mainly of internists) didn't feel competent to judge specialized techniques in these fields. Besides, surgery and obstetrics are not all-important in the average general practice. (During the study period, fewer than 16 per cent of the G.P.'s cases were surgical, fewer than 13 percent obstetrical. By contrast, 57 percent of their cases were essentially medical). Also, the researchers felt that correct diagnosis and good patient management were the real criteria by which to judge a man's handling of any case.

Summary.

A general practitioner is likely to be an above-average doctor if he:

1. Had high medical school grades (and is under 36)
2. Had more than three months' hospital training in medicine (the more, the better)
3. Spends forty to fifty-nine hours—no more, no less—in annual post-graduate study (including formal courses as well as hospital and medical society clinical sessions)
4. Subscribes to more than four medical journals
5. Belongs to the American Academy of General Practice
6. Has a spacious, well-equipped office staffed by two or more aides
7. Adheres to an appointment schedule
8. Practices in a group or partnership

The study shows no connection between the doctor's clinical skill and:

1. His father's occupation
2. His scores on the Medical College Aptitude Test
3. The type of medical school he attended
4. The type of hospital he trained in
5. The length of his hospital training in pediatrics, surgery, and obstetrics and gynecology
6. The number of medical societies he belongs to
7. His hospital affiliations (or lack of them)
8. His patient load, length of work day, and net income.

39   YOUR MALPRACTICE RISKS

By Medical Economics Staff

The facts in the following tables stem from a nine-year study in two California counties. From 1946 through 1954, a total of ninety-four malpractice suits were filed against physicians insured under the Alameda-Contra Costa Medical Association's group plan. There were thirty-one other claims that resulted in cash settlements of $100 or more. These 125 "malpractice incidents" are analyzed here.

How representative are they? "As professional liability experience goes, the period of study is brief," says Dr. Joseph F. Sadusk Jr., who compiled the basic statistics for his medical society's bulletin. And as two California counties go, the rest of the nation doesn't necessarily go, too. Most strikingly atypical are the high incidence of claims (one for every fourteen physicians annually) and the whopping damages asked in suits (an average of almost $65,000).

From *Medical Economics*, 32, (September, 1955), 121–123. Copyright 1955 by Medical Economics, Inc.

Such peculiarities aside, the Sadusk study seems reasonably representative of malpractice incidents everywhere. So the following tables may well illuminate the sources of trouble in your own medical community.

Who Generates Malpractice Incidents?

Women patients	54%
Men patients	34
Minor patients	12

In liability, as in lifeboats, women and children come first. Taken together, they generate almost twice as many malpractice incidents as do the men. "These differences are interesting," Dr. Sadusk says, "but no satisfactory explanation can be offered."

Who Gets Involved in Malpractice Incidents?

General practitioners	54%
Certified specialists	31
Noncertified specialists	15

These figures follow the percentage distribution of doctors in the area rather closely. A further breakdown of G.P.s—American Academy of General Practice members as against nonmembers—shows "no statistically valid difference." In other words, all types of doctors draw their share of malpractice incidents.

Who Gets Involved More Than Once?

Doctors with 2 incidents	0.7%
Doctors with 3 incidents	0.2
Doctors with 4 incidents	0.1

These "claims-prone" physicians comprise only 1 per cent of the medical society membership in the area studied. Yet in nine years they've run up 24 percent of the group's total malpractice costs; and suits asking $780,000 in damages are still pending against them.

Where Do Malpractice Incidents Occur?

Inside hospitals	70%
Outside hospitals	30

Not surprisingly, general practitioners are twice as likely as specialists to encounter malpractice incidents in their offices or in patients' homes. But even with G.P.s, the hospital is the usual scene.

Where Do Such Incidents Occur Disproportionately?

Median rate in hospitals per 100,000 admissions	12
Hospital X's rate per 100,000 admissions	56
Hospital Y's rate per 100,000 admissions	33

Fifteen of the seventeen hospitals in the area are fairly close to the median rate. The two exceptions are regarded as "astonishing." Do "claims-prone" physicians congregate in certain hospitals? Dr. Sadusk says only that "further investigations into the hospital factors are sorely needed . . ."

What Types of Work Produce Most Malpractice Incidents?

Obstetrics/Gynecology	20%
Orthopedics	14
General surgery	14
Internal medicine	10
Neuropsychiatry	6

The remaining 36 percent of malpractice incidents arise from just about every other type of work. "The large percentage of obstetrical and gynecological problems is quite surprising," says Dr. Sadusk. "It is quite possible that articles in lay magazines on this subject have contributed significantly to (Ob./Gyn.'s) emergence . . . as a leader in professional liability."

When Are Malpractice Suits Filed?

First year after incident	77%
Second year after incident	16
Third year or thereafter	7

As this table shows, it's possible for a physician to be sued because of an incident that took place years ago. Will he still have the insurance policy that covered him that year? Will he still have his records? If not, the time lag will have deprived him of his best defenses.

When Are Malpractice Suits Finally Disposed Of?

First year after suit	25%
Second year after suit	56
Third year or thereafter	19

These figures show the time lag between the filing of a suit and its final disposition. They make it clear that a malpractice case may hang over the doctor's head for interminable months. As Dr. Sadusk states it: "Professional liability is long and tedious."

What Percentage of All Claims Are Found Warranted?

Warranted	8%
Unwarranted	78
Still pending	14

This table covers not just the 125 "malpractice incidents" on which the other tables are based, but *all* malpractice claims in the area studied—a total of 609. Classified as *warranted* are thirty-one claims on which the defense committee recommended cash indemnities straightaway; eighteen claims settled later, "since they were considered meritorious"; and two claims that were upheld by jury verdict.

Classified as *unwarranted* are 436 claims dismissed by the defense committee as "totally without merit"; fifteen claims dismissed by a judge; and twenty-one claims denied by jury verdict.

Such clear-cut findings are possible only because of the way the defense committee operates. It made up its mind nine years ago, says Dr. Sadusk, that:

"If negligence or malpractice on the part of the physician appeared to be present . . . just and prompt financial remuneration would be made to the patient. On the other hand, if there was no merit to the charges brought against the physician, the doctor would be vigorously defended. Under no circumstances would a "nuisance claim" payment be made, as is so commonly done in other types of (professional) liability insurance."

This firm policy has helped Alameda-Contra Costa doctors. It has also produced firm facts about malpractice that may help doctors in other parts of the country.

40   SURGEONS AND THEIR PATIENTS: A STUDY IN SOCIAL PERCEPTION[1]

By Bernard Kutner

Introduction. Surgery today occupies a position of high prestige both among members of the medical profession as well as the public at large. While the favored status position of surgeons has been touched upon in the sociological literature, too little direct attention has been given to the interrelationships between surgeons and surgical patients. To the behavioral scientist the interpersonal problems in surgery offer a fertile field for investigation. The present paper concerns itself with the relationships between surgeons and their patients and primarily concentrates upon the problems of the surgeon in training, that is, the surgical intern and resident. Necessarily, also, we have aimed our investigation at the teaching hospital rather than the relationships that hold in the private practice of surgery. It is to be hoped that future studies will be designed to probe the relationships between the practitioner and his patient in the myriad of settings in clinical medicine. Because of its exploratory nature, we have raised more questions than we can provide answers. We begin with a brief consideration of the nature of private surgical practice.

1. Interpersonal Relationships in Surgery

a. Private Surgical Practice. The prototype of modern surgical practice is the surgeon who maintains a private office for purposes of examination, consultation, and post-surgical care and who is affilliated with one or more hospitals where his operations are performed. He may spend a portion of his time at a low-cost clinic or municipal hospital offering his services at minimal or no fees or he may lecture to and supervise medical students, interns, and residents in a local medical school or teaching hospital. The organization of his professional activities is usually so regulated that he has ample time for each of his manifold responsibilities. The largest portion of his time in practice is devoted to elective surgery and office consultation. While surgical emergencies occur, usually they are not too frequent.

The comparative orderliness of private surgical practice permits the surgeon, except in those instances where he is called in for emergency consultation, to develop rapport with both the patient and his family. The patient has a sense of security knowing that the physician who previously had examined him and "knows his case" will do the surgery, and in addition, will render post-operative care. Continuity of medical care is thus safeguarded throughout the period in which the surgeon is actively managing his patient. Thus, the individual's confidence and morale is strengthened in that he can better tolerate dislocations of living that are the normal consequence of entering the hospital and the discomfitures incident to surgery.

While the ideal practice of surgery is most closely approximated by the private practitioner, a considerable gap frequently appears between ideal practice and actual events in the context of general hospital wards. In this paper we shall attempt to explore the consequences of this schism for both patient care and interpersonal relationships.

b. The Surgical Resident and Intern. What we have described above is typical of the private practice of surgery and semi-private surgical and private surgical services of voluntary and proprietary hospitals. The situation is too often different in a teaching hospital and in the ward programs of general hospitals. It is estimated that about one-half of all operations performed in the United States in a given year are performed by surgical residents under the supervision of board-qualified surgeons. The "house staff" in a typical teaching hospital consists of interns who may "rotate" through surgery for three months or who may spend the whole year in a "straight" surgical internship. After a year of internship, the physician may become an assistant resident and in succeeding years of residency may arise to senior resident and finally to chief resident. Some institutions have extended the hierarchy to include a "junior attending surgeon" position. Training to prepare a physician to become a fully qualified surgeon requires a minimum of five years of graduated responsibility. Some residency programs, such as in neurosurgery, usually require a minimum of some seven years.

Sociologically speaking, the status hierarchy from intern to chief resident presumably reflects increasing competence. Unfortunately, as in most fields, greater experience in surgery does not always result in commensurate gains in skill. Hence, varying degrees of conflict over status, competence and promotion arise from the advance through seniority of less skilled neo-surgeons. A less experienced though more highly skilled resident must move forward at about the same rate of advancement as his less skilled colleague. A process of "natural selection" and the failure of complete surgical residency training reduces the ranks of potential surgeons during this period.

During his surgical residency, the trainee becomes increasingly immersed in the language, sights, smells and activities of the surgical clinics, wards and operating rooms. The exigencies of a heavy work schedule, a large patient load and the necessity of mastering the specialized knowledge and techniques of a field having manifold complexities, makes understandable the residents' tendency to place the technical medico-surgical aspects of each case in the forefront of his thinking. For these and other reasons we shall examine below, questions of a psycho-social nature tend to become obscured or obliterated in patient management. The low valuation of psycho-social factors in surgery among residents results in a series of distortions regarding the surgeon's role, the process of surgery and the future of the patient which we shall consider at a later point. It should be stressed here that the literature is amply filled with exhortations and urgings to "regard the patient's needs" and to "give the patient comprehensive care." Since the surgeon's skills and functions are shaped by his experiences in teaching hospital centers, we turn to a consideration of these institutions.

   c. *Surgery in the Teaching Hospital.* The majority of "ward patients" to be found in any teaching hospital are medically indigent.[2] That is, were they to undertake to pay for all services rendered in connection with their disease, they would deplete their financial resources to the vanishing point. Surgical ward patients generally are drawn from the lower economic and social strata of society and typically have less formal education, more tenuous occupational status and are older as a group than are private or semi-private patients in a given hospital. The typical house officer in a teaching hospital is obviously better educated, comes from a higher socio-economic group, is more articulate, commands a broader range of significant knowledge, occupies a position of prestige and is usually functioning under a different set of values than are his patients. These differences in background and outlook are frequently reflected in certain communication problems between surgeon and patients examined in some detail below. Here we should like to point out some of the differences in surgical goals as perceived by patient and physician.

   When a patient is admitted to a hospital, while he may suspect it, unless he has been so informed in advance by another physician, he has no certainty that he will undergo surgery. In fact, some patients, though aware that they are on a surgical ward are taken by surprise when informed that surgery is required to stem or correct their ailment. Most ward patients come to the hospital because of certain disturbing symptoms such as pain, bleeding, interference or loss of function due to injury, disease, or malformation. Some may arrive in an acute emergency such as an incarcerated hernia, a perforated ulcer or crushing injuries sustained in an accident. Others appear on referral for such conditions as chronic phlebitis, cholecystitis or suspected neoplasm. The primary concern of most patients is briefly: find out what is wrong, stop the disturbances and correct the cause of the trouble. Illness, disease, and injury are universally accepted as undesirable but while many will tolerate chronic illnesses over long periods, the average person does not long tolerate acute symptoms. Symptomatic relief, therefore, is the most common desire of the patient on a surgical ward.

   The practice of surgery in the teaching hospital has two major goals: service to the patient and the training of future surgeons. These goals can be compatible though in some instances they may be difficult to achieve simultaneously. Ideally, surgery attempts to intervene mechanically in order to correct, repair, alter, remove or otherwise modify the human body for the amelioration or cure of anomalies, diseases or injuries with a minimum of stress to the patient. Where and when feasible ideal surgery attempts to keep the patient informed of his condition, of plans for operating, and of likely results to be obtained in his particular case. It is these latter goals dealing with the psychological status of the surgical patient that most often are over-looked in the course of meeting the explicitly surgical problems the patient presents.

Usually, upon admission to the hospital, the patient is put to bed and one or more medical histories may be taken. To establish the diagnosis various laboratory tests may be ordered following one or more physical examinations. If surgery is indicated, during days or occasionally weeks pre-operatively, the patient receives a specified regimen of diet, drugs, blood, etc. Usually on the evening before surgery an attendant prepares the operative site, the anaesthesiologist prescribes the pre-operative sedative and subsequently the patient is taken to surgery. Post-operatively, the vital signs (breathing, pulse, and blood pressure) are checked frequently and the patient is watched care-fully for signs of bleeding, infusion reaction, pulmonary and/or cardiac com-plications, wound disruption, infection, etc. While these steps or stages in surgery are routinely followed in the teaching hospital, problems involving the patient's understanding of events, relationships and emotional difficulties are frequently handled in a casual manner or are deflected to psychiatric or social work consultation, to the patient's family or to the nursing staff. Management of emotional disturbances on the ward are often met by the judicious use of sedation or tranquilization. At least to surgeons-in-training, socio-psychological problems, the "human" dimensions of surgery, are com-paratively peripheral to the mainstream of thought and activity in surgery. To understand the factors underlying the resident surgeon's differential con-cerns with the multiple problems presented by patients in their care we must examine both their own as well as their patients' needs.

2. Some Social and Psychological Needs of Surgeons.

a. The Operator's Role. The prime locus of professional education and gratification in surgery is the operating room. No amount of reading, lectures or demonstrations can replace the experiences of performing surgery as an education method. For this reason, combined with the fact that necessary surgery *must* be performed in the teaching hospital upon an inexhaustible supply of patients, the major portion of a surgical resident's time is spent in operating or assisting at operations. Despite their obvious importance, most other functions of surgery such as establishing electrolytic balance, main-taining hemostasis, physical preparation, and post-operative management are generally not as much of concern to the house officer as are the techniques and procedures of the operation itself. Most of the non-operative problems are to be found in other departments of a hospital, principally, general medi-cine. What distinguishes surgical residency from other forms of medicine are the problems dealing with operative precedures. In fact, ratings of profi-ciency of surgical residents are often based primarily on the skill they show at the operating table. The role of the surgical resident is to become so skilled at general patient management and to perform as many and as varied a volume of operations as possible until he has reached a point of proficiency that qualifies him to be examined by the American College of Surgeons for certification. It is not surprising, therefore, that functions other than the operative one should play a less prominent part in the orientation of the surgical resident. Problems of a psycho-social order are regarded as extrinsic to surgery unless gross psychiatric or emotional symptomatology precludes or interferes with surgical plans. The typical low valuation placed on close interpersonal contact with patients by the surgical resident is highly overdetermined. The self-selection of surgery as a specialty is one factor that should be kept in mind. The choice of surgery as a career has often been spoken of as a successful device for avoiding patients while practicing medicine. This shibboleth is based on personal experiences rather than scientific evidence. Despite this fact, a degree of truth may be found in it. Interviews with thirty residents in one teaching hospital revealed that about half of them regard the psycho-social aspects of surgery as largely irrelevant—an attitude that must have played some part in the selection of this career specialty. (7, 8, 9, 20, 21). Other factors contributing to reducing the salience of psychological and social factors in surgical care include the comparatively high valuation placed upon success in diagnosis, physical work-up, surgical technique and post-surgical management; the comparatively low valuation placed upon the importance of social and psychological factors in illness by some surgeons in medical schools (22); the heavy pressure of work including large numbers of emergency operations done at night; the full schedule of conferences, seminars, rounds, and meetings the young surgeon is expected to attend; the relative inarticulateness of most ward patients; and differences in class and interest status of typical residents and their patients. We shall enlarge on this latter point below.

3. The Social and Psychological Needs of Patients.

a. The Meaning of Surgery. Since human beings respond variably to life crises, it is to be expected that responses to surgery should not be homogeneous. For some, a simple surgical procedure entailing a trifling risk of operative mortality or of post-surgical complications, such as the removal of warts, or skin blemishes, is an occasion of great moment. The patient may be hypertensive, feel weak, breathless, apprehensive, even panicky. On the other hand, some patients approaching major surgery are outwardly calm, relaxed, optimistic, confident. The meaning of these differences and individual variations in physical and psychological status before and following surgery will help clarify the role of the surgeon in meeting the social and psychological needs of their patients.

Whatever their ultimate causes may be, the majority of persons coming to an operation are gripped by anxieties. Believing that the patient lacks an understanding both of his own medical condition and the surgery contemplated, one prominent surgeon places the onus for anxiety upon the patient's lack of knowledge.

It is an unfortunate truth that most patients enter hospitals and operating room with unnecessary fears and anxieties. A great part of the apprehension stems from a lack of knowledge concerning their illness and the operative procedure which is to be performed on them. The persistence of these anxieties often interferes greatly with a healthy post-operative reaction and a smooth convalescence.[29]

While knowledge of steps, procedures and facts regarding surgery may help to alleviate destructive feelings of anxiety and hopelessness, it cannot entirely remove the symbolic elements of surgery. An operation, especially one necessitated by injury, disease or congenital anomaly presents an array of emotionally upsetting features:

1. It places the individual in a psychologically ambiguous situation. He must surrender his bodily autonomy to others and temporarily, at least, submit passively to an assault upon his person that is both harmful as well as helpful. The loss of voluntary control over one's personal activities and destiny may be the most distressing aspect of surgery to the individual.

2. The acknowledged existence of "risks" in surgery despite the high overall survival rate,[3] creates the possible situation that the person *may be* facing his imminent death. Such an eventuality, even though remote for a given procedure, induces those anxieties and fantasies associated by the individual with death.

3. Some types of surgery (i.e. colostomy, limb amputation, radical mastectomy, craniotomy, oopharectomy and orchidectomy) carry with them the actual or probable loss of a bodily part and the functions which that part serves. Such operations not only are feared because of ever present anxieties regarding mutilation but in addition there are fears regarding the consequences of the operation for the individual's future life.

4. Every surgical procedure entails a larger or smaller, but an invariably present measure of physical pain and discomfort, unusual and at times unnerving experiences and the relative social isolation of hospital life.

All of these factors may contribute to raising the anxiety level of a patient. Thus, while cognitive elements in surgical experience may, when lacking, add to the general level of anxiety in the patient, certain attributes of surgery bear intrinsic elements that are potentially traumatic. As will be indicated below, informational and emotional factors in surgery are closely related.

b. Social Traumata of Operations. Entering the surgical service of a hospital, the patient is thrown into contact with an array of others—physicians, nurses, technicians, aides, attendants and other patients—with whom he is required to interact. For some, exposure to the inspection, interrogation and observation of numerous unfamiliar persons is a trying experience. The norms of private life—autonomy of person, privacy of thoughts and acts, self-regulation of bodily functions, even conversation—must be modified and accommodated in varying degree. The hospital is a house of strangers, especially so for ward or open pavillion patients.

The hospital environment from a social interaction viewpoint engenders distortions in the relationships between the patient and members of the hospital staff. Thus, feelings of compassion and the desire to help are mingled with those of discomfort and avoidance. Ill persons may develop dependency feelings, investing professionals with "an aura of extraordinary ability" (6) while simultaneously disparaging them. Such types of conflicting feelings and perceptions arise from the socio-psychological context in which the interactions occur. While the dynamics of interpersonal relationships are at least as complex in the home, the latter does not present as great an immediate threat to the integrity of the personality as does the hospital. It is this threat, together with the passive-dependent-cooperative role thrust upon the patient that prevents normal human social intercourse. Further, distortions in relationships are enhanced by two added factors. The first is the limited time normally available for contact with the most significant persons in the patient's hospital world: physicians and nurses. Thus, Burling and associates report that one of the most frequently heard complaints about physicians in a hospital is "He won't take the time to explain things to me" (6). It is noteworthy that the form of the statement is a complaint rather than an explanation. In surgery this time limitation is especially acute since surgeons must spend a considerable portion of their time in the operating room—totally unavailable to patients wanting answers to questions.

The second complicating factor is the belief and practice of many surgeons that completely truthful answers to patient questions are sometimes contrary to the best interests of the patient (26). Thus, evasions, partial explanations, hedging and "white lies" are part of the daily interaction with patients. Since nurses and other professional workers are bound to silence by custom "to avoid confusion," the patient often finds himself unsatisfied and at times bewildered by a solid front of benevolent deception.

Thus, human relationships in the world of the surgical ward are proscribed by a variety of needs peculiar to patients and staff, by the structure of the situation in which they interact and by the customs and ethical considerations common to medicine. These modifications from normal relationships greatly affect communication between patients and surgeons. Since verbal communication in surgery is essential to the adequate preparation of patients and to post-surgical management, any deficiency or impairment of communication must necessarily lead to some inadequacy in pre- and post-surgical care. Addressing the American Surgical Association, a prominent surgeon advising a young surgical colleague stated as follows:

The most stimulating, gratifying, and at the same time, the most exasperating, experiences of your surgical life will be your relations with your patients and their families. It will be a simple matter for you to become careless and assume that they know as much about their illness as you do; or to become frustrated, after explaining carefully to them in as simple language as you can, to have them give evidence by their next questions that they have comprehended little of your effort. You may easily form the habit of telling them nothing, and rationalize it by believing that this is the best for their psychological state . . . the less personal the relationships, the more certain it is that the patient and his family will think bitterly in terms of percentage of recovery . . . when he is dissatisfied with the results of his surgical treatment.[14]

In surgery, one of the key factors in developing and maintaining a sound physician-patient relationship lies in the area of the psychological preparation of the patient. Such preparation is predicated upon the assumption that for most, if not all, patients the advent of surgery is accompanied by fear and anxieties, misconceptions and misunderstandings regarding all phases of the surgical experience. For some patients such preparation may consist merely of a reassurance that the situation is well in hand. For others, preparation may require exhaustive medical and psychological care to restore the individual's psychic equilibrium from the moment that surgery is contemplated to the time of discharge. There would, however, appear to be three areas in which such preparations is normally attempted although the frequency with which they occur is yet to be determined. These areas are the search for meaning, the need for social experience and the need for emotional support.

c. The Search for Meaning. Although it is many years since Bartlett (4) first enunciated the principle of "effort after meaning," the concept is still valid today. Human beings are constantly involved in a search for understanding of the conditions they experience in the world around them. Especially is this true as Sherif has shown when the individual is ego-involved in the situation (30). Thus, the surgeon who transmits information concerning the patient's condition and expected surgery takes cognizance of the fact that the patient desires to fill the cognitive void. Ignorance of the meaning of events related to surgery may have a stimulating effect on arousing hidden or overt anxieties. One prominent physician who has recently considered the role of explanation to the patient as an unrecognized omission in present-day medical practice, offers two reasons why explanations are indispensible to medical practice: as a therapeutic tool and as one of the best available ways of showing personal concern for the patient's welfare (17). Although taking as his point of departure the maintenance of good public relations through providing a sympathetic interest in his patients, this same author provides an excellent account of the need to enlarge the area of knowledge that the patient carries with him during his medical care.

The aim of the physician always should be to include in every consultation as much practical information as may be of use to the patient. Instruction of this kind, given unhurriedly and in understandable terms, convincingly indicates true interest and substitutes effectively for much that was included in the personal service of the old-school family doctor. To omit it constitutes not only neglect of a basic obligation to the patient, but also failure to do one's part toward correcting a major cause of discontent with present-day medical practice. (17)

Thus, giving information concerning the nature of his problem, the meaning of his symptoms and the likely course of the illness, would seem to increase the patient's confidence in his physician while bridging the gaps in his knowledge. Extensive explanations are frequently not given to patients despite the fact that many physicians may feel that patients should know much more concerning their ailment. (25) Pratt (27), in studying fifty-three doctor-patient relationships in a clinic in periods ranging from one to sixteen months, found that a major factor tending to reduce the physician's communications with patients was his perception of his patients as poorly informed. Thus, the average clinic patient, whose knowledge of medicine and disease, she found, tends to be seriously underestimated by the physician, tends to receive less information than patients regarded as possessing greater medical knowledge.

In his desire to learn the significance of symptoms and the possible events that are to occur in the course of surgery, the patient is often not only ignorant of the basic facts of his disease and of the normal operative process, but his surgeon may be reluctant to offer information if he feels that the patient cannot understand what he wishes to convey. Adequate communication between patients and surgeons, particularly in the surgical wards of a hospital, might possibly be enhanced, therefore, by attempts to discover the level of knowledge and understanding of the patient to whom the surgeon wishes to address his remarks and by an increase awareness of the points which the surgeon wishes to put across. The routine organization of this type of knowledge would help the surgeon in meeting what he may believe to be an essential aspect of the care he is rendering.

d. *The Need for Social Experience.* One commonly neglected area of medical care in surgery is the provision for adequate social experience during the preoperative and postoperative periods. Such experiences are not only valuable in and of themselves in rendering hospital life more tolerable for the patient, but can frequently be made use of as a therapeutic device. Not uncommonly, the brief time a patient may see his physician is sufficient to carry him through the day or through some especially difficult procedure. At the same time, it may act to prevent the patient from relying upon other patients for information concerning their disease. Szas and Hollender (32), in attempting to formulate a conceptual scheme for the physician-patient relationship, have pointed out that the model of mutual participation is largely unknown to medicine. In most situations, the physician does not gain the satisfactions from the relationship with patients that are presumed to be gained by patients. Thus, social interchange between physician and patient in a typical surgical ward is neither practicable nor usually possible. This is true since the physician's origin typically is from a different cultural and social background than that of the patient. This difference is accentuated by age, interests, experience and frequently, language. Normal social relationships, therefore, are often confined either to the current social grouping in the ward or between the patient and his relatives and friends. (32)

The social distance between surgeon and patient may be so great as to preclude all but the essential contacts necessary to establish a physical and social history and to receive indications from the patient concerning his physical and psychic status. Thus, social interchange may involve no more than the minimum medical requirements demanded. Under such circumstances the patient necessarily is thrown toward other members of the professional staff, such as nurses or social workers, or will seek out responsive non-professional staff members or relate to other patients. Coser (12), in her study of ward patients of a general hospital, reports the development of a "high degree of sociability and the formation of friendship ties" among fifty-one patients in her study group. Significant numbers of Coser's respondent's defined a "good doctor" as someone who is understanding, polite, kind, sociable, talkative, careful and attentive. She suggests that the warmth and receptivity that a patient may find in the ward of a hospital may be so great and their primary needs met so adequately that they are rendered less adaptable to the non-hospital role they must assume upon discharge. However, she feels that it is the regimentation and the receptive-passive role which the patient must adopt while in the hospital that are the fundamental conditions making for maladaptability.

The significance of meeting the patients' social needs while on the surgical service resides in the fact that these needs reflect more fundamental problems in the patient's emotional make-up and status. The relative social isolation to be found in a hospital ward, the threat implied to person and personality by impending surgery, the great physical discomforts of the early post-surgical period, and the common impersonal relationships of physician to patient which Fox has benignly termed "detached concern" (22) —all of these are social traumata of surgery having important psychological significance.

d. *Psychological Preparation.* There is little doubt that surgery, even of a minor sort, may stir emotional problems of a deep and lasting nature. There is equally little doubt that most patients benefit by a planned program of emotional preparation for surgery. William Kaufman in his presidential address to the Academy of Psychosomatic Medicine stated:

The patient must be emotionally prepared to accept necessary surgery without undue anxiety and fear. Everything must be directed toward reducing the psychological stress and trauma of anaesthesia and surgery to a minimum. The patient must receive the emotional support he needs and deserves during the immediate postoperative period. Measures must be taken which facilitate his total rehabilitation, despite ablations of his bodily parts and despite considerable post-surgical alteration in his bodily physiology. (18)

Dr. Kaufman believes that a properly employed half-hour or hour of such preparation may provide sufficient emotional security "to obviate preventable psychosomatic complications." He further believes that this type of briefing reduces anxieties, making anaesthesia more tolerable and producing less postoperative pain and discomfort.

"And he seems to make speedier recovery from the effects of surgery than the patient who is emotionally unprepared. This is equally true for emotionally normal patients as it is for neurotic patients, even though the latter may require somewhat more time to accomplish the necessary results." (18)

Fears are known to arise concerning every aspect of the disease, the surgical ward activities, the operation itself and from possible complications. What does the patient fear? Perhaps most of all is the fear of the unknown. (18) While specific anxieties may emerge, lack of a clear mental context leaves the person confused and uncertain. Fear of mutilation, castration, loss of function, paralysis and death may contribute heavily to the individual's disturbance. Blanton and Kirk (5) and Zwerling, et. al. (33) have reported a rather high incidence of emotional disturbance among surgical patients. Blanton and Kirk suggest that neurotic patients should have psychiatric treatment as part of their care to prevent protracted periods of convalescence. Kroger and Freed (19) have recommended that women having hysterectomies should be relieved of common anxieties regarding the effects of the operation on their sex life, appearance and aging. Cockerill (11) has likewise discussed the problems encountered in radical mastectomies. In reviewing the problem of psychological preparation, Michaels (24) stresses the importance of this procedure in surgery during early childhood, at puberty and at the climacteric. Operations involving the genital organs, eyes and skull are thought to harbor the greatest danger of psychological eruption. A similar conclusion is reached by Craig (13) who writes:

The importance of preparation of a patient for an operation is frequently proven by the fact that some of the patients even become psychotic prior to the operation.

Macgregor and Schaffner (23) have recommended, in the case of nasal plastic surgery that patients be screened psychiatrically before surgery is done to determine whether the patient is psychologically ready to face an operation that will change their appearance. Where the surgery is not elective but urgent, such pre-operative work must be done while the patient is in the hospital with its added potential traumata. Sutherland and his associates (31) have recently documented the potentially disastrous effects following radical mastectomy or colostomy. Bard and Sutherland (2) suggest that the surgeon may avail himself of the psychiatrist, social worker and nurse in the comprehensive management of patients with radical mastectomy. They report that patients are shocked, terrified, numbed, stunned and panicked by the revelation that breast surgery is required. Thus:

The physician should be prepared to spend considerable time with the patient interpreting the need for surgery. By encouraging the patient to express her feelings and fears freely, the physician can identify distortions and misconceptions. . . . In addition, he will find that patient's specific psychological difficulties will become quite evident. . . . It cannot be emphasized too strongly that an hour of permissive discussion when the diagnosis is established may be more advantageous in the management of the post-mastectomy patient than months of psychotherapy during and after convalescence. (p. 658)

An internist who carefully prepares his patients who face surgery has detailed the types of communication he employs to lessen their tensions and anxieties. These include information about the nature of the illness, why surgery is needed, when and where it should be done and about suitable surgeons. He also indicates what may reasonably be expected from both anaesthesia as well as surgery; clarifies misconceptions; reassures about the competence of surgeons; and reveals some optimism over the lasting effects of the work to be done. Moreover, he reviews details regarding hospital routines, the recovery room, post-operative procedures and the avoidance of certain complications. Information specific to the particular surgical procedure is also provided, such as the need for covering both eyes following surgery on only one of them. The author also suggests that post-surgical "preparation" should be given those who were not prepared pre-surgically. (18)

Beyond the fact that preparation for surgery may relieve a multiplicity of anxieties present even in emotionally normal persons, it may have an effect that lasts throughout and perhaps beyond the surgical experience. This derives from the feeling of acceptance and respect from a fellow human being, which taking the time and trouble to prepare, imply. Such feelings restore confidence and morale while reducing tensions built on fear.

The matter of psychological preparation may be summed up by referring to the words of two psychiatrists writing from different perspectives:

If we are to achieve and maintain good interpersonal relations in the practice of medicine, we need to have as much interest and concern for the feelings of our patients and their families as we have in the physical aspects of their illnesses. We need to regard our relations with each of them as significant as our scientific knowledge and the medicine we prescribe. (3)

It is well known that patients who are thought of as persons instead of just bodies before, during and after operations, recover more rapidly. (15)

4. *The Perception of the Surgeon's Role.* We have already reviewed the effect upon physician-patient communication of the social and educational differences between house officers and patients in the typical hospital ward and have noted in one study that the level of communication depends to a large extent upon the surgeon's interpretation of the ability of his patient to understand. There are other, less subtle, influences determining the quality and quantity of interpersonal contact between physician and patient in surgery. One such factor is the interpretation by the physician of the role he assumes in the teaching hospital. The results of one study have shown that:

In general, house staff physicians on the surgical service do not often conceive of the physician-patient relationship as an integral, important, part of their role. There is little agreement among them concerning the communicative aspect of their relations to the surgical patient, and a tendency to view this as quite incidental and peripheral to their "real" concerns. Some house staff physicians believe that the teaching hospital does not provide the proper setting or amount of time for developing their relations with patients, but that once they enter private practice this phase of their work will develop naturally or spontaneously. (8)

The "real" concerns referred to revolve about the learning role of the typical house officer. The teaching hospital is the proper locale to concern oneself with the technological aspects of surgery in all its phases. The psychosocial aspects of surgery are relegated to a low priority of factors to be considered in the preparation for carrying out and management of operative problems. Since the surgeon in training conceives of himself to be primarily a trainee in surgery rather than in "bedside-doctoring" he naturally assumes that patient-centered medical care should be a matter to concern him only in private practice. A paradoxical situation presents itself. The surgical trainee expects to learn the techniques of inter-personal management of surgical patients following entry into private practice. At the same time, since he is largely untrained in this area by the time he concludes his residency training, he is largely unprepared for this type of management among the private patients he is now to see. One criticism that has been leveled at the present system of surgical training is that the surgeon emerges as a highly skilled technologist who leaves the matter of the care of the patient to the internist or general physician who refers him for surgical consultation. The surgeon, therefore, remains more or less in the background and, as his experience has demonstrated in the training he received in the teaching hospital, sound inter-personal relationships are largely peripheral to the work for which he has been best prepared. The patient's perception of the role of the resident or intern who cares for him is all too frequently conditioned by the unresponsiveness of his doctors. One subject in a study of surgical patients exclaimed as follows:

I can't understand why a young person like me should have kidney trouble. I would like to ask the doctor about it, but he is always in a hurry when he sees me and I never get a chance to ask him anything. He doesn't talk to you like a person. (21)

While most patients accept readily the therapeutic role of the surgeon, they are often perplexed by the typical house officer's reluctance to adopt the informative and supportive role which they likewise ascribe to him. Gradually such unresponsiveness is accepted as a normal part of the routine and most patients thereupon confine their communications to circumscribed requests, demands or explanations. The resident or intern is seen as too harried by the demands of his work to adopt a posture of involved concern.

Surgical nurses are in constant contact with many of the non-medical needs of the patient. While they, like the physicians who are responsible for the patient, are efficiency and technology oriented, most recognize the gap in service to patients brought about by the orientation of professional staff toward the solution of the basically surgical problems involved. Some nurses regard the non-medical area of functioning as within the confines of the nurse's function. Others regard the social and psychological areas to be still within the framework of medicine and refrain from involving themselves in such problems. In both instances, however, nurses are in common agreement that whatever they may do, or be called upon to do, must have the explicit sanction of the medical staff. Patients' questions, therefore, are frequently brought to the physician for response or the physician is informed that the patient has a question which he should like to ask the doctor. The unresponsiveness of some nurses to some of the unmet social and psychological needs of patients may be understood, therefore, as not stemming from ignorance of these needs or a lack of desire to care for them, but from a fundamental disagreement or lack of concurrence as to the areas of professional responsibility legitimately to be covered by physicians and/or nurses.

The lack of unanimity among medical house officers, nurses and surgical patients concerning professional functions produces the general effect of reducing communication between all three groups. It is because of this lack of communication that patients come to the operating table emotionally unprepared for surgery and its aftermath.

5. *Implications for Medical Education and Research.* Since so many of the larger problems of surgery in the general hospital revolve about the question of communication deficits between practitioners and patients, medical educators and behavioral science researchers should benefit by a careful investigation of the patterns of communication in surgical services. The effects of a program of instruction in the psycho-social preparation of patients for surgery should test the hypothesis that patients prepared for surgery tolerate anaesthesia and the operative procedure better and make a faster, less complicated post-operative recovery. *It would appear that emphasis in undergraduate medical instruction in the field of interpersonal relations with patients should receive as high a priority in time and effort of instruction as is currently invested in the instruction of students in scientific surgery.*

Post graduate education of surgeons in the psycho-social area has recently been recommended.[9] Such a program would include an orientation to the total care problems of surgical patients, the presentation by house officers of cases at evaluation conferences from the social and psychological points of view, instruction in the psycho-social pre-surgical preparation of patients, and an emphasis upon similar problems during the usual teaching rounds. Where necessary, explicit instruction and supervision in techniques of interviewing and in discussing patient problems with their relatives should be instituted.

From a research point of view three major areas of investigation in this field would seem warranted.

1. A further elaboration of the role perceptions of surgeons, nurses and surgical patients to elucidate the effects upon communication and behavior.

2. The effects upon patients of changes in role definition and responsibility under controlled conditions, and

3. The effects of special programs designed to increase the competence of medical students, interns and residents in dealing with the psycho-social problems of patients on the attitudes and behavior of these groups in respect to medical care.

It is to be hoped that studies of these types might be undertaken not only in teaching hospitals, but on the semi-private and private services of voluntary and proprietary institutions. In this way, we may be able to compare differences in response to particular types of management where socio-economic status, education and articulateness of the patients are held constant.

41   **CULTURAL VARIATION AND THE**
PRACTICAL PEDIATRICIAN

By D. B. Jelliffe

The term "culture" is frequently used in a somewhat narrow sense to apply more or less exclusively to the artistic, academic, and spiritual activities of a community. However, the social anthropologist considers it too restricting to equate culture only with such important phenomena as architecture, literature, and philosophy—a wider definition is required, for "Culture covers not only the arts, sciences, religions and philosophies to which the word is historically applied, but also the system of technology, the political practices, the small intimate habits of daily life, such as the way of preparing or eating food, or of hushing a child to sleep."[1] Similarly, Foster[2] employs the

From *The Journal of Pediatrics*, 49 (December, 1956), 661–671. Copyright 1956 by the C. V. Mosby Co., St. Louis, Mo.

Based on the 1956 Presidential Address delivered in Bombay at the Annual Conference of the Association of Pediatricians of India. Published with permission of Dr. George Coelho, Chairman, Association of Pediatricians of India.

The views expressed are those of the author and not the official opinion of the World Health Organization.

following definition: "the common way of life shared by the members of a group, consisting of the totality of their tools, techniques, social institutions, behavior patterns, attitudes, beliefs, motivations, systems of values and the like."

CULTURAL VARIATION

Culture patterns vary all over the world and, although ideally a knowledge of all interrelated aspects of the particular culture would be of great benefit to the practical pediatrician, certain facets are of especial significance, particularly customs relating to pregnancy and childbirth, methods employed in child rearing, local food ideology, and indigenous medical beliefs.

Unprejudiced analysis, based on dispassionate and unbiased scientific observation clearly shows that both rational and irrational attitudes, and beneficial and injurious customs, are to be found in every part of the world, whether in Boston, Manchester, or Southeast Asia. The following examples may, for instance, be quoted as sometimes being of importance to a greater or lesser extent in the field of child health among different socio-economic groups in Britain—the prevalence of totally unnecessary "social" circumcision, overrigid attitudes toward toilet training and breast feeding, the use of proprietary "gripe-water" types of medicines and potentially dangerous mercurial teething powders, the belief that fish is a specific "brain food" for infants, and such superstitions as the belief that a baby boy born in a caul is lucky and, in particular, will not be drowned. From the general nutritional point of view, it is worth noting that the universal prejudice in Britain against protein-rich frogs, snails, dogs, and insects is so great that, even during the period of maximal food shortage during the last war, no suggestion was made that these might be employed for the supplementary feeding of children, despite the fact that these items form customary, much relished and nutritious foods in other parts of the world.

IMPORTANCE TO THE PEDIATRICIAN

If it is agreed that culture patterns, including the food habits and the practices associated with pregnancy and methods of child rearing, vary greatly in different parts of India, it becomes necessary to consider in what practical ways a knowledge of these beliefs and attitudes is important to the scientific pediatrician.

A description of what appears to be the present logical trend in pediatrics will show the main value of this approach. It has become apparent to the thinking pediatrician that an exclusively curative approach to child health is illogical, shortsighted, and overexpensive. It is, for example, unsatisfactory to treat children with ascariasis and Guinea worm infection, with malaria and malnutrition, if, at the same time, no effort is made to prevent the almost inevitable recurrence of these conditions when children leave the artificial surroundings of the hospital ward and return to their home environments. As a result of this mental evolution, the curative-preventive pediatrician has developed, with an appreciation of the importance of both overlapping and interdependent aspects of child health.

A consideration of the ways in which child health may be protected and improved suggests three main preventive approaches: (1) public health measures, such as an improved water supply, residual spraying with DDT, and immunization programs; (2) general socioeconomic measures, including increased employment and a higher standard of living, and the spread of adult education; and (3) health education. Important as are the first two of these, it is usually in the last—the field of health education—that the practical pediatrician has most chance to contribute personally, by means, for example, of counseling on infant feeding, given in the welfare clinic, or advice to parents when their children are discharged from hospital.

Although to the uninitiated, the art of health education in this or any other context may appear to be a straightforward matter, easily accomplished by a display of logic and a marshalling of posters, experience has unfortunately shown this not to be the case, especially among peasant peoples in non-industrialized tropical countries. The resistance, or lack of response, to standard health education measures so often found, is related to the fact that attempts at altering people's habits, ways of life, and customary behavior are never made *in vacuo*, but in competition with, and against the resistance of, deep-rooted and time-hallowed indigenous beliefs. Foster[3] expresses this view when he says: "The public health specialist is not working in a vacuum—rather he is working in an area in which the subject already has definite and hard-to-shake beliefs, which they are just as sure are correct as he is sure they are mistaken."

In brief, then, it has become clear—largely as a result of the work of Foster and his colleagues—that, in any health field, it is usually necessary to know a group's present attitudes and beliefs in order to modify them successfully by means of health education, and this applies perhaps with especial force to the field of child health. New knowledge will be accepted only in so far as it can be made to fit into the general pattern of custom and belief of the people.[2, 3, 4]

Second, from the point of view of scientific medicine, it has become increasingly realized that detailed investigation of methods used in child rearing among different cultural groups may often help to contribute to world knowledge of child care. For example, the rigid "by-the-clock" system of breast feeding has now been largely abandoned in Western countries in favor of the so-called "self-demand" method, partly as a result of observation of more natural methods employed in others parts of the world. This cross-cultural type of approach promises, for example, to be particularly rewarding in improving our understanding of the effect of child training on personality development.[5]

Finally, but certainly not least in importance, it seems probable that the pediatrician will be able to establish a better rapport with the families with which he is concerned, whether in the welfare clinic or as outpatients, and more easily earn their confidence, if he understands, appreciates, and learns to think in terms of their beliefs and attitudes.

INVESTIGATION OF CULTURAL VARIATION

The correct approach to cultural variation may perhaps be illustrated best by assuming that the pediatrician finds himself in a part of the world which is for him *terra incognita*—as, for example, if an Indian pediatrician were to set up a child welfare clinic in the center of Brazil. Under this type of circumstance, it would seem wise to conduct a preliminary investigation somewhat along the following lines: (1) investigate, so far as possible, relevant indigenous methods and practices; (2) make an *unprejudiced* analysis of these, based on scientific principles, but bearing in mind the local background (i.e., climatic, geographic, economic, agricultural, etc.); (3) divide the practices encountered into three groups—the beneficial, which should be encouraged, the harmless or neutral, which need not to interfered with, and the harmful, which should be overcome, if possible, by persuasion and demonstration, or integrated in some "neutralized" form, as will be described later.

CORRECT AND INCORRECT ATTITUDES

From a practical point of view, various attitudes may be adopted by the scientific pediatrician with regard to indigenous customs, and these may be considered as falling into two groups—the incorrect and the correct.

Incorrect Attitudes.—*Lack of awareness:* With a foreigner, working outside his own country, and sometimes even with a national pediatrician, who is often town-bred and from the upper socioeconomic group, there may be a considerable lack of awareness of the complexity of the indigenous beliefs and customs existing in the village. The fault here would appear to be mainly educational, as the pediatrician has usually not had his mind orientated during his training toward considering or investigating his patients' socioanthropological backgrounds.

Refusal to recognize: In some cases the pediatrician may be aware, to a varying extent, of local views and practices, but, often unconsciously, may adopt an attitude whereby he ignores them. In other words, he may compartmentalize his mind, so that in the clinic he deals only in terms of scientific pediatrics as laid down in the standard textbook, which is, anyway, usually written with a Western cultural background assumed.

Derision: Sometimes, unfortunately, the pediatrician may adopt an attitude of quite unwarranted superiority and look down on, or even deride, local village customs and traditional practices. This view that the methods of the villager are merely the inferior ways of an illiterate, ignorant peasantry is absolutely unwarranted—in many cases apparently strange practices may, in fact, represent time-tested and wise adjustments to a harsh and hostile environment.

Correct Attitudes.—Primarily, then, it is necessary for the pediatrician to be aware of and sympathetic toward local views, attitudes, and customs. Depending upon whether they are considered scientifically desirable or not, so one of the following lines of approach may be used:

Adoption: If a custom or practice appears to be beneficial in the particular local background, then it should be encouraged and adopted into the pediatrician's health teaching. For example, breast feeding prolonged into the second year of life may be judged biologically necessary for the growth and survival of infants in many sub-tropical and tropical communities, especially, for example, in the tsetse fly belt of equatorial Africa, where cattle cannot be raised. Under these circumstances, the pediatrician will have to reorientate his ideas and methods.[6]

Persuasion: Numerous indigenous practices may be found to be absolutely undesirable when judged by scientific criteria—as, for example, the use of cow dung as a dressing on the umbilicus of the newborn child, or the failure to introduce supplementary foods to an infant until he can walk. Under these circumstances, the correct approach for the pediatrician is undoubtedly to attempt to alter the parents' belief in the particular custom by means of persuasion, strengthened, wherever possible, by convincing, practical demonstration of the superiority of his methods. This may be extremely difficult, or even impossible, especially with an essentially pragmatic peasant population, when dealing with such long-term aspects of child health as the nutritional benefits of different methods of infant feeding. It is usually easier to convince when the results are rapidly and easily demonstrated, as, for example, the superiority of benzyl benzoate emulsion over herbal preparations in the treatment of scabies, or the efficacy of penicillin therapy in yaws.

In any case, in order to use persuasion to best advantage, the pediatrician must fully understand the resistances that are likely to arise against his advice, and this he can do best by being conversant with the local culture pattern.

Integration: Sometimes customs and attitudes considered undesirable by the scientific pediatrician may be rendered harmless by modification and integration. Thus, if orange and other fruit juices are classified as "cold" (*tonda*) in a particular food ideology and because of this cannot be given during the winter months, it would seem legitimate to make use of the culturally acceptable and scientifically harmless technique of neutralizing the essential inherent "coldness" of the juice by adding a little honey, which is "hot" (*garam*), if by this means the mother will be more willing to allow the infant to take the ascorbic acid-containing juice.

Similarly, sometimes by retaining and integrating, or at least not opposing, a particular custom, which to the scientific viewpoint may seem quite immaterial to the child's health, it may be possible to keep or increase the parents' confidence. In this avoidance of unnecessary conflict, major difficulties may be circumvented by carefully "charting a course along the reefs of culture, instead of crashing precipitously upon them."[7]

For example, in many parts of the world, the exact method of disposal of the placenta is felt to be of real moment. In these circumstances, allowing a relative to remove the placenta for burial, or whatever other method is employed, may encourage mothers needing special obstetrical care to come into the maternity hospital and so lessen the risk of birth trauma, a major pediatric concern.

In the same way, a knowledge of and, so far as possible, a respect for such conceptions as especially suitable days for medical procedures, such as vaccination, or of culturally defined efficacious times of day for taking medicines, should be cultivated. These practices can often be quietly adhered to —and many ensure that the patient will receive the main essentials of a particular form of therapy more willingly.

It may be argued that by adopting this type of method, the pediatrician is helping to perpetuate what are, when judged by present scientific knowledge, irrational beliefs. If alteration of ideas by persuasion were an easy matter, this sort of approach would certainly be unnecessary. Unfortunately this is definitely not the case, so that some type of integration may have to be employed as an interim measure until the spread of education causes many of these irrational attitudes to disappear. It is not suggested, however, that the health worker should give his advice using, for example, the terms and reasoning of the local food ideology, but rather that he should work within this framework, making use of it without supporting it. In the instance already cited, the pediatrician, knowing the customs and attitudes of the particular group, would advise the use of fruit juice with a little added honey, without either mentioning or condoning the "hot-cold" food classification, which he knows to be the basis of the difficulty.

The correct attitude toward any particular custom—whether for example, to attempt to persuade or to integrate temporarily—will have to be decided by the health worker. There is no absolute rule, and a decision will depend upon such factors as the pediatrician's estimate of local attitudes and resistances, and on the amount of time available in the clinic.

CHILD WELFARE CLINIC IN WEST BENGAL

The following examples, based on personal experience in a rural child welfare clinic in West Bengal, will illustrate a practical application of the type of approach outlined in the present paper. In almost all instances, mothers bringing their children to the clinic were illiterate Bengali villagers of the lower socioeconomic group and of the Hindu religion.

Foods and Illness.—Apart from the fundamental Hindu division of foods into *amish* (nonvegetarian) and *niramish* (vegetarian) the dominant food ideology among the village mothers attending the clinic was found to be the "hot-cold" (*garam-tonda*) classification, based upon supposed inherent properties of foodstuffs. [A similar classification of disease and diet (*caliente-frio*) is also prevalent among some Latin American peasant groups.[3] This appears to stem ultimately from the humoral pathology of Hippocrates and Galen, which reached medieval Europe via the Arab world and was transmitted to Hispanic America by the conquistadors. As this concept appears to be an ancient one in India, stemming back to early Sanskrit Ayurvedic literature, it is possible that it may have originated in India and spread to influence and mold early Greek thought in this respect.] According to this view, eggs, meat, milk, *musuri dhal* (*Lens esculenta*), honey, sugar, and cod-liver oil are regarded as being to varying degrees *garam;* while lemon, orange, rice, water, acid buttermilk (*lassi*) and curd (*dahi* or Indian yoghourt) are classified as *tonda.*

Apart from difficulties in infant feeding that may arise as a result of a reluctance to give such *garam* items as eggs and cod-liver oil during the

warm weather, of greater importance is the fact that illnesses are also classified as being *garam* or *tonda,* and that "hot" or "cold" foods cannot be given
during like illnesses.

Bronchitis.—For example, an upper respiratory tract infection, such as
bronchitis, is regarded as a "cold" or *tonda* malady. Scientifically, in this type
of case it may be desirable to advise the mother to give sulfonamides, together with plenty of water to drink and the lighter portion of the normal
diet, including rice preparations. This, however, would not be considered as
satisfactory by the mother, as both water and rice are classified as *tonda* and,
therefore, to be avoided in this type of illness.

In this instance persuasion may be possible but often may not be successful against such a deeply ingrained food belief, and, in this case, the two
attitudes—that of the pediatrician and that of the mother—can be successfully integrated by advising the mother to give sulfonamides, together with
water flavored with honey and rice cooked in milk. The mother will accept
this advice much more readily, as the honey and the milk are thought to
neutralize the "cold" in the water and in the rice, and scientifically the same
end point has been reached.

Diarrhea.—In children recovering from diarrhea, mothers are frequently
reluctant to introduce milk, even if diluted, as both the food and the illness
are classified as *garam,* so much so that continued feeding with carbohydrate
gruels may, in this type of case, act as the starting point for the subsequent
development of the protein deficiency syndrome known as kwashiorkor.

Frequently, in this sort of situation it is desirable, from a scientific point of
view, that the child should be given a bland, easily absorbable, low residue
carbohydrate gruel, a water-absorbing, pectin-containing food, and dilute
milk. In a West Bengal rural child welfare clinic, it appears that this is best
achieved by adopting three local dietary remedies, which appear to coincide
exactly with the scientific viewpoint. By using the carbohydrate *chira mondu*
(hand-mashed flat rice) and, as the pectin food, a sherbet made of the Indian
wood apple (*Aegle marmelos*), one is employing traditional dietetic treatment while, in dilute *lassi* (acid buttermilk), one has an acceptable and
familiar remedy. The buttermilk, being both acidified and defatted, and a
tonda food, is particularly suitable from all points of view.

Vaccination.—As in certain other parts of the world, smallpox, partly
perhaps because of its striking and characteristic appearance and its high
mortality, is often regarded by villagers in West Bengal as due to divine
visitation of the goddess *Shitala,* and, because of this, some years back, in
the early days of the health center, vaccination was actively refused. At the
present time, however, a great change has come about, so that vaccination is
nowadays welcomed and even sought after by village mothers. This, of course,
is an excellent example of successful health education by persuasion and
demonstration, as mothers have themselves come to observe that, if their
children are vaccinated, they are no longer liable to be blinded, disfigured,
or killed by smallpox.

Childbirth and the Maternity Home.—All over the world, the life crisis
of childbirth is associated with special customs, *rites de passage,* and pre-
cautionary practices. This is equally true in rural West Bengal and it is of

interest to see how these can be dovetailed and integrated into the otherwise alien background of the small maternity hospital attached to the rural center.

As no particular beliefs appear to be held concerning the length at which the cord should be cut, as in some countries, no difficulty arises here. With regard to the placenta, in the traditional home delivery this is buried by the *dai* (hereditary indigenous midwife). However, the exact details of this practice do not appear to be very important in this locality, so that mothers seem to be quite content for the placenta to be disposed of by the maternity home staff in a deeply dug rubbish pit. The ritual seclusion universally practiced by Hindu mothers after birth can be adhered to, at least functionally, by visitors' not approaching nearer than a few feet from the bed, and by the food's being brought from home by relatives and emptied into the mother's plate, which she leaves just outside the ward. In this case, care is taken not to touch the mother's plate with the food container during the process of pouring.

Attitudes toward the disposal of the shriveled umbilical stump vary. Many mothers do not seem to mind if this is thrown away, although some are in the habit of using it in a *maduli* (protective charm) worn round the baby's neck. In the latter case, the maternity home staff raise no objection.

Various ceremonies are performed in the neonatal period. One of these, *jata karman*, can be and is carried out in substance by the mother herself, putting a drop of honey on the neonate's tongue. Similarly, on the sixth evening, the mother will be anxious to be home for the night vigil kept during *Shosti puja* (dedication of the baby to *Shosti*, the goddess of children). However, if the mother has to stay in the maternity home longer than this, a satisfactory compromise can be achieved by the relatives' doing a part of the ceremony in the home, while the rest can be completed by the mother on the twenty-first day, when she has returned home. There are, however, two days on which the mother is very anxious to be home—the first is on the eighth day, for the ceremony of *atkore-batkore,* and the second on the tenth day, when the ritual purificatory bath is taken. Knowing this, the maternity home staff will make every effort to see that the mother leaves the hospital in time.

It can be seen, then, that, owing to the sensibly flexible attitude of the staff, an excellent working arrangement has been built up whereby the practices and beliefs of the mothers have been suitably integrated into the background of a modern maternity home.

Mixed Diet in Infant Feeding.—As in many parts of India, in rural West Bengal one of the ancient Hindu rites which is always observed is *annaprasan* (rice-feeding ceremony), which is here performed at 6 months of age for a boy and at 7 months for a girl.

It would seem likely that the original purpose of this custom was both to celebrate the baby's having survived the dangerous first half year of independent existence, and, at the same time, to commence widening the infant's diet. Investigation shows, however, that a not inconsiderable percentage of present-day villagers perform the ceremony punctiliously, but do not continue with rice and other foods thereafter, sometimes not introducing them until the child can walk or has teeth in both upper and lower jaws.

Nutritionally it is, of course, necessary for the infant to have foods other than milk, at least from about the end of the first six months onward, and it would seem profitable to use a reference to this wise and ancient practice as a practical lever in health education to persuade village mothers of the need for foods other than milk after the age of 6 months.

CONCLUSION

To understand fully the motivations behind the customs and beliefs of a particular people needs the skill of a trained socioanthropologist, who not only knows the language but has been able to live with the particular group unobtrusively and on equal terms. The assistance of such a person should always be sought—if possible in person, if not, in the available literature. Usually, however, the pediatrician working in a technically developing tropical region will himself have to attempt, somewhat amateurishly, to piece together at least the more relevant features of the particular culture pattern, especially the customs affecting children and pregnant women. He will then find himself better able to understand his patients' problems and to gain the parents' confidence more fully. In addition, he will be able to plan out and put into effect scientifically based preventive and curative measures in ways that are interwoven into the local pattern of beliefs and, therefore, the more likely to succeed.

From a wider perspective, it is highly desirable that world-wide investigation should continue into cultural variation and its effects on child health and development. Scientific medicine, of which pediatrics is one important discipline, has its ultimate historical roots in knowledge from all over the world. The next phase may well be the further incorporation and fusion of the valuable and worth while from all cultural groups into an enriched, expanded, and truly global system of child care.

42   ANESTHESIA: FROM NURSE'S WORK TO MEDICAL SPECIALTY

By Dan C. Lortie

It is not surprising that observers of the modern social scene take for granted the prevalence of specialization in our occupational life. The economic advantages of specialization were pointed out many years ago by Adam Smith and remain uncontested today. The great extent of specialization is dramatized by a compilation of occupational titles that lists 29,000 entries and carries an introduction warning that it is incomplete.[1] Our academic system is evidence of the need we feel to organize otherwise overwhelming quantities of knowledge into manageable packages. The development of specialization seems so "reasonable" that we rarely stop to question it; it looks both irresistible and automatic.

Specialization is, however, anything but a simple response to new knowledge and technique. It is a complex social process that involves important changes in a vast range of social relationships and institutional arrangements. We note that it operates selectively, and that the development often seems difficult to explain in terms of any inner logic. In medicine, as elsewhere, only some functions become the property of a formally designated set of specialists, while other functions are left inside conventional "fields." The creation of a new specialty means the emergence of a new group, and this involves difficult and even painful shifts in the relationships between colleagues, the patterns of economic rewards, and the distribution of power and prestige. Such changes do not come about "automatically." Our case in point, the medical specialty of anesthesiology, demonstrates that although there may be important impersonal forces lying behind specialization, these forces need a lot of assistance from active and interested human beings.[2]

This paper focusses on the human side of specialization—the process in which a new group of men move into the social system of a profession which is already a going concern. We will begin by seeing how they come to form a group and set objectives for themselves, and the part played in this stage by charismatic leadership. Then we will follow them as they move into the active phase of collective mobilization of power and seek to find niches in the complex structure of the medical profession. The functions they perform and the way in which these functions are expanded will be examined, and we will observe as well the uses to which they put "technology" in their struggle for a world more to their liking.

The medical specialty of anesthesiology did not form immediately upon the introduction of anesthesia into medicine and dentistry. Almost a century intervenes between Dr. Morton's use of an anesthetic agent in 1846 and the formation of the major organization of medical anesthesiologists today—the American Society of Anesthesiologists. A long period of "indecision" lies between these two dates as to how this new function would be allocated within the medical system. Historical materials are few on the conditions under which anesthesia was administered in the latter half of the 19th century, and we can only surmise that the actual tasks involved were taken on by whatever extra hand was around. By the turn of the century, however, a dominant allocation emerged. Nurses, under the supervision of surgeons, began to specialize in the work, and gradually came to view anesthesia as a specialty within their profession. Most doctors who gave anesthetics were but marginally involved in the field, and generally as "assistant" to the surgeon to whom they referred the case for surgery. Such conditions were hardly auspicious to the emergence of a medical specialty. On one hand it was work done by the nurse, on the other, it bore the stigma of a polite form of "fee-splitting."

A small number of doctors, however, who were more than peripherally involved, and who accorded to anesthesia a great deal of respect—saw possibilities in it which occurred to few others. They saw past the simple techniques of the day (the dropping of ether or use of the chloroform pad) to more advanced techniques that would prolong operative time, expand the range of surgical intervention and lower the rate of surgical mortality. They began, as individuals, to test new anesthetic agents and introduce new equipment. To become an effective group, however, they needed organization to replace their isolation one from the other, and leadership to give form to their hazy objectives.

Dr. Frank McMechan was the charismatic leader who arose to galvanize these men into action. Prior to a crippling disease which left him permanently confined to a wheel-chair, he had been highly interested in clinical anesthesia, and had come to believe that the field called for increased attention from the medical profession. Unable to practice, he turned his great energies to the cause—the cause he called "professional anesthesia." Despite his handicap, he travelled widely throughout America and other lands preaching the gospel of medical specialist anesthesia, addressing whatever assembly of physicians who would listen. On these occasions he would mobilize all the dramatic flair he had acquired as a young actor. The room would be darkened immediately before his entrance, and then a spotlight would follow Mc-Mechan's figure in the wheel-chair as it was slowly rolled to the center of the stage. In a voice resonant with emotion, he would begin his talk. He denounced those who treated anesthesia as a casual incident in the surgical sequence, and declared that human lives should not be placed in the hands of those who had not been trained as physicians. The speeches, however, were only one side of a highly active round of organizing groups of medical anesthetists, exhorting the profession, editing journals and encouraging the interchange of new ideas and techniques.

McMechan began this career in 1915 and continued it until his death in 1939. During this entire period, it was he who dominated organized medical anesthesia, and his role was that of agitator, prophet and statesman. In classic charismatic fashion, he relied for economic support upon "friends of the cause."[3] He was loved by his disciples, harshly criticized by others who called him a would-be tyrant.

McMechan's death came just before World War II and a key turning point in American anesthesiology. The American Society of Anesthesiologists, organized along the lines of established specialty societies, replaced the groups he had formed, and elements of conservatism were introduced. The unbending zeal of McMechan's day was replaced by more cautious policies and methods. Long-range policies for advancing the specialty joined the sharp demands for immediate action, democratic election procedures produced new leaders to take over from the unquestioned one, and quiet conferences with other medical groups replaced the dramatic appeals. The change, however, is more evidence of McMechan's success than his failure—the group was able to form stable organization to carry on the affairs of the specialty. The charisma was gone, but the spirit continued in national and local organizations who were pressing vigorously for the advancement of the specialty. McMechan left behind him a self-conscious and assertive group of men ready and eager to plant the standard of medical specialist anesthesia on new ground. On methods they disagreed; there was no disunity in their goal of nothing less than the status of "specialists among equals."

Dr. Morton's pain killer did not lead, therefore, to the smooth development of a new specialty group. For a century after his significant innovation, argument raged as to who should handle the new functions he had introduced.

The nursing profession took it as its own. After some seventy years, however, a group of doctors began to question this allocation, and under the inspiring leadership of a dramatic figure, developed an ideology to defend their claims. Gradually, the task became redefined as one involving life and death—as the proper right and duty of medical men. The leadership involved, the process of collective behavior manifested, the claims and counter-claims reveal a development similar to what we associate with the ecstatic phenomena of religious and political movements. This sector of the division of labor was an embattled one.

Reviewing their position at the end of World War II, anesthesiologists were inclined to express strong dissatisfaction with their lot. In many aspects of their status they saw strong evidence of the workings of a definition of their duties and rights as "nurse's work." They were salaried employees of hospitals more often than not. Many surgeons acted as if they had no more medical judgment or professional status than the nurses they usually replaced. Surgeons, accustomed to both medical and legal responsibility for their patients, were often loathe to reassess the role changes brought about by the introduction of another medical specialist on the team. Hospital administrations seemed unresponsive to the demands of the anesthesia department, and when pressed for more equipment or personnel, would point out that they had their hands full satisfying doctors "who brought in patients." Other doctors were sometimes scornful of the anesthesiologists, pointing out that they worked only on "other people's patients," and implied that they probably were men who could not handle the exigencies of private practice. The public at large offered little compensation—few members of the lay public even understood what they did in the surgical undertaking.

World War II, moreover, acted to bring new impetus to their dissatisfaction. A fresh supply of new men who had first handled anesthesia in the services showed strong interest in becoming specialists. The status of anesthesia in the armed services had somehow come to rise—and in many service installations, medical anesthetists carried high rank. The colleague group was at a pitch of activity developing new techniques, new forms of organization, certification and training, and editing new journals. There was an air of change in the atmosphere, and the years following World War II saw anesthesiologists conferring among themselves on how they could best achieve the professional recognition they wanted so fervently.

The position of these restless anesthesiologists can be analyzed in terms of the various sub-systems in which they participated.[4] They resented most, perhaps, their role in the operating room, the somewhat special and isolated world in which their core duties are performed.[5] The problems here can be summarized as those of subordination and a lack of functional autonomy—problems for which they blamed, often bitterly, the "Tin God Surgeons." Their position in the referral system was that of outsiders—they had no commodity to offer in this powerful system of reciprocal obligations.[6] In the hospital action structure, they found themselves isolated from the key centers of power, and complained that they were economically exploited.[7] Their voice was small in the political system of the profession as they were numerically weak in all parts of the complex of professional societies which rule the affairs of medicine.[8] Outside of medicine, in the wider community, they found indifference based on a total ignorance of their contribution—an ignorance dramatized by the inability of most laymen to even pronounce their occupational title. Overruled, subordinated, politically impotent, and invisible, the obstacles they faced were not negligible.

The group stood ready, however, to try and improve their status and began to develop strategies of various types to do so. We can review these strategies in terms of the sub-systems we have isolated. Such analysis reveals the pattern in the strategies, and tells us something of the moderations that take place when a group must operate within the institutional framework of an established profession.

We can begin with the position of the anesthesiologist in the community at large. The relationship between the public and the medical system is complex, but we can note that in two respects at least, the public attitude is important. It is the public of patients who ultimately demand and pay for anesthetic services, and it is selected representatives of the public who share control of medical institutions such as hospitals and health insurance plans. Some anesthesiologists decided to take the direct route to "educate the public." They initiated, with the help of public relations counsel, a series of popular articles using the fear theme by pointing out the risks in anything but physician anesthesia. The campaign ended quickly. The rest of the medical profession quickly condemned these activities and denounced them as violations of the codes proscribing "advertising." The response was so strong that anesthesiologists rushed to comply, and subsequently instituted controls over their colleague group to prevent a recurrence. The anesthesiologist found out a key fact—they would not be permitted to bring their case to the public at large, and they must not undermine public confidence in current medical practice. They could, of course, continue to do their best through individual contacts with patients and fellow community members.[9] The medical profession, however, would not tolerate any appeal "over its head"—such issues would be settled within the house of medicine.

At what points in the system could they hope for advancement of their cause? Could they do anything about their position in the operating room? In general, the operating room was not the place for a direct challenge. The anesthesiologist could hardly defy the surgeon who worked on a sick patient, and even if medical norms did not allow open dispute in the course of surgery, he had little chance of winning any power show-down with this powerful colleague. The anesthesiologist had, and still has, however, a most powerful ally —his constantly advancing technique. He might have to exercise tact and patience with the surgeon, but his long-range hopes could lie with the fact that his array of techniques, tools and special devices was increasing rapidly. New operative procedures called for more prolonged and dangerous anesthesia, and some procedures, such as spinals, were legally forbidden for anyone but doctors in several states. Younger men entering surgery were not even trying to master anesthesia, and were content to leave it to the anesthesiologist. The new specialists took the stance that time was on their side, and that the older, more rigid surgeons would not be with them forever.

Was it possible for the anesthesiologist, then, to hope for more immediate results in the referral system? Hardly. The movement toward specialization with its attendant limitation to anesthesiology meant that fewer than ever would have patients of their own to refer. They were stuck with being on the receiving end, and with whatever limitations in power and prestige this imposed.

The two areas that remain—the professional associations and the hospital action structure—were the only feasible battlegrounds. The anesthesiologists developed strategies in both these areas which did much to improve their position.

Anesthesiologists, working daily alongside the fee-paid surgeon, began to contest the salary mode of payment. They hated its connotations of employee, and nurse anesthesia; they resented the fact that anesthesia should be one of the hospital departments where income exceeded expenditures, and that this should be cited by hospital administrators who resisted their requests for other arrangements. Perhaps, as well, they suspected that the income they received did not match the rising incomes of fee-paid doctors in an inflationary period.

Anesthesiologists made the salary the issue, and turned to the organizations of self-government within the profession to bolster their cause. Numerically weak, they sought out pathologists and radiologists and urged them to join them in a joint cause. These "sub-specialties" managed to convince the wider medical group in the American Medical Association that salary arrangements by hospitals were actually the practice of medicine by a corporate body, and as such, constituted the "thin edge of the wedge" of "socialized medicine." Resolutions were passed in support of this general principle, and anesthesiologists could feel support in their battle against hospital administrations. One notes here that the group showed more than ordinary political discernment. The attitude of doctors toward hospital administrations is, to say the least, ambivalent, and the anesthesiologists managed to make this somewhat marginal body the butt of their attack. It may be the surgeons that they condemn in interviews, but when political action was undertaken, it was the hospital authorities who were made the target.[10]

Activity to change relationships with hospital administrations was taken, primarily, on the local level, and tactics varied with the terrain. Where effective demand exceeded supply, as in Canada, collective force was applied. One director of anesthesia, dissatisfied with the income he and his colleagues received, withdrew his doctors when negotiations came to a halt. The anesthesiologists left men available for emergencies only, and did not worry about others taking over: the word went out through formal and informal channels that it would be unwise for any other anesthetist to work in that hospital until matters were straightened out. The collective bargaining worked, and a successful strike of doctors brought about the desired results. This "strike" was not reported in the local press, and no unfavorable publicity resulted.

Such union-like activity, however, could hardly be the norm where competition was unregulated, or where medical anesthesia was still fighting for recognition from other doctors. In another instance, for example, a diplomatic strategy was developed to "knock over" a key hospital where surgeons still regarded medical anesthetists with distaste. The local group arranged the placement of a tactful woman anesthetist to bridge the gap from nurse to physician anesthesia. This stratagem paid off handsomely, and the woman was later replaced by a more aggressive and demanding male. Some anesthesiologists have heeded the old political saw about joining the opposition if you cannot beat it, and have taken on ill-paid administrative duties in order to advance the cause of their roles as anesthesiologists.

Two major patterns, however, can be identified in the welter of individual tactics developed by local groups. The first is the banding together of local anesthesiologists into "groups" which negotiate as an entity with hospitals. The second major theme is the extending of the technical functions of the anesthesiologist into new areas not formerly associated with the specialty.

The "groups" are generally partnership arrangements between collaborating anesthesiologists, and may even include all specialists in the area serviced. Where surgery is frequent enough to call for the services of specialists, and surgical recognition extended, these groups are powerful bargaining agents vis-a-vis the hospital administration. It offers a constant service without inconveniencing the individual anesthesiologist because assignments are handled on a rotation basis. Hospital administrations in more and more centers have been forced to accept an economic arrangement where the group bills the patient directly for the service rendered. In Canada, where anesthetics must be given by doctors as laid down in a court decision of 1939, this form of organization is now widespread, and is found even in smaller cities. The development in the United States, although not as general, is steadily gaining ground.

The second major strategy—that of extending the functions of the anesthesiologist and his department—is probably found in many new occupations. Elaborations have been made which would surprise the early practitioners. Within the operating room, the anesthesiologist has taken over whatever innovations are involved in maintaining the general condition of the patient, and sometimes follows these outside the operating room by assuming such responsibilities as the administration of blood banks. Many hospitals today have introduced "post-operative recovery rooms" for the surgical patient, and these are generally supervised by the anesthesiologist. Here, in the dangerous twenty-four hours immediately following an operation, the patient receives special nursing and attention close to the materials and machinery most valuable when a crisis develops. The anesthesiologists have assumed this not inconsiderable burden of risk and responsibility in exchange for the greater acceptance it gives them within the medical field. Anesthesiologists make similar transactions in their willingness to take on resuscitative work in the wards, and to attempt the therapeutic nerve blocks sometimes used to relieve chronic pain. The direction of these additions to the core function of surgical anesthesia is worthy of note. We see that they are generally in the direction of a more "doctor-like" stance, and often involve the key values of responsibility for the life and death of patients. Thus are the differences between the medical anesthetist and the nurse dramatized, and the gulf between the two steadily widened.

What insights does our case provide that might be useful in the study of the process of specialization in other situations? The initial assertion that the process is one involving much concerted human activity is demonstrated. We have noted the years of effort preceding the establishment of formal organization and training, and the gradually-increasing recognition that anesthesia is indeed work fit for a medical specialist. We note too that in this instance, the development has much in common with what we have observed in religious and political movements. Perhaps we have overlooked these more ecstatic elements in the tendency to view work as the result of purely economic, and hence generally rational, forces. If our case is any talisman, future analyses of the specialization process should broaden their perspective to include such mechanisms of collective behavior. Work functions, it would seem, must be recognized, promoted and organized before they become part of the regular division-of-labor.

Anesthesiology is steadily gaining in its battle for acceptance alongside the older specialties within medicine, and the strategies developed are those which are associated with some degree of success. What do these strategies suggest for our broader understanding of specialization? The specialty group must, if our case is illustrative, come to terms with the institutional setting in which it finds itself. It must mobilize the energies of its members, but it must also control the aggressions that are stimulated. Where colleague approval must be obtained, the strategies of choice are those which do not threaten the social system and its integration. Attacks are best mounted against those not at the core of the system, but against those marginal to it and somewhat unpopular with the professional leaders. The rationale put forth must be one consistent with the interests of the overall group and with its ideology. Whether it involves power play or the extension of functions, the key values of the profession must be observed, and taken into account at each point.

Many complex questions are involved in the relationship between technology and social organization. Our case shows that technology not only leads social change, but is in turn modified and used by those seeking new positions of power and respect. The group which wants to differentiate itself in acceptable fashion can do so by constant elaboration of its technical arsenal. With each advance it becomes more useful to others and thus accorded greater recognition.

For those whose concern is with the quality of medical care, it might be consoling to note that specialization as a social process is accompanied by institutional imperatives encouraging the development and use of new and superior techniques. Those who pine for the days of the general practitioner and his "holistic" approach might ask themselves whether the changes they would like to see in modern specialized medicine would carry with them any reduction in the premium on technical improvement. Whatever else may be its weaknesses, a system of specialties depends in large part upon the ability of the specialists concerned to demonstrate their special value in the daily work of the profession.

43   THE OSTEOPATHIC STUDENTS:
A STUDY IN DILEMMA[1]

By Peter Kong-ming New

When a person is entering a profession, he has many types of adjustment problems, both in terms of ideals which he has set for himself and in terms of practical problems which he encounters once he has committed himself. This would be true for the students who enter a well-established field, such as medicine[2] or law; however, these students may not need to do as much soul-searching as those who enter a profession which has only recently been recognized by the public as a legitimate field of endeavor. The latter are going to encounter numerous problems which require continual rationalizing so that they can live with themselves.

The students who enter osteopathy, from the time they matriculate to their graduation, constantly have to answer to themselves and to their publics the reasons for having entered such a profession. Osteopathy is a field which is undergoing rapid changes in its quest for recognition, and during the process its students are caught in this web of circumstances and must also redefine their roles.

Many of the changes which a "frontier profession"[3] needs to undergo cannot be appraised by examining the literature or the catalogues of the schools of osteopathy. Rather, the attitudes of the people within the profession, especially those who are entering it, give the clues to the changes which are taking place.

Osteopathy has experienced a series of changes, from the time Andrew Taylor Still, its founder, laid down the osteopathic concepts and their related philosophies. Certain onuses have had to be overcome and new ideologies have been introduced. Within the past ten years, the most pronounced shift has been the de-emphasis of manipulation and the infusion of "medicine and surgery" in the description of the function of osteopathic physicians. This paper will examine this shift in its relation to the dilemmas encountered by the students, as reflected in some of the interviews with one hundred students and three young osteopathic physicians in four osteopathic colleges.[4]

From Osteopathic **Manipulation** *to Osteopathic* **Medicine.** The responses from these interviews all point to a shift from Still's original formulation of manipulative therapy to the greater inclusion of "orthodox" medicine.[5] In the 1900's all prospective osteopaths were taught the art of manipulative treatment, and now this is only a minor part of the curriculum. A comparison between the stated objects of the catalogues of various osteopathic schools between 1900 and now indicates that radical changes have taken place. Emphasis has now switched from osteopathic manipulation to osteopathic medicine. In fact, the American Medical Association recently sent a committee into various osteopathic schools to investigate whether the osteopathic curriculum was any different from orthodox medical curriculum.[6]

The attitudes of the students and faculty alike seem to be in concurrence on these changes. These attitudes may be broken into three categories: (1)

"We are a *complete* school of medicine," (2) "A. T. Still never really looked down on orthodox medicine," and (3) "Manipulation is to be used as an adjunct of orthodox medicine."

The first category can best be characterized by the following excerpt from a lecture given recently by one of the instructors to the first-year students during the orientation period:

> I notice several of you students are wearing rings (points to the married male students). That's good. Now, when you and your wife go to some parties and someone should ask your wife where you are going to school, I hope you'll tell your wife not to mumble under her breath and say, "Myhusbandisgoingtoamedical school." She should say proudly, "My husband is going to the ——— College of Osteopathic Medicine and *Surgery*." Most likely the guest will say, "Oh, I didn't know osteopathy teaches surgery," and there your wife can have an opportunity to explain what we teach. Don't feel inferior to the other students of medicine. Say, "I go to the ——— College of Osteopathic *Medicine* and *Surgery*."

In an effort to allay any potential feelings of inferiority among the new students, stress was laid, throughout this talk, on the phrase of *medicine and surgery*. What has happened to manipulation? It is not forgotten, but deemphasized. In response to a question, "Do you think the medical schools will soon incorporate the term 'osteopathic specialty' in their teaching?" one of the students stated:

> I don't think that's likely, but the name isn't what's so important. Personally, I'm against "osteopathic concept." We take an entity but the term is badly chosen. I think that's why the allopathic schools are against it. Osteopathic—that means bone disease. Well, there's more to it than that. We shouldn't get stuck on a term. . . . I don't know what made Still pick up that term. It's the worst possible term. The name doesn't make much sense. But now we use something else. The Association is using a word that's achieving much more recognition: "Osteopathic medicine." That helps a lot. It brings in "medicine" and that helps. Now, we get stature and prestige, whereas before we didn't.

Thus, osteopathy represents a "complete school of medicine." As several students have indicated:

> In osteopathy we are taught medicine and surgery plus osteopathy. That's something the medical students don't get.

However, the same student will boast that "physical medicine" is used in the allopathic profession:

> Physical therapy is becoming more and more recognized. Naturally when electricity and electrical implements were in their infancy some of these therapy units were very crude mechanisms. And they didn't come up with standards that our present-day physiotherapy units do. Chiropractors jumped at the chance to pick up physiotherapy and use it and I think that's one of the reasons why M.D.'s were kind of reluctant to use it but nowadays you're well aware of the fact that diathermy and hydrotherapy are well recognized.

But one does not discard the use of manipulation without formal apologies to the founder of the school of osteopathy. In this second category, then, a certain amount of rationalizing is done. One student said:

But Andrew Taylor Still never was a man who completely denounced medical practice, nor completely denounced surgery—only indiscriminate surgery and indiscriminate medicine.

This is in direct contrast to the writings of Hildreth, a disciple of Still's who, in his biography of Still, exhorted the future students of osteopathy to respect and use fully "ten-fingered manipulation." Hildreth maintained that nothing could surpass manipulation in curing a patient of all ailments from blindness to gallstone attacks.[7]

The third category, manipulation used as an adjunct, is often little more than a rationale for less use of manipulation. As one of the students puts it:

But to think you can do anything with manipulation is absurd. You can't do anything with it. It's a modality, and adjunct—well, of—it's another modality of treatment.

But the real reason for giving less manipulative treatment might have been touched upon by a student:

Manipulation takes a lot of time and energy. Have you seen any of the manipulations being done around here? Some of the guys really sweat through their shirts when they're done. A lot of the students here say, "Now wouldn't it be a lot simpler if we gave him medicine instead?"

One would think that a primary requisite to enter osteopathy would be ten good fingers, two strong hands, and muscular arms. Yet, one of the students in a current class has an atrophied left arm.

An ideology serves some function, and here it could be assumed that a shifting of ideology is indicative of shifts in some broader functions: deemphasis of "manipulation" is one of the possible ways in which osteopathy could be recognized by the public. Manipulation is a symbol of minority-professional status in the same way kinky hair, thick lips, or dark skin are symbols of minority racial status. Thus, many students would rather go light on this point.

Similarly, students may not consciously admit to their choice of osteopathy as their primary goal, although one student had this remark to make:

Now a lot of students are going to tell you, "I chose osteopathy." That's just a lot of b—— s——. You don't choose to be a member of a minority group. You think [names a student] chose to be a Negro? To say I chose osteopathy would be like saying I chose to gain fifty pounds because I'm a racer. Or I chose to be discriminated upon. That's just a lot of crap. Anyone who tells you "I chose osteopathy" over medical school is just untrue unless he's being punitive about it and if he is, then he needs to see a psychiatrist.

However, once a student had made his choice, whatever that may be, he has to face the problem of living together with members of other healing-arts groups.

Equal But Separate or Together But Unequal. This problem may be characterized generally as a dilemma of being equal in status with the medical, or "allopathic," profession and simultaneously maintaining a separate organization, or being incorporated within the medical profession without the loss of the "osteopathic concept" but with the possibility of being treated as an inferior member of the healing-arts profession.

A profession, to be recognized as such, must, among other things, be able to legitimize its own existence through performing certain functions which characterize its uniqueness. In some cases, however, this very uniqueness or individuality may prevent the acceptance of the profession by the public which has been "conditioned" to some other professional groups which perform similar functions. A professional group, striving for recognition by the public, may wish to maintain its individuality, yet in doing so may appear to the public as an undesired deviant in our normative society and thus be ignored. On the other hand, if public recognition is to be gained, a certain number of the unique features have to be modified, so that the ultimate end may be a complete loss of orientation toward the original goal.

The problem is analogous to the U.S. Supreme Court decision with regard to desegregation of the public school system. Granted that separate but equal schools were not actually equal, it must also be conceded that integration does not guarantee equality. The Negroes who come from inferior schools with inferior faculty and facilities now have equal facilities, but socially they are still relegated to an inferior position. This same type of phenomenon looms as a possibility in the event of integration of osteopaths into the "allopathic" medical field.

With the osteopathic profession, differential treatment by the public is not determined by physical features, as in the case of Negroes, but rather by the osteopathic concepts. After years of struggle, these have now reached the point of some recognition. The osteopathic physicians, however, wish to reach their goal of "equal rights" with the "allopathic" brethren without giving up their basic concepts. At the same time, they realize that the speediest avenue to public recognition may come through the lessening of differentiation of the modes of practice between the osteopathic and medical professions. If the public no longer recognizes the two groups of physicians as being different, the osteopathic physician will not be expected to offer "osteopathic manipulative treatment," or OMT. With disuse, OMT may become Another Mode of Treatment and will not be associated by the public as a symbol of the uniqueness of the osteopathic profession. At present, the probable loss of the symbol is of the greatest concern to the members of the osteopathic profession.

The dilemmas are actually all ramifications of the one problem which confronts the osteopathic profession. The profession does not quite know whether it should continually stress the fact that "we are in a minority" and thus develop persecution syndromes or accept the role of a physician and surgeon in the fullest sense, with the chance of losing its identity as *osteopathic* physicians and surgeons.

A movie made recently to depict the osteopathic student's education was praised by a student:

That movie was wonderful. When you see it, you couldn't really tell that it was taken here. You'd have thought it was taken in Michigan or Stanford.

When it was pointed out that there was a very little mention of "osteopathy" and that some of the osteopathic concepts were totally neglected, the same student said:

Well, this movie was primarily intended to show the high school students and I think it's good that A.O.A. [American Osteopathic Association] shows these students that we're really no different from the M.D.'s. We're just every bit as good as they are.

Another student who is more perceptive to the message that the movie was trying to bring forth asked the writer's view. After being told that very little osteopathic manipulation was shown, he said:

Well, there's another thing in here. In all essence it showed we're no different than medicine. If you didn't see the title of the film: "D.O.—Doctor of Osteopathy" you wouldn't think this was about osteopathy.

Yet, it is constantly brought to the fore that osteopathy is a minority. The president of one college started off a convocation address by saying that "We are a minority. If you didn't want to recognize this you might as well leave now." This is, in effect, the same as saying, "We would like people to sympathize with our cause. If you come here to belittle us, you should not belong as members. If you are striving for goals other than those we are commonly striving for, then you are betraying us." This is common to the problems faced by ethnic minority groups. In a paper on Chinatown people in San Francisco, this observation was made:

A Chinatowner must maintain a certain amount of equilibrium in his associations: if he has both American and Chinese friends, it would be preferable for him to spend more time with Chinese or at least accept the values placed on in-group relationships. If a Chinatowner should spend more time with Americans and attempt to dissociate himself completely from Chinatowners, he will not have much status, no matter what his occupation or income might be.

In the minds of some students, the osteopathic physician should bear in mind that he is first an osteopath and secondly, a physician. Should be neglect to put "D.O." or the equivalent after his name on the shingle, he is betraying his own colleagues. However, this goes beyond mere D.O.—M.D. relationship, as one student indicated after being asked about the ethics of not having "D.O." after his name:

A lot of times, patients who come to you wish to see a D.O. especially. Now this would not be fair to the patient. Of course, you might lose a lot of patients by putting "D.O." after your name but I think you would gain a lot more.

The students, then, usually feel that the patients go to them for certain specific ailments, and the attitude of the A.M.A. prevents the public from getting what they want. One senior mentioned this when queried about the differential status of an osteopath:

We know we are a minority and I don't particularly care whether we join up with the A.M.A. or not. What I do care about is that the public gets what they want. Now, we've built ourselves up with private funds and we don't get any public or tax money. And for what we've got, we've done pretty well.

Here, the student feels that he is deprived of something, which, by all rights, he should have. Yet, if the question is put to him as to whether he would like to practice in a public—and usually this implies an A.M.A.-dominated hospital—he would say this, to quote one student:

I don't want to practice in an A.M.A. hospital until I have full recognition by them of the kinds of things we do. Could you imagine what would happen if I prescribed "O.M.T." for my patient in the records? Hell, the M.D. wouldn't know what it's all about and I'd be laughed at.

The result of being "laughed at" is withdrawal within themselves and refusal to face some of the issues at hand. One of the more important issues is the rationalization of their deprived status by blaming everything on the A.M.A. This is, of course, typical of any minority group which feels that its inferior position is the result of suppression by some dominant group of whatever legitimate initiative it may wish to carry forth.

The constant reminder by faculty, fellow students, inquisitive laymen, and friends of their own position does not help. Defense mechanisms are called into play. One student said recently:

I don't know what you're getting from the students. I always have four stories to tell to four different groups of people: to my relatives, I tell them one thing; to my friends, I tell them another; to my patients still another. Then finally to myself there's the truth.

Another student recalls bitterly that every time he meets a stranger and mentions that he is going to the osteopathic school:

. . . he'll ask me what osteopathy is. So, then I have to explain. And I don't want to get involved, so all I say is that we are something like medical doctors and I tell him a bit about what I study. Then he'll say, "Why, that's no different from any medical people. Why don't you go to a medical school?" But the worst people I come across are the ones who just say, "Oh, that's like those chiropractors, isn't it?" I get tired of these things.

Another student just gave up answering:

Everytime they ask me, I just ask right back what they think it is. They say, "Well, you're a bone doctor, aren't you?" I just say, "Yes" and let it go at that. They won't know any more even if I explain, so I give up.

The students have been taught in their curriculum that the osteopathic group believes in a philosophy which is somewhat deviant from the generally accepted position of a medical person. Hence, they consider themselves "unorthodox" as compared with the "orthodox physician." To maintain a sense of equilibrium in a world which is constantly presenting obstacles to their practice as a physician is at times a difficult task.

Throughout the four years in osteopathic schools, the students attempt to justify their existence, their position as osteopaths. This is made difficult in that for many of the students, osteopathy was an entirely foreign concept before they came to school. It cannot be denied that a large number of them arrived in osteopathy because circumstances prevented them from entering medical schools. The freshman is quite confused and gropes for some workable definition of osteopathy. Slogans about osteopathy are presented by the freshmen: "Body Unity," "We treat the disease whereas the allopaths treat the symptoms." "The body contains a vast storehouse of drugs." "Andrew Taylor Still didn't really say all of the things that are credited to him."

One instructor brings to his lectures voluminous literature from various medical journals to satisfy his students and help them "prove" the worthwhileness of the concepts. One senior mentioned, when asked about the position he holds on osteopathy, that:

. . . everything that's true in osteopathy is proven to me by all the literature that the medical men have written. Actually, they're just beginning to get our concepts now. At Michigan and Johns Hopkins Medical Schools, they actually talk about body unity all the time. We knew all along and they're way behind in our thinking. Stanford Medical School even uses manipulation, but in a very crude sense.

Another student dragged out a large textbook to show pictures of osteopathic techniques which are recommended in the treatment of low-back pains.[9]

Another way to bolster their feelings of inadequacy is to compare with students of orthodox medical schools the courses taught at the osteopathic schools. Upperclassmen often mention that a good deal of the time during their first Christmas vacation is spent visiting with college friends who are medical students. One student said:

When I was home my first Christmas, I saw a lot of my old buddies. They knew I was in osteopathic school and they were curious about what I was studying. Some of them thought that I was going to a bone-cracking school but I soon straightened them out. Usually after talking with them for a couple of hours, they're interested in what I'm doing and one of them said, "Hell, you're taking the same courses that we are" and that makes me feel proud. I won't take a back seat to any of them.

This same student went on to give a lengthy comparison on the basic science courses with other medical schools and concluded that "on the average, our basic science courses are about the same as theirs, if not a little better." These sessions with medical students are a very common occurrence. Those who do not have this opportunity feel rather frustrated. One sophomore who has not returned home since he started school in 1954, mentioned this:

Gee, I wish I could go home now. I would really tell my classmates who are not in medical colleges a thing or two. I just got a letter recently from a friend who's a sophomore at ———— Medical School. He said that if I applied there now I could get in. I'd love to tell him something about our school and compare calendars. I'm dying to get home.

By satisfying himself in terms of his ego-defensive mechanisms, the freshman feels that he has received a good Christmas present. He feels fortified to go the rest of the year relieved of his initial fears. Actually, whether his fear is diminished is dubious. The freshman and sophomore soon become junior and senior and their textbookish learning must soon be transposed into clinical diagnoses. For a number of students, this is a traumatic situation. Some of the knowledge must be organized because they see, for the most part, patients who need medical care. To be sure, OMT is prescribed by many of the clinical staff members, but this lies in the general area of "relieving pain" or "maintaining body unity." At this time the student uses his own discretion as to how much or how little OMT he wishes to apply. As they pass on to their internships, some of the men will have positions in hospitals which use practically no

OMT and this will bewilder graduates of more strictly osteopathically inclined schools.

Throughout their formative years in osteopathic schools, the students are told that they are equal to any medical physician and that they have had an "added tool," "an adjunct which the medical men do not have." Yet, it must be difficult to be told that they are "superior" to the medical men and still be surrounded by a seemingly cold and hostile world which really cares little about what they present and confuses them with chiropractors. The profession wishes to be recognized as one of full-fledged doctors; yet it wishes to appear different. In a society where people too readily accept the norm, the osteopathic profession will have to choose between being segregated and remaining equal or being integrated into the medical healing arts and held inferior.

Analysis and Interpretation. The problem of "What's My Line?" which confronts marginal professions is also in evidence with osteopathic students. Unlike students who enter well-defined professions such as medicine or law, osteopathic students require a lengthier period of adjustment to their present feelings of inadequacy. It is also difficult for them to identify themselves with the osteopathic profession, since many of the students, even at the time of graduation, envision themselves as medical practitioners rather than osteopathic physicians.[10] Rather than using their own colleagues as the reference group,[11] they constantly compare themselves with other medical students of medical practitioners.[12]

The faculty who are concerned with the task of orienting the students toward an osteopathic point of view are presented with a difficult problem. Most of the students have entered osteopathy as a second choice, and some of them wandered in only by accident. Only 34 out of the 103 interviewed had not applied to any medical schools. Forty-four students went directly into an osteopathic college after their undergraduate training. The remaining took a variety of avenues: to another undergraduate school (28), to a graduate school (16), to a medical school (4), or any combination of these. A good many of them were in some other type of profession (pharmacy or chiropractic). Thus, they have a positive need for the development of rationales to assure themselves that they have not entered medicine via the back door, a common accusation directed toward osteopathic students by some lay people.

One method of alleviating some of this fear is a constant comparison with the established medical profession. For the freshman, this occurs during the first Christmas vacation at home. He consciously seeks out those undergraduate classmates who are now in various medical schools in order to "compare notes." This has great cathartic value as well. From the medical students, the D.O. student discovers that the number of hours of teaching is about the same. Usually, "One-Upmanship" is practiced, whereby the aspirant M.D. would be asked subtle questions in a battle of knowledge gained in an osteopathic college. This is the *sine qua non* for the freshman student's ego. For those not able to get away during that first Christmas, the doubts of their "equality" persist for a much longer period. Once they become upper-classmen, the comparison is no longer on the subjects taught at school but how well the osteopathic students do on basic science examinations given by various state boards (sophomores), how well their clinical training compares with "other" medical students' (juniors), and how successful they are going to be as practitioners as compared with the M.D. practitioners (seniors).

The search for a favorable answer to the students depends on their relations with four groups of people: (1) the faculty who attempt to clarify specific views of osteopathy, (2) the patients who give them a view of the "public image," (3) the relatives and close friends who constitute the "ego booster," and (4) fellow students who are reflections of their own image.[13] The intensity of identifications with the osteopathic profession depends on the intensity of views expressed by any one of these four variables with regard to osteopathy.

The mixed reactions of these four groups with regard to osteopathy are reflected in the student's dilemma. Since none of these groups have a clear conception of the role of the osteopath in society, the student encounters difficulty in developing some self-conception of his role. The dilemmas expressed by the osteopathic students will abate only when role-expectations held by the public become crystallized.

44   A MARGINAL PROFESSIONAL ROLE: THE CHIROPRACTOR

By Walter I. Wardwell

The term "marginal man" became incorporated in the sociologist's terminology following its introduction by Robert E. Park[1] and its later elaboration by Everett V. Stonequist.[2] A marginal man is "a cultural hybrid, a man living and sharing intimately in the cultural life and traditions of two distinct peoples,"[3] and "in looking at himself from the standpoint of each group he experiences the conflict as a personal problem."[4] This conception has been severely criticized by Arnold W. Green[5] as being so lacking in precision as to be scientifically useless, and by Milton M. Goldberg[6] as needing qualification where "marginal cultures" furnish psychological security and "adequate facilities for participation in group life."

These writers assume that there are two different cultures (or social roles) to which the individual is marginal. Their type case is the half-breed or second-generation immigrant faced with the necessity of choosing between elements in his socialization experience. None of them considers that there can be marginality to a single well defined social role. Undoubtedly, some writers have used the word *marginal* in the latter sense, but there has been little explicit treatment of the meaning and implications of such a use of the term. An example of such a marginal role is the citizenship role of the American Negro. He is not in conflict over whether to adhere to American culture patterns or to those of a lower-caste, slave, or African culture. He wants to be accepted as a full-fledged American citizen, with all the rights and privileges thereof, but in attaining this goal he has only partially succeeded, particularly in the South. This constitutes the marginality of his role.

Reprinted from *Social Forces*, 30, (1952), 339–348.

A marginal role is also an imperfectly institutionalized one, which means that there is some ambiguity in the pattern of behavior legitimately expected of a person filling the role, and that the social sanctions attending the role tend to be inconsistently applied. The reason is that the role's very marginality implies inadequate fulfillment of some of the expectations associated with it. (In the case of the Negro, this would include violations of civil liberties, lower prestige, fewer economic opportunities, etc.) In common with other types of inadequately institutionalized roles, such as that of the labor organizer prior to the 1930's, the lobbyist, and the professional gambler, marginal roles usually result in personality strain.

The role of the chiropractor is structually comparable to that of the Negro, for it is marginal to the well institutionalized role of the doctor. Physicians are fully accepted as doctors, of course; osteopaths have become partially accepted; but chiropractors have attained little acceptance. In fact, the "official position of the American Medical Association" is that chiropractors are not doctors at all, but quacks—i.e., imposters in the doctor's role. The public is less harsh in its evaluation, but there is no question that the role of the chiropractor is a marginal one. This is true in regard to the following factors: (a) the amount of technical competence which chiropractors possess, (b) the breadth of scope of their practice, (c) their legal status, (d) their income, and (e) their prestige standing. On the average, chiropractors rank below physicians and osteopaths in all these respects although there are individual exceptions as regards items (a), (d), and (e). However, the chiropractor is not undecided as to whether he wants to be a doctor or something else—say, a business man (although his role tends to deviate from that of the doctor in the direction of "commercialism"); even more certainly he is not undecided as to whether he wants to be a doctor or a quack. He wants acceptance as a doctor (of a special kind), but society at large does not accord him this status. Hence his role is marginal.

There are two principal reasons why such marginal roles should be studied—first, to discover how they fit into the social structure (including the circumstances which give rise to them and permit them to continue, the functions they serve, their relationship to better institutionalized roles), and, second, to discover what sort of social adjustment takes place in marginal roles. In the present paper[7] we treat the first of these problem areas by characterizing the current role of the chiropractor in American society, and then attempting to discover why it is what it is. We shall investigate the functions served by the role for the chiropractor himself, for his patient, and for society as a whole, and then supplement his functional analysis by an evaluation of the sociohistorical factors in the situation.[8]

The data on which this analysis is based are derived from: (a) a study of the relevant literature, (b) interviews with a sample of twenty-four Massachusetts[9] chiropractors, comprising essentially all those active in the Greater Boston area, (c) briefer interviews with physicians, osteopaths, other chiropractors, and chiropractic patients, and (d) observation of chiropractors in their offices, at legislative hearings, and at professional gatherings in several different states. The available literature on chiropractic is extremely controversial—that of chiropractors being defensively *pro,* that of orthodox medicine being almost compulsively *con*. According to the latter, the chiropractic theory of disease (i.e., as being due to interference with the transmission of neural impulses) is scientifically invalid and the chiropractor is a charlatan "either too crooked to admit his deceit or too ignorant to know that his theory is erroneous."[10] There are indications in more technical medical literature, however, that the chiropractic principle of the "vertebral subluxation" (osseous impingement or irritation of a spinal nerve root) is accepted by certain orthopedists, although they would not grant it the general applicability which most chiropractors claim for it; for example:

The usual cause of pain and tenderness in the abdominal wall is an irritation of the spinal nerves where they make their exits through the vertebrae and . . . the commonest cause of this nerve irritation is bad body mechanics, and, further, . . . even partial correction of the bad body mechanics cures the abdominal pain and tenderness.[11]

From operating and widely exposing foramens in over 100 patients and making explorations in many more, I am convinced that foraminate constriction is a common cause of back disability.[12]

The Role Of The Chiropractor. We understand by *role* an institutionalized behavior pattern, defined in terms of rights and obligations betweeen a given "role-incumbent"[13] and the incumbents of other social roles. The role of the doctor involves three sets of social relationships, conventionally distinguished in codes of professional ethics as those to colleagues, those to patients, and those to society at large. Although usually the doctor's *obligations* are emphasized, he also has "*rights*," somewhat less well established, to social prestige, a relatively high level of living, etc. The corresponding aspects of the chiropractor's role, as well as such topics as the criteria for entrance into the role and the geographical distribution of chiropractors are discussed below.

Most chiropractors engage in independent private practice. A few of them share small "clinics" with one or more colleagues, usually close relatives. The typical chiropractor makes at least some house-calls, and does not employ an office assistant. Many chiropractors, but by no means a majority, own X-ray equipment, for the use of X-rays is deemed highly desirable for diagnosing the presence of subluxations. Chiropractors' fees usually approximate those charged for office visits by physicians in the vicinity; in the Boston area the modal fee is three dollars. Practically no studies of chiropractors' incomes have been made, but it is probable that the average net income of chiropractors in the United States exceeds $4500 per annum; there are some indications that it does not vary greatly from that of dentists, optometrists, and chiropodists.[14]

The standard chiropractic course of professional training now comprises four years of eight months each and not less than 3600 hours.[15] However, six states still license graduates of schools providing less training than this, and four other states do not license chiropractors at all. Eight states require, in addition to the four-year professional course, two years of pre-professional college work, and three other states require one such year. Eighteen states plus the District of Columbia have "Basic Science" laws, under which chiropractors must pass the same examinations in such subjects as anatomy, biochemistry, physiology, etc., that physicians do. Nowhere is graduate internship required for licensure but it is available in at least one large (640-bed) chiropractic sanitarium in Denver, Colorado.

More important than the length of the formal educational period is the quality of the instruction offered and the facilities available for training. Here is where chiropractic education is severely handicapped. Although nearly all schools are now organized on a non-profit basis, they still derive most of their income from tuitions. The majority of them have ill-equipped laboratories and classrooms. Facilities for clinical training are almost exclusively of the out-patient variety, and in at least one large school the burden of obtaining clinic patients falls mainly on the students. Faculties are overworked, often inadequately trained themselves, and frequently teach only part-time. A study of the catalogues of the eleven colleges accredited by the National Chiropractic Association reveals that, for a combined enrollment of 2748,[16] the eleven colleges have a total of 247 faculty members, with academic degrees as follows:

M.D.	5
D.O. (osteopath)	3
D.M.D. (dentist)	1
Ph.D.	4
M.A. or M.S.	21
B.A. or B.S.	47
drugless degree only	149
no degree	17
Total	247

Since chiropractors are not legally authorized to perform major surgery, prescribe drugs, or (in most states) practice obstetrics, some of them maintain that extensive training in these subjects is not necessary and that the lack of hospital facilities for training is therefore not a serious handicap. The trend, however, has been toward a more comprehensive training program of higher quality. The record of Basic Science examinations taken by chiropractors, while still poor, indicates some of this progress. (See Table 1.) The figures reveal a tendency during the period for a somewhat lower percentage of chiropractors to fail the examinations, for a greater number of chiropractors to attempt the examinations, and (hence) for a sizable increase in the number of chiropractors certified by Basic Science Boards.

Table 1—Record of Basic Science Examinations Taken by Chiropractors, Selected Years, 1934–1949

	1934	1938	1942	1946	1947	1948	1949
No. of Basic Science Boards	9	12	18	19	19	19	20
No. of chiropractors examined	13	32	24	40	61	216	807
No. of chiropractors passed	4	8	9	14	19	75	339
Percentage of chiropractors failed	69	75	62	65	69	65	58
No. of chiropractors certified by reciprocity	0	0	5	12	13	64	205
Total no. of chiropractors certified by Basic Science Boards	4	8	14	26	32	139	544

Source. These figures are taken from the *Journal of the American Medical Association* series on "Medical Licensure Statistics" which usually appear during May of the following year; the specific references are 104:17, p. 1519; 112:17, p. 1724; 122:2, pp. 111–2; 134:3, p. 283; 137:7, p. 638; 140:3, pp. 321–2; 143:5, p. 470.

At the present time there are about 30,000 active chiropractors throughout the world, most of them in the United States and Canada. There are about 6000 chiropractic students in twenty-odd colleges, all but one of which are in the United States. The highest ratios of chiropractors to population occur in California, Colorado, Iowa, Kansas, and Missouri; these states have at least one chiropractor to every 5000 of population. The ratio of chiropractors to physicians is one to two in Wyoming, and one to three in Oregon and Kansas. In general chiropractic is strongest in the Middle and Far West and weakest in the Old South (except Florida).

There are two national associations of chiropractors—the National Chiropractic Association ("NCA"), with 7764 members, and the International Chiropractors Association ("ICA"), with 3500 members.[17] The ICA advocates "straight" chiropractic—the doctrine that chiropractors should limit themselves to spinal manipulation alone—whereas the NCA is considered to be a "mixer" organization because it sanctions the use of heat, light, air, water, exercise, electric modalities, and diet regulation as a legitimate part of the practice of chiropractic. The straights regard the use of these adjuncts as "mixing" chiropractic and medicine and consider mixers as having "sold out" to the medical opposition.

Organized chiropractic is "a shaky structure" due to its small membership, the split between straights and mixers, and the lack of any realistic dependence by a practitioner upon the high regard of his colleagues in order to achieve professional success. There is no network of referrals to specialists, or hospital staff appointments to be courted, as in the medical profession. Primary activity of the professional associations is directed toward securing or retaining favorable legislation (i.e., that which leaves chiropractic free from medical control), and otherwise protecting the interests of members. Other activities include educational programs conducted at association meetings, a small amount of support of research and some financial aid to schools.

Relations between physicians and chiropractors are often surprisingly close in spite of organized medicine's tabu on cooperation with "irregulars." One reason for this seems to be the practice whereby patients with conditions considered outside the scope of chiropractic are referred to physicians for treatment; informal friendship ties often results. Twenty-one of the twenty-four chiropractors in the Massachusetts sample stated that they have cooperated on cases with physicians at one time or another. Five of them also stated that they are, or at one time were, able to send their patients to certain medical hospitals and treat them there. Eight chiropractors expressed themselves as certain that if a patient should die under their care, they could count on the friendly assistance of some physician, including his signature on a death certificate.[18]

The chiropractor-patient relationship is much like the physician-patient relationship except that it is often less formal and "professional." The patient often has to have chiropractic "sold" to him—a practice which may at times border on solicitation of patients. Although only "institutional advertising" is authorized by the NCA's code of ethics, it is difficult to distinguish between it and personal advertising when the advertising material is handed or mailed to the patient by the chiropractor himself. The vast majority of patients have originally consulted chiropractors only as a court of last resort—"when they have exhausted medical science and their money," as one of them lamented. The chiropractor cannot presume, as the physician often can, that patients will unhesitatingly accept him as a qualified practitioner of a healing art. He may boast of past cures or even make promises as to the benefits to be expected from chiropractic treatment. Sometimes he adopts a friendship orientation toward the patient instead of an impersonal professional one. It is the writer's impression that, although such a friendship orientation could be faked, informality and genuine friendships are prominent aspects of chiropractor-patient relations.

The social prestige of chiropractors is not very high. Only one limited public opinion study has attempted to obtain a status rating of chiropractors, along with twenty-four other "medical specialties."[19] In the composite rating of 250 respondents, "chiropractor" ranked twenty-second, higher only than "veterinarian," "midwife," and "manicurist." In the rural sample of 100 respondents, however, "chiropractor" ranked fifteenth, ahead of "osteopath," "orthopedist," "ophthalmologist," "roentgenologist," etc., which, along with other evidence suggests that chiropractors' prestige may be higher in rural than in urban areas. A more recent survey of 507 residents of the New York City area "from widely diversified sections of the population" showed that nearly half (47%) of them were totally ignorant of what chiropractic is,[20] and that only about 10 percent of the total had ever taken chiropractic treatment. Similarly, a survey of 1113 households in Michigan in 1948 showed that in only 14.7% of the families had one or more members been to a chiropractor.[21]

Chiropractors nevertheless appear to be well integrated into their local communities, even in Massachusetts. Of the sample of chiropractors interviewed only four are not members of some fraternal order; half of the total (i.e., twelve) are Masons, and six of these are Shriners. The average length of time that these chiropractors have practiced in Massachusetts is twenty-one years; in their present office locations, twelve years. Relevant also is the fact that nine of them now practice in their original home towns and that seven others located in their present communities because they had relatives or close friends living there. It is possible, of course, that a selective bias operates in Massachusetts so as to eliminate those chiropractors who fail to become well integrated into their communities. But even the degree of acceptance which they possess does not prevent them from being arrested for "practicing medicine without registration," for half of the chiropractors in the sample have been arrested one or more times. (Two have been arrested twice; two others, four or more times.) Approximately half of these arrests resulted in convictions, the usual penalty being a small fine, a warning, or a suspended jail sentence. This situation obviously would not hold for states where chiropractors are licensed, although in some of them (e.g., Ohio) some chiropractors practice outside the law because they consider it an unjust one.

Chiropractors get into public life probably as frequently as do the members of related professions. For example, three members of the New Hampshire state legislature were chiropractors in 1949. And, amazing as it may seem, one Massachusetts chiropractor has for a number of years been an active member of his city's board of health!

Motivations and Satisfactions of Chiropractors. The majority of chiropractors have been of humble origin and have advanced in socio-economic status through becoming chiropractors. This has not been the only reason for becoming a chiropractor, however, for there is little doubt that many of them have been motivated by a genuine desire to aid the sick. Some originally intended to become physicians but due to a lack of money or educational qualifications were unable to go to medical school;[22] thirteen of the Massachusetts sample had intentions of becoming physicians which later were diverted to chiropractic. Many chiropractors have been helped personally by their science; eleven of the sample stated that chiropractic benefit to them or to a member of their immediate family was a factor in their decision to begin the study of chiropractic.

Typical of a humanitarian motivation is the following statement by one of the chiropractors interviewed:

All my life my hobby has been sick people. When I was a kid, instead of playing baseball I would go visit sick people and do things to make them comfortable—favors and so on. I always wanted to be a doctor.

The following excerpt reveals status aspirations:

I was going with a girl who lived in the same house where Dr. ———— (a chiropractor) lived. She insisted that chiropractic was the career for me and that I must come over and meet him. I had always wanted to be a doctor. He told me that chiropractic is a fine profession for a young man and emphasized the good I could do with my hands. He also mentioned the remunerative side but didn't emphasize it so much. He compared it with salaried occupations and the slow promotions in a bank. . . . I always admired the horses and buggies of the M.D.'s outside the hospital in my home town. They had beautiful horses and fine blankets for them. And some had rubber tires on their carriages. That was something in those days! I wanted a horse and buggy like those. Then one day I helped carry an injured man to a wagon and went to the hospital with him. I got acquainted with an M.D. there and came back to see and talk with him a number of times. We talked about my being a doctor, but the course of preparation for an M.D. is long and hard, and what the chiropractor and the girl said made more and more sense to me.

Financial ambitions are evidently important to the spokesman of the following:

An osteopath friend used to tell me I should take up osteopathy, that I could make a lot of money at it. Another friend of mine did this and was very successful in California. His uncle was a chiropractor, so I went to see him. I investigated both chiropractic and osteopathy. I decided on chiropractic because I felt (and still feel) that it goes farther than osteopathy. It makes more specific adjustments. . . . I was probably a damn fool to choose chiropractic from the point of view of making money; I could be licensed like the other osteopaths around here. But I'm not sorry. There are plenty of osteopaths who make no more money than I do.

Some chiropractors seem to have entered on their calling without any specific motivation:

My brother went to the Palmer School two months before I did. I can't say why I decided to become a chiropractor, but I thought I would like the work and I liked the idea of going out West to school. I probably had as little reason as anyone for taking it up. A lot of the students had been personally helped by chiropractic, but I wasn't. Some of them went to the Palmer School for treatments and while they were there they took the course, too.

There is not sufficient evidence to determine whether the status, financial, or humanitarian motivation for becoming a chiropractor is of most frequent occurrence. Probably all three motivations co-exist to some extent in most chiropractors.

Advertising literature of chiropractic schools has always emphasized the three motivations illustrated above, though less subtly in earlier years than today. A study of chiropractors conducted under the auspices of the Committee on the Costs of Medical Care in 1932 reported that all chiropractic schools "held out to carpenters, baggage handlers, bookkeepers, pick wielders, and the like, the alluring prospect of making easy money and being a 'doctor.'" There is no question but that chiropractic schools have provided a channel of upward social mobility for many ambitious children of poor parents. On the other hand, there have always been chiropractors from other walks of life—lawyers, teachers, physicians, nurses, etc. The previous occupations of the chiropractors in the Massachusetts sample are as follows:

Professional	2
chemist	
mechanical engineer	
Managerial	4
shoe factory sup't	
leather plant sup't	
sales manager	
army officer	
Sales	3
X-ray equipment	
insurance	
magazines	
Clerical	4
Skilled work	2
Semi-skilled work	4
Unskilled work	1
Students	4
Total	24

In spite of the many handicaps of their calling, chiropractors at least are independent professional men having a fair amount of income and social prestige. They take pride in their skill and in the comfort they provide for the sick. Within their professional organizations some of them find opportunity to display leadership qualities and to exert influence; others can give their loyalty to the chiropractic group and derive from the ingroup feeling of the members compensation for the social rebuffs they encounter outside the profession. However, it is from fulfilling the American success pattern of getting on and up in the world and from providing relief to the suffering sick that chiropractors appear to obtain their major satisfactions.

Motivations and Satisfactions of Chiropractic Patients. Who are the people who become chiropractic patients? As far as their socio-economic status is concerned, there is some indication that, proportionate to the total population, more chiropractic patients come from the lower classes and fewer come from the upper-middle class. More women than men consult chiropractors. Chiropractors probably also have proportionately more ambulatory patients than do physicians, more patients with faulty osseous structure (the condition regarded as a chiropractor's specialty), and more hypochondriacs and psychoneurotics (because people without organic defects are the ones who are likely to become dissatisfied with orthodox medical treatment and try chiropractic).

Medical writers and chiropractors agree on one point—that the latter frequently help people with mental disturbances—though they differ as to the mechanism by which improvement is effected. Louis Reed says, for example:

It is evident that in any case the treatment has a large element of suggestion. The patient is told, with evangelistic fervor, that his troubles are due to just one thing, a sublaxated vertebra; the chiropractor sets about to 'adjust' that vertebra, using, perhaps, great force and causing the bones to 'crack.' He assures the patient that the nerve is no longer impinged, and that his troubles are over. The patient is quite likely to believe him and, if there is nothing seriously wrong, to be 'cured' by his belief.[24]

There is no doubt that suggestion plays an important part in the chiropractic treatment of mentally disturbed patients, as it does also in the medical treatment of such patients. In general, chiropractors are probably more "patient-oriented"[25] than are most physicians, who tend to be "illness-oriented." But chiropractors claim, in addition to this, that manipulation is of direct therapeutic assistance in cases of both psychosis and psychoneurosis. Their contention is that the physiological relaxation itself contributes to the easing of mental tension, particularly if the mental tension originally contributed to the physiological (i.e., muscular) tension that exists;[26] the adjustment " 'breaks' undesirable muscular fixations, i.e., abolishes habitual motor tensions linked with long-standing mental conflicts."[27] Whether or not this is a valid hypothesis it is not possible for the writer as a sociologist to determine from the data at hand. It would seem, however, to be a topic worthy of impartial scientific investigation.

Some patients may, in addition, derive neurotic gratification of sensual or masochistic needs at the hands of a chiropractor; the hypochondriac may receive friendly and sympathetic support. In the case of organic disabilities the evidence already referred to indicates that chiropractic manipulation is effective in certain types of conditions.

Finally, the chiropractor is in a position to "legitimize" the sick status of some individuals with whom the physician can find nothing wrong. If the patient is told that a vertebral subluxation is the cause of his disability, he is able to consider himself as genuinely sick rather than as just "imagining" it. The determination of who is "sick" is a function which all doctors perform, but since chiropractors and physicians adhere to different definitions of disease, it is possible for them to disagree as to which patients may properly be designated as "sick." In such a case the chiropractor performs an important service for his patient.

Functions Served for Society. Using a societal frame of reference, it is apparent that the chiropractic profession provides a channel of therapeutic innovation alternate to that of the medical profession. Just as homeopathy led to a decrease in drugging and Christian Science revealed medicine's deficiencies in the field of mental health, so chiropractic (and osteopathy) have focused attention on the importance to health of body mechanics, minor neurological disturbances, and manipulative therapy. Inasmuch as medicine, in spite of its emphasis on objectivity and scientific research, is resistant to changing its basic formulations, chiropractic performs the important function of furnishing another channel of medical innovation.

Socio-Historical Factors. In contrast to osteopathy, which was originated by a former medical practitioner (Andrew Taylor Still, in 1874), chiropractic has been developed (since 1895) almost entirely by men (1) who had no previous conection with medicine, and (2) who were of low socio-economic status. These two "historical accidents" have had important results for the subsequent history of chiropractic and its relations with the medical profession. Communication between the two groups has been minimal, consisting principally of the study of medical texts and professional journals by chiropractors. The informal contacts that have existed between physicians and chiropractors have been freest at the community level and almost nil at the state and national levels. As a result, chiropractors have learned less than they should have of the newer developments in medical science, and physicians know practically nothing about chiropractic manipulative therapy. The chiropractic findings which conceivably could be of considerable value to physicians working in related areas, such as the orthopedists, may never come to the latter's attention. Whatever chiropractic knowledge is introduced into medical circles has to be imported *sub rosa*, as it were, usually disguised as independent medical "findings" of neural disturbances, or as "experiments" with manipulative therapy;[28] for a physician who openly espouses chiropractic is invariably ostracized by his colleagues.

The initial gap in communication and in social standing between chiropractors and physicians has made it additionally likely that medical men should regard chiropractic as outright quackery. It has also given chiropractic educators a vested interest in perpetuating the notion that chiropractic and medicine have nothing in common with one another—the more so as chiropractors have gained in social and legal acceptance. Eighteen states now recognize chiropractic as distinct from medicine to the extent of granting autonomy to a board of chiropractors in the matter of examining and licensing prospective practitioners. The gap between chiropractic and medicine has thus been perpetuated as much by the chiropractic leadership as by the opposition of organized medicine.

Oswald Hall demonstrates the existence within the medical profession of powerful cliques able to exclude from full acceptance physicians of undesirable religious or ethnic background.[29] Such powerful in-groups would be expected to oppose even more strongly the acceptance of chiropractors (whom they term "uneducated quacks") as professional equals. Oliver Garceau, who has documented the control of organized medicine by a small minority, suggests that persecution of the out-group serves tension-reducing functions within the association:

Perhaps the active minority finds that quack-hunting is personally profitable. Such sporting events give evidence of conscientious attention to duty; they appeal to the professional idealism of the members, hurt no member's pocketbook, and contribute to a feeling of gratitude, obligation and even dependence on the active minority.[30]

There is some evidence, however, that the physicians who oppose chiropractors must vigorously tend to be the more unsuccessful ones.[31]

Physicians possess a stereotype of an illiterate, bumbling chiropractor mulcting the helpless sick, and this stereotype interferes with their making an unbiased evaluation of what chiropractors do. In this vein, a Basic Science examiner who was queried concerning examination questions has been quoted as saying:

We used to give them out, but the chiropractors memorized the questions and answers for future examinations. *We do not believe they know enough to answer them otherwise.* Now we refuse to give them out.[32]

It is significant that only chiropractors were accused of memorizing the questions and answers.

On the average, chiropractors are unquestionably not so well trained as physicians, have lower standards of professional ethics, and are greatly handicapped in therapeutic effectiveness by what amounts to a mono-causal theory of disease and cure. But over and above this the relations between chiropractors and physicians and the latter's evaluation of the former have also resulted in part from the sociologically significant historical accidents discussed above.

A Marginal Professional Role. According to the *Dictionary of Sociology:*

New (professions) emerge either *de novo* or as the changed status of what were formerly merely occupational groups, to meet the needs of a rapidly expanding complex civilization for experts and trained specialists.[33]

Chiropractic has emerged as a new profession in spite of intense opposition from organized medicine. Although the two professions may remain apart for many years, it is possible that chiropractic will eventually merge with medicine,[34] as homeopathy did with allopathy after years of bitter conflict, and as osteopathy seems to be in the process of doing at the present time.[35] The California Chiropractic Association has already proposed an amendment to its state's licensing law which would authorize chiropractors to use every device and technique of medical science except major surgery.[36] This proposed expansion of the scope of chiropractic practice will certainly be bitterly contested by organized medicine, as well as by some chiropractors, but it is a straw in the wind.

There is confusion in the minds of many people (and frequently in the mind of the chiropractor himself) as to what a chiropractor is and is expected to do. Especially is this true where chiropractors practice extra-legally. This is an important aspect of the imperfect institutionalization of the chiropractic role. Both the institutionalization of a role and role-marginality are relative matters permitting of degrees of more or less. Some such notion is inevitable unless we postulate a completely static society. For the dynamic nature of social systems implies incessant (though often minor) change in the definitions of social roles. Always some are in the process of becoming more fully institutionalized—others less so. Similarly, marginal roles may become more or less distinguishable from their primary role. Which sort of change is taking place obviously must be empirically determined in each given instance.

It is too early to predict what the future status of chiropractors will be. There is, however, some historical justification for the statement that the present antipathy between physicians and chiropractors provides no assurance that they will not some day find themselves in the same professional association.[37] The term "homeopath" has already fallen into popular disuse; homeopaths simply are physicians. Osteopaths are gaining increasing acceptance; it is relevant that they now insist on the use of the words "osteopath" and "allopath" as correlative terminology. Chiropractors are now becoming "chiropractic physicians" in many states. Though this practice is often opposed, particularly by the "straights," it appears to be the trend of the future. Among the forces pushing chiropractors in this direction are (1) stricter licensing laws, especially those with Basic Science provisions, which broaden the scope of chiropractors' professional competence, (2) the limited supply of medical doctors, combined with the need of various segments of the population for additional therapeutic services, (3) chiropractors' desire to offer a complete health service and not to have to defer to other types of practitioners, and (4) the increasing social, legal, and professional recognition of chiropractors, which has the effect of identifying them with physicians in the eyes of the general public, and which leads to such beliefs as the one that the chiropractor is simply another kind of doctor or that he is a "specialist" in treating certain types of conditions. The writer's "best guess" at this time is that chiropractors (and their distinctive therapeutic contribution) will eventually be merged into the medical mainstream.

The chiropractor is not marginal to two distinct cultures, as the term "marginal man" ordinarily would imply. He is simply an incumbent of a role that is marginal. However, since his is an occupational role, it is not as all-pervasive in his life as the Negro's marginal citizenship role is in his. In addition, the chiropractor does not have his status ascribed to him as does the Negro; at some moment of his life he made the "decision" to enter upon his role. But this does not necessarily mitigate the strain which occupying a marginal role produces, for the fact of having *voluntarily* entered the role may cause feelings of remorse which would not be aroused by the necessity to accommodate to a marginal ascribed role.

It is suggested that the type of role-marginality discussed in this paper is a prevalent phenomenon in modern society, due, in part, to the frequency and rapidity with which changes in role-definitions occur and new roles appear. Since most of these changes occur in the occupational sphere (including "occupations" in government, etc.), it may well be that those persons working in the area known as the "sociology of occupations" will find the study of role-marginality to be of particular theoretical and practical value.

45   THE DOCTOR-PATIENT RELATIONSHIP AND "FUNCTIONAL" ILLNESS

By R. S. Ferguson

Signs are not wanting that there has been some deterioration in the mutual trust which existed between doctors and patients before the introduction of the National Health Service (in England). There has certainly been an increase in the number of complaints and protests by patients and relatives to executive councils, and in the number of cases brought against doctors in the Courts.

Short of these dramatic and traumatic happenings, however, it is possible that subtler forms of deterioration in the doctor-patient relationship are occurring. The tyro in general practice, and this particularly applies to busy industrial practices, soon becomes inured, though the baptism is often painful, to arguments on the telephone and degrading and exhausting wrangles at the front-door, as to whether to visit "tonight or in the morning." Unpleasant pressure is experienced over the issues of certificates and, indeed, also prescriptions. Worst of all, a gnawing sense of insecurity arises in the young man as he wonders whether his older principal is fully enjoying his work or whether he is motivated, even partly, by fear. The astounding paradox is that with technique immeasurably improved, with great technological and therapeutic advances, the net result is less gratitude than formerly.

Little is left to chance nowadays—every injury of any moment (and many of no moment) is x-rayed and there must be precious few missed fractures; haemorrhage from the bowel, if its origin be not obvious, means that the patient will have a barium enema and sigmoidoscopy before the pile ointment is prescribed. A cough that will not clear up is no longer dismissed as bronchitis until the radiologist has pronounced on the chest. When doctors could cure few ailments they were held in high regard, now in an age of therapeutic excellence they often have to defend themselves (Needles, 1954).

Some Causes of The Deterioration. Needles has no doubts as to the principal cause—he lays the blame fairly and squarely on the great numbers of people who suffer from "functional" illness. They constitute what he calls a reservoir of ill-will. How do they fall foul of the doctor? A common source of irritation is of course that they have too little time spent upon them. The practitioner has too many certificates to issue, too many records to keep, too many demands on his services to take a leisurely and minute interest in the neurotic and his troubles. This unfortunately also applies to the non-neurotic,

From *The Practitioner*, 176, (June, 1956), 656–662.

and intimate knowledge of the individual is no longer always possible. In face of the extra pressure of work practitioners are more and more tending to aggregate into groups and the patient who does not pay close attention to details of time of consultation becomes nonplussed and confused when he finds himself consulting a new and strange member of the group. It seems a pity, too, that many doctors have given up maternity work. Childbirth is a primitive event deeply charged with emotion. A confinement successfully and sympathetically managed welds mother and child and the whole family to the doctor in a way that nothing else can do. No doubt there are good reasons for leaving this task to a specialized, though of necessity somewhat impersonal, expert but human values are unquestionably lost.

Aside from these professional considerations it is evident that the advent of the National Health Service has brought about a change in emphasis. A man now tends to think of his practice as so many thousand units—an administrative measure—and there is a holistic attitude to this aggregation: for example, payment is usually made by one huge cheque four times a year. Hospital clinicians have constantly to be on guard against conveyor-belt types of arrangements for patients—a concept beloved by administrators. The individual *per se* loses importance. These are some of the ways in which the bonds are being loosened. We need to keep awake in ourselves a lively self-criticism if we are to meet the changing needs of our role.

The Changing Attitude Of The Patient. In the third place it is undeniable that the attitude of ordinary citizens to the doctor has changed. This is not so much an isolated phenomenon in society. Twentieth-century man worships efficiency. Society is fast becoming a technocracy. Industry is now so big and so vast that the individual, as an individual, is quite lost. Sociologists and industrialists alike are concerned as to how to preserve human relationships in these leviathan undertakings (Ling, 1954). The inherited materialism of the last two centuries has made us concentrate too exclusively on externals, and human values have tended to disappear. Scientific and technical advances have rendered untenable centuries-old assumptions regarding the nature of the Universe, man's place and function in it, and the relation of the individual to his group. Individual unhappiness and widespread social disorder may be regarded as expressions of our disintegrating cultural traditions. In a recent survey (Frankl, 1954) it has been claimed that the spirit of our times is a collective neurosis made up of such elements as a planless day-to-day attitude to life, a fatalistic outlook ('après moi la bombe atomique'), a temptation for the individual to submerge himself into the masses, and a fatal tendency towards fanaticism. Needles quotes C. W. Mills:

The uneasiness, the malaise of our time, is due to the fact that in our politics and economy, in family life and religion, in practically every sphere of our existence, the continuities of the 18th and 19th centuries have disintegrated or been destroyed, and at the same time no new knowledge for the new routines that we live and must live has taken hold. The malaise is deep rooted, for the absence of any order of belief has left men morally defenseless as individuals and politically impotent. They have no culture to lean upon except the contents of a mass society that may shape them and seeks to manipulate them to its own ends.

There would seem therefore to be adequate psychopathological reasons for the vast increase in the numbers of people who are functionally ill, and who seek medical advice and treatment for psychosomatic illness, psycho-neuroses, and sicknesses of the personality.

Near-Deification Of The Doctor. In short, as a famous psychiatrist has said, Western man turned away from the priest to the doctor, someone who seemed to be more efficient, more practical, someone who seemed to incorporate the admired and worshipped science and devoted it to that most attractive goal, the perfection of human health and the alleviation of human suffering— *soluti et solatio aegrorum.* But the emphasis soon canalized exclusively on health; solace was not greatly in demand. Now this near-deification of the doctor I take to be a fourth cause of our difficulties for it has some not unexpected results. We had a good run. For a long time we have been good "copy." Medical journalism has flourished. Many best sellers, films and plays have been written about us. In a recent survey by questionnaire it emerged that the career which most parents in this country would choose for their sons would be a career in medicine and we are familiar with the vast over-application for places in medical schools which has been the rule in post-war years. Now the inevitable disenchantment is taking place before our very eyes. How could we hope to maintain our inflated pre-eminence? The age of technology and sub-human machine-like efficiency was bound to become dissatisfied with a science so incomplete, so fallible as medicine, and the keenest and most vociferous disappointment is felt by those who try us at our weakest point— the sufferers from psychosomatic and "functional" illness. Reliable observers estimate (Balint, 1954) that of all attendances at surgeries and clinics, anything from 25 to 50 percent are not suffering from any demonstrable pathological entity or nosological syndrome. If in applying our somatic remedies, we fail them, we need not wonder that they, having been led to expect so much, constitute in their chagrin a large reservoir of cynicism and ill-will against which we have to defend ourselves.

Is The Relationship Worth Preserving? If we feel therefore that our relationship with our patients has deteriorated, and if we know or can guess at some of the reasons for this state of affairs, then clearly we must ask ourselves whether we shall attempt to arrest or reserve the process, whether indeed the relationship has anything of value that is worth preserving. In the days when it was fashionable to regard medicine as an art as well as a science, physicians had no doubt that the doctor-patient relationship had value, both in therapeutic outcome and in human terms. It has hitherto always been recognized that this fact accounted for much of the best that was to be had in the medical life. Here lay much of the doctor's satisfaction in his work. It is noteworthy that in the least scientific branch of medicine, namely psychiatry (the branch most germane to "functional" illness, incidentally), the whole secret of the therapeutic process is believed to be locked up in this very human relationship: e.g. the transference beloved of the Freudian with all its fanciful and symbolical appurtenances. But the impact of sociology and anthropology and the increasing influence of Sullivan and the Washington school of psychiatry are making us familiar with the more forthright term—interpersonal relationships. There is no suggestion that the psychological understanding need always be very profound or complex. As an example of what is meant, Ozani (1954) may be quoted:—

"There is a point at which the values of democracy, religion and medicine agree —the value and dignity of the individual, the value of human understanding and kindly relationships with and assistance to another person who must himself continue his unremitting struggle to find an adjustment and meaning in his life."

This perhaps puts the matter rather too strongly and over-emotionally to suit our insular restraint.

Yet it is almost impossible to keep emotion out of the picture. Who has not knocked at the door of a sick person and been welcomed in with visible relief and diminution of tension before anything was done at all? Who has not been told at some time: "I felt better as soon as I saw your face?" Whether this be sympathetic magic or no, it seems to be an integral part of medical practice: a *sine qua non* of the good doctor. Gowers once said," if every drug in the world were abolished the physician would still be a useful member of society." Needles recalls Houston's teaching that the doctor himself is a potent therapeutic agent. So long therefore as 25 to 50 percent of the work in general practice consists of treating neurosis and functional illness—and there seems little indication that the numbers will diminish—the inference must be that the doctor-patient relationship should be retained as vigorously as possible, for on it does therapy depend. Two viewpoints from different quarters may be adumbrated in support:—

Balint (1954) is of the opinion that, although it is true that establishing and maintaining a proper therapeutic relationship needs much more time than prescribing a bottle of medicine, in the long run it can lead in many cases to a considerable saving of time, for both the doctor and his patient. This might be taken as a representative present-day psychiatric view. Speaking as a general practitioner, however, Pinsent (1951) describes how he deals with 40 to 50 percent of all his consultations in a busy industrial practice. These patients receive no medication, they are treated purely by advice and health education, their symptoms explained and worries put at rest. On the whole the replacement of medicine by advice was well accepted, few patients were "lost," and Pinsent considers this a return to the classical concept, etymologically sound at least, of the doctor as an adviser and teacher to his patients.

The Individual Neuroses. In an attempt at reform there would seem to be two main lines of approach: the individual and the collective.

If "functional" illness, or most hazardous of all, "functional" overlay on top of somatic illness, is the main reason for poor relationships between doctors and patients, need we go on treating it in quite the resigned fashion that we have been doing? The contribution that we can make here has been well mapped out in some recent articles which are reassuringly unanimous in their directives. Bennet (1953) is directly encouraging when he indicates that techniques are of less importance in this particular situation than in any other branch of medicine. He reiterates the view that in the relation between patient and doctor lie the essentials of cure or improvement. (In passing it might be emphasized to the patient that improvement is what is being aimed at; "cure" is fortuitous, even unlikely). As well as having an understanding and sympathetic attitude, and displaying a sincere and friendly interest, however, an appreciable degree of detachment should be maintained. Batchelor (1953) too, emphasizes that the attitude of the doctor is all-important: not censorious and, equally so, not too kind, or he will bring about undue emotional dependence on himself which becomes intolerable, and may actually hinder the patient's improvement.

Another factor which gives many practitioners qualms before leaving the beaten track of somatic medicine is that they feel that they have had inadequate instruction in psychological medicine. But, as just stated, success depends less upon the practitioner's theoretical principles than on his personality, the direction of his interests and his insight—the word has no magical connotation, anyone can have some degree of it, given sympathy, empathy and intuition.

Even though half an hour spent in talking with the patient (not to the patient) can actually be at once therapeutic and time saving, many will feel that these considerations are unrealistic while practices remain at their present size and pressure of work continues. If the point of view put forward here is accepted, it follows that many present-day practices are too large for the exercise of these skills. It is disquieting to note that the profession is now officially concerned at the prospect of the medical schools producing too many doctors in the next few decades. No doubt, since the cost of the Health Service is likely to remain as static as successive governments can maintain it, there is reluctance to welcome more colleagues into practice, since it will mean a progressively smaller share all round. This is a very human and understandable feeling. In addition there is the further chance that, having become used to large numbers of patients, we have also become accustomed to the superficial type of relationship which this entails, and in fact we may now be afraid of anything more profound.

Witthower and White (1954) put the matter plainly. Doctors should step down from the near divine role and give up the pose of omnipotence and omniscience. We ought to feel secure enough to admit our limitations and cease from reaching out for and taking on tasks beyond our capacities. "But we also have to live and support our families, and the temptation is often great to place self-interest before the interest of the patient, to promise 'miracle' cures against better judgment, to prescribe injections which are not needed or to play up to the patients' demands for gadgets which may not be required."

Not only could there be a great saving in time, money and effort (and the patient's happiness) if psychosomatic patients would not again and again be referred for specialist examinations and elaborate laboratory tests, but we should also prevent a good deal of neurosis from becoming permanent or passing over into psychosis. Overemphasis of the symptoms in this way leads to iatrogenic or doctor-caused illness—one of the psychiatrist's intractable problems. The practice of medicine consists not only in the application of biological knowledge, but also in the exercise of considerable degrees of social and psychological understanding.

The Collective Neurosis. If we believe that the collective neurosis is primarily a sickness of the community and society, we need not be afraid to say that medicine can only deal with part of the problem, and that the over-all solution lies in other spheres. It is a folly to claim to do more than we can.

Psychosomatic medicine is not yet established in its own right. It is practised almost exclusively by psychoanalysts and, although interesting speculations abound, one has to confess that so far, empirically speaking, they are barren. Not everyone will agree to consult a psychiatrist. It is doubtful if this is desirable even if it were feasible. The problem is one for society as a whole and, although politics have made medicine their business, there is no obligation upon us to pour millions of gallons of medicine down our patients' throats as a kind of twentieth-century *panem et circenses*. With the best will in the world, whatever therapy we use, it seems likely that results will be something less than satisfactory and, as is now happening, we shall be held responsible for the failure. The problem is not ours alone, it is not even the exclusive property of the Welfare State or the National Health Service, although it probably exists more acutely here; litigation against doctors flourishes also in North America.

We need not be ashamed to admit the limitations of our capabilities. Socrates was always saying that he knew nothing, and truth of intercourse was sound ethics long before economic expediency demanded that the customer be always right. To say all this is not to absolve us from the duty of continuing to try to help patients in their difficulties; but the extent to which we have recourse to placebos is a measure of our insecurity. When the nature of our daily work is such as to expose us to varying degrees of unpleasant pressures, there is then a special danger that standards will be lowered (Lewis and Maude, 1952).

But, even if the problem is at bottom a sociological one, we as a group are involved in society, and society looks to us to point the way out of the difficulty. As is so often the case, the main hope lies in prophylaxis. Public health is beginning to accept mental hygiene as its proper concern (M'Lennan and Small, 1955), although, as always in breaking new ground, progress is slow and often stumbling. There is sometimes a feeling among practitioners that patients often approach their problems in a wrong-headed way and cannot be made to see reason. Having been led to expect that popular education, ideally at least, would create a well-informed, stable and contented society, we are disappointed with the results. But that may not be the fault of education itself, so much as the way it is applied (*Lancet*, 1955). For example, the Socratic method of group discussion has been reintroduced of late years, with some success, into psychotherapy and now shows signs of becoming an increasingly important instrument of learning in schools, universities, and many other walks of life. The usefulness and applications of the method are described in a recent symposium published by the Central Council for Health Education (1954). Any method which encourages growth and development of the personality, with special reference to powers of self-expression and self-objectification, is a safeguard against ennui and the sense of frustration.

Here then are two spheres of activity where we can use the full weight of our influence, even though the results will not be appreciable for many years. Public health ventures into mental hygiene deserve our support and encouragement. We cannot expect to have a voice in general education programmes, but we can go on saying that the collective neurosis will only diminish when individuals are educated to accept responsibility. The developments and researches in medicine and sociology call for a re-examination of frontiers (Roth, 1956).

Summary. A deterioration of the doctor-patient relationship is postulated in the light of certain present-day facts.

Some reasons for the decline have been suggested by reference to changing conditions of practice. A powerful factor is believed to be the great increase in the amount of "functional" illness, which is itself a product of altered values in the social and cultural life of the community.

Evidence is presented that the doctor-patient relationship is therapeutically valuable, and certain suggestions are made for its preservation.

46   MEDICAL PRACTICE AND THE ALCOHOLIC

By Robert Straus

In recent years both professional and popular references to medical practice have reflected an increasing interest in the doctor-patient relationship. It has frequently been stated that the quality of rapport developed between the physician and his patient can directly influence the diagnostic acuity of the physician, the course which the patient's health problem may take, and the relative success which the physician and his patient are able to achieve in management of the health problems. The importance of rapport to the therapeutic process is especially evident in relationships between practicing physicians and their alcoholic patients. In this connection, Howard W. Haggard has written "There is no group of individuals—except children—which is more responsive to the attitude of the physician and senses his sincerity, or lack of it, more acutely than the alcoholic. It is the attitude of the physician and his depth of understanding which may be the deciding factors in the recovery of the alcoholic; if he understands him, and if he can make the members of the family and business associates likewise understand and cooperate, he has a good chance of steering the alcoholic toward recovery. Contrariwise, an adverse attitude, whatever its reasons may be, and may remain, is the insurmountable obstacle to recovery."[1]

The importance of a positive doctor-patient relationship is not limited to the patient's ability to benefit from treatment; it is also seen as a critical component of the physician's ability to serve his alcoholic patient. Florence Powdermaker has discussed the "acuteness of hypersensitivity on the part of the alcoholic patient" which she feels "makes it a *sine qua non* for effective treatment that the therapist have no hidden or overtly critical attitudes toward the symptoms." She notes that it is from "sincere appreciation of the patient's capacities and potentialities, and friendliness toward him . . . as well as from scientific interest in the problems of alcoholics, that the therapist derives the patience and objectivity needed for their treatment."[2]

From *The Annals* of the American Society of Political and Social Science, 315, (January, 1958).

Many observers believe that the remarkable effectiveness of Alcoholics Anonymous and the substantial help which lay therapists have provided for some alcoholics are in great measure made possible by sympathy, understanding and a positive interpersonal relationship.

In this discussion of relationships between physicians and their alcoholic patients it is desirable to consider two significant trends. One of these involves changes in the understanding and treatment of alcoholism. The other concerns ferment in the philosophy and patterning of medical care.

Changing Attitudes Toward Alcoholism. The last twenty years have witnessed dramatic changes in American society with respect to the general understanding of and response to the problems of alcoholism. Although the existence of medical ramifications in alcoholism have long been recognized, until recently it has been defined primarily as a moral problem associated with personal inadequacy and moral degradation. In fact, alcoholism carried such social stigma that the condition was considered unmentionable and great efforts were made to conceal or deny its existence. Many persons found comfort in the fallacious notion that the only real alcoholics were derelicts,—the homeless chronic inebriates of skid row. From this misconception, it was reasoned that men or women who, despite pathological drinking, were able to retain a degree of stability in their family, job, or community relationships, could not be true alcoholics because they did not fit the derelict stereotype. Although most persons could count at least one problem drinker among members of their family or close friends, there prevailed an ostrichlike denial that such "nice people" could be real alcoholics. Unfortunately this faulty reasoning enabled many alcoholics themselves to deny the serious implications of their drinking pattern and to rationalize a rejection of the idea that they might be ill or need help. As long as they could reason that alcoholics were personally to blame for their own condition, members of society could justify their rejecting the alcoholic and even excuse a righteous feeling of hostility toward him.

Physicians have not been immune to these negative attitudes which have prevailed in the larger society. Although they have long accepted responsibility for treating the damaged liver, the cardiological or respiratory problems, or the overt psychosis which may occur in individuals who are alcoholics and although they have provided emergency treatment for the effects of acute intoxication, physicians have been slow to accept the concept that they might also accept responsibility for the treatment of alcohol addiction. In some respects, the redefinition of alcoholism as a form of illness, a public health and medical problem, has gained more rapid and complete acceptance among the general public and alcoholics themselves than among some members of the medical profession.

The Physician's Dilemma. In 1945, Haggard discussed the dilemma which the redefinition of alcoholism would impose on the practicing physician. "The sound conception that the alcoholic is an ill man needing and deserving medical care and guidance has had wide publicity and gained sympathetic response. Increasingly in the future, alcoholics and their relatives will turn to the family practitioner for aid in controlling addiction. They will expect to obtain this aid. The practitioner will then be increasingly confronted by a condition to which, in the past, he has usually given little serious medical regard."[3]

For the physician, acceptance of alcoholism as a medical problem imposes a responsibility which he may well feel reluctant to bear. There are many factors which in combination help to explain this reluctance where it exists.

First, it is important to realize that many of the men and women who are practicing medicine today receive their medical education during a period when alcoholism was virtually ignored as a clinical entity. Although general hospital wards contained many alcoholic patients, these were usually admitted because of more medically acceptable symptoms. As a medical student the physician learned to think of the liver, the heart, the respiratory system, the skin disease, the psychosis, or the fractured limb as the primary problem. While he may have recognized that excessive drinking was an associated factor, he was seldom encouraged to pursue its real implications.

Furthermore, when the physician has given thought to alcoholism he has found that this is a uniquely evasive clinical phenomenon. Unlike many of the conditions with which he is accustomed to dealing, alcoholism presents no well defined diagnostic or therapeutic picture; there is no common etiology, no consistently characteristic course, no accepted method of management. There are, in fact, many alcoholisms but the various types are not clearly defined or delineated.

Alcoholism is a problem which involves many aspects of human behavior. It is a social problem, an economic problem, a psychological problem and its moral aspects must also be considered. Quite understandably the physician has considered these other problems beyond his own sphere of competence. Yet, treatment of the medical ramifications of alcoholism alone has seldom proved effective. Working with the alcoholic frequently is discouraging and an unrewarding investment of his time. Despite the pronounced emotional ramifications of alcoholism, most psychiatrists have been just as reluctant as their medical colleagues to become deeply involved in the treatment of alcoholic patients.

Studies of Physicians' Attitudes. In addition to its complexity and evasiveness, alcoholism presents other conflicts for the physician. Some of these are reflected by studies in which an effort has been made to ascertain the extent to which practicing physicians are dealing with the problems of alcoholism, the methods of treatment which they employ and their attitudes toward these patients.

In 1945, Riley and Marden[4] interviewed 455 physicians representing a ten percent sample of the practicing physicians in New Jersey. They found that a surprisingly high 65 percent of their respondents reported that they were seeing some cases of chronic alcoholism with an average of 7.3 such cases seen by each doctor during the course of the year. However, it was found that the methods of treatment in most frequent use were palliative in nature. Sedation, vitamins, and nutritional therapy accounted for the majority of treatments. On the basis of their findings, Riley and Marden concluded "The doctors who are currently treating for chronic alcoholism are taking few steps toward the long-term rehabilitation of their patients. They are giving temporary relief, but little else. This, however, must not be taken as an indictment of the doctors. . . . The rehabilitation of the alcoholic is . . . a long process. The general practitioner has neither the time nor the facilities."

While more than 90 percent of the physicians interviewed recognized that alcoholism has medical ramifications, the vast majority also discussed certain difficulties which they encountered in trying to work with alcoholic patients. Forty-three percent categorized the alcoholic as a "non cooperative patient" who fails to carry out the physician's directions or suggestions.

"They don't carry out treatment prescribed. They are not inclined to return for additional treatment when diagnosis is made, . . . They come with various complains and if you tell them it's alcoholism, they either stop or never come back."

Twenty-eight percent characterized the alcoholic as a nuisance, who may be unmanageable and may create specific annoyances:

"These people coming into a doctor's office create a bad impression, annoy other patients. They frequently don't pay their bills."

Finally, many of the physicians pointed out that the presence of alcoholism in a patient seriously complicated the treatment of other problems.

Responses to similar questions were reported in 1946 by The Committee on Public Health Relations of the New York Academy of Medicine.[5] The Committee distributed a questionnaire to all members of the five County Medical Societies of Greater New York. Replies were received from 1,609 physicians representing a 13 percent return. Sixty percent of the reporting physicians indicated that they did not treat alcohol addiction, and two-thirds of the other 40 percent indicated that alcoholic patients comprised less than one percent of their practice. In fact, only ten physicians reported that alcoholic patients comprised more than 10 percent of their patients and three doctors devoted more than 25 percent of their efforts to alcoholics. Authors of this report concluded that their findings reflected "a feeling of futility and a realization that specialized knowledge is required to deal effectively with the various phases of it (alcoholism)". They noted further "unless a physician deals exclusively with the treatment of alcoholism, he finds it a nuisance in his practice because of the time required and the unsatisfactory results obtained."

In 1952, Straus reported a community survey conducted in Jackson, Mississippi[6] in which 52 of the community's 126 physicians counted 851 problem drinking patients during the previous year. However, the majority of these were merely seeking relief from the effects of acute intoxication. Methods of treatment employed in Jackson, as in New Jersey, were overwhelmingly palliative in nature. Attitudes expressed by the Jackson physicians reflected a generally negative feeling toward the alcoholic:

"I don't like to treat them. A doctor could quickly develop a practice of nothing but alcoholics. They're usually insulting, hard to manage, and in most cases are soon drunk again.

"He is a sick individual. He needs confinement under proper nursing supervision.

"Disgusted. I do not feel many of them need a doctor, and resent the calls. I feel it is a moral problem, not an illness.

"More to be pitied than shamed.

"As a patient, he is ill mentally and physically, but as a citizen, he creates social and economic problems.

"The usual alcoholic has no motivation toward health, is unwilling to assume responsibility, deprives psychiatric patients of care by consuming the therapist's time in fruitless effort.

"The problem drinkers create special problems for the doctor. Special provisions should be made to treat them. My general feeling is a sympathetic one but I realize that I can offer little treatment to him.

"It is an illness and I am sorry for them but they are undesirable patients —usually uncooperative, poor pay, require night calls; not good for reputation to have too many—rarely accomplish any permanent good."

While these various surveys probably represent a fairly accurate reflection of prevailing attitudes, the data on numbers of alcoholics treated should be interpreted with caution. In this connection A. B. Hollinghead[7] has noted: "If data from physicians . . . are to be used as a criteria to determine alcoholism in a population we are going to have a very low rate of alcoholism, yet there may be a high rate of abuse in the society. We need another criteria of alcoholism than the impressions of medical practitioners." Commenting on 300 patients of private psychiatrists studied in his survey of mental illness in New Haven, Hollingshead found "Not a single patient is diagnosed as an alcoholic. The private psychiatric practitioner diagnosed the patient in terms of behavior he considered to be more basic to personality structure than excessive use of alcohol."

As we have already suggested, the physician prefers to classify his patients according to basic organic or body system disorders, and the hospital administrator frequently will not admit the alcoholic patient unless he has some associated symptoms which are medically respectable.

The Alcoholic as a Patient. Attitudes expressed in these studies substantiate the impression that most practicing physicians have great reservations about treating patients for alcoholism. In fact, the average physician may have much greater difficulty accepting the redefinition of alcoholism as an illness than members of society at large. Redefinition brings to the physician a responsibility which he may feel unable to discharge. The assignment is far from comfortable. As suggested by the attitudes quoted above, the alcoholic symbolizes many problems for the physician and considerable conflict. This patient often appears uncooperative and unappreciative. He causes many minor and some major disturbances. If given a little attention and sympathy he may demand much more. He may present some personality eccentricities which are personally offensive to the physician. Although intellectually the physician may know that these traits are a manifestation of the illness, emotionally he may struggle to maintain professional objectivity. He may find that he cannot identify with his alcoholic patients or establish empathy. He may even find that the alcoholic introduces personal conflict over his own orientation to the custom of drinking. Few persons growing up in American society during the last century have been immune from the impact of the "wet-dry" controversy. For most persons, whatever their drinking or non-drinking habits, the question of drinking carries emotional overtone. Whatever his drinking custom, the physician may find difficulty in detaching his personal orientation from his professional relationship with the alcoholic.

In addition, the physician is faced with the very practical dilemma of not knowing how to help his alcoholic patients. His efforts to provide palliative relief bring no real solution. In order to hospitalize an alcoholic he must often resort to an alternative diagnosis and he is subject to rebuke if his subterfuge is discovered. Furthermore, the demand for medical attention for alcoholics is so great, and the supply of sympathetic physicians so small, that the average physician finds it difficult to treat only a few alcoholics. Yet once word is spread that Doctor "R" is "treating" alcoholics he fears that he will become so labeled that other patients will stay away. Faced with this combination of complex forces, it is understandable that relatively few physicians have welcomed alcoholic patients.

"Special Problem" Emphasis. Although the recent era of enlightenment with respect to alcoholism has included the definition of alcoholism as a medical and a public health problem, one aspect of this "movement" has actually provided the practicing physician with a rationale for giving little attention to the problem. This is the "special problem" emphasis which has characterized much of the organized community effort to deal with alcoholism. Proponents of the "special problem" approach argue that unless the disease is singled out for emphasis it is invariably lost among traditional health and welfare services. This reasoning is by no means unique to alcoholism. It has characterized the voluntary health movement in the United States. Because alcoholism is a particularly complex phenomenon and one historically subject to so many gross stigmas and misconceptions, there is unquestionable need for a concentrated effort to better measure, understand and interpret this illness and its associated problems. However, special concentration has frequently resulted in narrow conceptualization and a possessiveness on the part of alcoholism workers who feel that only the specialist can fully understand and effectively deal with the problem. Faced with such possessive and sometimes antagonistic zeal on the part of a small but vocal number of alcoholism workers, physicians and other professional persons, whose interest might be stimulated to work with alcoholics in the course of their general practice, have sometimes completely disassociated themselves from any effort to serve alcoholics or even families which include alcoholic members.

The wide publicity afforded Alcoholics Anonymous, and community "information centers" and special alcoholism clinics have provided the practicing physician with a rationale for referring his alcoholic patients elsewhere, despite the fact that many of these other resources are not equipped to deal with the medical and psychiatric aspects of the problem. However, even the best of these special resources can work with only a small segment of the alcoholic population. If significant numbers of alcoholics are to be helped it is essential that the general health resources of the community, including the practicing physicians, be a part of this effort. Overemphasis on the need for a specialized approach can seriously impair the attainment of this goal.

Trends in Medical Care. Thus far we have considered the conflicts which have arisen for the practicing physician in connection with his alcoholic patients. It has been suggested that while society at large has appeared to accept the concept of alcoholism as a form of illness and has manifested an increasingly sympathetic attitude toward the alcoholic, the physician, who acknowledges medical and public health ramifications in alcoholism, still finds it difficult to accept alcoholic patients. Most of the physicians who report that they treat alcoholism do so in a limited way and with considerable reservation. A distinct lag is apparent between society's definition of alcoholism as a medical problem and the readiness of the medical profession to accept full responsibility for dealing with this problem. This lag is in part attributable to the fact that society's definition oversimplifies the complex nature of the problem. Alcoholism is not generally responsive to medical treatment alone. In part the lag is explained by the fact that alcoholism does not fit compatibly into the traditional categories of disease which have characterized the philosophy and organization of medical practice during recent decades. However, medical practice is now in a state of ferment, and there is reason to believe that current trends in the philosophy and patterning of medical care may actually lead to a distinct interest in the treatment of alcoholic patients.

Comprehensive Medicine. A significant concomitant to the rapid scientific development which has characterized medicine for more than fifty years has been the pattern of segmentalization in medical education and research and specialization in medical practice. Medical education is now undergoing a trend away from the unilateral consideration of body systems and distinct disease entities toward a more comprehensive conceptualization of the patient's health and disease. Many medical schools are experimenting with multidiscipline patterns of teaching which seek to provide a broad orientation to the basic relationships between all aspects of human biology and behavior without sacrificing the specific competence and depth which more traditional approaches have developed. Not only is there stress on relationships among the basic medical sciences, the clinical areas and between clinical and basic science subject matter but the horizons of medicine are undergoing expansion. It is recognized and taught that human adaptation to illness is not restricted to man's organ systems but includes factors in his personality, his social group relations, his customs and beliefs and the physical environment in which he lives. The philosophy of comprehensive medicine stresses the importance of all of these factors in the maintenance of good health and in recovery from or adaptation to disease.

Under segmentalized forms of medical education little attention has been given to alcoholism. It is a highly complex phenomenon which does not fit neatly into any of the traditional categories of disease. It's etiology and management are evasive and unorthodox from a medical point of view. As noted above, physicians have long recognized that medical treatment alone seldom is effective therapy for the alcoholic. In order to teach comprehensive medicine, medical educators have had to re-evaluate their choice of case material. It is suggested that the alcoholic patient, whose alcoholism has been virtually ignored in the past, even while his neatly categorized cirrhosis has provided teaching material, now has become an "interesting" patient. When medical education focuses on the whole man, the alcoholic in whom organic disease, personality stress, and multiplicity of health problems are so often combined with well discernable social and environmental problems, appears to be an ideal vehicle for demonstrating the interrelatedness of problems in health and disease.

New Medications. Not only is alcoholism medically respectable to the young physician trained in the philosophy of comprehensive medicine, but through the use of recently developed medications, including the various tranquilizing drugs, the physician now has a new feeling that he can do something for the alcoholic. Only time will tell whether tranquilizing drugs can have a prolonged role in alcoholism therapy. However, because these drugs enable the disturbed alcoholic patient to behave in a less eccentric fashion he will less often be classified as a nuisance, as noncooperative, or as an undesirable patient. The use of tranquilizers certainly appears to enable the physician to feel less uncomfortable with his alcoholic patients and thereby achieve a more satisfactory relationship with them.

The Health Team. Also significant to the medical handling of alcoholic patients has been the emergence of the health team approach to medical care. Specialization in medicine permitted a high degree of concentration and competence but resulted also in a segmentalized form of care in which patients were frequently shunted from one specialist to another for the episodic treatment of specific complaints. Seldom was the health of the patient evaluated in its total context. With specialization, there have emerged also a number of ancillary professional and technical groups of medical personnel; the laboratory and X-ray technicians, physical, occupational and diversional therapists, social workers, clinical psychologists, and others. Frequently, the services of these adjunctive personnel have been employed only in a limited and highly specialized way. With the philosophy of comprehensive medicine new patterns of medical practice are developing in which groups of medical specialists and ancillary personnel combine their skills in the total evaluation and management of health problems. For alcoholism, which invariably carries complications beyond the strictly medical sphere, the health team form of organization may offer still further encouragement and potentiality for success to the physician who undertakes to provide therapy. It is noteworthy that the team concept was employed in the first out-patient alcoholism clinic established in 1944 and this pattern has served as a prototype for most alcoholism treatment programs which have been developed since that time.

Together, the various trends in medical philosophy, organization and practice which have been considered—comprehensive medicine, the health team, and newer forms of therapy—provide promise that newer generations of physicians will develop the positive attitude toward the alcoholic as a patient which is an essential component of effective rapport and treatment.

It is suggested that this attitude will emerge when, with continuing research, the physician can feel more hopeful and confident of helping the alcoholic; when through health team organization he can supplement his skills with persons trained to deal with psychological and social ramifications of the problem; and when his philosophy of medicine enables him to define alcoholism as an interesting and medically respectable problem.

VII

The Medical Setting:
Hospital, Clinic, and Office

THE SETTING in which medical treatment is given and medical personnel perform their duties and practice their skills is a special realm of investigation and study by behavioral scientists. The social structure of hospitals, the interrelationships of the medical, administrative, nursing, ancillary, and technical staffs in the hospital system have constituted a most fruitful subject of research. The study of various out-patient clinics and day-patient populations are included in this section, along with the analysis of the problems of the office-setting of the physician.

One of the most extensive sociological studies of the hospital has been conducted by Albert Wessen. In his original article, he summarizes some of the outstanding findings of his analysis of hospital ideology and communication between various categories of personnel in the hospital ward. Some conflicts and problems involving hospital authority are analyzed in the paper by Harvey Smith.

Some intriguing differentials in organization, staffing and operations between public-supported and privately-operated mental institutions are presented in an original contribution by S. Kirson Weinberg.

Robert Wilson offers a new and intensive analysis of the functioning and structure of the hospital operating room that includes aspects not often recognized by both medical and non-medical people.

The effect of the status system of an out-patient psychiatric clinic upon patient care is presented in a pioneering study of Jerome Myers and Leslie Schaffer, M.D.

The financial aspects of medical practice are presented from the standpoint of a business consultant to physicians in an original contribution by Robert Albright.

The social process whereby new medication becomes introduced into the practice of medicine, particularly in office practice, is studied in the article by Herbert Menzel and Elihu Katz.

Behavioral scientists have, for the past several years, been engaged in extensive studies of the nursing profession in a myriad of phases. Lack of space unfortunately prevents the presentation of a number of other excellent studies of the nurse. In an original contribution, Sam Schulman analyzes some of the basic components of the nursing profession. Some of the ways in which the culture of patients in the hospital have an impact upon nursing care are presented in an original article by Lyle Saunders.

47   HOSPITAL IDEOLOGY AND COMMUNICATION
BETWEEN WARD PERSONNEL

By Albert F. Wessen

A modern hospital requires a large number of highly trained individuals for the provision of adequate patient care. Their efforts must be supported by the ministrations of many others, perhaps less well trained. If the care of individual patients is not to be unduly fragmented, the efforts of all these people must be well coordinated. If the members of the ward "team" work together in reasonable harmony and with full efficiency, there must be a certain degree of "give and take in hospitals."[1]

At least three factors appear to be essential if adequate coordination or integration of any human group is to take place. *First,* there must be adequate channels for communication between all group members. *Second,* there must be some agreement between members concerning common purposes and presuppositions. And *third,* there must be clearly defined allocations of role and authority.[2] It is the purpose of this paper to examine certain aspects of the social structure of the general hospital in light of these requisites of organizational effectiveness. It will be argued that the rigidity of the institutional status system and certain imperfectly assimilated changes in ward organization have created barriers to free communication among hospital personnel. Moreover, differences in institutional ideology will be shown to be related to these factors.

Although it is believed that the evidence to be presented is generally applicable to all general hospitals, what follows is a case study of one large, private, general hospital of some eight hundred beds, situated in a metropolitan New England city. This institution will here be called "Yankee Hospital." Data for the study were drawn from intensive observations on the wards of this hospital, from informal interviews with members of the staff, employees, and administration, and from detailed formal interviews concerning role relationships and attitudes toward the hospital held with a sample of seventy-five doctors, nurses, dietitians, laboratory technicians, and nonprofessional ward personnel.[3]

I. THE HOSPITAL WARD AS A SOCIAL SYSTEM

The "heart" of any hospital is the patient ward. Here, the basic work of the hospital is done: patients are received, cared for, diagnosed, treated, discharged. Practically all of the other facilities of the institution—ranging from technical services such as operating room, laboratory, or social service department to "hotel" or administrative services such as laundry, kitchen or business office—exist to support the needs of patients and personnel on the wards. And in the bustle or stillness of each ward, both life and death dramas and the tedious routines of therapeutics, training, and research are consummated each day.

How may a sociologist conceptualize the culture of a typical medical or surgical ward?[4] A full delineation would require a monograph. Here, it will be possible simply to identify the main actors in the ward social system and to indicate some of the principal features of the social structure which orders their interaction.

In the typical general hospital ward, the patient is less an actor than a passive observer of the ward social system.[5] This fact differentiates the general hospital from such institutions for long term care as mental hospitals and tuberculosis sanitaria; it also distinguishes the contemporary hospital from its forebear of a half-century and more ago.

Dependent upon ward personnel for the satisfaction of his simplest needs, the average medical or surgical patient tends to focus his attention upon himself, his condition, and his anxieties. Although he may carry on an active social interaction with patients in nearby beds, in most cases he has little inclination to participate in, or to discuss, the life of the ward except as it directly impinges upon him. Replacement of the old fashioned open wards by private or semi-private rooms in modern hospitals has further acted to restrict the patient's potential involvement in ward affairs.

From the point of view of ward personnel the patient is not considered to be part of the ward social life. He is assumed to be neither interested in nor informed about the complicated medical culture which is ministering to him (except, of course, as it affects him directly.) He is believed to have little interest in the problems of hospital organization and management beyond seeing that he gets the most service for the least price. This was the unanimous opinion of ward personnel—doctors, nurses, and auxiliary workers —with whom we discussed this matter. As one physician put it, "The patients? All they are interested in is getting themselves out of the hospital. They take our word for what must be done, and they don't care what happens, or how, so long as it helps them." A similar attitude on a different level was expressed by a janitor who said that although he liked to talk with the patients "I never talk about my job; they've got enough troubles of their own to worry about."

Thus, for hospital people, the patients are not so much a part of their social system as a vital *reference group* in the midst of which the personnel operate, which they serve, and toward which they orient many of their actions and attitudes. Because the hospital's dominant purpose is to serve patients, it is only natural that explanations of the behavior of all groups of personnel tend to be formulated in terms of its relationship to patient welfare. As we shall see, many of the ideological differences found between the various occupational strata in the hospital come from the fact that these tend to conceptualize patients' needs in different ways.

Representatives of at least twenty-three different occupational status groups are represented on a typical ward at Yankee Hospital or have frequent business there. These are the following:[6]

Physicians:
1. Visiting staff physicians (of various ranks)
2. Residents (and assistant residents)
3. Internes

Nurses:
4. Clinical supervisors and/or instructors
5. Head nurses
6. Staff nurses
7. Student nurses

Paramedical professionals and technicians:
8. Dietitians
9. Laboratory technicians
10. X-ray technicians
11. Social workers
12. Occupational therapists
13. Physical therapists

Semi-skilled workers:
14. Trained attendants (licensed practical nurses)
15. Medical technicians
16. Dietitian's aides
17. Ward receptionists and clerks

Unskilled workers:
18. Nurse's Aids
19. Male Aids
20. Ward Helpers ("Pinkies")
21. Floor service maids
22. Cleaning maids
23. Janitors

Like all of its kind, Yankee Hospital organizes these classes of personnel according to a relatively rigid status hierarchy in which doctors are accorded highest prestige, followed by nurses and the several groupings of paramedical and "non-professional" workers. This hierarchy is popularly justified in terms of the necessity for quick, precise, and responsible action in the medical crises which are almost routine in the hospital setting. It is sanctioned by the practice of generations, and presently reflects the very considerable social distance which exists between the various groupings of hospital personnel as members of the larger society. Within the past few years, this hierarchy has been transformed into a full-blown bureaucratic organization patterned after the example of business management. Yet in many respects, the observer is tempted to describe the hospital social structure as almost castelike.

These sharp status-distinctions are manifested both upon the ward and throughout other areas of Yankee Hospital. Their maintenance is simplified and facilitated by the distinctive uniforms worn by the various categories of personnel. Thus, at least twelve different uniforms can be found on a typical ward—and, as in the case of nurses, small variations in the basic uniform often signify further status differences. Although the basic purpose of uniforms in the hospital is without doubt the validation of the status of the various types of personnel who care for patients, they undoubtedly facilitate the maintenance of rigid status distinctions between the various occupational groups.

These status lines are further sharpened by the fact that separate dining rooms are provided for three major groups of personnel—doctors, nurses, and all other employees. The exclusiveness of dining rooms is enhanced by the fact that there are two cafeteria serving lines, one of which is patronized by doctors and nurses, the other by non-professional personnel. Habitual seating arrangements within the dining rooms themselves further underline the status differences. Thus it is rather unusual to see full-fledged staff nurses eating at the same table with trainees. It was observed, too, that at a typical meal the doctors' dining room may be roughly divided into four sectors. Along one side of the room may be found the surgeons, while the other side is largely filled with practitioners following the medical specialties. These groups both divide themselves so that the section of the room nearer the window is largely reserved for visiting staff members, while internes and residents occupy the opposite half of the room. Within the nonprofessional employees' dining room, moreover, there is a marked tendency for employees of the different departments to lunch with others in their own category. Commensality—that principal setting for informal conversations in our society—thus tends to be restricted in the hospital to those who belong to the same occupational group.[7]

Segregation between the three major classes of personnel is not rigid. Nurses who desire to do so frequently eat in the general employees' dining room. Physicians and surgeons sometimes bring individuals other than doctors into their dining room as guests. On the other hand, it is quite unusual for nurses to bring non-nurses into their dining room, and doctors rarely lunch outside their own room. These distinctions are to be seen in full force only at luncheon and at dinner. At snack hours, at breakfast, and during the midnight lunch, occupational distinctions tend to break down. In fact, as a general rule it may be observed that occupational segregation is most marked during the day shift, is seen to a lesser degree on the evening shift, and to a minimal extent at night when the smallest numbers of personnel—and practically no wakeful patients or visitors—are active on the ward.[8]

The implications of these occupational status distinctions for the social structure of the ward can be fully understood only when two other characteristics of ward organization are noted. *First,* on every ward there are dual lines of authority and responsibility.[9] One of these "chains of command" governs the care of patients. In over-simplified form it may be represented as passing from doctor to nurse to non-professional personnel. The other deals with matters of hospital management and administration. Here the staff physician is typically completely outside the chain of command. He is not directly responsible to hospital administration; technically he has the status of a "volunteer" who is accorded the privileges of membership in the hospital's medical staff. Rather, authority passes from the hospital administrator through various departments heads and supervisors to members of specific occupational categories. Thus, while each individual staff-nurse into whose hands care of a patient is assigned is responsible for executing the orders of the patient's physician, she is also responsible to her head nurse, her supervisor, and to the upper levels of the nursing administration for matters concerning ward management, technical procedures, and discipline. Similarly, a male aid, like other auxiliary personnel, is responsible not only to the head nurse—and through her to doctors—on the unit to which he is assigned, but also to the supervisor of male aids. That ward personnel appreciate the possibility of playing off one authority against the other is indicated in the comment of one male aid who said "It sure makes me feel good sometimes to know that Mr. _____ is down there to stand behind me if the nurses get unreasonable." The same dual system of authority holds for housekeeping personnel and for most of the other personnel having business on the ward.[10] Thus, communication and loyalty of personnel tend to be channeled within the major occupational lines by this "administrative" chain of command, while at the same time clinical authority tends to move *across* these lines.

Second, as has been implied, the personnel of a ward differ markedly in the extent to which they become a part of a given unit. Some persons are assigned permanently to a "floor." Of these the most important is the Head Nurse, who is responsible for its administration; in large part, according to our informants, she is able to "set the tone" of work and interaction in her unit. Ideally, the full complement of staff nurses, auxiliary nursing personnel, and dietary and housekeeping employees will be assigned permanently to a given ward unit. But shortages and high turnover of personnel, unpredictable changes in work load, and the necessity to set up work schedules to assure full around-the-clock coverage of essential skills, combine to create a situation in which the make-up of the "permanent" personnel of a ward is constantly changing.

Other types of personnel are expected on the ward only sporadically. Most staff physicians appear on the ward only for such regular exercises as rounds or according to the particular needs of their patients. Similarly, laboratory and X-ray technicians, social workers and occupational therapists are apt to come to the ward only when a referral makes necessary their presence there. And the identity of these part-time actors in the ward social system is also subject to change from day to day. The educational purposes of the hospital tend to intensify the instability of the ward social group. Student nurses and physicians-in-training must be given experience with all kinds of patients. The organization of modern hospitals into discrete ward units serving patients of a given type therefore forces the development of a system of rotation of trainees from unit to unit, usually for short periods of time on each.[11]

All this makes for a situation in which it becomes difficult for primary group associations to develop on the wards of a large hospital. New faces appear too constantly. Moreover, since many of these persons constantly face situations in which their responsibility is not only to ward authorities but to superiors of their own occupational category, normal formal mechanisms for developing an integrated group are weakened. Structural pressures in the hospital thus seem to accentuate rather than to minimize occupational difference among personnel.

Contemporary hospital administration makes much of the idea that those who work on a ward comprise a single therapeutic "team." In many quarters, emphasis is placed upon the necessity for free participation on the part of all concerned if the most effective planning of ward activities is to take place. The application of "group dynamics" has become an important part of recent blueprints for better ward administration.[12] It may perhaps be suggested that these emphases indicate that hospital people are trying to recover the integration and order of a simpler social system which modern hospitals have outgrown.

II. COMMUNICATION BETWEEN WARD PERSONNEL

What are the patterns of communication between personnel as they work on a given ward? To what extent does interaction encompass all the members of a therapeutic team?

Answers to these questions were sought through systematic observation. Personnel on two units—one semi-private and one "charity" ward—were observed over a period of thirty hours (scattered through various parts of the day and over a period of several days). Each time two individuals were seen in conversation, it was noted who was speaking with whom. If there were more than two individuals in the conversation, the members of the group were divided into pairs. Thus, if two nurses and one doctor talked together, it was assumed that three conversations were taking place: one between the two nurses and two between a doctor and a nurse. Each conversation observed was designated as a single unit except that if it was observed to last more than three minutes, a second unit was scored—and so on every three minutes. Because some conversations may not have been seen by the observer, the results to be reported below must be considered as suggestive rather than rigorous. Personnel were divided into three categories—doctors, nurses, and all others. The numbers of conversations held between members of one of these groups or between members of different groups are summarized in Table One below.

Table 1—Distribution of Conversations Between Members of Various Occupational Groups on Two "Yankee Hospital" Wards

Group with which Interaction was Observed:	Doctors (N=223)	Nurses (N=562)	Others (N=441)
Interaction within own group:	74.12%	61.57%	61.68%
With the remaining groups of relatively higher status:	23.24[A]	9.43[C]	1.36[C]
With the remaining group of relatively lower status:	2.64[B]	29.00[B]	36.96[A]

A=Nurses   B="Others"   C=Doctors

(N's refer to the total number of conversations observed involving members of each group.)

The fact which stands out in this table is that ward personnel tend to interact mostly with others in their own group. Thus the doctor is three times as apt to speak to another doctor while on the ward as he is to a nurse, and he almost never talks with other personnel. Likewise, the nurse is more than twice as likely to speak with another nurse than to other workers, while her in-group communication is almost seven times as frequent as is

her interaction with medical men. The other personnel rarely speak with
doctors but do interact with nurses about sixty percent as often as with others
of their own group. These facts may be stated in another way: the greater
the social distance between occupational groupings on the hospital ward,
the less interaction is observed between groups. Moreover, the highest
status group—the doctors—are more apt to interact within their own group
than are the nurses or other personnel (mostly non-professional workers).
It would seem that insofar as this data is valid it strongly supports the impression that communication on the hospital ward is channelized along occupational lines.

The hospital status system was described as involving an almost caste-
like set of segregatory patterns which quite effectively limit informal interaction between hospital personnel of different ranks. One would naturally
expect these barriers to interaction to carry over into the work situation. Moreover, there seems to be a well nigh universal tendency for those of high social
rank to be freed from the obligation to interact with those of lower degree
except on their own terms; or as Homans phrases it, "a person of higher social
rank than another originates interaction for the latter more often than the
latter originates interaction for him."[13] The data in Table I can provide only
indirect evidence on this point. This table shows, however, that physicians
tend both to interact within their own group to a greater extent than other
ward personnel and also to allocate a relatively higher percentage of their
conversation to nurses and other (non-professional) personnel than do the
latter groups to them; these differences are consistent with Homans' hypothesis.

This tendency for interaction across status differences to move from above
downward is in part a result of the necessity for authority to move along
a chain of command. It is also a result of the respect accorded to higher status.
Within the hospital, this is to be seen most clearly in behavior toward physicians. Respect for the doctor's prestige—already a very strong element in
general American culture—is systematically indoctrinated in hospital personnel. Deference patterns are most marked, interestingly enough, among
the group whose status is second only to the doctors—the nurses. They are
painstakingly taught at Yankee Hospital to fledgling student nurses in their
"Professional Adjustments" course. The manner in which this is done is made
clear in the following excerpt from an interview:

"Insofar as possible, we try to utilize the technique of 'role playing' in
teaching our course. And in teaching the girls how to get along in the ward
situation, we do little more than help them to apply ordinary rules of common courtesy. For example, at one of our sessions, the girls were acting out
what a nurse should do in case of meeting various people at a doorway. And
they correctly showed that a nurse should step back to allow a visitor or a
doctor to pass through the door first. After class, one of the students came up
to me and said, 'Miss ———, I can see why I should stop to let some one like
you go through a door ahead of me, but I can't understand why doctors
should go first. I was taught that gentlemen should wait for ladies.' So I had
to explain to her that not only do men show their respect for ladies in this
way, but also that we show respect for other people in similar ways. I ex-

plained to her that not only are the doctors older than she and entitled to respect on that account, but that they *contribute more to the community* than she will and hence deserve respect for this reason too."

Of special interest in our present discussion is the deference which makes nurses "bow out of the picture" when physicians are present. In its most typical form, it involves the nurse stepping back out of the picture if a doctor enters into the conversation which may be going on between a third party and herself. It also is seen in a tendency for nurses to speak only when called upon in formal sessions (such as ward rounds) in which physicians are present.[14]

The average nurse expresses a strong sense of mingled respect and fear of the doctor. This was spontaneously reported by ten of the twenty-two graduate nurses interviewed. As one nurse put it, "You have to be pretty 'Yes sirrish' to the Visiting Staff—they demand a lot of respect." And another pointed out that practically "everyone doesn't like some of the doctors and are afraid of those they don't like." This attitude is most marked among the students, although as one senior pointed out, fear of the physician tends to pass away as increased experience is gained. Nonetheless, six of the seven students interviewed reported that their relations with doctors tended to be tense and fear-laden. As one put it, "You have so much respect for them that you watch yourself and listen for what they say to get it right."

What may be said of the nurse's relationship to the doctor may be said—in somewhat attenuated form—of the nonprofessional personnel. As one old janitor put it, "I just keep out of their way . . . I wish they'd put a sign on those doc's backs so I'd know when they're coming my way." On a somewhat more sophisticated level, a male aide, in explaining that in his contacts with the doctors he never initiates conversation unless he has to ask for information, said, "We have respect for the doctors and realize that they are in a different circle than we are." At the same time, many of the menial employees express their respect for the doctors in their almost pathetic pride that "the doctors are real nice and speak to me when they see me in the hall."

Paramedical professionals—and particularly the laboratory technicians—fail to show this general deference for physicians to the same degree. This independence seems to be based both on the fact that these people are removed from the ward and its line of clinical authority for much of each working day and upon their status as technical specialists to whom physicians refer particular problems or tests for analysis and solution. As one technician put it, "Technicians can talk to them straighter; they will talk back to the doctors and not let them browbeat them." Another explained the situation by the fact that "the doctors are more polite to us and take our word more than on the floor where they rule supreme." This lack of deference to the doctor allows the technicians to "take them for what they are." As one put it, "Eighty five to ninety percent of the doctors are in a cloud. They walk around in another world of medicine alone and are absent-minded about other things. 'Oh, he's a bird' is a favorite expression of ours that more or less sums up how we feel about them." It is perhaps not surprising that several of the physicians interviewed spoke spontaneously of the "snippiness" and "impertinence" of the technicians.

While the doctor may walk in spendid isolation behind the walls of deference his superior knowledge and authority have built up, the position of the nurse as supervisor of non-professional ward workers means that she must be in interaction with them to some degree; the testimony of several nurses to the effect that they have to "talk and talk" to these workers in order to make them perform effectively indicates that this purely "supervisory" interaction accounts for a substantial proportion of the on-the-job conversations between the groups. Most nurses, moreover, consider auxiliary nursing personnel as part of the ward family, and a good deal of chit-chat certainly goes on between the groups. The comment of one male aide, however, throws light on what may motivate some of this informal conversation: "When they want something done, they consider you as an equal; at other times, no."

There is evidence, furthermore, that the amount of informal interaction which takes place between nurses and non-professional personnel tends to vary according to the status of the nurse involved. Thus almost all the non-professional ward employees interviewed agreed that a head nurse is more difficult to speak with than are other nurses. As one male aide put it, "The head nurses make you jump through the hoop. I wouldn't have the confidence to talk to them as I would to the other nurses on the ward."

In any case, there is little doubt that the higher status of the nurse affects both the content and quality of her informal conversation with non-professional personnel. Jealous of professional properties, she may sometimes be somewhat abrupt in her insistence that everything "be in apple-pie order." The effect of this is to make non-professional people shy away from her. As one supervisor put it, "The nurses and head nurses are not inclined to have much to do with our people. They feel above them. And our folks, once rebuffed, do not try to make friends again." And one of the auxiliary personnel spoke for himself in saying "You don't like to be dirt under people's feet. Working with the nurses isn't too pleasant, and I avoid them when they act that way."

The status differences just discussed involve both those set up by the hospital as an institution and those of the larger society. Typical differences in education and socioeconomic background differentiate doctors from nurses, other paramedical professionals, and from non-professional workers. These differences—between upper-middle, lower-middle and lower class persons—in themselves are apt to minimize communication. Moreover, there are a series of age and sex differentials which complicate the situation as well. Thus, for example, while free and easy communication might be difficult for a student nurse and a senior Visiting Staff physician, it might be both easy and attractive to the same student and an interne.

While such differences may either reinforce or mitigate the effects of the hospital status system, two other factors act to reinforce them. One of these lies at the very basis of the status system itself. This depends upon differential kinds of training for various groups of personnel. And these various levels of training involve both jargons of their own and differences of emphasis which seriously inhibit communication between groups. Naturally, this tendency to difficulty on the part of one group in understanding others is most marked among those of lower status categories. Most non-professional workers cannot understand much of what the doctor says when he is speaking on his own technical level. And even though nurses may understand the gist of what physicians say, they miss many of the fine points. They very frequently report their contacts with a doctor in terms of his explaining something to them. But what is true with respect to understanding of the doctor by other groups tends to a lesser extent to be true with relation to jargons and special emphases of all other occupational groups. Even though one may understand in general what the other fellow is talking about, it is difficult to grasp its full significance unless one has "seen the system from the inside."

Furthermore, interaction between occupational groups tends to be severely formalized. Doctors and especially nurses feel that their behavior on the ward should be strictly "professional"—an attitude that tends to limit the scope of communication to necessary, job-relevant considerations. Much of the communication necessary to coordinate the work of the therapeutic team takes place in formal conferences of one sort or another—ward rounds, "report" conferences, and the like. And prescriptions of physicians for patient care must normally be written in the "order book" rather than simply being given in the course of conversation. On the one hand, this rule guards against verbal error or misconceptions concerning what the doctor wishes done. On the other, it sometimes acts to relieve the doctor of any necessity for verbal interaction with the nurses. As one nurse put it,

"Too often the doctors simply come in, see their patients, write orders in the order book, and leave without our knowing they have ever been around. This means that we must constantly check through the order book to see if any orders have been written up that we don't know about."

Yet if certain of the activities of the Hospital tend sharply to restrict interaction across occupational lines, a few of them tend to break down these barriers. It is likely that younger personnel—and particularly those new to the ward situation—perceive status distinctions less sharply than others. (And, sometimes, as between young physicians and nurses, a romantic interest adds its stimulus to communication!) Moreover, interesting cases— particularly those involving important persons or particularly dramatic medical problems—become a common source of interest to all personnel. It has been suggested that a good index of the degree to which a worker is integrated into the life of a ward might be the extent to which he learns about such cases.

Interestingly enough, the interaction across occupational lines seems to be best developed in surgical units. It is characteristic of surgical procedures that they require intense cooperation between physicians and nurses. It might therefore be expected that operating rooms are thus places in which members of these groups might be especially likely to communicate freely with each other.[15]

According to our informants, the preliminary stages of an operation and the final "sewing up" stage are times in which there is a good deal of joking and chit-chat among surgeons, anesthetists and nurses. On the other hand, during delicate portions of operations or at times of crisis, interaction may either subside to a minimal series of orders—"scapel . . . sponge . . ."—or explode in fits of anger. It seems to us that the tension involved in surgery accounts for much of this ambivalent character of operating room interaction. On the one hand, much of the horse-play and joking acts as a tension-reducer; on the other, the surgeon who shows his temper during an operation does so largely because of the tension that his concern for his patient and his difficult technique have built up within him. At the same time, the fact that in the operating room the patient is usually unconscious seems of great importance. And Parsons[16] has shrewdly observed that one of the major reasons medical men are loath to allow laymen to witness operations is that they do not wish them to observe the joking and small talk that goes on during an operation which may involve the life of an acquaintance of the observer.

III. THE IDEOLOGY OF HOSPITAL WORKERS

Thus far, two of the essentials for integration of a group have been discussed with respect to the situation on a typical hospital ward. It has been shown that there are real barriers to communication between ward workers which tend to follow occupational and status lines. More briefly, it has been pointed out that lines of authority on the hospital ward tend to overlap because of the existence of both administrative and clinical chains of command. The matter of the extent of agreement between members concerning common purposes and presuppositions remains to be discussed.

We may expect that members of any group will develop a body of beliefs which serve as a rationale for their behavior within the group. Insofar as these ideas are directed toward the aim and character of the group itself, they may be called an "institutional ideology."[17] What is the nature of this ideology at Yankee Hospital? Do personnel have similar beliefs about their hospital? Or do their ideologies follow the lines of cleavage manifested in the ward social structure?

It is a sociological truism that barriers to communication within a group tend to foster the development of disparate attitudes and patterns of behavior among members. Homans has formulated this idea positively,[18] "the more frequently persons interact with one another, the more alike in some respects both their activities and their sentiments tend to become." If occupational status differences have the significance indicated above, therefore, each major occupational grouping in the hospital ought to have a distinctive ideology.

We may begin this analysis with an investigation of opinions of Yankee Hospital personnel concerning the aims and purposes of their institution. Study of the operations of the hospital, of its historical development, and of its stated aims revealed *five* broad ends or purposes for which it exists— and for the fulfillment of which its personnel are presumably to work. The oldest and most basic of these, of course, is the primal purpose of *giving care to its patients*. A second, in which the hospital has been engaged for more than eighty years is the *education of personnel* through formal programs— an aim so comprehensive it now touches at least eight health service occupations. A third purpose, much emphasized in the last twenty-five years and the watchword of the hospital's public relations program, is to be of *service to the community*—to provide health services valuable to all residents of the area whether they be sick or well. The fourth purpose, though a fond hope for years, is still largely programmatic at Yankee Hospital; this is the aim of doing *research*. The fifth purpose is common to all institutions, and may be called *instrumental*; it refers to the hospital's aim of self preservation—its "desire" to maintain the esteem of the community, to provide satisfaction to patients and employees alike, and to remain solvent.

In an effort to determine the extent to which hospital personnel perceived the basic purposes for which they cooperate, the following types of questions were asked of the seventy five hospital people who were formally interviewed:

1. What is the purpose of Yankee Hospital? What does it exist to do? What are its basic aims?
2. What are the basic policies of the hospital directed toward? What is it aiming to accomplish now?
3. What would the hospital do if it had unlimited funds at its disposal? Why?

Responses of the interviewees to these questions were combined and analyzed according to the basic purposes to which they referred. The results are shown in Tables 2, 3, and 4 below:

Table 2—Summary of Responses Made by Hospital Personnel Concerning Institutional Purpose & Policy

Type of Purpose or Policy	Doctors (N=16)	Nurses (N=29)	Other Employees (N=30)	Total
Patient Care	20	47	37	104
Community Service	26	22	4	52
Education	36	13	7	56
Instrumental Aims	1	13	18	32
Research	2	7	3	12
	85	102	69	256

(Responses re research were omitted in computing Chi Square. Chi Square = 64.01, p = less than .001.)

Table 3—Percentage of Personnel Recognizing Various Institutional Purposes

Type of Purpose	Doctors	Nurses	Skilled "paramedical" Personnel	Unskilled Non-prof's	All Sample
Patient Care	100.00%	82.76%	88.24%	61.54%	84.00
Community Service	43.75	41.38	11.76	0.0	28.00
Education	68.75	37.93	23.53	0.0	34.67
Research	6.25	10.34	0.0	0.0	5.33
Instrumental Aims	0.0	10.34	41.17	46.15	21.33

Table 4—Average Number of Responses of Personnel Concerning Institutional Purposes*

Optimum Expected Number	5.00
Doctors	2.19
Nurses	1.83
Other workers	1.40
(Skilled paramedical personnel)	1.64
(Other non-professional workers)	1.08
Average, all personnel	1.73

* (Computed on the basis of Question #1 only.)

These tables reveal that there is no unanimity among hospital personnel concerning what the basic aims and purposes of their institution are. It is striking how few of the well-publicized and rather obvious basic purposes could be verbalized by our interviewees—the average for all personnel was but 1.73 out of a possible score of 5.0. As might be expected, the better educated, higher status personnel were better informed than their lower-status associates. But of special importance in the present connection are the systematic differences—of statistically significant quality—in the perception of basic hospital aims by the different status groups. Although the primal purpose of patient care was recognized quite universally, the doctors emphasized the highly publicized educational and community service purposes more heavily than any other group. On the other hand, the non-professionals —most dependent on its fulfillment, perhaps—were most insistent upon the importance of the hospital's instrumental aims. One is forced to conclude that status differences in the hospital are associated with diversity in the ideologies of the institutional group.

We may now characterize these ideologies in somewhat greater detail. The members of Yankee Hospital's Medical Staff who were interviewed not only elaborated a more extensive ideology than did members of other groups, but one which was qualitatively different as well.[19]

These doctors' ideology is basically conservative. New trends toward complexity of hospital organization and administration were seen by the doctors as real dangers. As one physician put it, "I guess we've got to have all these business departments, but again, there's a tremendous overgrowth. Their expansion has been terrific and out of proportion to the increase in beds." Perhaps because he eschews all interest in day-to-day problems of the administration, the doctor's conception of the ideal hospital seems somewhat unrealistic. He is embarrassed by the tremendous costs of medical care, yet at the same time he inveighs against the "dollars and cents attitude" of the administration. He wants his hospital to supply all the technical facilities necessary for the most modern patient care. But though he has gotten these special services and facilities, he sometimes fails to see that it is in large part precisely these services which have complicated the work of the administration he so readily condemns as being too bureaucratic. In his emphasis on the education and community service purposes of the hospital, the average doctor has lost sight of the importance of its instrumental purpose.

Similarly, physicians tended to object to new developments leading to higher standards in the nursing curriculum. Their ideal nurse seemed to be one who faithfully serves patient and doctor without benefit of much more than a thorough practical training. One physician stated this position clearly: "The trouble with our nursing schools is that they give too much theory and too little practice." Another elaborated saying, "They're educating our nurses out of existence; there's too much of a gap between the kind of training the graduate receives and the kind of reality she faces. It has gotten to the point where some of us feel that nurses are practically becoming doctors. So they will do a beautiful technical job, but won't do such necessary things as preparing food, changing linens, and so on." The animus of the doctors is not as a rule directed primarily toward students or staff nurses. These are thought of as "good gals" whose superiors are leading them on a dangerously independent road. The doctors are almost unanimous in their indictment of supervisors and higher nursing administrators, even though they concede that these groups have improved somewhat over the years. One physician was blunt: "Heads of nursing schools are old battle-axes and don't give nurses enough responsibility."

The doctor also sees nursing as becoming unduly bureaucratic. As one physician put it, "a great deal of the brass in the nursing department is unjustified. There is too much inter-office communication and too much writing among the nurses." Or, as another said, "Many times on the ward, the patients' lights are not answered because the floor nurses have to chart, do record work, or maybe are just above nursing. The house staff have to do many procedures without nursing help even though they need it because the Training School Office just won't allow it. Their attitude is 'It's not our job.'"

These attitudes are not just those of a group which is wary of change; they are also motivated by the doctors' concern to maintain what they feel is their rightful power and prestige in the hospital. They seem to interpret much of what goes on in the hospital as directed against them. Thus several physicians remarked that always some staff members feel that "the administration is trying to put something over on us." Nine of the sixteen physicians interviewed believed that the actual center of power in the hospital was rightly in the hands of the Medical Staff. Three others gave this body a measure of authority almost equal to that of trustees and administration. And four reported that "although laymen run Yankee Hospital, this situation is (somewhat unfortunate)." As one of the doctors put it, "We doctors are frightfully fearful of direction by lay-people. But although we want our prerogatives, we don't always accept our responsibilities." Another said that "The doctors are losing their intrinsic influence in the hospital and that's bad." On the other hand, many of the physicians would agree with one who pointed out that "any administration tends to run away on half-baked tangents, but we don't let them get away with it."

The ideology of the physicians is profession-oriented in another sense. They often tend to think of the hospital as the "doctor's workshop." As one explained the basic purpose of the institution, "the hospital should be a place where a doctor can get extra care for his patients which he cannot give them in his office. It should be the place where he can get a combined consultation over and above that which he can obtain by sending them to specialists." This physician was thinking primarily of what Yankee Hospital could do to help him manage his private patients; like others, he felt that "we are lucky that the charity load has not had an enormous part in the hospital's program. The pauper load is handled at the City Hospital and elsewhere. Here, charity is properly pigeon-holed, not an inherent load which overburdens the hospital." Or, as another put it, "this hospital is directed primarily at the middle class—those who can pay their own way and are in the habit of doing it." Still another said "all kinds of people come here, but it is encouraging how many of the very rich do come to Yankee Hospital." No doubt this emphasis upon middle and upper-class patients in the minds of these physicians is related to their strong belief in "free enterprise in medicine."

The foregoing feelings about the charity load are carried over into the opinion of physicians about the out-patient clinic—a department of the hospital which has been little developed. In general physicians oppose much increase in out-patient service because it "would be competing with the G.P.'s." They are frank to say that its principal justification is that it is a necessary part of the program of medical education.

There is whole-hearted support of this program because it helps raise the standards of the medical profession as a whole. Yet many staff doctors desire a program that is oriented toward practice; there is strong opposition to the approach of "academic medicine." As one doctor put it, "Our contribution to the region lies in our ability to give excellent patient care. We would make a second or third-rate medical school teaching hospital. I feel this is because our staff wouldn't want to teach; we don't have one iota of the medical school point of view." Or as another said, "we aim to be one of the few hospitals in the country to train good practicing doctors and not professors."

But when the physician talks of education, he refers largely to the program of *medical* education. Thus, 30 out of 36 responses of physicians concerning the hospital's educational aims had to do with training programs for doctors. When the physician looks at the hospital, he tends to see in it only what is relevant to his own professional needs.

The physician tends also to equate good patient care with the fulfillment of his demands. In terms of clinical criteria, this equation is obvious, but it also carries over into his perceptions of hospital organization as may be seen from his attitude toward nurses and the nursing administration. The opinions of several doctors will bring out the dynamics of these attitudes.

"I feel strongly about the modern attitude of the nurses. It seems as if they've lost sight of their primary purpose—to take care of the sick and help the doctor do a better job."

Another physician saw himself and his colleagues as being at the top of a great pecking order.

"The doctors of the visiting staff want all the prerogatives of doctors— want the nurses to be valets to them and not to the patient. The staff uses the nurses, and the nurses use the trained attendants and technicians and so on."

Still another said,

"The courtesy shown by the nurses toward the doctors is improving. It has been very poor. But you can't raise too much hell about it or you lose nurses."

On the other hand, another point of view was expressed by the doctor who felt that,

"The average doctor considers the good nurse as a co-worker and not a servant. I think nurses have their real function in treating the patients' whole personality—this we can't handle."

Another believed that,

"The average doctor takes nurses as a matter of course. They are supposed to be there and do what he wants. The trouble is that we are not getting nurses who are interested in helping patients. They aren't interested in carrying bed-pans, making beds and so on. They want to be administrators."

A final change on the theme was rung by the doctor who declared that, "Most doctors here feel that the nurses should get their orders from the medical team and they resent supervisors and administrators as invaders of the doctor-nurse relationship."

We do not wish to impugn in any way the motives of the doctors. Like other hospital people, they have what they consider to be the best interests of their institution at heart. Their standard of ethics and intention to render good service to their patients is as unquestioned as is their competence. At the same time, as members of a profession whose status entitles them to an influential voice in determining hospital policy, it is only natural that their ideology includes provisos which aim to protect what they consider to be their legitimate interests. And because the doctors honestly seem to feel that what is good for physicians is also good for the hospital, they assert themselves in all good conscience.

The ideologies of the nurses and non-professional workers are by no means as consistent and well-developed as that of the medical staff. They have no need to be, for they perform different functions. The doctor is in a position to influence, if not to dictate, hospital policy and must have an ideology which will guide him in exerting this influence. His platform, therefore, needs to be "political" in nature. The nurses and non-professional workers, on the other hand, are not in position to influence policy to the same degree; for most of them, as hospital employees, institutional life is largely regulated by directives from above. The character of their ideology, therefore, tends to be expressive. Its functions are, on the one hand, to express those attitudes and desires which arise from the work situation and on the other hand, to justify the activities of personnel within the organization.

The status of the nurse, midway between that of the physician and most other hospital employees, is ambiguous. Hers is a professional status; nevertheless, at every turn she finds herself pressed down by the overwhelming authority and prestige of the doctor. And although her upward mobility has been blocked, her status is being more and more invaded by non-professional workers such as trained attendants. It is not surprising, then, that her ideology should cling to and emphasize her special responsibilities in the work of the hospital. In emphasizing the care of the whole patient, the nurse is staking out for herself a field of competence which, for the moment at least, seems secure from invasion.

The ideology of the nurses, moreover, is an outgrowth of the history of their profession. The very basis for the professionalization of nursing was rooted in the necessity for improving the quality of personnel who served hospital patients. In order to improve personnel, it was necessary to implant in them ideals of service of a very exalted sort; the profession of nursing thus became, in the eyes of women like Florence Nightingale, a sacred calling. Their service, from the beginning was conceived of in diffuse terms; the nurse was to minister to all the needs of the patient as ordered by the doctor. Although its verbal expression is a relatively recent development, the idea of treating the whole patient thus goes back ot the beginnings of the modern profession of nursing.

This idealistic aim of treating the "whole patient" involves not merely a desire to care for the patient's mental and spiritual condition as well as for his body; it extends also to the nurses' taking full responsibility for all the care which is given to the patient (other than by the doctor). Thus as auxiliary workers increasingly relieve the nurse of the more routine tasks of patient care, the latter feels a need to take charge of their actions and see that everything is done correctly. The holistic element in the nurses' ideology thus affects her relations with other hospital employees. It has been especially noticeable in affecting the relationships between nurses and dietitians. For although the installation of the latter on the wards has relieved the nurses of a very onerous work load, the nurse resents the intrusion of the dietitian into what was originally her own sphere. One nurse justified this attitude on the grounds that "we feel we know more about patients than the dietitians do." The ideology of the nurse will not permit her easily to accept the competence of people other than herself and the doctor to deal with patients.

Because the nurses believe very strongly that the hospital is an institution dedicated to works of mercy, they do not easily accept the hard facts of medical economics. Neither does the expansion of the hospital into an organization which operates on a large scale and in an efficient, impersonal manner accord well with their ideals. As one nurse put it, "There's too much emphasis on making the patients pay. The hospital is money-mad. This makes it hard and unidealistic." Another noted that, "The need is for supportive nursing. You're a woman, the patient is too, and you're the liaison between her and the doctor. But we haven't time for anything except vital signs. There's too much emphasis on speed and too much mass production. Things have become too impersonal; with penicillin, much of the personal part of nursing has gone. Someone has to prove to me that all this is progress." Still another nurse noted that "The hospital is no longer the big family it once was. Conveyors and tubes have changed all that and made the hospital an impersonal place. Now, you often don't know anyone except in your own department."

For the nurse, the purpose of patient care is the outstanding aim of the hospital and all other aims are interpreted in terms of how they tie in with this basic purpose. Thus the nurses tended to interpret the community service purpose of the hospital primarily in terms of a ministry of preventive medicine, out-patient clinics, and public health education. Moreover patient care in the eyes of the nurses is not simply a matter of physical treatment. Rather it involves both "getting him well as quickly as possible, ministering to his mental and spiritual welfare as well as to his physical body." In this endeavor the nurses consider that they play the crucial role; as one said, "It is our job to care for the patient. We must try always to be friendly and treat the patient as a personality and not as an 'it' with a disease." Or as another nurse said, "the nurse has the biggest part in the work of the hospital. She has the closest contact with the patient and the first responsibility to him. Without the nurse, I don't believe we could have a hospital, just as we wouldn't have an army without soldiers. Not that the doctor isn't in the picture—he is a very close second." In an institution which has been rendered more and more impersonal by expansion and new techniques, nurses feel that

they are the representatives of the human qualities, and as such, the execu-
tors of its highest ideals.

Although they consider themselves quite competent to criticize doctors'
orders—which they believe are sometimes "crazy"—nurses readily agree that
it is the physicians whose knowledge makes possible the healing work of the
hospital. Therefore, they are willing to pay them the respect they deserve.
It is the hallmark of the professional nurse to be dignified, and to have respect
for "those in authority." Nurses believe that the hospital demands the highest
standards of conduct on the part of its personnel; sometimes too, they think
that it is the professional employees who must bear the responsibility for
maintaining these standards. As one put it, "One and all should uphold the
dignity of the profession they are in. I doubt, though, if we can trust the
intelligence of the laboring classes to do this."

If the ideology of the nurses is idealistic and altruistic, it is also imbued
with a certain missionary zeal. It is a keystone of nursing belief that in teaching lies the way to the fulfillment of the purposes of the hospital. They are
enthusiastic about the whole gamut of Yankee Hospital's teaching programs,
and are tremendously concerned with the academic standards of their training school. And the nurses feel that teaching should go beyond training of
health service personnel; to them, one of the principal ways in which patient
care could be improved is by developing more adequate methods of teaching
patients to avoid future illnesses and to live with their infirmities. In this
endeavor, they feel that their concern for the "whole patient" is crucial.

Perhaps because they believe that their approach is basic to the success
of the hospital, nurses are concerned about their status in the institution.
As one put it," The policy toward personnel should change. Some people still
think that students should be looked down on and that the nurse is so far
below the doctor that she shouldn't even be talked to." And another insisted
that "the days of Florence Nightingale are gone. You can still love humanity
and get paid—you have that feeling long before you think about wages."
After decades of what they believe to have been little short of exploitation,
nurses are begining to feel that the instrumental purposes of the hospital
should extend to employees as well as to patients.

It is this kind of thinking which characterizes the average nurse's attitude
toward the hospital. She identifies herself extremely closely with it. The
institution is, for her, a concrete means of making her ideals come alive in
reality. Not only does it actuate her altruistic motives, but it satisfies her desire for prestige and respectability. As one put it, "Yankee Hospital is a very
nice place to work, and I'd advise anyone to work here. It gives one prestige
in the community to work here because of the very fine doctors who are on
the staff, the nurses—who are fine women—and so forth." Yet sometimes the
pressure of the work blots out both the nurse's feelings about what the hospital is and ought to be and her sense of identification with it. The work
load on an understaffed floor can make the nurse see in her job nothing but
drudgery, fatigue, and techniques, and in her hospital nothing but the insistent white call lights that mean more and more work. As one nurse tiredly
protested when we asked her questions concerning her ideology, "The hospital does so many things—and we're too busy to think of them. There are

so many departments that you don't have time to think of. And there are so many patients to take care of and so many lights to answer that we don't know what we're doing or why we're doing it."

Thus the ideology of the nurses sometimes is honored more in the breach than in the observance. Because many think of education for their profession as "training," and of their service in terms of performing procedures properly and efficiently, it becomes difficult for these nurses to see in their work anything but drudgery—or any compensation other than to lean on the stiff, starched proprieties of professional status.[20] And because they feel a real responsibility for the administration of the ward—and, perhaps see in this area opportunity for enhancing their status—they tend very often to emphasize administrative matters, (the execution of which is quickly recognized and controlled from above.) The more intangible matter of care for the whole patient thus sometimes becomes more a theoretical goal than an actual achievement. But all this is simply to say that it is not always possible to live up to high ideals.

The ideology of the other paramedical workers is much more fragmentary than that of the nurses. Two principle facets characterize it. On the one hand, there is a great consciousness of the service orientation which working in a hospital involves and a strong sense of identification with the institution. This generalization applies to ideological statements made by dietitians, laboratory technicians, and housekeeping employees alike. As one put it, "We are working for the patient not just for the boss. Our main object is to make the patient well and comfortable. This is vaguely in the back of all our minds. Don't I sound like I had a halo?" On the other hand, the ideology of these workers seems to be strongly focused on the technical aspects of hospital operation—on how best to do their job, on the physical facilities which characterize the hospital, and on how to make it run more efficiently. While the dietitians and technicians and unskilled workers largely tend to see only the problems of their own occupation as needing attention, their overall interest is strongly centered upon the instrumental purpose of the institution. Because they feel proud to be a part of it they want to help it. The non-skilled worker particularly tends to make the more dramatic technical operations of the hospital the symbol of its work. On the other hand, the dietitians tend to think of it in administrative terms.

Most employees wish naturally for better hours and higher pay. However, there is little tendency toward a "union" point of view. Even the menial employees are acutely conscious of the financial limitations under which the institution operates. As one put it, "with conditions as they are, they do about as well as they can. If they had more money, they would do more. We read in the paper about their terrible expenses and how they work to overcome them." And they are conscious too, of the financial plight of hospital patients; "There's one thing I don't like: many patients are injured and keep talking about how the credit office asks for money the first thing they come in. They have to charge enough anyway." For these reasons, there is not a strong feeling among employees that management is exploiting them. There is a general realization on their part that higher wages are available elsewhere. But such intangible advantages as security and the satisfaction of "helping people" mean more to them than the increased salaries they could earn on the "outside".

There are, of course, differences in the ideology of the paramedical and non-professional employees. The interesting thing, however, is that the broad outlines of the ideology of the male aid is rather like that of the laboratory technician; and the janitor believes much the same sort of thing as does the dietitian. The skilled employees, of course, have an ideology which possesses greater scope and refinement than that of the unskilled employees, but both groups build upon their identification with the hospital's purpose of patient care and their concern for the achievement of its instrumental aims.

The three basic ideologies which we found among hospital personnel each tends to have its own organizing theme. Thus, the doctors conceive of a hospital as an institution whose basic function is to help the medical profession in its efforts to provide the best possible medical care. And the nurses feel strongly that the hospital is an institution which should minister to the health of an entire community in the spirit of altruistic service; this ministry in their eyes should be directed toward the "whole patient." Finally, other ward workers tend to believe that service to patients subsumes the whole aim of the hospital; to them, it is a miracle-working institution to which they are willing to dedicate their working hours, and the instrumental aims of which they are greatly concerned to see achieved. There is unity among all groups concerning the tremendous importance of good patient service in the life of the hospital. But there is a great deal of difference among the groups as to the implications of this primal purpose. And the way in which these implications are conceived constitutes the core of the ideology of each groups, and helps determine its actions within the institution.

Conclusion. There are in the hospital certain tendencies which appear to set limits upon the degree to which integration of the organization's personnel can take place. It has been shown that communication tends to be for the most part channeled within occupational lines, giving rise to a tendency for those who work together on the wards to know and associate principally with those of their "own kind." Associated with this tendency to isolation on the part of the various occupational status-groups is a set of disparate institutional ideologies. Each group expressed divergent ideas concerning hospital purpose and policy, and these attitudes point up areas of latent conflict between the groups. These tendencies, together with the strain imposed by a dual hierarchy of authority upon the hospital ward, may go far to explain much of the tension which from time to time appears in hospitals.

But one should not dwell solely on the negative implications of hospital social structure. Diversity of opinion can be productive of new approaches which would otherwise be difficult to conceive; each of the institutional ideologies depicted above gives emphasis to an integral part of Yankee Hospital's mission which might otherwise tend to be obscured. Similarly, considerations of efficiency and interest justify much of the tendency of hospital personnel to interact primarily with members of their own group. And it is hard to see how the execution of clinical needs of patients can ever be fully rationalized into the hospital's administrative chain of command without endangering the quality of medical care.

What can be said is that these structural tendencies cannot be taken for granted without risking the snowballing of legitimate differences of interest and approach into major misunderstandings. Moreover, they must not only be recognized and acknowledged but held within limits. Hospital workers—like participants in any other division of labor—do constitute an interdependent team. And teamwork demands the free contribution of all those involved. Rigidity of status, undue limitation of inter-group communication, and unresolved differences of opinion can be disruptive. There is need in the hospital, as in every institution, for tolerance and understanding of why others behave as they do.

48   TWO LINES OF AUTHORITY: THE HOSPITAL'S DILEMMA

By Harvey L. Smith

Certain organizational problems distinctive to hospitals become apparent when they are viewed alongside other complex human organizations. These distinctive features provide a set of constantly recurring problems to which people working in hospitals must adapt. It is proposed here to analyze the bases of such organizational problems and to indicate the dilemmas they entail for the administration of both lay and professional hospital personnel.

George Washington once reported, after a hospital inspection, that he had found no principal director, and no subordination among the surgeons. He expressed his belief that this led to disputes which would continue until the hospital was reduced to some system. This might still be considered a valid capsule criticism of many modern hospitals.

Understanding the details which underlie such criticism requires study of the human (social) matrix of hospital administration. As a sociologist, I have undertaken such study over a period of years in a variety of hospitals in several regions of the United States. I have had, in addition, several years of military service in hospital administration. Research and some practical experience therefore underlie this sociological report on hospitals.

Analysis Of Hospital Structure. Basically, a hospital may be viewed as an organization at cross-purposes with itself. It is the kind of human institution about which people constantly complain that they are caught "in the middle." What they are caught in the middle of, is a direct function of what we shall call the basic duality of hospitals.

A clue to the nature of this duality is provided by the statement that one frequently hears in hospitals—"The big thing here is the difference between what they say we do and what we actually do." A closer look at this difference brings us closer to the operating problems of hospital administration.

Let us start with the system of controls, the hierarchy of authority, through which a hospital operates. Here are found very great differences between what the hospital says it does and what it actually does.

Take, for instance, the formal organization charts which many hospitals believe reflect a true picture of their pattern of operation. A comparison of the patterns indicated on such charts with the observed relationships among people actually working in the hospital reveals that usually the hospital organization chart portrays a complex system of administrative controls over lay people. Thus, there is the hierarchy from board of trustees to hospital workers. Hospitals vary in the degree to which the authority and responsibility at each level, and the channels of communication among them, are explicitly developed. But a closer look at an operating hospital reveals that this is far too simple a portrayal of its actual organization for work. The primary difference involves the role of professional persons—especially the physicians. There is almost no administrative routine established in hospitals which cannot be (and frequently is) abrogated or countermanded by a physician claiming medical emergency—or by anyone acting for the physician claiming medical emergency—or by anyone acting for the physician and similarly claiming medical necessity. Upon close observation it is found that the actual authority of the medical man in the hospital is very great indeed. Although the conventional organization chart portrays the position of the medical staff as outside the line of authority, we observed physicians to be exerting power throughout the hospital structure at all levels—upon nurses, ward personnel, upon patients, and even (where physicians were trustees) directly upon administrators themselves.

Thus, two main lines of authority—lay and professional—exist in the hospital. And there are sectors of the hospital which may not clearly be assigned to either, and in which the authority of both may overlap. We have called these the "hybrid areas"—and they are typically represented by pharmacy, pathology, x-ray, admissions, and medical records. These are mixtures of lay and professional competence and authority.

Authority May Overlap. This duality of controls is a product of the complexity of hospital organization—a complexity shared by other human structures (i.e. universities) where professional competence is exercised in a matrix of lay administration. In essence, it involves the attempt to handle two different principles of authority within one institution. The work of Max Weber[1] provides us with ideas for analyzing and understanding such complexity. The authority vested in (exercised by) lay administration is of a type familiar to us all. It is close to what Weber has classically described as bureaucratic authority, functioning in a clearly defined hierarchy with "packets" of authority and prestige prescribed for each level. But the problem for the hospital is that the authority of the bureaucrat confronts that of the medical professional, who represents what Weber has called charismatic authority. This sociological term, borrowed from theology, and meaning literally "gift of grace," represents the kind of authority which a person exercises by reason of having a set of followers who attribute special powers to him. By virtue of these special powers attributed to him he is held somewhat in awe. Weber recognized that the physician was a charismatic person.[2] One of the primary characteristics of charisma is that it is defiant of administrative regulation. Possessors of charisma resist being encompassed in bureaucratic organization. It is, in these terms, the special problem of the hospital that it is an administrative structure which must contain and regulate charismatic professional persons who are defiant of lay regulation. Thus, both administrators and physicians are authoritative figures, but for different (and basically conflicting) reasons. This provides, so to speak, a built-in conflict situation for hospital administration.

Conflict Between Systems. This problem may be seen in another way—as a conflict between two systems of status in the hospital. The ideas of Chester Barnard[3] are useful in understanding this. Barnard has noted that two kinds of status may be found in human organizations. One of these he calls "scalar" status—or the status inherent in a position within some hierarchical system. High rank in an organization and high status thus coincide. The other form of status he calls "functional." Such status inheres in certain kinds of work, regardless of the position of the worker in a ranked system. Thus, in the hospital, administration represents a system of scalar status, and the physicians carry high functional status. Orders normally came from those whose status is higher than the recipient of the orders. Hospital personnel find themselves receiving orders from carriers of both forms of status—from the administrative side whose "right" to "boss" them is explicitly recognized, and from the physicians whose "right" to "boss" them is not so clearly recognized but orders often reflect the conflicts which inhere in the dual status system.

A dual system of values, expressing these conflicts, pervades the hospital. A hospital is, of course, many things: a place where the sick are cared for and treated, a place to which physicians bring their patients, a hotel, a laundry, a healing institution, a business organization. These many "purposes" of a hospital are rarely subsumed under any single "master symbol." Rather, these many activities tend to be justified, by persons working within hospitals, in terms of two dominant values or symbols: "money" and "service." And frequently these are expressed as considerations of money *versus* service (or vice versa). This means, in brief, that a hospital is not quite sure of the kind of organization that it is, or should be. Is it a service institution or a business institution? Or something of each? Hospitals are faced with the need to come as close to balancing their budgets as possible while being sensitively aware of their task of serving the health needs of a public which includes those who cannot or will not pay for their care.

In the main, administration is forced to focus upon the contingencies of fiscal survival and the physician more often appears as the person dedicated to the service aspect of hospitals. The fact that administrators and physicians often switch sides tends to point up the reality of this dichotomy of values. The employees of the hospital who have to mediate between the often conflicting demands of "money" or "service" are again confronted with a conflict situation which is built into the hospital.

All of this makes the hospital a peculiar form of power structure. Its distinctive aspects may readily be seen if we compare an "idealized" picture of the power structure of an industrial plant with a similarly idealized picture of the "flow" of power within a hospital.

Consider industry. Here, in a non-unionized plant, we find the flow of authority from management to the worker. Where a union is present in the plant the workers are able to exert counterpressures upon management. Staff members ordinarily act in an advisory capacity to top management, although in a functionally organized plant they may exert specific authority over particular segments of the plant organization. The crucially important productive work is performed at the worker level, low in the status hierarchy. Characteristically, conflict in such an organization appears as worker resistance to management.

Crucial differences appear when we consider the power structure of a hospital. We have the similar "line" of authority from management to the worker, with little union-organization resistance in hospitals. But, at the staff level, the physicians do not act merely in a passive advisory capacity. They intervene actively and powerfully throughout the structure, exerting power upon hospital operating personnel, defiant of administrative regulation, and, where they are members of boards of trustees, are able directly to control "top management" itself. Furthermore, it is at the staff level—the high status level of the physicians—that the crucially important productive work of this institution is performed. And it is here, characteristically, in hospitals that we find the important resistances to management (administration) generated. This distinctive aspect of the hospital power structure highlights the problems of hospital administration.

Illustrative Cases. Such basic problems appear in many guises and in many parts of the hospital. They represent a complex interweaving of the controls, status systems, and values which have been described.

The kinds of crucial problems which may arise between lay and professional people in hospitals are illustrated by the following case. A medical director readily admitted that he was so discontented with his job that he was prepared to resign. In fact, he showed us his letter of resignation which he kept on hand in his desk. He gave as the main reason for his discontent in the hospital the fact that he, a medical director who was a physician, was under the immediate supervision of a hospital administrator who was a layman. It was the opinion of this medical director that laymen simply did not know enough about the basic things which were involved in hospitals to do such a job adequately. As he said, "You cannot put a layman over a doctor in a hospital and have it work." He stated that not only he but other physicians in the hospital felt that this was an unworkable relationship. Furthermore, he quite explicitly indicated the belief that his job involved him in something of a status dilemma. He felt himself caught between the requirements of administration and his role as a physician, and said that he no longer knew for certain whether he was a physician or an administrator. This case quite clearly reveals the dilemmas which may be experienced by those two systems—the administrative and the professional.

Physicians Break Rules. In another case, an elevator man reported a hospital rule stating that there should be no smoking in the elevator. When some physicians had entered the elevator while smoking he informed them of this rule. These physicians had been extremely angry and had reported him to the director of the hospital. He had been summoned to the director's office and reprimanded for trying to give orders to the physicians. Here is a case where the charismatic person of the physician was somewhat inviolate in the face of fairly legitimate lay regulations.

The medical record librarian reveals another kind of dilemma-situation along another kind of axis. This lay person, who is charged with approval of the contents and format of medical records, often has to use what we have called a system of indirect sanctions to effect her job. This is a kind of adaptive behavior which works more or less as follows: Instead of giving physicians a direct order concerning the charts she tells them that unless they do thus and so the reputation of the hospital will suffer, especially at the next inspection.

This use of indirect sanctions by appealing, not to the rules and regulations which give one the right to give the order, but rather to the value system of the dominant persons (here the physician), is also clearly revealed in the case of a laundryman. He said that he never had any trouble in the hospital. Whenever he needed something he simply told the person from whom he wanted it that he was asking for that the patients needed. Thus, no direct order is given. Rather, there is an attempt to motivate the person to cooperate in terms of his own value system.

Or, take the case of an old pharmacist who made explicit and expert use of the dual conflict of authority within hospitals at a time when his pharmacy was to be moved to a new place in the hospital. What he had done was simply to play both sides against each other by going and saying to one side, "Don't you think it would be splendid if my pharmacy were in such-and-such a place?" Upon receiving a noncommittal "Yes" he would immediately go to the other side and say, "I have been told by Doctor So-an-So that my pharmacy should be in such and such a place." He then interpreted demurrers by the hospital administration as wanton disregard of professional opinion and wisdom.

It is pertinent to add that this pharmacist actually sewed up the entire system by appealing directly to members of the board of trustees in this fashion. He would visit their homes, bringing medicine for them or their children, and solicit their approval for the place he wanted his pharmacy moved. He would then tell members of both the medical staff and hospital administration that the board of trustees, the ultimate source of authority in the hospital, had suggested a good place for his pharmacy. This old-timer, with 40-odd years of hospital pharmacy experience, revealed a very acute manner of exploiting the divided authority system of the hospital to achieve precisely what he wanted. The result of two bosses for him was independence.

Another problem was reported by the chief of a pathology service who said that every physician in the hospital was a boss for his technicians. They claimed to know what the lab reports were supposed to contain, how much time analyses of various sorts would require, and which methods of analysis should best be used. The girls were constantly badgered to be quicker and more accurate. He felt that every physician in the hospital was a competing expert for his job as chief of the pathology service. Here is a point where lay and professional competence overlap to the confusion of the working personnel.

In still another case we talked with the registrar of a Veterans Administration hospital. He also reported himself as being "in the middle" and went on to add that he was really caught between the demands of the physicians in the hospital and the administrative requirements of operating the hospital. He was, in fact, caught in the classical conflict between lay and professional contingencies in the hospital, especially over the matter of the availability of beds. Administration wanted to adhere to the directives concerning criteria and categories of admission and discharge. Physicians wanted beds occupied by cases that were medically and professionally interesting. Here again there was a clear-cut conflict between the demands of the administrative and professional components of the system and this registrar, mediating between the two, stated the classical dilemma quite clearly, of being "caught in the middle."

"Money" vs. *"Service."* The problems of admissions offices reveal the confusions caused by the hospital's duality of values. Here, the demands of "money" and "service" are often in conflict for operating personnel and plainly reveal the ambivalence of the hospital as to whether it is a "service" or a "business" institution. This is certainly the case where the hospital is involved in the collection of money. Hospitals are urgent, yet apologetic, about the question of collections. The "front office" (the admissions office) is often caught in the cross-fire of these feelings of urgency and apology. For example, an admitting officer in one of the hospitals told us of her problem of assigning a private room to a man of uncertain means who was moribund. She said that almost against her better judgment she had assigned him to a private room. He died soon after and she was very glad that she had done so. But just the same, she said, she was immensely relieved when his wife came in and paid the hospital bill immediately after his death. Here again we see clearly the dilemma of a person who is weighing equally important humanitarian and fiscal considerations against each other. It is perhaps necessary to point out that there may be no ideal solutions to this kind of problem. This may be a kind of recurrent conflict which is, so to speak, endemic to the hospital as a human organization. Administrators who understand this are better equipped to deal with the strains of their organizations.

This conflict between fiscal and humanitarian demands, as they were interpreted by two different persons in positions of authority, made for a constant duel in one hospital that was observed. They were both persons high in administration—one with training as a nurse, the other with training in business administration. Neither was clearly assigned a position superior to the other. Each constantly berated the other. The administrator with training as a nurse stressed the cold, heartless inhumanity of the business manager, who, she, said, tried to screen patients entirely in terms of whether or not they could pay. The business manager complained of the idle, welfare orientation of the nurse, saying that if she had her way she would have the hospital filled with local indigents (a Skid Row was quite near) and they'd have to close their doors in bankruptcy. The conflict between these two for the position of authority was so great that there did exist in fact two organization charts. One, which was more or less publicly distributed, showed the nursing administrator as chief of the hospital. The other, privately distributed but adhered to by the trustees of the hospital, showed the business manager as the "boss" of the hospital.

There are many other problems which seem to be rooted in the peculiarities of hospital organization. Certainly many of the personnel problems faced by hospital administration appear to be more acutely difficult than those faced by administrators of other kinds of organizations. For example, certain hospitals which we observed could have been characterized as "weeping organizations." As a kind of bitter jest we could have established a "weeping index" in which the copiousness of tears shed by members (usually women) of the hospital was some measure of the effectiveness of its organization.

There are several important reasons for this, all of which the hospital must realize, as it must also realize that none of these is susceptible to magic solution. One of these, for example, is that the hospital is a structure of what we have called "blocked mobility." That is, the skills which are developed in one small component of the hospital, for example x-ray or pathology or housekeeping or admissions, are not readily transferrable to other departments. When the question of promotion to another department comes up, persons within the hospital who merit consideration often do not actually possess the skills needed to occupy the new position. In addition to this their skills continue to be required in their old department and very often department heads who have trained their personnel may resist their transfer to other parts of the hospital. This problem of "blocked mobility" is a constant source of frustration for hospital employes. Frequently, the only way to rise in the hospital structure is to leave the hospital, secure outside training, and then return at a higher level of status and competence. This means that a hospital cannot offer many of the same incentives of continuous promotion to its employees as can other institutions.

There is, of course, upward mobility available within the hospital. But some of it is of a peculiar kind and involves particularly difficult problems of inter-professional competition. For example, if we look at a hospital as a total number of certain set of functions, or operations, some of which have high prestige and others low, we find very often that professional (or subprofessional) groups within the hospital try to improve their status by taking on some of the functions of the occupation above them in the prestige scale, at the same time trying to drop off operations that are lowest in their own prestige scale. This has been true, for example, of the relationships among nurse's aides, nurses and physicians. The professionalization of nurses has included their taking over functions which previously were the physician's prerogative alone—for example, the emphasis upon the role of the nurse on the therapeutic team. In their turn the nurse's aides have attempted to focus upon basic nursing operations—some of which the nurses have been only too happy to relinquish as they themselves moved upward.

We have here a kind of dynamic relationship among members of various professions (or occupations) within the hospital which involves basic competition regarding the use of their skills and of certain functions which are assigned to them. This particular kind of competition is, of course, often disrupting to organizational stability. Frequently we find that the reapportioning of functions does not solve the conflict but simply changes its place. For example, the Veterans Administration in one hospital met the demands of the nurses by assigning some of their lower level functions to the attendants in the hospital. Within a short time, however, the conflict had shifted from the nurses to the attendants who were trying to drop some of their lower level functions into the hands of the janitors. In consequence, we frequently have within hospitals a kind of dynamic balance involving the functions of physicians, nurses, practical nurses, aides, maids and janitors in which the symbolic bedpan gets passed from one to the other. Removing odious functions from one occupation assuages it temporarily. We soon find, however, that another occupation is trying to get rid of the invidious task.

This pattern is often complicated by explicit efforts to "improve" the lower echelons through training, pay raises, raising standards of selection and performance, and so on. Such efforts tend to hasten and augment the upward drive of subordinate groups. The superiors who set about to improve their "help" may find themselves facing competitors. Thus, a successful program of recruitment and training of psychiatric aides may frighten nurses into formal reiterations that psychiatric aides perform nursing functions and should be controlled by nurses. These are some of the problems entailed by the peculiar nature of hospital upward mobility.

Professionalization. All of this points up the fact that a hospital is a seed-bed of professionalization. This makes for special kinds of motivation, and provides peculiar personnel problems. It is of help to hospitals that some persons who find satisfaction in the role and prestige of being professionals may be less concerned with the salaries of their jobs. Laboratory technicians, aides, medical record librarians, nurses—all these groups are striving toward recognition as professionals—striving for secure organization around special sets of skills, recognition by other occupations of their changed status, and increased prestige. It is important that the significant organizations of workers in hospitals are not unions demanding higher pay, but proto-professional organizations asking for changes in status and recognition. This development tends to reinforce the "service" value in hospitals rather than the "money" value.

But general problems for hospitals are also entailed by this drive toward professionalization. Each such group carries with it the beginning of the charismatic behavior which we noted for the physicians. Each wants to become its own "boss" and is sensitive to the interference of (which may mean administration by) other groups. Again, the general authority of the hospital confronts groups of specialists, secure in the unique possession of their skills, who can say, and perhaps make it stick, "They've got to do it my way. Otherwise I'll quit—and just let them try to do it without me." Thus the nascent professions in hospitals may provide a set of motivations which aid the work of the hospital, at the same time that they complicate the organization needed for such work.

Labor Market Competition. Hospitals also, for many categories of workers, come off second best in the labor market competition. The higher pay scales and larger benefits in other kinds of enterprises remove hospital work from the consideration of many workers. These same advantages tend to draw many good people out of hospital work toward more lucrative jobs. In many hospitals this leads to what has been called "seniority by default"—the good people get out and entrenched mediocrity prevails. Also, the continuous nature of hospital work, which doesn't respect nights, week ends, holidays or family responsibilities, may be responsible for mobilizing a certain proportion of "queer people" into hospital work. This may in some respects be an asset—many of these "queer people" may devote their entire lives to the hospital, literally almost never leaving it. Their usefulness is attested by the remark of an administrator that if he only had enough "queer people" to handle the long hours and dirty work he could obtain an excellent office force. However, it is often the case with such isolated people that they present "personality problems" which are disruptive to hospital organization. This becomes crucial in those hospitals which represent a "closed community" of many people living-in 24 hours a day. Family-like interpersonal pathologies and mutually hostile cliques readily develop. Certain types of "queer people" can devastate such a situation. Since it does not operate purely according to the logic of profit a hospital may have greater tolerance for such deviants than does business, for example. But they represent a recurrent problem of hospital administration nevertheless.

The particular functions which a hospital performs for its medical staff also set the stage for administrative problems. It would take us too far afield to do more than sketch this out. Briefly, one can indicate that, for physicians, a hospital affiliation may include the following functions: provide prestige among colleagues, and within professional associations; condition the size and type of practice; permit the advancement of career by extending treatment facilities; provide a system of referrals and sponsorship, of mutual claims and obligations among fellow physicians, through which practices may be established or maintained, or specialties developed; may even provide office space for them in clinics where private patients are seen. The hospital, then, is an arena for medical professional development. Administration needs to understand how its hospital is involved in this since crucial matters such as size and type of case load and applications for staff and house-office positions may be importantly affected.

Recent research has stressed another dimension of hospital organization— its functions as a milieu of therapy. Studies, particularly in psychiatric hospitals, have shown that disturbances in the social field (social environment) of the patient, and these include inter-professional conflicts, are directly related to the course of patients' illnesses. Thus disturbances arise, and therapy may be hindered or implemented, because of factors in the hospital organization. The task of administration thus takes on hitherto unsuspected dimensions of therapeutic relevance.

This is probably particularly complicated in psychiatric hospitals. In these the task of the therapist often involves considerable individuation of patient treatment. Hospital administration, whose task includes that of establishing organizational patterns, is seen as the enemy of this therapeutic practice. Now, however, with our growing awareness of the relationship between a patient's milieu and his illness and recovery, there is good reason to believe that the establishment of proper organizational patterns by administration may very well conduce to patient health. Thus the dimensions of a new research problem emerge: the study of the relationships between the needs of individuation and organization in hospitals as these affect the health of the patients.

One of the things that emerges from the material presented is the clear need for further research to provide needed knowledge. This is true of the problem areas already addressed as well as of areas of hospital organization not yet explored.

In the latter category, for example, studies are needed of the community relationships of hospitals. What are the most effective means of community support and how may these be mobilized? What are the crucial relationships between different kinds of hospitals (*i.e.* by size, specialty and so on) and different forms of community (*i.e.* by size, region)? What are the real communities served by hospitals and how are these related to the localities in which they operate? Who are served from these communities, who not, and why? What are the community expectations of hospital service and functions, and how closely do these coincide with the survival contingencies of the particular hospital?

What about the recruitment of operating personnel? Do small-town hospitals need small-town people to operate them? Should they be local people or strangers, and for which kind of jobs? Do local people get caught in a web of kinship obligations that make it difficult for them to perform professionally? Can a stranger more easily be professional? Is he, however, so excluded from local community understandings as to be made less effective? Who, in a community, are best selected as trustees? These are part of a host of community problems involved in the administration of hospitals. Knowledge in these areas could greatly help administrators.

Administrators' Functions. And, finally, study of the growing profession of hospital administration itself would be greatly rewarding. What are the observed functions of hospital administrators in different sizes and kinds of hospitals? How close are these to what administrators say they do and think they do? What are the intrinsic operating problems of hospital administrators? We have cited some of them—much more needs to be developed in this area. How close together are the expectations developed in professional training and the realities of this work? What is the image of this profession in the minds of other professions and of patients and the public? Is this a satisfying self-image for the hospital administrator, and if not, why? What and why are the relative advantages of being a physician of a layman in this job? The former feels guilty about not practicing medicine. The latter is denied intimate participation in many of the central interests of the institution. Is the professionalization of hospital administration tending to reduce this dilemma? Surely much new knowledge is needed here.

49   ORGANIZATION, PERSONNEL AND FUNCTIONS
OF STATE AND PRIVATE MENTAL HOSPITALS:
A COMPARATIVE ANALYSIS

By S. Kirson Weinberg

The influence of formal and informal facets of institutional organization upon the behavior of its members has been studied for the factory, prison, and more recently, for the mental hospital.[1] This characterization of mental hospital life is especially pertinent because it repudiates the former view that the condition of the psychotic person is unaffected by contemporary social influences.[2] Furthermore, the organization of the mental hospital affects its custodial and therapeutic effectiveness. Hence these criteria must be considered when we compare the state mental hospital which provides custody for most mental patients in this country, with the private hospital, especially the psycho-therapeutically-oriented private hospital.[3] In this comparison we shall deal successively with the demographic features, the social structure, personnel, and functions of these types of hospitals pertinent to their effects upon the patients, and shall ascertain what, if any, aspects of private hospital organization can be applied successfully to the state hospital to augment its therapeutic effectiveness.

I. Comparative Composition, Mobility, and Size of Population. Private and state mental hospitals attract patients from distinct social classes. The private hospital is composed largely of patients from the middle, upper-middle, and the upper classes, while the state mental hospital is composed largely of people from the lower and middle classes. Sprinklings of over-lapping classes exist, however, in the two hospitals. On the one hand, some middle-class patients are sent to the private hospital for a brief period by the financial sacrifice of the family. On the other hand, some hopeless psychotics from the upper-middle and upper classes are sent, as a last resort, to state hospitals.

Admission into the two types of hospitals also carries divergent social and legal meanings. The patient admitted into the private hospital is not defined as insane, and he can leave when his family so desires. In fact, his discharge from the hospital may result largely from the financial considerations by the family rather than from his emotional condition. Hence, statistics on the condition of discharged patients are not recorded for private hospitals. The patient in the private hospital can retain his civil and property rights. His committment can be concealed and defined as a "rest." The person committed to a state hospital, even though he may, in many states, enter voluntarily or as in "need of mental treatment," still in many instances, he may be committed as "insane," temporarily lose his civil and property rights, and have no voice in determining his release. Moreover, regardless of the manner of admission, the very presence of a patient in a state mental hospital tends to carry a stigma of "insane," despite the increasing public tolerance towards the mentally ill. In brief, the meaning of being admitted to the two types of hospitals varies considerably in its social definitions, and this also may influence the oriented patient's definition of his hospital situation as well as of himself.

The discrepant degrees of mobility of patients in the two types of hospitals are indicated by the contrasting rates of resident populations and the much closer rates of annual first admissions and discharges. In 1953 the number of resident patients in 205 state hospitals was 19 times the number in the 208 private hospitals: the respective figures were 293,303 and 14,757. The population in the average state hospital (2,969 patients) was 38 times that in the average private hospital (76.7 patients).[5] But the state hospitals had only 2.8 as many annual first admissions as the private hospitals (115,048 to 41,425) and only 1.6 times as many discharges as the private hospitals (102,179 to 67,571). In fact, the private hospital discharged 1.2 times as many patients from intra-mural care than did the state hospitals (59,741 to 46,805), while the state hospital discharged 23 times as many patients who were in the community on conditional discharge on furloughs or on trial visits as the private hospitals (55,374 to 2,369).[6] In brief, the state mental hospital has many more static patients than has the private hospital, and as such has different problems of custody. But where is this static population in the state hospital?

The state mental hospital has a large proportion of residual patients who are unresponsive to treatment, and who cannot be discharged. In one typical state hospital, this unresponsive group comprised about 70 to 80 percent of the hospital patients, as contrasted with one private hospital where only six percent of separated patients had been in the hospital over four years and 16 percent of 45 resident patients over four years.[7] For one thing, custodial care is too expensive in private hospitals to permit extended periods of stay except for the very wealthy patients. Secondly, the diagnostic types of patients who enter private hospitals seem more responsive to treatment or to temporary improvement than patients admitted into the state hospital. In 1953, neurotics, affective psychotics and alcoholics constituted about 67 percent of the first admissions to the private hospital. By contrast, the slight majority of first admissions—51 percent—in the state hospital were schizophrenics and the senile disordered, but these diagnostic categories of patients constituted only 32 percent in the private hospitals.[8]

But even schizophrenics vary by chances of improvement, which affects their length of hospital stay. The broad category of schizophrenia ranges from the transient schizophrenics, on the one extreme, who recover quickly, to chronic schizophrenics, on the other extreme, whose condition resists treatment. This difference in amenability to improvement can be indicated by length of stay. In a study of patients who had died in a state hospital, it was found that schizophrenics had an average length of stay of 14.6 years. In one Midwestern state hospital about 67 percent of the schizophrenics were hospitalized for five years or longer. Yet the present author's study of transient schizophrenics pointed up that the average length of stay was 6.2 months.[9] In one private hospital, 77 percent of the schizophrenics left the hospital within two years, and 72 percent within one year. Even though in 1953, schizophrenics comprised about 23 percent of the first admissions to private hospitals, the vast majority of them very likely left within the first year.[10] Of course, this does not always denote improvement, but may mean, too, lack of funds for further treatment.

II. Comparative Social Structure and Personnel. The extent to which the mental hospital emphasizes therapeutic or custodial functions results from its formal and informal organization. The character of its organization affects the staff's orientation towards their duties, their official relationships among themselves, and, most important, their relationships with the patients.

The staff mental hospital, with a rigid, caste-like structure, segregates the staff from the patients into two distinct categories of people. This broad divisive structure, while characterizing many private hospitals, especially the biologically-oriented type, is less rigid and has a different meaning in the psychologically-oriented private hospital. The difference in the meaning of a social hierarchy resides in the way the staff uses its dominance in treating and caring for the patients. This difference can be illustrated by an incident which reflects upon the patient-centered private hospital and the institution-centered state hospital.

In one of the psychoanalytically-oriented private hospitals, one patient complained about the lack of drinking fountains in the ward. Within a reasonably short time the hospital had a drinking fountain installed.[11] Had this episode occurred in an average state hospital, the patients and others would have been incredulous and would have considered the event a delusion of grandeur. On the patient's part, the extent to which the needs of the patients become the focus around which the social structure is built, indicates the extent to which the hospital is patient-centered. While this patient-centeredness characterizes the most effective, psychotherapeutically-oriented hospitals, it is an institution-centeredness that characterizes the state mental hospital. The divergent social structures of these institutions also affect their collective orientations.

Social Structure Of The Staff. The social structures of both types of hospitals include the professional personnel on top, the superintendent as the chief, followed by the clinical director and psychiatrists or physicians, and sometimes other clinical personnel, such as the psychologist and psychiatric social worker, then the quasi-professional and technical persons, such as the registered nurses, adjunct therapists such as occupational therapists, physiotherapists, recreational leaders, and finally the psychiatric aides, attendants, and maintenance persons.[12] In addition, every ward had a specific hierarchy and structure. This ward structure is important because of its direct impact upon the patient. Although general hospital policy and practice was formulated and implemented by the top hierarchy, these policies and practices had to be mediated through and interpreted by the ward personnel.

In both hospitals the professionals had the most authority, prestige, and salary; they limited their informal relations largely to each other, ate in separate dining rooms, and had an ordering relationship with the other staff members. In both types of hospitals the clinical and administrative personnel were distant in orientation, and sometimes at cross purposes in their policy. In the state hospital the clinical personnel were concerned with the patient's condition, while the maintenance personnel emphasized the hospital maintenance and the patient's job.[13] In the private hospital, the clinical personnel concentrated upon the patient's personal condition and welfare, while the administrative staff stressed his payment of fees. The staffs of the two types of hospitals can be compared with regard to the scope of, and orientation to, their duties and their coordinated efforts in treating or in caring for the patients. But the effective discharge of their duties depends, first, upon the number of patients in their care.

In 1955, state hospitals had a doctor-patient ratio of 1 to 201. But this ratio was far short of the doctor-patient ratio recommended by the American Psychiatric Association of 1 to 30 for patients in intensive treatment, and 1 to 150 for patients in continued treatment. The psychologist-patient ratio is 1 to 1106, but the recommended APA psychologist-patient ratios are 1 to 100 for patients in intensive treatment, and 1 to 500 for patients in continued treatment. The graduate nurses had a patient ratio of 1 to 82, but the recommended APA ratios for graduate nurse to patient is 1 to 5 and 1 to 40 for patients in intensive treatment and patients in continued treatment respectively. The ratio of attendants and nurses to patients is 1 to 7, but the recommended APA ratio is 1 to 4 and 1 to 6 for intensive and continued treatment patients respectively. Finally, the ratio of social workers to patients is 1 to 163, but the recommended APA ratio is 1 to 60 for extra-mural patients and 1 to 80 for first admissions.[14] These ratios are limited to the clinical personnel who are concerned directly with diagnosis, physical care and treatment of the patients.

What about the competence of the personnel? In 1950, less than 16 percent of the certified psychiatrists in the United States were connected with state hospitals. Of 382,047 graduate nurses, only 1.3 percent were employed in state hospital work. In 1949, of 3600 accredited clinical psychologists, about 3 percent were employed in state hospitals. In 1950, of 2,253 trained psychiatric social workers, 22 percent were employed in state hospitals.[15] In short, many state mental hospitals do not have competent clinical teams to do the diagnostic and therapeutic work. This means that diagnosis and therapy are frequently thrust into the hands of a psychiatrist who, with his many duties and many patients, as well as his limited psychological training, tends to pursue the traditional hospital routine, and hence, accords the patients the necessary medical attention and superficially inquires about their condition on his rounds.

Yet this condition, with all its shortcomings, represents an enormous improvement over the state hospital situation of a decade ago. For example, from 1945 to 1955 in the state hospitals psychologists have increased by over 575 percent, social workers by over 200 percent, graduate nurses by over 150 percent, and physicians by 82.4 percent, and attendants by over 125 percent.[16] The state hospital professional staffs are increasing in quantity, and because of improved training, are increasing in quality.

But in one private psychotherapeutically-oriented hospital, there were 165 personnel and 116 staff members to 60 patients, which is about two staff members to one patient. There were 27 full and part-time therapists, or about one therapist for two to three patients.[17] Furthermore, nearly all these therapists were trained, and perceived the patient as a therapeutic problem. But this ratio very likely does not obtain in medically-oriented private hospitals. The problem is whether this ratio is needed in the state hospital, because physical treatment requires fewer therapists and less contact with the patient. Another important consideration is the attitude and concerned work of the staff in their treatment of the patient.

The doctor-patient relation in the state hospital tends to be superficial, impersonal and distant, while the patient, on the other hand, regards the doctor as one who controls his hospital destiny. Frequently, he tries to approach the doctor, but the doctor has so many patients that any single patient cannot get much time from the doctor. Doctors who are medically oriented feel that their relations with the patient require merely a cheerful "bedside manner" or reassurance and no concerted conversations.

But since state hospitals tend to be medically-oriented, even adjunct psychotherapy, when indicated, may not be administered. Younger doctors who want to conduct prolonged psychotherapy, find that such tends to be discouraged, because it neglects other patients, and at best carries no collective approval or reward. In time, the younger psychiatrist loses interest, becomes discouraged, and conforms to the norms for the professional staff, or he leaves the hospital. Other physicians feel overburdened by administrative chores. As a result in Southern state hospital, 80 percent of the physicians remained less than three years. Furthermore, the doctor's relationship with the attendants directly and indirectly affect the patients.

The attendants are another significant broad category of personnel. They are with the patients for longer periods than any other members of the staff, and influence the patients decisively. One attendant phrased their influence as follows: "The superintendent may run the hospital, but we run the patients."[18] The doctors, despite the wide gap in status, are dependent upon the attendants for ascertaining the patients' condition and for having their orders carried out. Attendants feel that their activities are unrewarded and unrecognized, and are sensitized to slights and rebuffs by the professional staff. They can displace their hostilities and aggressions upon the patients, who are vulnerable and defenseless in this situation. Thus an attendant can harass a patient to the point of agitation or can contribute to the patient's relapse. These actions, however, are not characteristic, because the main reaction of the attendants is indifference to the patients so long as they do not get out of line.

Attendants, because of their subordinate roles, are on a distinct social level, with a distinct occupational sub-culture. Their common understandings and concerted techniques for handling patients are transmitted informally, usually by example, to the novice, who also learns by reprimand, for supposed infractions of the rules. Formal rules, however, do not coincide with attendants' practices, which are oriented towards keeping the patients "in their place," preventing escapes and towards overseeing the patients' work. Attendants remain socially distant from the patients, but are motivated by preconceived notions of insanity and of psychotic behavior.

Regardless of an individual attendant's desires to help a patient, he has to conform to the attendant culture by refraining from being too friendly or too sympathetic with the patients.[19] The attendants' aims are oriented towards controlling the patients and keeping the ward in order, not necessarily toward improving the patients, although some attendants do contribute positively to a patient's improvement by kindness and sympathy. However, their reactions are not necessarily rewarded by the hospital or encouraged by other attendants. Since the pay and work incentives for attendants are quite low, unskilled persons with only limited education can be recruited for these jobs. Some are personally unstable transients who float from job to job. Other attendants from farms and small towns have normal paternal and maternal sentiments, despite meagre schooling, and can be of help to the patients. The psychiatric aide as a category of trained personnel on the attendant level, has increased during the past decade in some state hospitals, but considerably more remains to be done to improve the caliber of the attendant.

The doctors in the psychotherapeutic hospital are oriented differently than in the state hospital.[20] In one private hospital, the 22 doctors were psychiatrists and were psychoanalytically trained; that is, they were students at the local psychoanalytic institute, and hence, were psychologically-oriented to the patients. The standard career of the psychiatrist began as a clinical administrator, followed by beginnings of administering psychotherapy. He then devoted himself two to three years to the hospital, after which he began to see private patients as well as to attend to hospital duties. He continued this mixed practice for another two or three years. Then he either became an administrator, teacher, or researcher in the hospital, or withdrew for private practice. Within eight years, at the peak of his experience, he usually withdrew to private practice. As a result, there was a continual turnover of psychiatrists in the hospital, with the hospital losing its trained psychiatrists.[21] Psychiatrists, and especially psychoanalysts, aspire to private practice. Hence, they regard institutional work as a training period. In this respect, the majority of psychiatrists have a polar experience to many long-time state hospital doctors who have somehow "had it" or failed in private practice, and have turned to the state hospital as a source of livelihood. Thus, the private hospital psychoanalysts regard private practice as the optimum situation, while the state hospital doctor experienced private practice with disappointment and failure. Furthermore, the psychoanalyst has had enough psychological training to find psychotherapy purposive and satisfying. The long-time state hospital doctor, as a physician, approached psychiatry as close to a medical specialty as possible, and viewed treatment in terms of medication or physical manipulation, such as electric shock.[22] Without the preparation for psychotherapeutic training, he was not always clear as to whether his conversations with the patients really affected any change. Furthermore, the patients themselves frequently wanted their illness to be a kind of physical malady, because it spared them from facing their conflicts. Thus the organic approach to disordered behavior prevailed in the state mental hospital, and it prevails, too, in many private hospitals; and furthermore, it prevails in the psychiatric societies, with psychotherapy definitely on the defensive as a treatment for psychosis. But the implication of this discrepancy between the physical or medical and the psychological approach to treatment, makes for a different doctor-patient relationship and leads to a different mental hospital atmosphere. The psychiatrist, by developing close rapport with the patient, affected the patient's outlook and created a therapeutic atmosphere in the private hospital which was minimized in the state hospital.

In some private hospitals attendants and psychiatric aides are not much better than in the state hospitals. Even in one of the best psychologically-oriented private hospitals, the staff category at the attendant level, psychiatric aides, were students and persons in marginal positions and were uneducated in psychiatric matters. They had very little incentive to remain in their hospital capacity, and their turnover was very high. Of a total of 41 psychiatric aides, the complement for the hospital, there were 79 separations from the hospital during a two-year period. Of these separations, 43 were unsatisfactory.[23]

The caliber of the psychiatric aides while somewhat superior in the private hospital than in the state hospital, is not markedly so. Furthermore, their status distance from the doctor, their discontent and high turnover in the private and state hospitals, are common shortcomings. In the private hospital, nurses starting at the hospital had almost an even chance of leaving under a cloud, while aides had one chance in four of failure; and if leaving without notice was considered failure, then there was an even chance that psychiatric aides would leave discontented. One chief difficulty with this private hospital, as with many others, is that it did not provide a satisfactory career for the psychiatric aide.

Social Structure of the Patients: The kinds of patients who are in private and state hospitals vary inversely by numbers. In the private hospitals the majority of patients are considered responsive to treatment or to improvement. In the state hospitals the majority of patients are the chronic patients, who are considered not responsive to treatment. In one midwestern state hospital the chronic patients comprised about 66 percent of all patients, while at least 19 out of 39 wards were chronic wards, not including the physically ill and chronically agitated patients. About 44 percent of the patients were in the hospital longer than 10 years, and about 66 percent were in over five years. By contrast, in one private hospital only 16 percent had been in the hospital longer than four years. Thus the *esprit* of the two hospitals differs considerably.

In the state hospital the hopeful patients are on top of the patient hierarchy in terms of institutional attention, not power, followed by the broad category of chronic patients, and lastly the agitated patients, with the physically-ill and bed-ridden, in a peripheral category.

The career of the hopeful patients in the state hospital compares with and even resembles the career of the hopeful patients in the private hospital. Their stay is relatively short, usually under one year. They get the most intense attention from the doctors, the most frequent use of treatment facilities such as drugs and electric shock, and are usually in the best furnished wards.

They have the most frequent contacts with the outside world by trial visits at home and by visitors and letters. Their orientation is towards release, and they do not necessarily consider themselves in the same mental category as the chronic patients who are the long-time hospital patients and the agitated patients.

The chronic or static patients are in the hospital longer than two years, and have to define their hospital role in a different manner. They realize that their chances of release diminish, because they are in a ward where fewer patients are released. Hence, they reorient themselves towards the hospital and try to make it as habitable as possible. This group, ranging from "institutional cures," the privileged patients, through the patients with limited privileges, and finally to the apathetic and listless patients who can do very little for themselves.

The chronic patients are the preponderant group of hospital residents at any given time. They markedly influence the pattern of hospital behavior. They are the workers who find, by necessity, that they must come to terms with the hospital, and they are the ones whose length of stay give the hospital a continuity and a tradition. This cumulation of these chronic or static patients makes the state mental hospital predominantly a custodial, somewhat self-contained, institution.

The agitated patients represent a distinct diagnostic and administrative category. In this category are not only disturbed patients, but also those who constitute a problem to the hospital by their continued defiance, escapes, or assaultive behavior.

Culture Of The Patients: The culture of the patients in the state hospital has emerged out of their defensive and helpless position in the hospital hierarchy. It has become consolidated and reinforced by their relative isolation from the staff, and it has achieved definite continuity by the long-time patients. Thus hopeful patients are determined to soften the stigmatized meaning of their sequestration in the hospital, and foster ways of trying to get released from the hospital. Chronic patients strive to make the hospital as habitable as possible, avoid the punitive staff members, especially the attendants, and devise ways to overcome the hospital monotony. But the important aspect of the patient-culture is that it disrupts communication with the staff, as much as the staff, by its indifference and impersonality, blocks communication with the patients.[24]

The culture of the patients in the psychotherapeutically oriented private hospital is centered around therapy and personal improvement, as well as being released from the hospital. They do not feel stigmatized by their presence in the hospital, and they do not feel helpless and defenseless with reference to the staff. Hence, the flow of communication between the patients and the staff is not blocked, and this unimpeded social process can contribute to the patient's improvement, and especially to his added self-assurance. Thus the culture of the patients in the psychotherapeutic hospital emerges from a relatively free and non-constraining therapeutic process. By contrast, the culture of the patients in the state hospital emerges from a constraining custodial process.

III. Social Structure and Functions. State and private hospitals are, in varying degrees, organized to carry out the 1) protection of the public and the patients, 2) custody of the patients, 3) physical and psychological treatment of the patients, and 4) the peripheral functions of training hospital personnel and conducting research.

Protection Of The Patients And The Public: The hospital's role in protecting the public directly affects its position in the community. Both types of hospitals tend to be isolated from the community. Frequently the personnel of the hospital are hired from other communities and tend to be segregated from the residents of the community. Secondly, the residents in many of these communities, motivated by their stereotypes about the insane, tend to be alerted to the possibilities of escaped patients and the irresponsible damage which they believe patients can conceivably commit. Thus the private hospital, like the state hospital, must avert alarming the community. Private as well as state hospitals are also responsible for the safety of the patients, and must see that patients do not escape and hurt themselves, and that they do not get harmed inside the hospital. The private hospital may be more lenient about patients' escapes, but they cannot be too lenient, because the community may react by revoking its license. The state hospital staff realizes that escapes can create very adverse publicity, which they strive to avoid.

Custody: The state hospitals, despite increased budgets, still have difficulty in providing adequate shelter, food, clothing, entertainment, medical care, in addition to the therapies for their patients. In the area of custody, the private hospital is, on the average, superior to the state hospital, but this custody varies with the fees the patients pay and the amount of profit the private hospital realizes. By tradition the state hospital is an isolated, largely self-contained custodial institution. The 19th century so-called "therapies" were ineffective and brutal, with beatings, emetics, and blood letting. When sheer humanism, as well as added knowledge, dictated their abandonment, the absence of effective physical therapies emphasized the state hospital's custodial function. And the funds allotted by the state legislatures indicate the low level of custody for the state hospital patient. Since World War II it has consistently improved. In 1951, the average annual expenditure for each state mental hospital patient was $828.24, but these average expenditures vary regionally and by state. Wisconsin had the highest per capita expenditure, $1508.98, and Tennessee had the lowest per capita expenditure, $360.39.[25] State hospital custodial conditions are improving, but do not come up to APA standards, and are, of course, far below those of the most expensive private mental hospital. In two hospitals of this type the average monthly cost for each patient was over $800, and primarily because of the many personnel who are present to help the patient.[26]

The state mental hospitals in the densely populated areas are overcrowded. This over-crowding affects the proper sleeping conditions for patients, as well as their privacy, and intensifies the pressure upon the hospital for prematurely discharging patients.[27] To what extent private hospitals are over-crowded is unknown from available writings.

Of more decisive influence in hospital custody is the place of work by patients. The state hospitals which must conform to a low budget have a large proportion of patients in some work capacity. In one Midwestern state hospital, 520, or 20.8 percent of 2,494 patients worked, and 101 patients who were paid received a total stipend of only $261.00. In a hospital in the deep South, 56.0 percent of 4,390 patients were employed in some capacity.[28] In many hospitals, the patients had no choice but to work. In other hospitals, the patients had the alternative of not working and becoming bored, or working and receiving privileges. Most of them preferred work, because work indicated status, and even facilitated discharge. Although work was supposed to benefit the patients, it was never definitely established as to just how they were helped, except to prevent deadly monotony. Patients worked primarily because it was necessary for hospital maintenance. In a few instances, good workers were even delayed in their discharge. Furthermore, the patients' work-roles obscured their patient-roles. The patients as cheap and available labor in the state hospital could and did give the professional staff a depreciated estimate of people. In one particular instance, a patient who had attended college was assigned as a domestic, and she refused to work at such an assignment. Her only recourse was to remain idle, deprived of the "privilege" of walking the grounds. As a result, with the doctor's assurance that the work would facilitate her improvement and her discharge, she reluctantly returned to work.

But in the expensive, patient-centered private hospital, patients are absolved from hospital chores, which were performed by domestics and maintenance workers. Hence their roles as patients were not obscured by work assignments. Second, they retained status by not being ordered about except as patients.[29] The more opulent patients could even perceive technical and professional personnel as subordinates whom they must obey for their own welfare. In this role they did not feel the same type of inferiority to the staff that characterized the attitudes of state hospital patients.

Physical Therapy: Electric shock and drug therapies have an effectiveness which is independent of the physicians who administer them. On a physical level, whether a patient receives these physical therapies in the state or private hospital, is of secondary concern, because the therapies would have similar effects. The margin of difference would be based superficially upon the number of shock treatments or the amount of dosage administered. But the basic criteria for comparison would be the way the hospital staff and the patients are oriented towards and use the physical therapy, and the way physical therapy is supplemented with psychotherapy.

The aura of mystery about therapy which has been traditional in medical practice, pertains in the state hospitals and thus the patient is kept in the dark about his treatment and its effects. This can arouse misgivings in the patient, who may then become quite anxious about the therapy. One patient complained: "If I go to a doctor for medicine, I expect him to tell me what's wrong and how the medicine is going to help me. That's the least he can do. But here they tell you nothing. You just have to obey."[30] There is the further twisted meaning of physical therapy as a kind of punitive instrument for maintaining order in the hospital and insuring the patient's obedience. One patient who talked back to her physician was labelled "disturbed," and had electric shock prescribed for her. Since the patient regarded electric shock as punishment, she sought out other doctors to intercede for her, and tried to amend her behavior to avoid the electric shock. She believed her resentful behavior to the psychiatrist, and not her condition, prompted the "treatment." This attitude formerly pertained to hydrotherapy, which is a means for quieting agitated patients. Electric shock treatment becomes interpreted by the patients as punishment, and creates intense fear of the treatment. In Southern State Hospital, the attendants who supervise the patients most of the time could report their actual or presumed condition. They once placed some patients on a list of those in need of shock therapy because these patients resented ill-treatment by the attendants and because they refused to eat the objectionable hospital food. Many attendants considered any patient who deviated from ward routine, as mentally disturbed and hence, in need of shock therapy. Some attendants even believed that the shock therapy was good for all mental patients because it deterred them from worrying about themselves, and actually improved their physical health.[31]

To what extent does this orientation characterize the private hospital? At the psychologically-oriented hospital, physical treatment, when administered, was minimal, and hence represented no problem. The patients were informed of the effects of shock, and had no extraneous anxieties concerning physical therapy. In most private hospitals the nurses and attendants had less need for resorting to shock treatment as a disciplinary lever for conformistic purposes. But in some less adequate private hospitals, where the attendants were not highly trained or qualified, a somewhat similar emphasis upon control was implemented. Since private hospital patients were committed for shorter periods, there was less need for transforming physical treatment into a disciplinary medium.

Another problem is the complementary use of psychotherapy to consolidate the effects of physical therapy. Shock or drug therapy can transform an agitated and non-communicative person into a communicative human being, but some psychotherapy to resolve the person's conflicts as well as to reassure him, is vital. The relative emphasis of complementary psychotherapy in the private or state hospital would enhance the effectiveness of the physical therapy. Since many state and private hospital psychiatrists doubt the efficacy of psychotherapy and regard psychosis as an organic illness, they also made minimal use of psychotherapy, except perhaps for purposes of reassurance.

Custody Versus Therapy In The State Hospital: Since the state hospital emphasizes its custodial function, it has to reconcile its therapeutic program with the custodial routine and orientation of the staff. In some hospitals, some therapy such as hydrotherapy, was not used because the staff felt it was unnecessary. With this equipment to implement physical therapy in the state hospital, the staff even had to be reoriented. Belknap has described the dilemma of the superintendent, as a medical man in a southern hospital, as follows:

If they conformed to the structure of the hospital as they found it, they could carry out a reasonably good, routine custodial administration. If however, they attempted to establish modern psychiatric treatment of patients, the procedures necessary called for changes in the traditional routines. This change amounted to a change in habits of most of the older employees, and immediately upset the routine custodial structure, thus preventing the Superintendent from acting efficiently as an executive. But the professional training of any physician has been for at least the past hundred years in the direction of seeking and finding improvement in the condition of his patients. Thus, the superintendents of Southern State Hospital have found themselves confronted with a choice between being good doctors and poor administrators, or good administrators and poor doctors.[32]

Thus, in the conservative, tradition-bound state hospitals, therapy represented a departure from the custodial emphasis, and created or intensified anxiety among the long-time staff members. But the state hospitals were more receptive to organic therapies, whether shock or drugs, than to psychotherapy, because this form of treatment is consistent with the impersonal relations and social structure prevalent in the state mental hospital. For physical therapy can be administered relatively simply and impersonally, and can affect an improvement in symptoms in a relatively short time. Hence, its use does not change drastically the attitudes of the staff, but merely calls for some new routines.

Psychotherapy: The Hospital As A Therapeutic Community. The caste-like, tradition-bound structure of the state mental hospital impedes psychotherapy because it impedes communication between staff and patients, because it confuses the role of the patients, and because it represses instead of stimulates the expression of their feelings. Despite these deficits, the state mental hospital affords a reservoir of therapeutic push by the collective influences among the patients and by the hospital setting itself.

The barrier between staff and patients, which impedes therapy, exists mainly for administrative control, staff convenience, and custodial effectiveness, and not for the patient's benefit. But this barrier also results from the patient's culture, which is oriented towards shortening their hospital stay. Many patients, as a result, conceal or disguise their condition in order to create the most favorable impression for the doctor, whom they regard as an authority figure facilitating their release. This barrier, in part, has resulted from the social distance, impersonal attitude, even indifference, of the staff. Hence, the conflicts, irritations, and problems of the patients are not confided to the doctor. The doctor can penetrate this barrier when he has the time to allot to the particular patient, when the patient is not oriented to the patient's culture, or when the patient is so lonely that he craves an outlet.

Second, the patients who are assigned as workers in the hospitals are obscured, or at least confused, in their roles as patients, as we have emphasized, although conceivably some might have benefited from the jobs. Third, the patients were intent upon controlling their feelings in order to conform to the rules of the hospital, because they were aware that any agitation or spontaneous behavior was frequently punished. Hence, they were afraid to be spontaneous or to manifest feeling.

Still a high percentage of first admission patients in state hospitals recover within the first year. Certainly the intervention of somatic therapy had an important influence upon their recovery, but other forces inherent in the hospital social process also influenced their condition. First, the patients are removed from the conflict-creating settings of the family, job, and neighborhood which precipitated their breakdown. Second, the patients are placed amidst a group of patients who accept them. Third, their peer-like collective living arrangement disrupts their past frame of reference and impels them to view and do things in the hospital from a different orientation. This collective living also has an impulsion which facilitates the socialization of the patient. The social pressure of doing things on time and with others, work so that the patients feel the push of others. Fourth, their desire to leave the hospital and resentment against the stigma of insanity, are shared collectively and reinforced by other patients. This collective reinforcement of the patient's desire to leave the hospital has varied effects. It intensifies his desire to improve in order to be released. It idealizes the "outside community," which ceases to be a cruel world, but a free world, a world of release. In short, as he feels this social push to leave the hospital, his past conflicts become less incapacitating and he acquires a divergent perspective towards his surroundings as well as a feeling of belonging, and a fighting hope to leave the hospital. Fifth, he acquires a series of rationalizations for his condition which may help him improve.[33] Some patients found that the leisure and the daily conversation with other patients had a positive effect upon them. Since many hopeful patients improve spontaneously, even if left alone, this group pressure, at the least, enhances their tendencies to improve.

The psychologically-oriented private hospital, however, mobilizes all its clinical personnel to foster a therapeutic community. From this orientation, the private hospital instructs the staff to help the patient improve.

Two general therapeutic approaches can be discerned in the psychologically-oriented private hospitals. One approach is directive, and consists of prescribed attitudes by the staff towards the individual patient in order to improve his personal condition. The other approach is less directive, and provides a permissive setting for the patient so that he can express himself freely and obtain insight into his behavior.[34] The directive approach which has been used at Menninger's clinic, can best be described as follows:[35]

A set of attitudes was developed over the years, covering a wide variety of psychodynamic constellations. These attitudes were designed to meet the total needs of the patient, both conscious and unconscious. The term "needs" is not used in the sense of discerning only what the patient wishes, but rather what conditions are necessary in order to restore emotional balance. These attitudes have been defined and explained in a guide booklet that is available to all the professional personnel working in the hospital. When each patient's case is discussed in staff conference, a specific attitude to be maintained by all personnel toward the patient is prescribed. It is written on the orders for the patient, and is communicated to all professional personnel, which includes nurses, psychiatric aides, recreational therapists, dietician, and any others who will have important contacts with him.

For example, an attitude of firm kindness is ordered for a depressed patient to help him expiate his guilt feelings and externalize his aggressions. But this this attitude does not mean superficial cheerfulness nor acquiescence to pleas that he be left alone to suffer for his unworthiness. While this program in principle should prove effective, we do not have the results which would show the extent of its effectiveness for diverse types of patients.

The second less-directive approach which was implemented at Chestnut

Lodge aims to cultivate an environmental setting which reveals an understanding of the patient's difficulties which led to his breakdown, and the conditions which impede his improvement. It aims to help the patient reorient himself to these difficulties by individual psychotherapy and by a tolerant staff who accept the patient's problem and encourage his needs for friendship and security. In brief, this hospital environment is almost diametrically opposed in philosophy to that of the state mental hospital.

IV. Conclusions. In brief, the state mental hospital, despite a predominantly custodial emphasis reinforced by traditional procedures, has contributed to the improvement of many recently admitted, hopeful patients. The inherent milieu therapy within patient interaction contributes to this therapeutic process, supplementary to drug and electric shock therapy, by incorporating certain features from the private, psychotherapeutically-oriented hospital.

First, it must acquire trained and competent psychiatrists and adjunct personnel, especially nurses and attendants. It must make their hospital careers satisfactory to recruit them and to prevent their leaving.

Second, the attendant as a crucial figure in the patient's hospital stay would be trained as a psychiatric aide who would devote his time as a kind of group leader for the patients. Although the physical work in the ward would be done in part by the patients, it would not be their main function and it would not obscure their roles as patients.

Third, the competent clinical personnel who would not be overburdened with clerical duties would probably be able to disrupt the patient's defensive culture and reestablish lines of communication between the staff and the patients.

Fourth, the clinical personnel would channelize and direct the collective pressure in the patient-milieu to help the individual patient become reoriented.

Fifth, it would discard those traditional procedures that impede the patient's improvement.

Sixth, the patients would be oriented in concerted ways about hospital life so that they would not experience needless anxieties about the physical therapies or about their adjustment to the hospital. This orientation would be continued throughout the patients' careers to the time of outright discharge from the hospital.

50 TEAMWORK IN THE OPERATING ROOM

By Robert N. Wilson*

Introduction. Like all dramas, a surgical operation has certain important plots and subplots, a cast of characters, and a spatial setting. In narrative form, surgery at a large general hospital often occurs in a sequence such as the following:

From *Human Organization,* 12, (Winter, 1954), 9–14. Copyright 1954 by the Society for Applied Anthropology.

"At seven o'clock in the morning, nurses have arrived on the surgical floor. They find maids finishing the cleaning of the operating suites and corridors. Notices of scheduled operations for the day are posted in prominent places, listing the patient's name, type of case, operating surgeon, and appropriate operating room. Orderlies and nurses aides are wheeling small tables into the rooms, with sterile equipment laid out ready for use. The charge nurse assigns to their respective cases the scrub nurses (who will actually assist the surgeon) and the circulating nurses (who will perform general tasks around the operating room such as fetching water and counting sponges).

"As the hour of surgery, eight o'clock, approaches, the scrub nurses are washing hands and arms in the small scrub rooms next to the operating rooms; when they are thoroughly washed, according to specific procedures and an allotted time, they slip into sterile gowns and gloves. Their scrubbing must precede that of the doctors, since the nurses will be expected to assist the latter in their scrubbing and gowning. The first patients are in the corridor or preparation room where they have been wheeled by an orderly, and they are already in a semi-conscious state from drugs of a sedative type.

"With the arrival of M.D.'s on the scene, the tempo of preparation increases. Nurses are now untying the sterile bundles and spreading instruments out for instant use. Usually, orderlies and the charge nurse are checking lights, suction hoses, etc. The anesthetist is setting up his tanks and dials at the head of the operating table. Internes and their more advanced colleagues, the surgical residents, are ordinarily scrubbing before the operating surgeon appears. Much joking and chatter occurs between these younger doctors and the nurses. When the operating surgeon, an older and more dignified M.D., starts to scrub, the tone of levity may decrease markedly. His appearance signals an even more alert and faster level of preparation on the part of other members of the operating team. The nurses assist the doctors in dressing for surgery; they hold gowns ready for the doctors to step into when scrubbed, and when the gowns are on they tie them securely. They hold rubber gloves up so that the doctors can put them on more easily. At this stage, before the incision has even been made, the motif of watchful cooperation has been established between nurses and doctors in the process of gowning.

"Now the patient has been wheeled into the room and the anesthetist is busily caring for him, making him comfortable and applying anesthetic. (The anesthetist is the patient's direct 'companion' in this venture, the person who reassuringly sedates him and establishes a close personal connection). In a difficult case, the surgeon has perhaps previously consulted a colleague about the technique he plans to use and what conditions he expects to find. As the moment of cutting draws nearer, however, he is 'on his own' as the captain of the team; his lonely responsibility is mitigated by the presence of younger doctors and nurses, but he must be the key decision-maker.

"At the signal from the anesthetist that the patient has reached a proper depth of unconsciousness, the surgeon makes his first incision. (The patient has already been draped and painted by the cooperation of house staff and nurses, under the surgeon's direction.) Immediately, by spoken word or conventional hand-signals, the surgeon calls on the nurse for sponges and instruments; the young doctors assisting at the operation are brought into play to hold retractors and clamps which staunch the flow of blood and keep visibility good in the operative field. At each stage in events, the surgeon consults the anesthetist to keep check on the patient's condition. Some portions of the operation may actually be performed by the surgeon's assistants, although he is always in close supervision and handles the critical moves himself. It is a mark of status to be allowed to work in the operative field, and actual surgery is done only by well-trained resident doctors. Nevertheless, the familiarity gained by simply holding the wound open for the surgeon is a vital part of the young interne's experience.

"There are two parallel status lines at work in the room. The surgeon passes on commands to the senior resident, who in turn passes them to junior residents and internes. The scrub nurse likewise initiates action for the circulating nurse and any students present. These chains of authority are criss-crossed by orders from the surgeon to the scrub nurse, and from any doctor to any of the nurses; however, action is seldom if ever initiated in reverse: nurses do not issue orders to any doctors and the lower echelons rarely direct the activities of the higher.

"The operating surgeon, after finishing his major task, consults the anesthetist again with respect to the patient's general condition and the length of time required to close the wound. As the closing process begins, there is a visible relaxation of tension and vigilance; joking becomes more frequent, and the pace of work more leisurely. Before a stitch can be taken, however, the nurses must count the sponges used in the operation, as a safeguard against leaving foreign objects in the patient's body. Here, at least, the nurses do initiate action, for the surgeon waits for their assurance that the sponge count is correct.

"During the sewing-up phase, the junior members of the surgical team usually take a more prominent role than they have in earlier stages. Often the chief surgeon will remove his gloves and stand around chatting, or even leave the room entirely. The resident is left in charge, and he and the internes proceed to apply the finishing touches. After the sutures are all in place, the anesthetist takes charge of dressing the patient and moving him from the table to a cart which will return him to his bed. In this he is assisted by nurses and, usually, an orderly; sometimes the junior doctors will help out, but the chief surgeon is not engaged in this phase.

"At length the patient, anesthetist, and doctors leave the room. The nurses are last to leave, as they were first to arrive. They pick up the doctors' discarded gowns and gloves, and prepare the room for the next case. The whole process, requiring from 30 minutes to six or more hours, has included a large cast of characters exhibiting much communication. Yet they are so familiar with their jobs that the number of spoken words may have been slight."

A marvelous example of teamwork has taken place. Although innumerable orders have been given, most of them have flowed from the dictates of the patient's presence and condition. In a very real sense, few of the directives issued during surgery are arbitrary decisions on the surgeon's part. Rather, in the last analysis, the patient's needs have been the controlling element in the entire situation. Thus the person who seems to have been least capable of exerting authority—the prone, unconscious "object"—has in fact assumed the star role and has exercised the preponderant influence on the course of the drama.

In the days before modern techniques of asepsis had been developed, but after the idea of cleanliness had begun to be accepted in medicine, it was the custom to spray the operating area with an antiseptic solution. A certain noted surgeon, therefore, used to pause before the operation and intone, "Brethren, let us spray." Somehow this irreverent remark typifies an important aspect of life in the surgery; where the job to be done is intrinsically abnormal and fraught with anxieties, the atmosphere is deliberately made as mundane and casual as possible. In this most serious of situations, efforts are directed toward pulling the psychological climate into "normalcy." Like the small boy whistling past the graveyard, the inhabitants of the room make things prosaic; further, there is reason to think that energies must be mobilized for the work itself, not allowed to drain off in unproductive fear and trembling. While operating rooms are not truly places of levity, and *Ars Chirurgica* advises the surgeon to be "fearful in dangerous things," the pattern of joking and small talk is perhaps the most striking feature of surgery to the outsider. There is drama, but only a fraction of total operating time looks anything like the Hollywood stereotype of tightlipped tenseness and mute solemnity. The self-consciousness which one would expect to characterize a person invading another's body, and literally "holding a life in his hands," is for the most part dispelled by technical considerations; a job must be done, a careful exacting task, and this is the focus of energy and intellect. Operating rooms, then, are workmanlike. The first impression dispels any thought of "constant crisis."

Every operating room is:

(a) like *all* other operating rooms
(b) like *some* other operating rooms
(c) like *no* other operating rooms

This logical scheme was originally applied to the field of personality, but it fits the operating room equally well. In fact, it might well be said that the surgery *has* a personality of its own, a distinctive blend of characteristics setting it apart from the rest of the hospital. It is perhaps a misnomer to speak of "the" operating room; rather, there are probably many types which may be classified in several ways.

A. *Every Operating Room Is Like* ALL *Other Operating Rooms.* What do all operating rooms share as identifying marks? At least the following features are proposed:

(1) Drama, excitement, intensity: an air of importance.

Surgery is so obviously worth while and effective that it may be trite to comment on its importance. Yet there are many other aspects of medicine, and many aspects of every job, which lack the immediacy and lauded purpose of surgery. In the operating room, there can be no doubt that what is being done is dangerous and vital. Because we all share a belief in the importance of the body, because it is a basic part of the human being's security, any drastic manipulation (such as cutting) is cause for excitement. Further, the power to enter and change the body[1] signifies an immense responsibility on the surgeon's part, and insures that the atmosphere shall include a sense of awe. And there is an element of drama, despite the stricture that it does not resemble the movie version. Each operation is a problem, a challenge, whose course can be plotted but not thoroughly predicted. One piano chord in the old-fashioned cinema announced that "something is going to happen." Just so, in an operating room everyone knows that "something is going to happen."

As one graduate nurse expressed it:

"Down here you have the patient at the most critical time of his life and you know by the time he leaves the operating room what his chances are. You feel as if you are really important in his life. You're only with him a little while but still its the crucial time so far as he is concerned."

We have stressed the mundane aspects of operating room life, and pointed out the joking air which often precedes and follows the surgery. One can hear much talk of fishing trips, much mutual kidding, etc. All these contribute to a reduction of tension. But the tension exists; everything is *not* sweetness and light. A recurrent index of tension is the tendency to quick flareups of "temperament," of irritated and antagonistic remarks. Some impression of this index is gained from a record of part of an operation by an observer seated in the gallery.

"At this point, we have an interesting piece of interaction between the scrub nurse and Dr. M. The nurse hands him one swab, retaining another in her hand. He takes the swab as she hands it to him, and throws it angrily on the floor on the other side of the operating table. He asks, 'Is this phenol?' (referring to the swab left in her other hand). The nurse replies (pointing disgustedly to the floor) 'That one was phenol. This one is alcohol.' Dr. M: 'When I called for phenol twenty minutes ago, I *meant* phenol. I've got to swab that whole end off. Now get me some phenol.' The nurse then fills a small cup with phenol and hands it to Dr. M. with a swab. This procedure he accepts.

"Dr. M. is now under great tension. It shows. His remarks become more brusque, irritated, profane. When the nurses have trouble getting a hose fixed up, he says, 'Let's get going here. Dammit, it takes twenty minutes to do a thing and there is one way to do it right.' The nurses begin to count sponges in a fairly loud voice. M. shouts to them, 'Stop counting sponges! Don't do *anything* until I stop this bleeder.' A moment later he shouts at Y (the assistant resident), 'Pull back those fingers. Jesus, let's see this thing.'"

(2) Emphasis on teamwork and cooperation.

It might be said that every operation is a *co*-operation. In surgery, no one can "go it alone"; each person is dependent on many others, and the patient is of course dependent on all members of the team. So necessary is teamwork, in the nature of the job, that even individuals who are personally antagonistic often act in concert during the course of surgery. (In this, the operating team is like a jazz band or baseball club. Legend has it that the members of the famous double-play combination of Tinker to Evers to Chance did not speak off the field for many years.) The individuals composing an operating team are so close-knit, and understand the task at hand so thoroughly, that verbal signals are often unnecessary. A language of gesture has developed whose meanings are crystal clear to persons following the operation intently. Perhaps the outstanding examples of intuitive co-operation occur in these pairs of team members:

surgeon—nurse
surgeon—anesthetist
surgeon—assistant surgeon

To the nurse, the intimate comprehension of the surgeon's technique, and his recognition of her competence, may become a prime reward of her job. The desirability of a close harmony is recognized as is illustrated by the comments of an operating nurse and a surgeon respectively:

"Morale is high in the operating room because there is a team spirit. The finest point in the nurses' life comes when she is finally taken in and fully accepted as a member of the team. On a certain day, everything changes. There is almost a clean break with the past . . . the surgeon will recognize you and call you by name. A kind of emotional block is broken, and you know you are accepted. Any nurse feels very wonderful about this. The main reward for doing operating-room nursing lies in a special relationship with the surgeon."

"Both instruments and nurses have to be worked with for a couple of years before you know them. If she (nodding at nurse) stayed with the same guy for two years she would do everything before he even asked for it."[2] [a senior resident.]

It is obvious that the surgeon and anesthetist must work together. The degree of anesthesia to be given a patient depends on the type of operation and the various stages in its progress. Conversely, the surgeon must be kept informed of changes in his patient's condition. One interview note states:

"We then got into a discussion of how the anesthetist works. Dr. D. described as perhaps the most important point a close cooperation with the operating surgeon. He said it is desirable that the anesthetist know the surgeon well, know his technique, and be able to co-operate with him almost automatically."

(3) Technical criteria and "the religion of competence."

All operating rooms place great stress on efficiency and expertness. In part, this is due to the complicated nature of surgical work; the fact that it rests on an exacting knowledge of multiple factors. The irascible surgeon who is highly skilled, and thereby gains respect, is a familiar figure. Unpleasant personal characteristics may often be overlooked if competence is high enough. The judgment of colleagues and nurses soon enough labels any doctor according to the degree of mastery he is observed to exercise, and the palm goes to the expert.

In part, too, the importance of cleanliness contributes to a desire for efficiency. The rituals connected with sterility promote a precise mode of behavior which infuses the non-sterile portions of technique. Surgical work is, by definition, careful.

The surgical job itself is such a demanding one in terms of exactitude that it draws all related jobs into the orbit of mechanical perfection. Because surgery must be orderly, the tasks which facilitate it are also orderly. "A neat job," then, can describe everything from a virtuoso performance by a heart surgeon to the measured folding of towels by a nurse's aide.

In the surgery, all tasks are "obvious" and can be quickly judged by ideal criteria; nowhere is the American talent for the admiration of "know-how" more clearly expressed. It is plain that the emphasis on technique and precision is necessary to high-level effort in surgery. Yet we may also mention the possibility that some portion of this emphasis serves a subsidiary function: it keeps the hands and mind busy on detail in a setting where excess imagination or sensitivity might interfere with the psychological boldness required. Inspection, not introspection, is the imperative of operating room activity.

(4) The surgeon's authority.

"The surgeon is the captain of a ship. He is ultimately responsible for everything that happens in the operating room."—Chief of surgery.

Huge responsibilities demand huge grants of power, for responsibility and power must be in some way commensurate. The surgeon's authority is unquestioned, it would seem, because of three interrelated factors. First, there is the right relation between authority and responsibility; a person held to account for something must, fairly, be in a position to affect the process by which the thing comes about. Second, the surgeon stands at the very top of a skilled hierarchy. He is not a replaceable part, and, ideally, he knows more about the job at hand than anyone else in the room. Therefore, it is natural that he would be vested with the authority to direct the work on grounds of competence. Third, there is an aura of magic and reverence surrounding the figure of the surgeon; this aura has its roots in the ancient connection of priest and healer. When the three factors are combined, one sees a potent basis of authority. Although the authority is mitigated in several ways, it is a "constant" characteristic of the surgery. Relaxation of power may occur when long acquaintance and close work relations, especially those between doctor and nurse, have vitiated the third factor, the priestly aura or "charisma." Implicit or explicit resistance (or rarely, transgression) to authority often stems from a surgeon's failure to fulfill wholly the standards of competence, so that respect is weakened. At any rate, the overpowering nature of the surgeon's position is almost certain to produce an under-current of resentment among lower-status members of the work team. This is illustrated in the exasperated aphorism of an operating room nurse: "Nurses spend half their lives waiting on doctors, and the other half waiting *for* them."

(5) Physical and psychological isolation from the rest of the hospital.

For reasons of sterility and general work flow considerations, the operating suite is always separated from the hospital as a whole. It has its own floor, or part of a floor, and is for most purposes a "closed system." Although patients must be brought to surgery and taken back to their beds when the operation is over, this task is performed by orderlies, and other hospital personnel rarely visit the surgery. Of course casual visiting is prohibited since non-essential onlookers would tend to disrupt the precision of work, and might increase the danger of infection.[3]

The isolation of the operating room means that, in the eyes of other employees, this area is strange and forbidding. All non-surgical people are in a fundamental sense on the "outside" and may be curious about what occurs in the sanctum. They have, further, a definite attitude of awe and admiration for the activities that go on there and the "initiates."

Conversely, the surgical staff, from doctors to maids, develop a strong feeling of comraderie. They recognize their status and role as a special group. Their world is the surgery, not the hospital. This implies great warmth and cohesion, as well as agreement on a variety of values. They must and do learn to live together as an elite corps.

B. *Every Operating Room Is Like* SOME *Other Operating Room.* There seem to be a number of *types* of operating room, which share certain secondary characteristics. These qualities are like an overlay, supplementing and modifying, but not drastically changing the conditions noted above. They include:

(1) The extent of teaching carried on.

On this factor, operating rooms may vary from those that include no personnel in training to those that involve students, nurses, internes and residents. Obviously, in the teaching situation, part of everyone's energy must go into the initiation process. The presence of students keeps people on their toes, keeps an air of questioning and striving alive, which infuses the surgery. Outdated and incompetent elements, be they surgeons, nurses, or surgical techniques, have little chance of survival.

Methods and attitudes undergo constant changes, as the operating room keeps pace with the advance of medical science. And the surgery is "conscious" of its work, measuring and evaluating it in the light of high criteria of excellence. The stress on *competence* is heightened because every case is in one sense a model for the learners.

Division of labor is pushed further in teaching hospitals. For one thing, more hands are available; for another, there is a constant effort to split off suitable practice tasks which can give a student experience and afford him a gradual introduction into the core of the operation. Both nurses and doctors in training follow a series of stages, whereby they approach ever more closely the condition of standard excellence. Nurses move from circulating duties so scrub nurse, from easy to hard cases. Internes and residents progress from holding retractors and stitching incisions to the actual work of the operating surgeon. The accentuated division of labor means that coordination of all the parts is more difficult to achieve, and therefore planning is essential. Since a very large number of people are involved, interpersonal relations take on added significance; morale and skill must be high to insure smooth functioning.

Differences in prestige are multiplied in the teaching situation. The ladder of status has many extra rungs, within both medical and nursing staffs. Thus, we find not only the invariant distinction between surgeon and nurse, but finer distinctions between scrub nurse and circulating nurse, between chief surgeon, assistant surgeon, resident and interne. These gradations have the advantage of inducting "raw" individuals through manageable stages, so that they are not thrust from student to full professional in a single immense jump. However, they also tend to increase social distance and multiply the opportunities for friction. An amusing account of status-laden behavior, as told by two operating room nurses, will illustrate the theme:

"They asked the question, 'Who is the first person to leave the operating room after an operation?' And immediately answered it with, 'The surgeon, of course.' They said first the surgeon steps back from the table, takes off his gown and gloves, throws them in a heap on the floor any place. They described how even the young resident will rip off a towel from the operating table, perhaps with several instruments on it, and just throw it to the floor while preparing the patient to go back downstairs, and then the resident will wait for the nurse to untie his gown and stalk away. After everyone has gone, the nurse or nurses and the anesthetist are left to clear up the place and to get the patient back downstairs. Miss R. exclaimed, 'After the great big doctors are all finished, who do you think moves the patient back on to the stretcher to take him downstairs? The nurse, of course.' At this point, Miss M. interjected, 'Yes, that is what happens. They just walk out after shouting at you for two solid hours.' "

The fact of teaching means that each stage in surgery itself will be carefully scrutinized and explained. Although not all surgeons converse during the course of an operation, it is usual for the surgeon, his assistant, and/or the senior resident to carry on a running commentary, describing the significance of the work at hand. In recent years, there has been a shift away from didactic teaching in medicine: one demonstrator or lecturer confronting a mass of students. The stress now falls on clinical teaching which introduces material to the student through his active participation in a case. Thus the learners at an operation will be scrubbed up and actually assisting, rather than watching from the gallery. (Few operating rooms are now being constructed with amphitheaters, as a result of this trend.)

Problems are introduced by the teaching emphasis, many of them concerning the amount of participation allowed to the student. In surgery, only one man can operate; in the teaching of medicine, multiple diagnoses of the same individual may be made for practice purposes. There is a story of a young interne which points up the dilemma. After a particularly impressive piece of surgery, the doctors retired to the surgeons' lounge just off the operating room. The chief, who had performed the operation, began discussing it with his team. At length, turning to a very young interne whose duty at the operation had been to hold the distal end of the retractor, the great man asked, "And what did you learn from this operation, my boy?" The interne replied, "I think I have definitely established, sir, that the assistant resident has a terrible case of dandruff." Yet a chief of neurological surgery has commented that in his own experience the gradual progression up the ladder of responsibility was an excellent introduction to his specialty. He noted especially the fact that the slow rise to a central position in the operating team insured that he would not feel too much pressure where he at length held full authority, that he would not feel "on the spot" in his first cases as operating surgeon.

Non-teaching hospitals lack the special difficulties involved in this sort of on-the-job education. On the other hand, they also lack the detailed explanation to members of the team, and the general air of competence and easy expertness which the presence of distinguished chiefs instills.

It might also be pointed out that non-teaching hospitals have no scape-goats as ready at hand as students. A latent function of student nurses and internes would seem to be found in their position as legitimate targets for the impatience and anxieties of graduate nurses or surgeons. Without disrupting the rapport of key team members, it is possible to vent anger at the circulating nurse who trips over her own feet, or the interne who is wool-gathering when he should be watching the operation.

(2) The difficulty of the case in progress.

The relative seriousness of an operation determines many features of an operating room. For instance, in general terms, more difficult cases imply the involvement of more personnel, greater lengths of time, greater number of instruments, etc. In these important ways, a chest operation in Hospital X will be more nearly like a chest operation in Hospital Y than like a hemorrhoidectomy in Hospital X. While it is true that no two pieces of surgery are ever *exactly* alike, the major varieties show definite similarities.

In a fairly easy case, the atmosphere of the room tends to be rather relaxed and the requirements of strict attentiveness and speed on the part of all concerned are less rigorous. The tension which introduces friction into casual interactions is largely absent. However, in avoiding the extremes of pressure, the operating team misses the excitement and feeling of importance that accompany a major challenge to skill. Thus there may be complaints that the work is dull or routine, that the challenge is not great enough to hold one's interest at a high, sustained level.

Because fewer people work on a minor operation, the need for precise coordination is also less pronounced. In the teaching hospital, these cases are often used as opportunities for the young student to begin testing his own skills. A surgical resident may be given a vein ligation as his first solo flight, or a student nurse may serve as scrub nurse on the same type of operation. It is not true that these cases are taken "casually," but they do include a greater margin for error and seldom require split-second timing.

Since minor cases are usually short, the factor of fatigue is also less critical. In a long exacting surgical effort, physical exhaustion may cause outbursts of temper; mistakes may be less well tolerated toward the close of a lengthy job. Often a long case will involve shifts of personnel, especially nurses, thus adding to the need for tight coordination. The more difficult work, sometimes requiring six or even eight consecutive hours, points up the need for physical endurance in surgical personnel. A noted surgeon once remarked the possession of "good legs" as one of the qualities of a competent surgeon, since long hours of standing are so often necessary.

These two characteristics—the extent of teaching and the nature of the operation—may be viewed as scales having various values. Any operation will fall at a certain point on each scale, and share the qualities of that point with other operating rooms to form a "type." Thus we might speak of "major surgery in a teaching hospital," or "minor surgery in a small, non-teaching hospital," and find many elements in common with the designated category. There are undoubtedly other characteristics which contribute to a classification of operating rooms (for instance, whether the surgical staff is "open" or "closed") but these seem to be the most critical.

C. *Every Operating Room Is Like* no *Other Operating Room.* Three elements appear to account for the *unique* quality of each operating room— and, for that matter, of each single operation. They are:

(1) the personality of the surgeon
(2) the personality of the nurse
(3) the creative course of surgery itself.

Certain facets of the surgeon's and nurse's personality have already been discussed, those features which seem to be invariant. Such, for example, are the factors associated with tension and fatigue (stereotypes of the "irritable" surgeon or the "snippy" nurse) or connected with formal lines of status and authority (the "authoritarian" surgeon, or "sub-servient" nurse). But over and above these behaviors which seem to be determined by "the situation" are a host of actions, attitudes, and traits which make each individual, in surgery or anywhere, unique.

An interview with a clinical instructor, a graduate nurse, provided an interesting illustration of the variations introduced by the surgeon's particular tastes in the matter of talking and joking during an operation:

" 'The operating room,' said Miss D., 'Takes its tone from the personality and attitude of the surgeon. It is not a joking place if the surgeon does not like to talk while operating.' She described several different staff members and their variations in operating-room leadership and atmosphere. She said that Dr. T's operating room was always very friendly and filled with witty exchanges, while Dr. H's, although friendly, was strictly business. One distinguished surgeon allows no talking whatever in his room, while another is so jovial that he always remarks during an operation that he considers himself very lucky to have been given the very best nurses available for *his* operation."

Nurses, too, may be impersonal or warmly involved, although they do usually follow the surgeon's lead. When a nurse and surgeon are extremely well-acquainted, and have between them the bond of countless shared experiences, their mutual personality adjustment may greatly enhance the technical efficiency of the team.

Surgery takes a different course each time it is performed. This is natural, since the bodies of patients are by no means uniform. But the truly individual character of some few operations stems from the creative element in new types of surgery. Perhaps a maneuver is being performed for the first time; perhaps the operation is exploratory and uncovers an unexpected cancer; perhaps a dramatic turn of events provokes an unanticipated crisis. In any event, something has been added to routine, and the operating room acquires a distinctive aura of excitement and discovery. In surgery, as in any other creative activity, there is room for novel aspects which thwart the attempt at rigid classification. Part of the peculiar charm and attraction of the operating room lies in this creative facet, the fact that routine may always be upset. If there were no possibility for innovation and inspiration, if surgery were really "routine," it is unlikely that it would attract the caliber of persons who are attracted to an operating room team.

51   SOCIAL STRATIFICATION AND PSYCHIATRIC PRACTICE: A STUDY OF AN OUT-PATIENT CLINIC*

By Jerome K. Myers and Leslie Schaffer

This paper is an analysis of the relationship between social class and the selection and treatment of patients in a psychiatric out-patient clinic. It grew out of another research project in which the authors are engaged.[1] In that study a significant relationship was found between the social class background of patients and the type of psychiatric treatment they received.[2] There was a

From *American Sociological Review*, 19, (June, 1954), 307–310. Copyright 1954 by The American Sociological Society.

distinctly higher percentage of patients receiving some form of *psychotherapy* in the upper social classes. In contrast, the percentage of persons receiving *custodial care* only or some form of *organic therapy* was greater in the lower social classes.

Because of the significance of these findings, the present authors studied the relationship between social class and psychiatric treatment in more detail, examining a setting where only one type of treatment (psychotherapy) was administered and where most patients had the same disorder (neurosis). In the process was tested an economic explanation offered by many psychiatrists for the findings of the study mentioned above.

Most psychotherapy is administered in private practice and is expensive. It was argued, therefore, that lower class people cannot afford such treatment. There is reason to believe, however, that the economic explanation is not wholly satisfactory. Therefore, the authors examined the records of all cases (195 in number)[3] that came to the clinic from October 1, 1950 to September 30, 1951, to determine if social class was related to: (1) acceptance for treatment, and (2) nature of treatment as measured by (a) training and status of the therapist, (b) duration of treatment, and (c) intensity of treatment.

The institution is a training and community clinic where treatment is oriented around expressive psychotherapy. Such therapy is verbal and interpersonal in nature, and based upon fundamental psychoanalytic principles. It requires relatively long and intensive contact between patient and therapist. Anyone with an income of under 5,000 dollars a year and residing within a given geographic area is eligible for care, and the fees charged are nominal and scaled. On theoretical grounds, if ability to pay were the important component in psychotherapy, we would expect that acceptance for therapy and the character of subsequent experience in the clinic would not be related to the patient's social class. This hypothesis was deduced from the economic arguments advanced by psychiatrists to explain the differential association of therapy with social class in the earlier, more comprehensive study.

Analysis of the Data. The clinic's procedure in selecting patients was as follows: If an individual seeking psychiatric help met the clinic's residential and financial requirements, he was referred to an intake interviewer who was either a social worker or a psychiatrist. This interviewer obtained from the patient necessary information to present his case to an intake conference at which all the clinic's psychiatric personnel decided whether or not therapy should be administered. All of the patients accepted by the intake interviewer became the subjects of our study. We classified these individuals operationally according to a method described in a previous paper,[4] using a five-class system developed by Hollingshead, in which the highest status group is labeled class I, with the others following in numerical order, class V being the lowest.[5]

The social class distribution of persons seen by the intake interviewer was as follows: class II—9 percent, class III—28 percent, class IV—39 percent, and class V—23 percent.[6] It is clear that persons from all social classes, except the highest, sought aid at the clinic. Whether or not an individual was recommended for treatment, however, was directly related to his social class position as can be seen in Table 1. Nearly two-thirds of class V persons were not recommended for therapy, compared to about one-fifth of persons in class IV and only one-tenth of those in classes II and III. Certainly the economic hypothesis is not supported by these findings.

Table 1—Percentage Distribution of Patients by Social Class and Intake Conference Decision

Conference Decision	SOCIAL CLASS			
	II	III	IV	V
No treatment recommended	11.8	9.6	22.2	64.3
Assigned to staff	35.3	17.3	2.8	.0
Assigned to resident psychiatrist	29.4	38.5	30.6	2.4
Assigned to medical student	.0	9.6	26.4	23.8
Assigned to other therapist (Social workers, psychology students)	5.9	7.7	9.7	7.1
Referred to other agencies	11.8	17.3	4.2	2.4
Unknown*	5.9	.0	4.2	.0
	100.1	100.0	100.1	100.0

Chi-square = 81.7924, p less than .001 N = 183.
* Unknown cases were not included in the chi-square computation.

Just as interesting is the fact that there was a significant difference in the training of the personnel assigned to treat patients in the various social classes. The trained staff psychiatrists treated mainly class II and class III patients; resident psychiatrists in training treated class III and class IV patients; and medical students, taking a four week course, treated class IV and class V patients. The fully trained staff did not treat any patients in class V and only two in class IV. In contrast, medical students with no previous experience in psychotherapy treated no patients in class II and only five in class III.

The third relationship between class position and treatment was that the duration of therapy varied significantly from one class to another. The data in Table 2 show that the higher a patient's social class, the longer his treatment. The percentage of persons receiving treatment for ten or more weeks increased from 14 in class V to 59 in class II. On the other hand, nearly half of all class V patients were seen less than one week, but only 12 percent of those in class II were seen for such a short period.

Table 2—Percentage Distribution of Patients by Social Class and Duration of Contact with Clinic

Length of Contact	SOCIAL CLASS			
	II	III	IV	V
Less than one week	11.8	26.9	37.5	47.6
1-9 weeks	29.4	26.9	33.3	38.1
10 or more weeks	58.8	46.2	29.2	14.3
	100.0	100.0	100.0	100.0

Chi-square = 17.5029, p less than .01. N = 183.

The intensity of treatment, as measured by number of contacts with therapist, was also significantly greater in the higher social class. The percentage of persons seen ten or more times rose from 12 in class V to 53 in class II, and the percentage of persons seen only once declined from 45 in class V to 18 in class II.

This relationship between the nature of treatment and the patient's social class is illustrated even more strikingly by analysis of only those cases assigned to a therapist at the intake conference, instead of all cases accepted initially.

As indicated in Table 4, the percentage of patients seen ten or more times declined from 75 in class II to only 29 in class V. These findings indicate clearly that lower class persons did not receive as long and intensive treatment as those higher in the class system.

Table 3—Percentage Distribution of Patients by Social Class and Total Number of Times Seen in Clinic

| Times Seen | Social Class | | | |
	II	III	IV	V
One	17.6	23.1	38.9	45.2
2–9	29.4	28.8	40.3	42.9
10 or more	52.9	48.1	20.9	11.9
	99.9	100.0	100.1	100.0

Chi-square = 22.5410, p less than .001. N = 183.

Table 4—Percentage Distribution of Patients Accepted at Intake Conference by Social Class and Duration of Therapy

| Times Seen | Social Class | | | |
	II	III	IV	V
1–9	25.0	36.8	70.0	71.4
10 or more	75.0	63.2	30.0	28.6
	100.0	100.0	100.0	100.0

Chi-square= 15.4446, p less than .01. N = 114.

It must be recognized that factors other than social class may be related to acceptance for treatment and subsequent therapeutic experience. Sex and age of the patient and professional status of the intake interviewer, suggested by psychiatrists as perhaps being relevant, were not. The chi square test was used, and significance was defined at the .05 level. Diagnosis, however, was found to be significantly related to acceptance and subsequent clinical experience. Although most patient were neurotics, approximately one-quarter were suspected of being psychotic and were treated differently. They were not accepted for therapy as frequently as neurotics and did not receive as long and intensive treatment by as highly trained personnel. This did not account for the differential treatment of patients by social class, however, since there was no significant difference in the class distribution of suspected psychotics and neurotics.

Conclusions and Interpretations. In summary, it was found that in a situation where the economic factor was held constant, acceptance for therapy and the character of subsequent clinical experience were related significantly to the patient's social class; the higher an individual's social class position, the more likely he was to be accepted for treatment, to be treated by highly trained personnel, and to be treated intensively over a long period.

Although the necessary data to explain these findings are lacking, some tentative explanations which might lead to further research are offered. It may be that differences in the social class backgrounds between psychiatrists, who are mainly from classes I and II, and class IV and V patients are important factors in the differential acceptance rates and subsequent clinic experience. Variations, according to social class, in the conception of the psychiatrist's role and the meaning of therapy seem important. For instance, the psychiatrist's values concerning who should be treated appear to influence the acceptance of patients. Also, lower class persons do not seem to share with psychiatrists the conception of therapy as a process by which the patient gains insight into his problems. Frequently, such patients conceive of the therapist's role in magical terms.

Psychotherapy involves intimate communicative interaction between the patient and therapist. Therefore, it may be facilitated if a certain similarity in culturally determined symbols and learned drives exist in both patient and therapist. Differences in value systems and patterns of communication, on the other hand, may hamper the establishment of the therapeutic relationship. At present, it appears possible that lower-class patients need to acquire new symbols and values to participate in expressive psychotherapy. Since this is a difficult process, many of them may be considered unpromising candidates for successful treatment. According to the clinic's staff they often "lack motivation for psychotherapy" or are not "psychologically minded." Perhaps psychiatrists need to acquire new symbols and values in dealing with lower class patients; or perhaps new approaches are necessary to bring psychotherapy to such persons.

A somewhat more comprehensive statement, particularly of some of the theoretical problems posed by these findings, will be found in another paper by the same authors (v.i.).

Since 1954, when our two papers were written, several other investigators have reported essentially similar findings in two other clinics. In addition, Frank and his associates at the Johns Hopkins School of Medicine have been concerned, among other things, with the problem of "drop-outs" in psychotherapeutic work, although their concern has been largely with group therapy. We append here a bibliography of literature relevant to this paper which has appeared up to the end of 1957:

Schaffer, L., and Myers, J. K., "Psychotherapy and Social Stratification" (*Psychiatry, 17*, 1, February 1954, pp. 83–94.)

Auld, F., and Myers, J. K., "Contributions to a Theory for Selecting Psychotherapy Patients" (*J. Clin. Psychol., 10*, 1954, pp. 56–60.)

Winder, A. E., and Hesko, M., "The Effect of Social Class on the Length and Type of Psychotherapy in a Veterans Administration Mental Hygiene Clinic" (*J. Clin. Psychol., 11*, 1955, pp. 77–79.)

Imber, S. D., Nash, E. H., and Stone, A. R., "Social Class and Duration of Psychotherapy" (*J. Clin. Psychol., 11*, 3, July 1955, pp. 281–284.)

Imber, S. D., Frank, J. D., Gliedman, L. H., Nash, E. H., and Stone, A. R,. "Suggestibility, Social Class and the Acceptance of Psychotherapy" (*J. Clin. Psychol., 12*, October 1956, pp. 341–344.)

Jessor, R., "Social Values and Psychotherapy" (*J. Consult. Psychol.*, 20, 4, 1956, pp. 264–266.)

Frank, J. D., Gliedman, L. H., Imber, S., Nash L. H., and Stone, A. R., "Why Patients Leave Psychotherapy" (*A. M. A. Arch. Neurol., and Psychiat.*, 77, 1957, pp. 283–299.)

52   ECONOMICS OF DOCTOR-PATIENT RELATIONS

By Robert Albright

In a topic as controversial as this one in which very few facts are available, but many opinions exist, disagreement can be expected. While expecting, in fact encouraging honest disagreement, it should be kept on a level where there is actual grounds for it. Here are a few areas where disagreement has been found in the past, where no actual disagreement is necessary.

In any discussion of medical economics, the question of the indigent patient is always brought up. The status of indigency is variable. The patient who can't afford to pay *anything* for medical care, is a true indigent. This is the pauper. Fortunately, in America today, the number of *true* indigents is very small. Nothing that may be stated later should be construed as a reference to this type of patient. Each doctor must decide for himself whether he will treat the true indigent or see that proper treatment is obtained from public authorities

The type of indigent patient most doctors are talking about when they refer to the "poor person" is the type that can't afford to pay the normal fee for services. Here again we state that the individual doctor must make up his mind just how much of this work he wishes to do and is physically capable of doing. I would advocate that he should make this decision on the basis of facts, rather than hearsay or opinions.

"Doctor Smith is my doctor." "Doctor Jones is my doctor." "Doctor Brown is my doctor." The names are different. The persons making the statements are different. They may be male or female, short or tall, skinny or fat, rich or poor, black or white, sick or well; as different as only humans can be. But one thing is similar. The statement is made with assurance and is always made in the possessive sense. "Doctor Smith is *My* Doctor!" The question that often occurs to me is, "Why?" Why is "Doctor Smith *your* doctor?" Why is "Doctor Jones *your* doctor?"

As one who deals with medical collections, I have heard hundreds of patients voice their reasons why "Doctor So and So is not *my* doctor any longer." Listening to these reasons we have formed some opinions on why people choose a doctor. Often times these reasons are not apparent on the surface. Neither are they always apparent in the statements a patient will make.

If it were possible to list ten reasons in the order of their importance, on why people select a doctor I believe you will find the clinical and medical ability of the doctor is *not first*. I don't know where among the ten it would fall, but it *would not be first.* What you would find first is this: "He is considerate, by treating me as an individual."

"Doctor Smith is *my* doctor because I *think* he is the best doctor in the world." Does this mean the patient thinks Doctor Smith knows more about medicine than anyone else? On the surface, yes! But:

(A) Since the patient is untrained he is not qualified to judge the doctor's knowledge of medicine.

(B) Because the patient is average he has never had to question the doctor's knowledge of medicine because he is not the victim of a rare or incurable ailment.

"Doctor Smith is *my* doctor because I *like the way he treats me.*" His treatment covers everything from the comfort of his chairs in the waiting room to the manner in which he gives an injection; the way his nurse looks, speaks and acts; how the doctor speaks and acts, how long I wait before I see him, his fees, his bills and his manner of handling these matters.

The very root of most difficulties between doctor and patient are not those of a clinical nature, but rather those involving non-clinical treatment. The most common difficulty between doctor and patient is the *bill*—the fee for services performed. Insurance companies tell us the basic cause of many malpractice suits lies in a disagreement over the bill rather than one involving medical treatment. Even though the suit itself may be brought for medical reasons, the ultimate cause of many suits is a disagreement over fees. Since the very basis of American medicine revolves around the private practice of medicine, the question of the bill or the "Economics Of Doctor-Patient Relations" is of primary importance.

There are those who, in their attempt to solve this problem, would do so by simply eliminating the Economics entirely—in short, socialized medicine, national health plan, subsidies of health insurance companies, etc. These all have as their end result, "curing the cold by burying the patient." The clinical advances in modern medicine have come about as a *result of* our private practice system, not *in spite of it.* Each time the relationship between physician and patient breaks down on an economic issue, it lends fervor to the cries of the proponents of various health plans.

People choose a doctor because of the way he treats them, not solely his clinical treatment, but also his treatment of them as individuals. A great deal of his treatment of them as individuals is reflected in his fees and his bill. The physician's handling of these economic problems not only affects him directly, but indirectly each and every member of the medical profession. In view of these facts, it behooves every medical student to learn more about the business side of the practice of medicine. If doctors engage in the private practice of medicine, *then he will be in a business.* Doctors practice medicine to make a profit, because they like their field, because they are needed, and because they obtain personal satisfaction in easing pain and bringing comfort to the afflicted. Making a profit does not detract from the merit of these higher motives. If in the practice of medicine the physician fails to make a profit, then it becomes extremely difficult to practice good medicine. For out of profits will come his livelihood and the livelihood of his family. Out of profits will come the funds for research, hospitals, clinics, equipment and the leisure time to develop new techniques. There is a distinct ratio between "good medicine," "good public relation" and "sound business." They walk hand in hand.

I have found in my business and in talking with members of my profession throughout the country that the doctor whose clinical ability is respected by his own colleagues, is also the doctor who has one of the best practices, one of the nicest offices, is well liked by his patients, is fair in his fees and has the least bad debt loss. "Good medicine, good public relations, and sound business."

The biggest problem in the doctor's office is collecting the fee for his services. We assume here that the fee schedule, in itself, is fair and equitable to the doctor, his patient and his profession. The setting of fees is a problem all in itself. Many good publications are available through the American Medical Association that will aid a doctor in setting a fair fee schedule.

A new patient walks into the doctor's office. He or his nurse secure the patient's name and address and what clinical information deemed necessary. The physician renders some medical services and the patient leaves. At the end of the month, the doctor sends a bill and hopes to get paid. All too often this is the picture in the doctor's office. Why? Would one expect to walk into a store where he is not known, give his name and address, pick out a suit of clothes and walk out with it? Of course not. But a doctor's office is different! Of course it's different. It doesn't follow, however, that because of a difference he must operate like a free clinic. There are things that can and should be done. The doctor benefits by them. His patients benefit by them. The medical profession will benefit by them.

There is an old axiom in the credit business "That an account opened properly is half collected." This is as true of a medical account as it is of a commercial account. Keeping this in mind, let's start again. A new patient walks into the doctor's office. His nurse or receptionist secures the desired clinical information. She also has the patient fill out (or she may fill it out for him) a form, commonly called "New Patient Information." It has *at least* the following information: Name, residence address, home phone number, wife or husband's name, employment, address of employment, position with the company, name and address of a close relative, name of person recommending the doctor, insurance company if any, address of insurance company, and policy number. There may be additional information but this is basic. At the same time, or after the doctor has seen the patient, the nurse or receptionist should explain to the patient his office hours, and whether he works by appointment or not. Preferably this information should be printed on a small sheet of paper together with the doctor's phone numbers and how he can be reached in case of an emergency. Many doctors print this information on a small sticker that can be posted on the patient's telephone directory.

The receptionist should explain to the patients the physician's policy on charge accounts. It will be of tremendous advantage to the doctor to set his policy *before* he starts practicing medicine, rather than to set a policy *after* he has several thousand dollars of unpaid accounts.

Here is how it can be accomplished with just a little time and planning. The receptionist can say:

"Mrs. Smith, we mail our statements on the 26th of each month. YOUR statement will cover all charges and payments up to and including the 25th of each month. Your account is payable each month. If at any time you need longer periods, please don't hesitate to call me, as we will be glad to cooperate. Let me assure you that the doctor or myself are available at any time to discuss your account or his charges."

Patients will appreciate this attitude. They like to know where they stand. They like to know what they are entitled to. The task of collecting delinquent accounts is made much easier if the doctor's policy is discussed with each and every new patient when they first come into his office. Of course, this takes time, but the economic relationship he will build with his patient, through this policy, will more than offset the time spent in establishing it with each patient.

Every office should contain the A. M. A. plaque inviting each patient to "discuss your fees or their accounts with you and the fact that you welcome such discussion." This plaque should hang above the doctor's desk in his office, not above his secretary's desk, since she is not issuing the invitation, nor in a corner of the waiting room, since no patient will discuss anything with him there. It should hang in the doctor's office in a position of prominence.

"Let me assure you that I am at your disposal at any time to discuss my fees, your account or any other information you may require." Many times this happens: a patient says to a doctor: "Doctor, I sure am sorry about my bill. I haven't been able to clear it up." Too often the response is: "Don't worry about it." Then a pat on the back, a hearty laugh and a walk to the door. If that patient had said: "Doctor, I'm sure worried about this cold, I can't seem to shake it." Would you tell him "Not to worry" and let it go at that? Or would you ask for more information and prescribe a treatment?

When a patient brings up the matter of his account, he is asking for help, not compassion. He expects the doctor to be able to offer some plan that will help him to pay his account. Ninety-five percent of all people are conscious of their obligations and worry about them. The physician must be willing and able to suggest a plan of action for the patient that will help him clear his account. Certainly the doctor is not expected to be a financial counselor. Since this money is owed to him, he should be willing to attempt to find a solution for his patient's problem. Many times the patient wants reassurance. They want to know that its "O.K." with the physician either to pay a little each month or that the doctor is willing to wait another sixty days. Whatever type of arrangement the doctor makes with the patient, it should be written down right then, and given to his bookkeeper. The doctor should tell the patient he is going to give it to his bookkeeper. This does several things. It shows the patient that the doctor felt the matter was important enough to take time out and tend to *his* problem. It also impresses him with the fact that his promise has been written down. He will be more apt to keep his promise, knowing it will be noticed if he doesn't. It also gives the patient a feeling of relief to know what he is supposed to do and when he is supposed to do it.

There is an attitude prevalent among some in the medical profession, that by never mentioning the bill, never discussing fees before the service is rendered, never asking for their money, never pressing a patient for payment, they are doing their patients a favor. Actually, they are helping a certain percentage of their patients become proverbial "deadbeats." They are also forcing their paying patients to pay the cost of medical care for an unnecessary number of non-paying patients.

In 1956, the average doctor in the United States collected an average of 85% of his charge volume. It means that for every doctor collecting 90 percent, there is one collecting 80 percent. For everyone collecting 95%, there is one collecting 75% and so on. This means that every group of 8½ patients who paid their medical bills were also paying the cost of 1½ patients who failed to pay their medical bills.

When you or I purchase a suit of clothes, we know that included in the price of the suit is a charge to cover the bad debt losses of the store. We expect that. But is it right to expect each patient paying a $5.00 office visit to have 75¢ of that office visit go for the care of people who *can pay* but don't? I don't think it is. Remember, we are discussing people who have the means and ability to pay, but lack the will to pay. It is the will to pay that must be fostered and encouraged by the doctor.

Credit, particularly open account credit, which includes medical credit, is basically the promise of one individual to another. Since the vast majority of people are basically honest, this "promise to pay" is one of vast importance. The people who normally pay their obligations do so for ten major reasons. One or more, or all of these reasons will apply to the patient who pays their medical accounts. The ten major reasons why people pay their accounts are: self respect, reputation for fair play, satisfaction of doing the right thing, freedom from worry, favorable credit record, security on the job, security for family, good example for children, opportunity for further credit, and saving of additional expense.

One or more of these ten reasons motivates each and every patient who pays his medical accounts. In the remaining 15% of patients who don't pay their medical accounts, these motivating factors must be cultivated and their importance emphasized by the doctor. This can be accomplished by having a sensible, business-like manner about his accounts from the moment the patient first walks into his office. Prompt and complete billing for service, together with routine methods of collection follow up, all serve to impress the patient with the importance of the medical account. This importance in turn leads to an increasing awareness, on the part of the patient, towards the ten motivating factors.

What are the rewards a doctor gains by employing good business methods in his practice? There are many. Increased income, more leisure time, and a very definite improvement in his patient relations. I once had a doctor tell me that it was better to collect 80% of a $50,000.00 a year practice than 90% of a $40,000.00 a year practice. Four thousand dollars better, in fact. This seems to be an opinion widely held. That if you employ firm business methods you collect more money but do less volume. Nothing could be further from the truth. We have clients on our accounts receivable management service, who collected 75% to 85% of their accounts receivable prior to using our service. Since then, year after year, their collections have averaged anywhere from 90% to 98% of their charge volume. In no case has volume fallen off. In most cases there has been a decided increase.

There have been surveys for many years showing average collection percentages in the various fields of medicine. While they could be quoted here, their value is lost unless you ask the question: Why? Why does one specialty have less trouble than another collecting medical accounts? I believe that when you delve into this question, you find yourself back at the basic doctor-patient relationship, and exactly what in that relationship motivates a patient to pay his account. If we can better understand what motivates patients to pay their medical accounts in a particular field of medicine, perhaps we can apply that same motivation in other fields, in different ways. Here are some observations I have made in handling medical collection accounts.

The more preventive medicine a doctor does, the less trouble the doctor has with patients not paying their accounts. One example is the field of pediatrics. Generally speaking, collection percentages are high in this field. A large portion of a pediatrician's volume is made up of periodic examinations of children, periodic immunization shots and so forth. This is preventive medicine rather than treatment of illness, as we generally accept the term.

Another thing I have noticed is that the collection problems of medical accounts increase in a direct ratio with the seriousness of the illness. The majority of the medical collection volume we handle is made up of large accounts involving surgery or long periods of confinement in the hospital. The accounts patients run up for their, let's call them, "day to day ills" are usually handled in a proper manner, maybe not paid every thirty days, but paid eventually. Here is another observation concerning large bills. The sooner a *new* patient has a large bill for a major illness, after coming to a doctor for the first time, the more chance of never collecting the account. The more tangible the medical service becomes, the more the patient understands the nature of the service. The more time spent in explaining the nature of the illness and the method of treatment, the easier it is to secure payment for services rendered.

The very nature of preventive medicine holds an attraction to the patient. All of us would rather prevent an illness than have treatment for it. Serious illness is something we didn't desire, never wanted, and wished we didn't have. Consequently, anything attached to preventive medicine holds an attraction to the patient, even a bill. And vice-versa, anything attached to a serious illness has a stigma attached to it, especially the bill.

Another reason for this difference is a purely economic one. Everyone keeps a personal budget of one type or another. Some by accurate written records, others by mental arithmetic. The monthly or quarterly trips to the doctor are planned, the cost is known, and money is set aside in the budget for them. But the serious illness is unexpected and unplanned. Consequently, the question of payment is a financial problem as well as a physical one.

What can doctors in private practice learn from this? First, it should encourage extra effort on his part to better educate his patients to the value of preventive medicine. Actually, this is his responsibility as well as to his advantage, both as a doctor and a business man. Thus, you have "Good Medicine" and "Good Business." Along with it will come "Good Public Relations." Patients like this type of medicine. How much more pleasant, both for the doctor and the patient, to send a bill for services pronouncing them "fit" rather than a bill for treatment of "ill health."

I also stated that the quicker a new patient has a large bill for major medical care the more chance of never collecting the account. The reason for this is the new patient has not had time to establish any sort of relationship with the doctor. His first meeting is composed of nothing but bad news, his second with major treatment and often times his third is in the form of a bill. There is a certain amount of gratitude on the part of the patient for the doctors help. When he receives your bill, however, his expressions are oftentimes "shorter" and "more concentrated" as to his exact feeling. This should serve to emphasize the importance of the first meeting of the doctor with his patient. Here is where he should be impressed with the doctor, his methods, and his business-like way of handling his practice. This includes, not excludes, his fee and bill.

"The more tangible the medical service becomes, the easier it is to secure payment." Too often the patient feels that his treatment is routine, of not much importance. Many times this is because he doesn't understand the treatment nor does he understand exactly what the physician hopes to accomplish by the treatment. If the patient gains this impression, it carries over to his bill, which also becomes routine and not very important. A little more time in making the patient feel that this treatment is "for *him*," "to help *him*," "to make *him* well" will work wonders in the doctor's collection percentage.

This is not an attempt to tell doctors how to practice medicine. It is an effort to state that the way a doctor practices will govern the extent of his collection problem. This is sometimes referred to as "Bedside Manner," the *extra* touch a doctor has, the ability to make each patient feel important. This ability, together with sound business-like methods, will help any doctor collect 90% to 98% of his charge volume.

The doctor's first concern is the welfare of his patient. It is this ideal that has given the profession its high stature. The welfare of the patient, both physical and mental, is and always should be, the doctor's first consideration.

Is the economic welfare of the patient also the doctor's concern? To the extent that it involves the medical account, it is. A patient burdened with medical debt has an impediment to his physical recovery. The importance of this impediment will vary according to the makeup of the individual patient. With some it may be important enough to actually retard or at least impede the treatment the doctor is prescribing. With others it may be no more than another obstacle to overcome in the daily task of living. The patient who is suddenly confronted with large medical accounts he is unable to pay, as he paid them in the past, is frustrated in one or more of the ten basic desires. If the patient *feels* he is losing his self respect or worried about his inability to pay the account; if he *feels* he isn't being fair with the doctor;

isn't it possible for the burden of medical debt to affect his physical recovery? This is another argument in favor of the doctor discussing the patient's medical account with him, showing him a manner in which he can pay his account, and assuring him this manner of paying will be satisfactory to the doctor.

Too often we are prone to judge all debtors by the actions of the "Deadbeat"—the individual who never pays his accounts unless forced to pay them. This individual goes through life spending more time dodging his creditors than he does trying to pay them. The "deadbeat" is the individual to whom the ten basic motivations have no value or meaning. He has no self respect, he doesn't know the meaning of self respect. He doesn't worry, he doesn't think of his job or his family. In fact, his moral character is shattered. I have seen many responsible people confronted with unexpected debt, with what appears to be a hopeless situation, throw up their hands and give up. Most of the time they need help and advice. Among the thousands of cases of this type that have reached our office, I have never found one that couldn't be straightened out. Since the greatest single source of unexpected debt is medical expense, it would seem that as a doctor, for his patients' welfare and because it is also "Good Business," this should be his concern.

Doctors are asked to heal the sick, comfort the afflicted, and ease the burdened. Most of them are family men. Thus he will have the normal cares of wife and children. He belongs to a profession whose advances in knowledge occur daily. He is expected to remain informed of them. Since a doctor is a "pillar of the community," he is expected to assume his share of civic responsibilities. Many of them start their professional life deeply in debt, so they have their own share of financial problems. Now I have said that the doctor should share the economic problems of his patients; that under our system of private medicine, he cannot separate the physical well being of his patient from his economic well being, any more than he can separate the blood from the body and still have life.

There have been, and still are, two major obstacles in the path of the doctor who desires to employ "Good Business Methods" in his practice: knowhow and time. The latter of these, time, is by far the most serious obstacle. It's true that business techniques, tax work, office systems, collection techniques and management ability are not exactly the subjects taught in medical school. The average doctor is certainly capable of acquiring knowledge in these arts, but he lacks time. He is hard pressed to maintain a practice, keep up with advances in medicine, have time for his family, and time for himself to enjoy the fruits of his labors.

These circumstances led to the formation of Medical Bureaus, agencies operated by business men, offering various business services to the doctor, such as collections, bookkeeping, tax service, financing or budgeting, professional management, telephone answering, employment service, office systems and records, credit reporting, and others. For many years, these bureaus operated as individual units with no contact among themselves. A doctor desiring the services of such a bureau had no guarantee that he would be dealing with a reputable and ethical agency. Some thirty years ago, several of these bureaus recognized these facts and met in St. Louis to do something about it. Out of these meetings came the Medical, Dental and Hospital Bureaus of America, Inc.

The Bureau owners themselves laid down standards of membership and ethical procedures of operations. They went one step further and had these standards and procedures approved by the Medical Economics committees of the American Medical Association, American Dental Association and the American Hospital Association. Today the Medical, Dental and Hospital Bureaus of America, Inc. maintains its executive offices in Chicago and has liaison committees that work closely with the Medical Economics committee of each of the three associations.

Membership standards in this association are high. Any unethical practice on the part of any member bureau leads to immediate expulsion from the association. In over thirty years no member of this association has ever been accused of *any* unethical practice by *any* member of the medical fraternity. The basic creed of this association is "Better to lose a collection, if in making it, you would destroy the patient-physician relationship."

Many of these services such as tax service, telephone answering service, employment service, nurses registry, printing and mimeographing service, and office systems and records are self-explanatory in their very title. The major difference in being offered by a medical bureau rather than a commercial institution is they are designed specifically with the doctor in mind. They are operated solely for the medical professions and thus their methods of operations are geared to the specialized problems and needs of the professions.

Financing Or Budgeting. Many times the patient who owes one doctor a large bill also owes several other medical accounts. This usually happens due to the fact that most large bills are incurred along with a period of hospitalization. Thus the patient may have a bill from physician, hospital, pharmacy, anesthetist, surgeon and possibly even other physicians called in as consultants. Each creditor is usually willing to accept monthly terms. The patient, however, may not be able to make a reasonable monthly payment on each medical account. Also there is a certain amount of psychological pressure exerted on some patients, when they have several outstanding accounts.

Here is where the medical finance plan plays a large part in strengthening the physician-patient relationship. The patient is referred to the medical bureau. Upon approval of his loan application, the bureau pays each creditor the amount owed by the patient. The patient signs a note for the total sum plus charges and makes one payment on his entire indebtedness. Each creditor endorses the patient's note for the amount they receive. If the patient fails to pay all or part of his note, the bureau asks each creditor to pay back their pro-rata share of the unpaid balance. The endorsement by the creditor permits the bureau to make loans to patients who otherwise would not be financially entitled to a loan on the basis of their collateral. Actually, the creditor is endorsing something he never had in the first place.

Each doctor should familiarize himself and his office staff with the details of any medical finance program offered in his community. This gives him an opportunity to suggest a concrete plan of action to his patients who have incurred large medical expense. It provides a sound solution to many of their problems.

Centralized bookkeeping provides the supervision and credit executive ability so desperately needed in handling the doctor's accounts receivable. It takes the routine drudgery of billing and bookkeeping out of the doctor's office. Bills are itemized to each patient. Everything is done in the doctor's name and address. All monies are handled in the doctor's office. Daily records of charges and payments are sent to the bureau, where they are posted to the patients' accounts. At the end of each month the doctor is furnished with a record of the transactions on each patient's account.

"Collection follow up" of accounts is handled by the bureau in a policy *approved by the doctor*. The doctor *at all times* retains control over his accounts. In fact he exercises greater control over his accounts, under this system, since he takes time each month to review his delinquent accounts and approve a course of action for each patient. Doctors using this system will collect 5% to 10% more of their charge volume than under another system. Increased collections pay the cost of the service many times over.

Too often the bookkeeping and billing procedure in a doctor's office is something done, *"when you have the time!"* It assumes secondary importance to everything else. The result is sporadic and inadequate billing, which alone accounts for half of the bad debt losses in a doctor's office. Accounts receivable management service provides the executive supervision, follow through, and labor to accomplish the job and cut this exorbitant and senseless loss. The use of a straight collection service without proper billing and proper collection follow through is a waste of time, both yours and the bureau's. With proper billing and collection procedure, a good collection service can recover dollars, patients and good will.

In choosing a collection service, there are nine points to keep in mind. If an agency doesn't meet all nine qualifications, better not to use any collection service at all.

1. Select a local agency with a reputation for reliability and good standing in the community.

2. Avoid out of state or mail-order type agencies.

3. Investigate the methods used (ask to see the type of notices and follow-up material)

4. Check the ownership and financial responsibility of the agency, and its promptness in settling for monies collected.

5. Don't sign anything—Better agencies don't use contracts.

6. Can you be assured that no legal action, or threat of it will be taken without your consent?

7. Will the agency be governed by your instructions to collect only within the scope of good public relations?

8. Will it agree to report cases deserving your special consideration and accept adjustment, withdrawal or cancellations of an account when, in your opinion, such action is advisable in the interests of good public relations?

9. Once an account has been turned over to an agency, the agency is entitled to a share of any sums paid by the patient either to you or to the

agency. One should be fair and recognize the assistance given in collecting this amount. Be fair with your agency.

Most agencies operate on a 50% contingent basis; no charge unless a collection is made. Many doctors consider this too high. An A. M. A. booklet entitled "Collecting Medical Accounts" contains the following chart:

Value of Accounts Receivable

Age of Accounts	Value Per Dollar
30 days	98¢
60 days	83¢
90 days	65¢
4 months	50¢
6 months	30¢
9 months	20¢
1 year	10¢

Many times I have seen doctors stop using a reputable agency and give their accounts to an agency who claimed they could obtain better results. A good agency will not promise any specific amount of collections because of the unknown factors such as age of the account, previous handling of account and local collection laws.

Professional management is the "grandaddy" of all services. The average medical practitioner cannot afford to hire a full time business manager. Professional management service fills this need. The service supplies the business executive ability necessary to a doctor's office. The service is responsible for efficient office system and records. Good systems save time and permit doctor and staff to devote more time to patients. The operators of this service not only design and install these systems, but they are responsible for training the office staff in their use. They will make a periodic analysis of the doctor's practice to help him factually measure his progress; to determine how he is doing and what he can expect to do in the future. The service provides an efficient income tax system, to insure that the doctor is in a position to take advantage of every tax break but at the same time keep him on a correct basis with the treasury department. The service provides the doctor with the competent executive ability needed to manage his financial affairs. It permits the doctor to devote more time to his practice, his family and his own personal leisure, while at the same time giving him the peace of mind that can come with knowing his "house is in order."

53   SOCIAL RELATIONS AND INNOVATION IN THE
         MEDICAL PROFESSION: THE EPIDEMIOLOGY
         OF A NEW DRUG*

         By Herbert Menzel and Elihu Katz

In the last few years, research on communications and opinion formation has taken more and more account of the various ways in which interpersonal relations may "intervene" in the communication process. Thus, for example, the role played by personal influence in affecting individual decisions has received increasing attention. Events in the world outside, be they political acts, technological innovations, or fashion releases, seem to impinge upon the individual not so much through the direct channels of the mass media, as through the mediation of face-to-face contacts with other individuals— some of whom, in turn, are affected by the mass media.[1] This realization of the role of so-called "opinion leaders" has been accompanied by another awareness: sources of influence which are not inherently relevant to the subject matter at hand must be considered even where expert opinions and specialized sources of informations are available. Among the sources which influence a very wide arc of the individual's behavior with very little respect for the boundaries of subject matter are enduring networks of social contacts. Thus, for example, in politics, neither the newspaper editor nor even the ward heeler appear to affect the individual's vote as powerfully as his parents, his spouse, or his ethnic and religious loyalties.[2]

But personal influence is not the only aspect of interpersonal relations which is relevant to an understanding of the flow of mass communications and their effects on individual decisions. The extent of an individual's integration in a group may be an important variable, for example. Thus, one study has shown that children who are relatively well integrated in groups of peers tend to make quite different use of adventure stories on the radio than children who are relatively isolated from such contacts.[3] Or, an earlier study has shown that Allied propaganda to German troops did not take effect until the soldier was cut off from his intimate, interpersonal ties—when his own small unit of peers and non-commissioned officers broke up.[4]

If "belonging or not belonging" is a key variable, so is belonging to one group rather than another. An individual is ordinarily reluctant to depart from the norms of his particular group, unless the departure itself receives some form of group support, and a communication aimed at influencing his thoughts or actions may therefore fail. When changes occur, it is usually only when the individual perceives that his group approves, or that support comes from a dissident sub-group, or from an outside group toward which the individual sees himself moving or whose presumed standards he accepts.[5]

Communication In The Medical Profession. A current study on the flow of scientific information in the medical profession has provided an opportunity to apply these ideas to a new and substantively different sociological

From *The Public Opinion Quarterly*, 19, (Winter, 1955–56), 337–352. Copyright 1955 by Princeton University.

field. By contrast to earlier studies of opinion formation and decision-making, we are dealing here with a relatively closed community of specialists. We are not concerned with topics where everybody is supposed to be entitled to his own opinion, but with matters based on scientific findings, where the relevant expert sources are generally recognized, easily identified, and universally available. The hypothesis of the roles of less expert sources and of interpersonal channels as mediators of influences is therefore put to a more crucial test.[6]

The general concern of this project is physicians' reactions to innovations in therapy, particularly with regard to new drugs. Drugs, unlike other matters of medical practice, have standardized names and easily ascertainable release dates, and it is possible to pinpoint the time of first use of a drug by each physician. In this sense, then, the process of diffusion of a new drug can be traced through the social structure of the medical community.

The data we shall draw upon are from a pilot study conducted in May, 1954, in a New England city of approximately 30,000; 33 of the 40 doctors practicing in the community were interviewed. Since the behavior in which we are interested (prescribing of new drugs) can take place only among physicians, we have thus interviewed 83 per cent of the relevant members of the community. But because of the small number of cases, the findings must be treated as highly tentative. We present these early results primarily for the purpose of calling attention to the clues implicit here for research in the flow of influence and innovation. The analysis of later interviews with over 200 doctors in the Midwest is now in progress at the Bureau of Applied Social Research.

In this paper, we will consider the ways in which the doctor's position in the social structure of his local medical fraternity affects his acceptance of new pharmaceutical products. Our procedure differs from that of most previous studies which have sought to trace the role of personal influences in individual decisions. Typically, in these other studies, individuals who have recently made some decision are first identified and whenever their account shows that another person has figured in the decision, they are asked to identify this "opinion leader." The nature of the social relationship between the influential person and the person influenced, as well as the characteristics differentiating the two, are then determined.

In our study, however, we first interviewed *all* the local doctors we could, and, by means of three sociometric questions, determined the network of social relations among them without reference to any one particular decision. The channels of information and influence which entered into a recent drug decision were also ascertained in all interviews, and compared with the doctor's position in the social network. Only then did we superimpose on the social network the flow of adoptions of a new practice, as indicated by the precise sequence of dates on which each respondent introduced a certain new medication. This latter information was obtained through an examination of the prescription files of local pharmacies.

Sociometric Questions, Stars, And Isolates. To locate each of the 33 physician-respondents in the structure of his local medical community, three sociometric questions were asked. The first question was, "Could you name the three or four physicians you meet most frequently on social occasions?" The resulting picture is shown in Sociogram I.[7] Three major networks of choices appear, designated A, B, and C. (B and C may also be regarded as sub-groups of the same network, since their segregation from one another is not as definite as that of either from A.) There are also two isolated individuals and five "neutrals", who choose into Cliques A and B equally.

A second sociometric question was aimed at a more specialized kind of social contact: "Who are the three or four physicians in your conversations with whom the subject of drug therapy most often comes up?" A comparison of the resulting map (not shown here) with Sociogram I shows that the basic pattern holds for both, with two differences: fewer drug-talk companions than friends are named, and there is increased concentration of attention around two top leaders.

A third map of informal social relations was obtained by still another question: "When you need added information or advice about questions of drug therapy, where do you usually turn?" This question was designed to elicit the names of individuals to whom a position of authority is accorded. As might have been anticipated, the responses in this case were even more heavily concentrated on a small number of stars.

As we have indicated in the introduction, the role of interpersonal relations in individual decisions is not confined to the conveying of information and to the channeling of influence. For example, a doctor who shares an office with another may feel less hesitant about the risk of trying out new drugs in general, and not merely because of anything the other doctor may have said about any particular drug; or, a doctor whose friendship is not reciprocated by other doctors may develop quite a different relationship to other channels of information—he may become more friendly with the pharmaceutical salesman, for example—than the doctor who is well integrated in the medical community. Thus, a doctor's association with other doctors may serve (1) as an important source of information and influence on a particular innovation, and (2) as an important determinant of his response to innovations in general, and to information and influence emanating from other sources.

For this reason, the sociometric data will be related to doctors' behavior in two basically distinct ways. The first of these is the examination of certain characteristics which differentiate individuals who have received many and few sociometric choices. What, for instance, is the use made of the diverse channels of communication by the sociometric stars—by those receiving many choices? How does it differ from the use made of these channels by their less popular colleagues? A second use of the sociometric data will be to ask what difference it makes with *which* doctors a given doctor is associated, rather than *how many* name him, say, as a friend. For example, is a doctor more ready to adopt a new drug if he has friends who have already adopted it?

The Channels of Influence. Each respondent was asked how he had learned about two of the drugs he had recently adopted. Table 1 cross-tabulates the replies with the popularity of the doctor among his colleagues. An interesting pattern emerges. Journal reading plays a much larger role in the

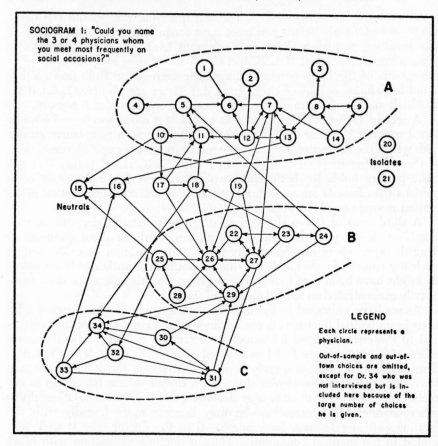

SOCIOGRAM I: "Could you name the 3 or 4 physicians whom you meet most frequently on social occasions?"

LEGEND

Each circle represents a physician.

Out-of-sample and out-of-town choices are omitted, except for Dr. 34 who was not interviewed but is included here because of the large number of choices he is given.

adoptions of doctors who receive one or more designations than among the isolates. This conforms to the hypothesis of the "two-step flow of communications," which states, in essence, that messages originating outside of the individual's face-to-face group do not impinge on him directly, but are mediated by a few members of his group, who expose themselves to messages from the outside world more than their conferes.

The source of this hypothesis is in mass media research, where it has been found that opinion leaders are in closer contact with the mass media than their followers. But doctors can keep in touch with the outside world in other ways than through the printed media—e.g., by attendance at medical meetings in other cities. The two-step flow hypothesis therefore leads one to expect that out-of-town meetings as well as journals would be more important in the decisions of the most popular drug discussion partners than in those of their less popular colleagues. Table 1 bears out this expectation: only those who receive three choices or more report that what they learned at meetings entered into their decisions. It would seem that the star does indeed serve as a relay: he incorporates what he has learned at the meetings into his own decisions and, it may be assumed, into his conversations with others.

Table 1*—Drug-Talk Choices and Channels Employed in Decisions on Two Recent Drug Adoptions

	NUMBER OF DRUG-TALK CHOICES RECEIVED		
	None	One, Two	Three or More
Mail and periodicals from drug houses	30%	18%	21%
Articles in journals	10	39	32
Detail men (salesmen)	40	25	21
Colleagues	15	15	16
Meetings	0	0	11
Other Channels	5	3	0
	100%	100%	100%
(Number of channels)	(20)	(34)	(19)

* The percentages are based on the total number of channels mentioned, which exceeds the number of doctors in each category, since many doctors reported on two decisions, and the average number of channels per decision was 1.88.

The drug decisions of the sociometric isolate, by contrast, are marked by heavier reliance on commercial sources—direct mail advertising from the pharmaceutical companies and the "detail man" as the drug house representative is called. These sources, to be sure, also come from out of town. What differentiates them from journals and meetings is that, being commercial sources, they carry less prestige, and that it requires less effort to keep up with them. Evidently the two-step flow hypothesis does not apply to *all* channels from the outside world. Some of the channels *do* impinge on most members of their intended audiences directly, and are not disproportionately utilized by the opinion leaders.

Incidentally, the differential importance which the detail man has for the social isolate is not limited to his role as a purveyor of information about new medicines. Two of the four doctors who received no friendship choices volunteered the information that very often talked with the detail man on subjects other than drugs: "We'll get off the track sometimes on economics, politics, family affairs," said one. Another relatively isolated doctor commented on the detail men as follows:

They are helpful—they know all the doctors in the communities around here and give you all the dirt and gossip and incidental news about what is going on amongst the doctors in this community.

This pharmaceutical salesman evidently serves as a near-professional companion for men who are relatively cut off from informal contacts with other physicians.

A final observation from Table 1 yields a surprise. The classic model of the two-step flow of communication provides that it is the rank-and-file members who are influenced by the opinion leaders, while the latter are influenced by the mass media. But in Table 1 "colleagues" are mentioned exactly as frequently by opinion leaders as by the rest. The most likely explanation is that the opinion leaders may themselves turn to colleagues of even higher status, and that it may take three or four steps, perhaps rather than two, before a level of leadership is reached where dependence on personal contacts is markedly decreased.[8]

Revision of the model to allow for multistep flow of communications would thus seem in order. A second revision has already been pointed out:

that messages from the outside world need not come through the printed word or other mass media. In the case of physicians, we have seen that attendance at society meetings may take over this function. As the multistep flow hypothesis is applied to still other publics, it may be found that the opinion leader can keep in touch with relevant parts of the outside world in still other ways. Finally, the model may not apply to channels of low prestige and unusually easy accessibility.

One more finding, still tentative, regarding the channels of information used in recent drug decisions is especially worthy of attention. Medical problems differ widely in the degree to which their answers are well-structured and generally established. Table 1 includes the reports of doctors concerning their adoptions of a variety of different drugs. We can, however, divide these into two broad classes: one class of drugs is applicable to certain acute conditions which call for immediate action and present a very small number of alternate methods of treatment; success or failure is visible in a day or two. The other class of drugs is applicable to chronic conditions where many dozens of treatments compete, and the effectiveness of therapy is very difficult to gauge. We find that colleagues constitute only seven per cent of the channels reported as leading up to the adoption of a drug for the acute conditions but represent 22 per cent of the channels concerned with the chronic diseases. In other words, the role of colleagues increases substantially in the relatively more ambiguous situation. In a sense, this recalls the studies of suggestion and influence by Sherif and others: the role of personal influence is more important in the relatively more unstructured situation.

Table 2—Use of Channels of Communication in Decisions Regarding Acute and Chronic Conditions*

| | PER CENT OF TOTAL CHANNELS MENTIONED | |
	Acute Conditions	Chronic Conditions
Mail and periodicals from drug houses	23%	17%
Articles in journals	26	27
Detail men	33	27
Colleagues	7	22
Meetings	0	5
Other channels	10	2
	100%	100%
(Number of channels)	(30)	(41)

* The percentages are based on the total number of channels mentioned, which exceeds the number of doctors in each category, since many doctors reported on two decisions, and the average number of channels per decision was 1.88.

The Social Network And The Diffusion Of Drug Adoptions. To explore further the workings of person-to-person relations in this realm, we shall now turn from correlates of the number of sociometric designations received to the question, "What difference does it make to *which* clique you belong?" Age, ethnicity, religion, father's occupation, and pursuing a specialty practice were all found to be correlated with clique membership. The existence of these background correlations lends some feel of reality to the division into cliques which the sociometric data indicated.[9] In order to relate the social network to the adoption of a new item of behavior, the local pharmacists were asked to search their files for the first prescription written by each of the interviewed doctors for a certain drug which had come on the market a few months before. Table 3 is a presentation of the chronological order

Table 3—Date of First Prescription of a Specified New Drug by Each Doctor*

No prescriptions before July 1:
Drs. 7, 9, 10, 20, 22, 28

		Drs. 2 5 6 8 19			Drs. 25	
Dr. Dr.	Dr.	33	Dr. Dr.	Dr. Dr.	26	
31 / 12	1/	34 /	17/30	18/23	/27	
December 1953	January 1954	February	March	April	May	June

* Each doctor is represented by his identifying number. Doctors following specialties not usually prescribing drugs through commercial pharmacies are omitted.

in which doctors in the sample adopted the drug. (Surgeons and other specialists not normally prescribing drugs through pharmacies are excluded from this table.) Intervals on the table correspond roughly to the time intervals involved.

Our original intention was simply to correlate early or late use of the new drug with characteristics of individual doctors. But after Table 3 was drawn up, we were intrigued by the strange alternation of slow periods and spurts which it shows: first, three pioneers adopt the new drug at three-week intervals. Then, suddenly, during a period of only eleven days in February seven doctors start writing prescriptions for the new drug. During the next three months, only four doctors start prescribing the drug, at widely spaced intervals. Then, again, three doctors initiate use of the drug within a period of only five days in mid-May. No further doctors appear on the table after this, although our data are complete for an additional month and a half. There thus remain six doctors who either do not prescribe the drug at all, or do so only at an unknown time very much later than any of their colleagues.[10]

How is this alternation of slow and fast periods to be accounted for? One possibility is, of course, that the fast periods are those when there is more need for this particular drug in the community—times of epidemics, for instance. However, the slow and fast periods do not coincide with the known seasonal variations in the incidence of diseases for which this drug is indicated. A second possible explanation for the alternation of slow and fast periods is that the two fast periods correspond to two sales campaigns that may have been carried on by the pharmaceutical companies involved. This may be the case but fails to explain why certain doctors responded to the first campaign, while others did not.

The third possibility is that the alternations can be accounted for by social relations. During the initial slow period a few hardy individuals try out the new product—perhaps watched with interest by their more conservative colleagues. Each spurt then represents the almost simultaneous adoption of the drug by a well-integrated group of physicians. This hypothesis, unlike the other two, would not only explain why spurts occur at all, but also why it is the *particular* doctors who participate in each spurt that act in unison—e.g., why Drs. A, B, C and D act simultaneously, but not Drs. D, E, and F.

We therefore decided to bring together the data on first prescription dates with the data on social groupings. The result is Sociogram II which is identical with Sociogram I, but adds information on the date of each doctor's first prescription for the new drug. Different shadings denote the time periods during which each doctor first prescribed it. Triangles indicate doctors following specialties not normally prescribing drugs through pharmacies. Solid circles indicate other doctors who did not prescribe the drug at all during the period covered by the survey. Let us now trace the flow of the innovation through this map of friendships among the physicians. Two questions will occupy us as we do so: (a) are doctors who adopt the drug on successive dates in contact with one another? (b) is each spurt of adoptions located within one of the cliques?

(1) *Initial slow period.* The first three doctors are symbolized by blank circles. Their initial prescriptions took place on December 1, December 22, and January 10.

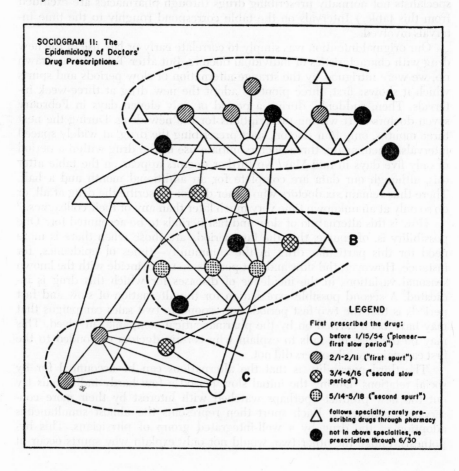

SOCIOGRAM II: The
Epidemiology of Doctors'
Drug Prescriptions.

A

B

C

LEGEND

First prescribed the drug:

○ before 1/15/54 ("pioneer—
first slow period")

◐ 2/1-2/11 ("first spurt")

⊗ 3/4-4/16 ("second slow
period")

⊕ 5/14-5/18 ("second spurt")

△ follows specialty rarely prescribing drugs through pharmacy

● not in above specialties, no
prescription through 6/30

(2) *First spurt.* Seven physicians represented by single hatched circles adopted the drug between February 1 and 11. Four of them are in direct contact with a pioneer (i.e., a blank circle), and the remaining three have second-order contact with a pioneer.

At the end of this February spurt, three out of four doctors in Clique C have used the drug; so have six out of eight doctors in Clique A; but not a single member of Clique B. (Surgeons and other non-prescribing specialists are excluded.) Even more striking than this contrast between the proportions of each clique who have used the drug by February 11 is another fact. One might think that the remainder of Cliques A and C would follow suit after some lag—perhaps two or three weeks later. But in fact only one of them ever filed a prescription for the new drug with the pharmacies reporting to us throughout the period covered—i.e., through the end of June. In other words, after the first pioneering period and the February spurt, only real diehards still hold out in Cliques A and C.

(3) *Second Slow Period.* Several more doctors (recorded as cross-hatched circles) adopt the drug during the next few weeks; their dates are widely dispersed over a long period of time (March 4, March 29, April 9, and April 16).

(4) *Second Spurt.* Then suddenly, between May 14 and 18, three doctors in Clique B, represented by dotted circles, prescribed the drug, leaving only two doctors as non-prescribers in Clique B. Again, these two are not merely a little behind their colleagues, but they are "diehards," having no prescriptions for the new drug on record throughout the period covered by our survey.

We have now traced the sequence of prescriptions of a new drug through our map of friendships among the doctors in this city, much as doctors themselves do when they trace the "epidemiology" of an infectious disease on the map of a city. What we have seen can be summarized in three propositions:

(1) That half or more of the members of each clique who are ever to adopt the drug do so within a few days of one another.

(2) That for each of the three cliques it is possible to state a cut-off date such that those members who have not adopted the drug by that date do not adopt it at all during the survey period. Only one respondent deviates from this generalization.

(3) That no one (except the three pioneers) adopts the drug unless he has a direct sociometric contact with a doctor who adopted it before him. Three respondents deviate from this generalization, and it is therefore restated as follows: that drug adoptions on any particular date are more frequent among doctors who are in direct sociometric contact with others who have already adopted the drug, than among doctors who lack such contact.

Tables 4 and 5 constitute quantitative expressions of the empirical deviations from these three propositions. Table 4 shows no deviations from the first proposition. It also shows that the one doctor who actually deviated from the second proposition and prescribed the drug after the cut-off date for his clique constitutes but 14 per cent of the deviations that *could* have occurred Table 5 tabulates the deviations from the third proposition. It was necessary to compute separately for each date on which an adoption occurred the number of eligible doctors who had not already adopted the new drug but were in contact with others who had, and the number of similar doctors lacking such contact. Summing for all the dates, we find 49 contact situations and 34 non-contact situations. Each of these could have led to an adoption on the date involved. Actually, 22 per cent of the contact situations and only 9 per cent of the non-contact situations eventuated in a drug adoption. The corresponding percentages for the case of complete dependence of contacts and adoptions would be 29 per cent and zero per cent; for complete independence, 17 per cent and 17 per cent.[11]

Table 4—Cliques and Spurts* of Drug Adoptions

Clique	Cut-off Date	Total Adoptions	Adoptions prior to Spurt	Adoptions During Spurt No.	Per Cent	Adoptions after cutoff Date (Deviations) No.	Per Cent of total adoptions	Per Cent of possible deviations	Non-Adoptions
A	2/10	6	2	4	67%	..	..	..	3
B	5/18	4	1	3	75	..	..	..	2
C	2/11	4	1	2	50	1	25%	50%	..
All Cliques		14	4	9	64%	1	7%	14%	5
Neutrals		3							1
Total		17							6

* "Spurt" is defined as the seven days ending with the cut-off date. Doctors following specialties not normally prescribing drugs through pharmacies are excluded from Table 4.

Table 5—Adoptions of the New Drug among Doctors who, on the Day the Adoption Occurred, were and were not in Direct Sociometric Contact with another Doctor who had already Adopted it*

Number of Doctors, who, on the date indicated, had not yet adopted the new drug and:

	Were in contact and—			/ Were not in contact and—			
Date	Adopted	Did not adopt	Total	Adopted	Did not Adopt	Total	Grand Total
Feb. 1	0	6	6	1	7	8	14
Feb. 5	2	5	7	0	6	6	13
Feb. 6	1	6	7	0	4	4	11
Feb. 10	1	5	6	1	3	4	10
Feb. 11	0	5	5	0	3	3	8
Mar. 4	0	4	4	1	2	3	7
Mar. 29	1	3	4	0	2	2	6
Apr. 9	1	2	3	0	2	2	5
Apr. 16	1	2	3	0	1	1	4
May 14	1	1	2	0	1	1	3
May 18	2	0	2	0	0	0	2
After							0
Total numbers	11	38	49	3	31	34	
Total percent	22%			9%			

* Doctors who never adopted the drug during the period covered by the survey, as well as doctors following specialties not normally prescribing drugs through pharmacies, are excluded from Table 5, as are the three earliest adopters. The results are not substantially altered when the length of the intervals between the dates in Table 5 is taken into account and the three earliest adoptors are added.

We therefore feel justified in proposing that the spread of this innovation in the medical community flows through social channels, and that each of the spurts of adoptions in middle February and middle May does indeed represent the simultaneous adoption of the drug by a socially close-knit group of physicians. There are a variety of ways in which such simultaneous decisions may be reached: (1) perhaps a decision, once reached by one member of a clique, is easily accepted by his associates who trust his judgment; (2) perhaps members of the same clique share norms of reliability and criteria of judgment to such an extent that whatever is convincing to one member is likely to be equally appealing to the rest; (3) perhaps each group shares exposure to channels, so that they are homogeneous as to stimuli received; (4) perhaps they even look at a case in the hospital together and are apprised on such an occasion of the success of a new treatment. (The occurrence of two sales campaigns for the new drug, which was mentioned as a possibility, would be compatible with items (2) or (3).) Whatever the process by which a group of doctors reaches such a near-simultaneous decision, it would be followed by a slow period of sporadic adoptions by doctors in other groups until some event—perhaps endorsement by a respected leader—triggers off a new spurt of adoptions in one of these other groups. In each group certain "diehards" would be left over, who cannot be convinced of the usefulness of the new drug.[12]

What sort of doctors are the three pioneers who prescribed the new drug as early as December and January? Contrary to our expectations, they are neither outstanding specialists, nor outstanding leaders by any available criterion, nor in possession of an unusual degree of access to outside information. By contrast, the outstanding sociometric stars in our sample are predominantly late-comers in the adoption of the drug.

This inverse correlation between early prescription for the new drug and leadership is surprising, and one is tempted to conjecture as to the process that might be at work if the finding is a reliable one. It would almost seem as if each clique had its early experimenters or "advance scouts," who were willing to try out an innovation before any of their local colleagues. In each clique, the sociometric stars are among the last to adopt the drug; but when they finally do, all the other members except the real diehards fall in line immediately. This would account for the sudden final spurts of adoptions which we have observed. We must caution, however, that the reliability of this finding is in doubt. Our later Midwest data show a direct correlation of leadership and innovation. We do not know whether this is due to a true regional difference, or to error in one of the sets of data. It is noteworthy that the study of the diffusion and acceptance of new farm practices has given rise to equally contradictory findings concerning the extent of overlap between innovators and influentials. Eugene Wilkening's North Carolina study finds little overlap; Herbert Lionberger's Missouri study finds considerable overlap. A recent study by Marsh and Coleman implies a possible basis for reconciliation: in a "low adoption" neighborhood—that is, where the neighborhood norm is conservative with respect to farm innovations—the leaders or influentials did not have significantly higher adoption rates than non-leaders; in "high adoption" areas, however, the leaders were far ahead.[13]

In summary, we have found that the bringing together of independently established information on social relationships, on innovating behavior, and on the use of channels of information in decision-making supports the hypotheses of the role played by face-to-face contacts in mediating innovations from the world outside.

We have seen that the notions of the importance of interpersonal relations are applicable to a case of decision-making among specialists concerning matters based on scientific findings where well-recognized expert sources of knowledge exist. This, we noted, is particularly the case when decisions are required for relatively ambiguous situations.

Finally, we have found it necessary to propose amendments for the model of the two-step flow of communications: by considering the possibility of multi-step rather than two-step flow; by noting that sources other than printed publications may be the channels to the outside world maintained by the opinion leaders; by noting that the model may not apply to channels of low prestige and unusually easy accessibility; and by differentiating various kinds of leadership, especially by emphasizing the differential roles of the innovator or pioneer on the one hand and the opinion leader or arbiter on the other.

54   BASIC FUNCTIONAL ROLES IN NURSING: MOTHER SURROGATE AND HEALER

By Sam Schulman

All men who live together in whatever time have faced problems common to societal existence: group living has brought with it debits as well as assets. For one reason or another there have always been members of society who could not assume full responsibility as group members and, conversely, others who have had to accept a greater share of social responsibility. In the life cycle of each man there are times when he is dependent upon others and times when others are dependent upon him. There are times when his dependence is so great that without assistance and guidance he ceases to be a functioning member of society.

Witness the infant. Without the guidance of adult minds and the protection of adult hands human infants are vulnerable to destructive elements of an inimical environment. The need to shield the littlest members of society have called forth the complementary supportive activities of adults. Without this kind of social mutuality group existence would shortly cease to be. Under normal conditions society makes every attempt to rear the children it has reproduced.

There are many areas of social mutuality involving dependent and supportive actors where individual needs cannot be met by the efforts of the dependent individual himself. Such an individual is a patient;[1] one who is temporarily unable to meet his social responsibilities because all, or part, of his body (or mind) has been afflicted by external agents. Such external agents may be demons, destructive gods, natural catastrophe, germs, stress, hostile persons. The intervention of other external agents—constructive gods and spirits, situational change, medicine, ministering persons—is seen as necessary to abolish sickness, or to delimit it, and to allow the stricken member to return to society.

Both the infant and the patient are dependent, but there is a qualitative difference in their dependence. An infant is all of society's concern. The pathos of a lost and weeping child is shared by adults and will initiate palliative efforts on their part. An adult, merely by being an adult, feels qualified to afford minimal care to a child; he has lived through childhood and it is everywhere about him a stage of development of his community co-members. Society itself, through its norms, defends and perpetuates this attitude. The child necessitates the very generic complementary role of the adults who meet his needs. Within this total structure of responsible adults certain of them are recognized as having primary responsibility. A father figure, regardless of actual biological kinship, is present. But always, where possible, the adult member most responsible for the welfare of a child is its actual biological mother.

A patient, too, is all of society's concern, and, in a very basic way, most adult members of society would feel it necessary to initiate action, however minimal, to assist him. Unlike the child, however, the patient cannot depend upon the experiential universality of his state to be preparation for alleviating it. Unlike the child's, the role of patient has grown out of a socially deviant situation: being sick. Sickness may, in fact, call forth rather negative feelings in some societies (including our own) where great emphasis is placed upon health. It would be difficult to imagine a societal setting where the state of childhood was abhorred. Like the dependent child the dependent patient requires the complementary role of adults who meet his needs and in every culture there are, indeed, such persons. In our own society, where the patient's needs have been segmented like nowhere else in the world, such responsible adults are members of the health professions, their auxiliaries, and allies. One such patient-focused group is nursing.

The modern American professional nurse does many things for the patient. A statement frequently heard from nurses (usually none too happily) is that the "nurse is all things to all people." A visit to a hospital ward where the nurse is seen writing charts, directing janitors, giving medications, bandaging wounds, consoling relatives, taking pulses, bathing bodies, administering parenteral solutions, fixing flowers, answering telephones, repairing equipment, teaching students—an almost unending list—fortifies this statement. The nurse does many things: the nurse plays many roles. Role is meant here as a set of behavior expectations which are closely associated and are oriented to the achievement of specific or latent objectives: both actual overt behavior and conceptualized ideal behavior are facets of any role.[2] It is the purpose of this paper to develop a theoretical scheme which seeks to describe the modern nurse in terms of two basic functional roles: mother surrogate and healer. This does not preclude other roles with which the nurse may be identified, but it is the feeling of the writer that these are her principal roles. It is a further purpose to suggest that much of the disequilibrium encountered on both interpersonal and intrapersonal planes in the nursing profession is due to essential areas of conflict between these two roles.

In a recent publication George Devereux has noted that every science has its "key concept:"[3] in essence there is a systematic segregation of disciplinary interests by a basic concept or theme. He thus identifies the science of anthropology by "culture." Extending this idea beyond the realm of the pure sciences it would seem that such a key concept for nursing would be "patient care." Regardless of whatever other activities enmesh the nurse her job, immediately or mediately, is to minister to those whom society recognizes as patients.

Patient care presents two aspects involving ministration: that which centers about the everyday tasks of living which the patient must have others do for him which, for the time, he is unable to do; that which centers about the process specifically oriented towards having him regain his normative healthy state. Theoretically these aspects would call for distinct behavior expectations of those who minister to the patient: mother surrogate and healer. The mother surrogate role is basically multifunctional: she does many and varied things to insure her patient's wellbeing, running the gamut from washing his feet to passively sitting by his side and listening to his innermost feelings. The healer role is basically unifunctional: to complete those tasks specifically necessary to combat the patient's affliction and restore him to society. Such fundamental distinction does not prohibit the overlapping of qualities of both roles in a single individual. It would not seem incorrect to assume that all health practitioners, from primitive shamans to members of the health team of a modern American hospital, exhibit characteristics of both mother surrogate and healer in varying proportions.

The roles of mother surrogate and patient are reciprocal and are here intended to convey a similarity to mother-child role reciprocality. The nurse as mother surrogate should feel towards her patient as the mother feels towards her child. An exact analogy is not possible, of course, nor is it intended. Many of the important behaviors found in the mother surrogate-patient relationship are also found in the mother-child relationship which permits collateral comparison and justifies the label "surrogate" which the writer uses in defining a nurse role.

The mother-child relationship[4] is characterized by intimacy. Physical intimacy dominates the initial phases of the relationship, is gradually lessened as the child grows and develops, and, in most societies, is minimal or absent if not prohibited as the child assumes the body, mind, and social functions of a mature member of society. For the mother a prevailing sentiment is tenderness and compassion for her child. She is protective of his interests and shields him from the abuse of others. To her child a mother gives freely of herself and of things which she commands. A fundamental ability which seems to characterize all higher animals allows the mother to intuit much of her child's needs and, within the dictates of her culture and of the immediate situation, she will seek to meet them. She identifies with her child; the fears and frustrations of her young one are hers also. A further characteristic of the mother role, obvious but important in its analogy to the role of mother surrogate, is its femaleness; i.e., regardless of whatever further requisites are demanded of the mother role, it is always assigned to women. (Even where the unique customs of the *couvade* obtain, the newborn is given over to a "lying-in" father not to be cherished and cuddled, but to absorb strength and prowess as early in life as possible.)[5]

The mother surrogate role closely approximates that of the mother. Certain differences are obvious. The sickroom is not the home. The patient has not been the product of a sexual liaison involving the nurse. The relationship of the patient and mother surrogate is short-lived when compared to that of the child and its mother. The list is long. In spite of these differences the similarity is strong. The role of mother surrogate is a feminine role characterized by affection, intimacy and physical proximity (greatest at the onset and least at the terminal phase of the relationship), orientation towards the meeting of general needs of a dependent ward, and identification and protection of such a ward.[6] Frances Kreuter approximates these dimensions of the role when, in discussing "nursing care," she describes the component "care" as "tending to another, being with him, assisting and protecting him, giving heed to his responses, guarding him from danger that might befall him, providing for his needs and wants with compassion as opposed to sufferance, tolerance; with tenderness and consideration as opposed to a sense of duty; with respect and concern as opposed to indifference."[7]

Regardless of whatever cultural circumscriptions or additions are made or of its manifestation in combination with the role of healer, the role of mother surrogate is universal for activities identified as nursing. Not only is it universal in a cross-cultural sense, but it is a constant characteristic of nursing in an historical sense. Wherever and whenever nursing is encountered, the role of mother surrogate is its indivisible core. In its simplest application in the precedent state of a mother-child relationship, the mother who binds the wound, soothes the emotions, and supports the injured pride of her child who has been hurt in sandlot play is nursing him. In a remote application, the director of nursing service in a large metropolitan hospital, who is many times removed from the patient's bedside and only through channels affects his wellbeing, still identifies as a nurse: the role of mother surrogate is a function of such identification.

The writer knows of only one relatively uncluttered example of the mother surrogate. She is the *tsukisoi*, a low level sub-professional nurse in Japanese hospitals.[8] *Tsuki* is derived from the verb "to attach," and *soi* indicates nearness: an apt description of an individual who is employed to do simple continuous nursing of a patient while he is hospitalized. *Tsukisoi* are women, some who are matron-spinsters or widows who have reared their families, some who are young and are not yet married. They are employed to create a homelike atmosphere for the patient while he is in the hospital and to minister to all of his personal needs excepting those involved in the curative process and those which are culturally condemned (such as his sexual needs).

A *tsukisoi* is employed by the patient or his family when it is known that he will enter a hospital. A *tsukisoi* dormitory is called and a woman is summoned. She brings to the hospital those things that she will need to do her job as well as her clothing and her pallet. For as long as her patient remains in the hospital she stays with him. She is constantly at his side or immediately available: there are no hours or days off and there are no work shifts. She prepares her patient's food as well as her own and eats with him in the confines of the sickroom. She grooms her patient and bathes him within the bounds of propriety. She attends to his excreta, mends his gown, perfumes him, holds his book as he reads, talks to him, bears the abuse of his ill-temper, listens to his innermost fears and joys, and sleeps on her own mat by his side through the night. When a patient is too poor to employ a *tsuksoi* (and their compensation is pitifully little) it is expected that a female member of the patient's family will serve in her stead; and, if he has neither money nor family, his physician may ask for governmental support to employ a *tsukisoi* which the patient may share with another indigent and famililess patient. The only procedures which may be done by the *tsukisoi* which are associated with the curative process are simple massage and the administration of oral medications, both done under the direction of a professional nurse or of a physician. *Tsukisoi* represent a level of nursing that only barely has left the confines of the home; it does, in fact, bring the home into the hospital. (Visiting American physicians frequently find the "apartment-house" atmosphere of Japanese hospitals disturbing.[9]) *Tsukisoi* may be an incipient stage in occupational specialization reaching its apex in the American professional nurse. *Tsukisoi* are trained, but such training is rudimentary and fragmentary. It is presumed that any normal woman can, with little preparation, assume the role of *tsukisoi*. Although the modern nurse practices at a much "higher" level of nursing, it is important to note that her immediately preceding historical counterparts did not and that this same basic presumption prevailed in European and American cultures until very recently.

The impress of this long historical orientation cannot be underestimated. In Western cultures it has been traditionally assumed that preparation for nursing was to be a woman or to possess womanly virtues. Christianity further strengthened this assumption. It was, and is, considered spiritually exalting and praiseworthy to walk among the sick and Christ-like to comfort those in pain or distress. How much like a sainted and warm maternal figure is the nurse in this charge attributed to Vincent de Paul in the seventeenth century:

She shall greet him gayly and kindly . . . approaching his bed with a mien modestly cheerful . . . shall raise the pillow for him, arrange the covers, place the small table near the bed, and on it arrange the napkin, the plate [and] the spoon [and] rinse the gondola. She shall wash the hands of the sick, pour out the porringer and put the meat in a plate, arranging all on the said small table; then she shall kindly invite the sick person to eat for the love of Jesus and of His holy Mother: all with love as though she were treating her child, or rather God, Who considers done to Himself the food she does to this poor person, and she shall say to him some little word [of] holy joy and consolation for the purpose of cheering him. [She] shall cut the meat into morsels . . . pour out the drink, [and] invite him anew to eat. Having thus set things going, if there is someone at hand [to continue], she shall leave him and go to find another whom she shall treat in like manner. [If, however, there is no one to continue the work she remains and] when he [the patient] has finished eating, having washed the dishes, folded the napkin and removed the table, [she] shall say grace for the sick and take leave of him immediately in order to go and serve another.[10]

Nursing literature abounds in documents which describe the nurse in similar terms from early Classical times to the very dawn of the Industrial Era. The Christian deaconess orders and nursing sisterhoods—and nursing brotherhoods and clerical orders as well—are based upon self-denying service and love for the unfortunate and afflicted. A short half-century ago the American nurse resembled her earlier and universal craft-level predecessors. Lyle Saunders[11] portrays her as an independent entrepreneur who was employed directly by a patient's family to work in his home. She worked alone but under the authority of a physician. Like the *tsukisoi*, she did numerous things for her patient "from giving skilled technical care to doing housework and looking after the patient's children." She was in constant attendance and her services were continuously available to her patient since she lived in the patient's home all during the period of her employment. Without knowledge of such terms, and with little reason to be concerned about them, this American nurse, two generations removed, gave "comprehensive nursing care." "What she had been trained to do and what she did were in close conformity, and she undoubtedly derived much satisfaction from the fact that what her job required was what she understood as nursing."[12]

Saunders' mention of skilled technical care as a component in total patient care introduces the functional role in nursing which the writer has termed "healer." W. H. R. Rivers has observed that every society has among its occupational specialists one "whose special business it is to deal with disease."[13] This would be the healer with, perhaps, the further elaboration that the healer's goal would be to overcome the disease and to restore socially the afflicted person. The healer's relations with the patient are thus centered about the curative or therapeutic process. Ideally any action which does not concern therapy is out of his province. If massage is indicated it is meant as a curative rather than a comforting procedure; a diet is prescribed which will supply nutrients to aid the body in health restoration and not to please the palate of the patient; the patient's body is touched to palpate organs and record vital signs and not to emotionally support him through the warmth of physical contact. The healer stands in sharp contradistinction to the mother surrogate: the healer "heals" and the mother surrogate "mothers." Realistically archetypical healers and mother surrogates are not encountered: they are, however, approximated. On one hand there is the *tsukisoi*, and on the other hand the highly specialized medical practitioner who does not see the patient as a "whole person," but as an upper respiratory case, a multiple fracture, a cardiovascular accident, or even as a layer of tissue or a radiological plate. For purposes of analysis the roles of mother surrogate and healer are seen as distinct entities which not only stand as contrasting but possibly as antagonistic to one another.

In their emotional and attitudinal aspects these roles are quite disparate. Within situational and societal limitations the mother surrogate is allowed freedom of affect. The nurse as mother surrogate is expected to express herself and to support her patient with words and actions of comfort. She is a friend to the patient and her approach to their relationship is informal. Her dictum might be: succor the patient. The nurse as healer is limited to her vital function and is permitted no latitude of affect. Her words and actions are limited to the performance of the therapeutic tasks at hand. Idle and non-informative conversion has no place in her relationship with her patient and their interaction is characterized by formality. Her dictum: save the patient.

The mother surrogate attempts to meet a host of supportive needs which keep her patient alive and as well adjusted to his deviant situation as is possible. The healer meets a single great need: to overcome the deviant situation as quickly, as thoroughly, and as successfully as possible.[14] The goal of the mother surrogate is to sustain, her desideratum a static state of adequacy. Her activities are governed by her situation. The healer, on the other hand, is change-oriented and dynamic; she attempts to command the situation and alter it. The very temporal character of the patient relationships of these roles differs. A continuous relationship is expected of the mother surrogate so that the diverse needs of her patient may be met. The healer's relationship is basically discontinuous and fragmentary; like any other specialized service functionary she is present when the curative process demands her specialized ministrations.

It does not seem an overstatement to note that according to the values most cultures associate with these two roles there is a difference in sexual tenor between them. The complex of behaviors which make for the mother surrogate role is essentially feminine; the complex of behaviors which make for the healer role is essentially masculine. This does not mean, of course, that the role actors are (or should be) manifestly male or female, but that the behaviors are more easily psychologically assignable to one side or the other of the sexual ledger. (Balinese men are no less men because they walk with "feminine" gait; Spartan women no less women because they can look dispassionately upon the remains of a son slain in combat.)

Regardless of the comparisons made of two distinct roles, they are always found in combination among members of the health team or any of their historical counterparts: mother surrogate and healer are part of physician specialist as well as of shaman, of medical social worker as well as tsukisoi. It is possible to think of a perfect state in which the biological mother nurses the minor afflictions of the members of her family and, only if they worsen or if the malady is tabu to women, a healer is called. The demands of reality, however, reduce such a perfect state to conjecture for it nowhere exists. Even the modern physician, pressed by time and patient load, is forced to consider more than the "case" he treats. Talcott Parsons has observed, in fact, that the modern physician achieves a depth of intimacy with his patient that is unequaled in our society:[15] the patient is never so naked a creature as when he is with his doctor.

The collateral existence of the roles of mother surrogate and healer is never better seen than in the modern American professional nurse practitioner. She is an agent in keeping her patient alive and relatively need-free; she is also, as partner to the physician, an agent in the curative process.[16] There are areas in which role expectations do not collide and, hence, there is no basis for the nurse's psychic or social confusion. Where, however, the nurse is faced with a clash in role expectations and she is caught between the poles of mother surrogate and healer, problems in role conflict are engendered. Role conflict, notes Parsons, is the "exposure of the actor to conflicting sets of legitimized role expectations such that complete fulfillment of both is realistically impossible. It is necessary to compromise, that is, to sacrifice some at least of both sets of expectations, or to choose one alternative and sacrifice the other."[17] In some role conflicts such compromise is easy to obtain. When, however, the roles in question are those of mother surrogate and healer, both of which are of intrinsic importance to the modern nurse, some conflicts take on great magnitude and compromise becomes difficult to achieve.

In terms of this frame of reference there are numerous examples of mother surrogate-healer role conflict for the professional nurse. Analyses of nursing problems will perforce contain those which stem from such conflict.[18] It is not the function of this paper to elaborate on these conflict areas nor to present yet another listing of them. As a means of illustration of the thesis of this paper— that these roles exist and that conflict comes out of their disparity—it seems appropriate to examine one such difficult area. An elemental conflict lies in the affective character of the mother surrogate role and the intellectual or dispassionate character of the healer role.

The ideal nurse as seen by the lay public, by other associated occupational groups, and by nurses themselves is an affective person. However the multitude of technical, clerical, administrative and managerial duties may have tarnished the ideal, it still exists. Young women go into nursing with this ideal in mind. Many serve year after year "in harness," and, in the obituary notices, their virtues, a restatement of the ideal, are extolled. The mother surrogate role is institutionalized in American culture.

When nursing students are asked why they wish to enter the profession the response seldom is, "I wish to be a highly technical medical worker in charge of the therapy of patients in a hospital." It will be, more than likely, like this response of one of the writer's students: "I want to spend the rest of my life helping others. I feel it is a very worthwhile profession and, at the same time, very soul-satisfying to know you have helped to ease the sufferings and pains of someone."[19] In an analysis of the responses of a class of students to such a question, words like "love," "help," "God,' 'and "soul" stand out as thematic indicators. Several studies have shown this to be a major theme associated with student career-choice everywhere.[20] It is so constant that questions which seek to discover reasons for entering nursing have been dropped from the application forms of a prominent Eastern religious school of nursing. "Why read them," remarked an informant, "they're all the same!"[21]

Nurses actually practicing see the ideal subjected to many alterations but, amazingly, it persists.[22] Physicians, closest of all the professions to nursing itself, hold the same ideal for nurses. As part of a larger study of the nurse in a metropolitan area, about 200 physicians were asked whether a nurse should be kind and sympathetic (indicative of a type described as "ministering angel") or businesslike and efficient (indicative of a type of "starched, businesslike, efficient, trim, technically expert, coolheaded nurse.") More than eight out of ten physicians preferred the "ministering angel" which ap-proached the role-ideal of the mother surrogate.[23] Further investigations of this same research group indicate that the general public coincides in favoring the ideal of the mother surrogate. In responses to open-ended questions de-signed to elicit favorable and unfavorable descriptions of nurses, the general public generally described mother surrogate characteristics as favorable and healer characteristics as unfavorable. Among the favorable terms were: "affec-tionate," "agreeable," "cheerful," "considerate," "generous," "gentle," "human," "kind," "sympathetic," "thoughtful," and "understanding." Among the un-favorable terms were: "brusk," "coldly efficient," "hardboiled," "immune to suffering," "masculine," "unemotional," and "unsympathetic."[24]

There is little doubt that the hospital system has played a major part in diminishing the mother surrogate role in nursing. The great exigencies of its life-and-death business (and how difficult it is to speak of such activities as a "business"), the developments in medicine and other fields which have simpli-fied and routinized usual patient care and have flooded the wards with pa-tients but have not supplied sufficient personnel to cope with them, the changing philosophy of nursing education: all have contributed to its dimuni-tion. The hospital provides the scene in which curing takes place; it provides little else. It sanctions the healer role and delimits the mother surrogate role. Nurses, however, are obstinate in relinquishing their ideal. They complain of each development which takes them further from bedside care of patients. They feel uncomfortable and guilty when they go up in the nursing hierarchy for this same reason.[25] Interestingly enough, a recent study shows that nurses have persisted in seeing affective qualities in their present patient relation-ships while the patients in these same relationships have seen their nurses as rigid authoritarian types.[26] Another analysis, written by a sociologist and based upon his observations as a patient, describes nurses as disinterested, oriented to getting their rather specific tasks accomplished, and lacking in affect.[27]

Avenues for affective expression are gradually closing for the professional nurse. The "care" in patient care retreats before "cure." Other hospital work-ers are assuming the affective characteristics of nursing, and professional nurses are loathe to surrender them. The trend towards greater professional-ization foretold by Esther Brown a decade ago,[28] continues, and with it the nurse as healer assumes greater and greater importance. Devereux and Weiner castigate the modern hospital and compare its socially sterile atmosphere to the worst of the therapeutic environments of the past. A major element in this sterility is the inability of nurses to dispense that which the dependent patient most needs: emotional gratification.[29]

The affective aspect of the mother surrogate-healer role conflict is far from being resolved. Surfacely, the healer predominates; below the surface, the mother surrogate exists as the basic psychological orientation of the nurse. She is torn between values of a traditionally ideal role and role performance of an antipodal nature. This has evidenced great concern in nursing circles. The professional nurse of today, laments Dorothy Smith, is a "displaced person." She adds that the nurse is in the "unenviable position of being tied by emotion, tradition, and education to a way of functioning that—for good or bad, and for reasons largely beyond the control of nurses—no longer exists. For the most part, though of course there are exceptions, we teach students to handle, enjoy, and find satisfaction in kerosene lamps and then send them out to cope with electric lights."[30]

A further illustration of the concern of nurses with this is seen in the 1958 curriculum conferences of the National League for Nursing, the educational standard-setting professional organization in nursing. In a series of eleven regional conferences where representatives of all schools of nursing, hospital affiliated and collegiate, met in three day work sessions, the central theme of every conference may be said to have centered about nursing's concern with the antagonistic facets of the mother surrogate-healer role conflict.[31]

In terms of a single broad variable—the presence or lack of affect—the roles of mother surrogate and healer are seen to be in conflict. In its developmental or historical aspect there has been a transition from behavior expectations associated with the ancient ideal of the woman and mother towards those of the technical healing specialist, a transition never easy or simple. Each of the steps leading to the dominance of the healer role is marked by opposition, especially from nursing itself but also from associated groups and from the lay public. In its present phase this role conflict is evidenced in repeated attempts to "redefine" nursing and the great emphasis now placed on "just where the nurse fits" in her relations with other occupational groups and in the community. Even more, one sees the conflict in stark evidence when the question is repeated a thousandfold in American schools of nursing and at every meeting of nurse-educators: "Just where are we going?"

There seems to be every reason to suspect that, in terms of this variable, nurses and nursing may be going along divergent paths. In hospitals—where almost all of today's nursing takes place—there is little reason to deny the diminution of affect among all professional groups. It is, in fact, a distinct mark of the professional to limit emotional involvement with patients to only those affective mechanisms directly related to therapy. Sub-professionals, on the other hand, have not been subjected to professional norms or stress and, as has been shown in many current studies, they have assumed much of the affective function in patient relationships.[32] If present trends are indicative, this function in the future may be lost to the professional nurse. Ultimately, the nurse ideal will change: in the future she may be the healer, not the mother surrogate. Affect in patient relationships, however, will still continue: it is too basic a characteristic to change. But this aspect of patient needs will be met by others. Nursing, with which the role of the mother surrogate is so completely associated, will still be nursing, but it will be carried on by persons of other occupational affiliations, not the professional nurse.

55   CULTURE AND NURSING CARE

By Lyle Saunders

Our topic is cultural and sub-cultural difference and its possible relevance for the work that nurses do. And perhaps a place to begin is with a couple of illustrations of widely differing kinds of situations in which cultural factors were found to be of significance to nurses and related health workers.

Since most nurses now work in hospitals, let us first look at an illustration from a hospital setting. For a number of years a cultural anthropologist, Mark Zborowski, has been interested in the ways in which people characteristically respond to the stimulus of pain. Now pain is basically a physiological phenomenon—but the meanings pain has and the kinds of responses to pain that are deemed appropriate by various people are matters of cultural prescription. One of *our* cultural expectations with respect to pain, for example, is revealed in the remark attributed to Abraham Lincoln and used by Adlai Stevenson in his talk conceding defeat in the 1952 presidential campaign: "I feel like the boy who stubbed his toe and who, when asked how it felt, re plied that it hurts too much to laugh and I'm too big to cry." A child may cry and run to his mother to have his small wound kissed and made well; a man, we feel, should bear his pain with stoical reserve. We can be at ease with a crying child; but even those of us who meet such situations professionally tend to be disturbed by a crying man. These response patterns derive from our cultural norms relating to pain. Other peoples have different norms that specify the appropriate pain responses of individuals of every age, sex, and social position.

Studying the patient population of a large metropolitan hospital, Zborowski found significant differences in the reactions and attitudes to pain among the four cultural groups into which patients were classified. How a patient reacted was found to be related to his cultural background. Some groups tended to be quite emotional in their responses, moaning, complaining, demanding relief, exaggerating their pain experience, giving an impression of extraordinary sensitivity. Another group reacted by withdrawing, by crying only when alone, by assuming an unemotional, matter-of-fact, almost detached attitude, by bearing their pain with a minimum of outward expression. And, as might be expected, the attitudes and behavior of doctors and nurses towards particular patients were found to be, in part, reflections of their cultural expectations. Patients who behaved as the professional people's expectations led them to think patients ought to behave were regarded as "good" patients and were rewarded with approval and support; those whose reaction patterns were not those considered appropriate were seen as "bad" or "problem" patients deserving disapproval and subject to the risk of being viewed as deviants, hypochondriacs, or neurotics. (See Chapter 27 herein.)

Prepared for the New Mexico State Nurses' Association Convention, Albuquerque, October 9, 1956.

Something of the importance of culturally related differences such as those he described, was summed up by Zborowski in these words:

In the relationship between the doctor and his patient (and between nurse and patient as well, he might have added) the respective attitudes toward pain may play a crucial role, especially when the doctor feels that the patient exaggerates his pain while the patient feels that the doctor minimizes his suffering. The same may be true, for instance, in a hospital where the members of the medical and nursing staff may have attitudes toward pain different from those held by the patient, or when they expect a certain pattern of behavior according to their cultural background while the patient may manifest a behavior pattern which is acceptable in his culture. These differences may play an important part in the evaluation of the individual pain experience, in dealing with pain at home and in the hospital, in administration of analgesics, etc.[1]

If people react to pain in culturally patterned ways, and if, as Zborowski's studies and those of such persons as Hollingshead, Redlich, and their Yale-colleagues suggest, doctors and nurses respond to patients in terms of their culturally-acquired expectations and definitions, then cultural difference must be a matter of concern to nurses since it has something to do with what they do in their work and with why and how they do it.

A second illustration, relating more to an area of concern of the rural public health nurse than to that of the hospital nurse, is a case study by Edward Wellin of the efforts of an agency of the Peruvian Ministry of Health to persuade the people of a small town in the Ica Valley of Peru to boil the water they used for drinking and household purposes. In the village of Los Molinos there were three sources of water: an irrigation ditch that flowed seasonally; a spring; and a town well. Repeated tests had shown all three to be contaminated. And so a hygiene worker—a person somewhat like a public health nurse, but with less training—was assigned to the village to see what she could do to improve nutrition, sanitation, and general health practices, but in particular to get housewives to boil the water they gave their families to drink. Now it would seem that persuading people to do such a simple thing as boiling water in order to avoid illness should be an easy thing to do. But in Los Molinos it turned out not to be. When the hygiene worker first came to the village, fifteen of the two hundred families were boiling water. When she left after two years of effort, eleven additional families had become water boilers. Eleven converts in two years! And the questions naturally arose: is this a fair return for so much effort? What does it mean? What are the differences between those who boil and those who do not; between those who were persuaded by the hygiene worker and those who resisted? To answer questions like these, Wellin, an anthropologist with WHO, was called in. What he found is too complex for telling here in detail. The essence of his findings, however, was that even such an apparently simple act as boiling water is linked through a myriad of intricate and complex bonds to many other cultural factors that, in their totality, are highly resistant to change. In Wellin's words:

It is axiomatic of all human culture that customs, like men, are not islands unto themselves. Beliefs and customs are parts of cultural systems; they relate to, support, and are enforced by other beliefs and customs. . . . It is not enough that

action workers know the items of custom that characterize the community's way
of life; they must also understand how these customs are linked with one another.
Otherwise, one may perceive strange, different, or 'illogical' customs as fortuitous
things or (as) the vagaries of ignorance; one may also fallaciously assume that
new health habits can be introduced by simply adding them to pre-existing sequences, or that old habits can be 'subtracted' and new ones 'added' in their
place. . . . As we have seen (Wellin continues) water boiling is not a simple or
merely additive thing in Los Molinos, and the relatively meager response to the
issue is not due simply to apathy, ignorance, or stubbornness. That housewives
should boil drinking water and that healthy people should drink it are matters that
run the gauntlet of many factors, including the group's ecology, its economy, social
differentiations, and cultural convictions and behavior."[2]

This case has many implications for the work done by nurses and other
public health workers in a multi-culture area like New Mexico. It illustrates,
among other points, the great complexity of apparently simple social organizations; the pressures all people (even ourselves) are under to conform to the
standards and practices of social and cultural groups; the difficulties created
by poverty and the consequent lack of facilities and materials for following
good health practices; the difficulty of arousing interest in ideas or practices
that do not fit existing patterns of cultural perception or existing value systems; and the lack of appeal of 'knowledge' that does not relate to something
already known.

I have been using "culture," "value systems," "social organization" and
similar jargon terms just as if everyone were a sociologist or anthropologist
and accustomed to communicating in such high sounding lingo. I had forgotten for the moment how frequently, in their brief association, doctors and
nurses have had to say to eager social scientists the same thing that many
generations of patients have said to them: why don't you talk so we can
understand you? So perhaps it would be well to detour a bit to say something
about what this phenomenon of culture is and why people who already have
their heads crammed to the bursting point with knowledge about physiology,
anatomy, bio-chemistry, bio-physics, pharmacology, bacteriology, psychiatry,
group dynamics, personnel administration, hygiene interpersonal relations,
ethics, and public relations should be expected to concern themselves with
it.

First the *why*. Increasing knowledge about human behavior has led us to
view it as a complex whole whose parts are intricately and dynamically interrelated. The alliance of medicine with the biological and physical sciences,
that began about a hundred years ago, has brought to bear enormous resources and energies on the problems of understanding man as a biological
organism interacting with a physical environment, and has resulted in a vast,
though still incomplete, knowledge of this aspect of human behavior. During the past half century or so a concurrent emphasis on the psychological
and emotional aspects of human behavior has led to a great understanding
of individual personality and of the importance of mental and emotional aspects of health and disease. More recently, we have come to see that a full
understanding of the behavior of these engaging and baffling creatures that
we are must include consideration of those aspects of behavior that derive

from the fact that we are all members of social groups and the bearers, creators, and, in some sense, prisoners of this phenomenon we have come to know as culture. The development of ideas of "comprehensive medicine" and "comprehensive nursing care," with their emphasis on providing for the care of an entity called the "total patient," has focused increasing attention on the social and cultural dimensions of behavior and has led to a growing interest by educators and practitioners of the medical and nursing arts in possible contributions of use to them that might be forthcoming from social scientists.

This point was briefly and clearly presented by Esther Lucile Brown in her talk to the Public Health Nursing Section of the APHA at their annual meeting in November, 1955:

In recent years, it has become increasingly necessary to admit that although much has been learned about personality structure and the use of oneself in establishing and maintaining a warm and healthful relationship, achievements have often been minimal when working with persons appreciably different from ourselves. Failures, for example, in persuading Puerto Rican persons to go regularly to clinics for obviously necessary examination and treatment, in convincing mothers from working-class families of the value of following diets prescribed for them or their babies, in getting Southern Negroes to furnish essential but very simple information—such failures have left us with grave frustrations. So serious has been our sense of defeat that we have not infrequently fallen back upon meaningless and destructive name-calling: stupid, lazy, good-for-nothing people.

Later perhaps we have had an opportunity to learn how much beliefs, customs, and value systems differ from one ethnic or racial group to another, from one socioeconomic class to another, and how differences in beliefs produce differences in behavior. . . . Then we begin to realize that an additional kind of understanding must be added to that of understanding personality . . .

Throughout the medical and health services today and particularly in public health, reference is made to the necessity for being concerned with a total person, for individualizing care to meet the varying needs of patients, for viewing the patient or client in his family and community matrix. But how can any of these things be done effectively unless we know far more than at present about how attitudes and patterns of behavior—our own included—are conditioned by educational, economic, religious, national or racial, and geographical backgrounds.[3]

Nurses of all kinds are, in their work, still largely preoccupied—and properly so—with matters and interests that pertain to the biological aspects of their patient's behavior—with medicines and treatments and therapeutic routines, with diets and immunizations and sanitary precautions. Increasingly they have become concerned about psychological and emotional factors—anxieties, tensions, fears, hostilities, aggressions, frustrations that arise in and influence the relationships between them and their patients. And now, rapidly, they are coming to see that if they wish to do the kind of job that they want to do, they are going to have to take account of values, expectations, status, roles, norms, social class, ethnic membership group and similar matters from the province of the social scientists.

It is a truism that the providing of any sort of service—including public health and nursing care—involves both provider and recipient in the establishment and maintenance of a set of interpersonal and intergroup relations.

It is equally obvious that the course and outcome of these relationships is influenced by the expectations, beliefs, knowledge, goals, values, and perceptions of all concerned. It is thus important for persons who organize and dispense nursing and other health services to know a great deal not only about how human beings respond as biological organisms to preventive and therapeutic measures, but also how they behave as individual personalities and as members of social and cultural groups. This latter category falls squarely into the field of interest and professional competence of social scientists, and suggests one reason why more and more sociologists, cultural anthropologists, and social psychologists are being drawn into collaborative activity with persons in nursing and other health fields.

So much for the *why* of talking to nurses about cultural difference. Now a brief word about the *what*. With respect to culture, most of us are in the position of the school boy who discovered in an English class that for years he had been writing prose without knowing it. Since we are born into a cultural environment and thereafter in our lifetimes are never separated from one, culture comes to seem so natural, so omnipresent, so taken-for-granted that we are usually no more aware of it than we are of the air we breathe or the skin in which we are encased. Only at times like this when someone calls it to attention or when we must interact with someone conditioned in a different culture do we become aware of the extent to which our behavior and the meanings other people's behavior has for us are oriented by the fact of our having been molded in the image of the cultural groups into which we were born and in which we associate.

Culture is a distinctively human characteristic, possessed, if at all, only in the most limited degree by any other species. Its function is to enable us to find our way around in our physical and social environments with a minimum of trial and error fumbling, and to aid us in the business of surviving, reproducing, and satisfying our physical, psychological, and social needs. Culture encompasses every aspect of living from the form of government to the direction a revolving door turns, from the poetry of, say, Keats to the scrawls on the walls of public toilets, from the atomic reactor to the children's game of one-old-cat, from neurosurgery to the aspirin tablet. It includes the gestures we make in conversation, the use of buttons for holding garments together, the rules for calling people by name or title, the proper distance to stand when talking to another person, the volume and pitch of voices, the colors we are able to distinguish, and our definitions of what constitutes illness. Culture provides for us, as Paul Walter has said, ready made and tested solutions to the recurring problems of life—whether they be problems of what to feed a husband for dinner, how to treat a sick baby, what to wear to the Santa Fe fiesta, or how to go through a revolving door. A revolving door, incidentally, illustrates very well the utility of cultural traits as well as the degree to which we are mostly unaware of the cultural foundations of our behavior. All revolving doors, so far as I know, turn in the same direction. It is doubtful that any of us could say what that direction is without stopping to think about it, and yet any of us can approach such a door, thinking deeply about something else, and without hesitation pass through on the right side.

What a mess there would be if some revolving doors turned in one direction and some the other! Every door would be a problem to be individually solved, and what a hubbub would arise when the person passing in and the one passing out reached different solutions! I suspect that in such a case there would be a lot of muttering on both sides about how any fool ought to know how to go through a revolving door, just as, in other areas of culture, we sometimes feel, even if we don't always say it, that any fool ought to be able to see when a baby is dehydrated, or know that a copper bracelet won't prevent rheumatism, or recognize the need to stay in bed to recover from tuberculosis, or see the relationship between infant diarrhea and screens, or understand that a nurse knows more about health than a grandmother does.

The most difficult thing about culture difference is the recognition that 'difference' is a two-way word. It is very easy to observe that other people are 'different'; it is much harder and takes some imaginative effort and a bit of detachment to realize that we are 'different' too. Our own ways—whether they be ways of thinking, believing, perceiving, or acting—are so much a part of us and are so reinforced through repetition and through our observation of other people following them, that it is most difficult to appreciate how any people following different ways can still be reasonable or normal or, we sometimes think, even human. And yet this effort must be made if we are to work successfully among people culturally or sub-culturally different from ourselves.

In a talk to the California State Nurses' Association earlier this year, I had occasion to mention several sources of cultural and sub-cultural difference that affect the relationships between professional health workers and the people they serve. These were rural or urban residence, socio-economic status, ethnic group membership, and the differences in knowledge, training, interest, motivation, and value that exist between laymen and persons who have received any type of professional training. Any nurse employed in New Mexico will certainly have had abundant opportunity to observe how her work is affected by factors such as these.

New Mexico in 1950 was still about half rural, and although rural and urban ways of life are everywhere in this country becoming more alike, there are still differences that complicate the giving of nursing and other health services. Consider, for one example, how the duties, the responsibilities, and the facilities available to the nurse in the small rural hospital differ from those of her colleague in an urban teaching center.

Socio-economic differences, too, exist in New Mexico as they do everywhere and they operate here, as elsewhere, in many ways that affect the work of nurses. The types of disease people get, what they do about them, how well they cooperate with health personnel, how they rear their children, what kind of family relations they maintain—to mention only a few variables —are all to some extent related to social class position.

New Mexico, too, is exceedingly complex in the ethnic distribution of its population. A recent report from the Ramah area mentioned five distinct cultures that were found in a single small town. There is not a nurse in New

Mexico whose work is not at one time or another influenced by the fact that the state contains sizeable Indian and Spanish-American populations.

Finally, the sub-cultural differences that exist between laymen and professionally trained persons are as great here as anywhere and they interpose many barriers to affective communication about health matters. This point has been nicely summed up by Benjamin Paul who reminds us that

"Any specialist has a unique point of view which sharpens his perception within a restricted area of interest. For this benefit he pays a price; he finds it hard to recapture the unspecialized way of seeing things. The health professional is no exception to this rule. With health at the center of his perceptual system, he often finds it difficult to view health as laymen customarily perceive it. This may not matter much if he remains in the laboratory or acts as a technical consultant. But if he wishes to work effectively with groups of people, he must overcome his trained incapacity and learn to see health from the standpoint of the man in the community."[4]

A very wise physician who works in public health in northern New Mexico says much the same thing in these words:

". . . we must realize that when we work with people of another culture we frequently have no status. They have never heard of the schools where we have been educated or the hospitals in which we have been trained or the many fine institutions with which we have worked, so that what we say will not bear as much weight as what the accepted local source of medical advice says, be it doctor of medicine, osteopath, chiropractor, medicine man, or respected elderly aunt. If we don't face this, we don't get to first base."[5]

These factors of rural-urban residence, ethnic group membership, social class affiliation, and lay-professional differences are important sources of many problems that complicate the work of nurses. Much could be said about each of them. But since most of what I might say is available in print and can be read by anyone who is interested, I should like to devote my remaining time to a mention of two or three areas of knowledge or relationship in which there are in New Mexico real cultural differences that affect nursing care.

The first of these centers in the notions various groups have about the causes of disease. Nurses, of course, have quite sophisticated ideas about disease causation. As a group they accept the germ theory; they know a great deal about the reasons why people get degenerative diseases; they understand the role of emotional factors in the etiology of some diseases; they are aware that there are some ailments whose cause or causes remain unknown. Few of their patients, however, have this degree of sophistication. Many have a different set of ideas; more than a few are vague and fuzzy in their ideas; and some are close to having no ideas at all about how diseases happen.

The forty or fifty thousand Indians who live in New Mexico are the inheritors and bearers of cultural traditions that, in many respects, are radically different from those of the dominant population group. The nurse who works with Indians may find from time to time, that her patients have ideas about disease causation that she cannot accept as valid. She may find disease attributed to being out of harmony with the cosmos, or thought to be caused by a failure to observe appropriate rituals, or resulting from a spell worked by a malevolent enemy, or stemming from the influence of ghosts or other supernatural beings. I suspect, that, in the past fifty years, many a stalemate in treatment has occurred because Indian patient and Anglo doctor or nurse did not see eye to eye on the causes of a particular set of symptoms.

Nurses who work among the quarter of a million Spanish-Americans in New Mexico may also at times encounter ideas that their training did not prepare them for: the belief, for example, that disease is an expression of the will of God about which nothing can or should be done; that fondling a child can cause it to become sick; that witches are able to produce incurable ailments in people; that cold air can be a dangerous substance to come in contact with.

Likewise, the nurse who works with Anglos quickly learns that she and her patients are not always in complete accord about the causes of illness. Some disease, she finds, is thought to come from bad blood; congenital defects or blemishes are believed to arise from unpleasant emotional experiences of prospective mothers; ulcers are causd by eating greasy foods; appendicitis from biting fingernails; cancer from improper alignment of the spine. In a series of some 300 interviews carried on this past summer with hospital patients of low socio-economic status, we found that few had any clear conception of the germ theory of disease, and almost none could give us any information about possible causative factors in more than a small proportion of the fifty disease entities we called to their attention.

Considered without reference to anything else, it is probably not very important what ideas people have about the causes of disease. Such ideas, however, do not exist in isolation but are closely related to what people consider appropriate measures for the prevention and treatment of disease conditions. If some disease results from being out of harmony with nature, as Navajo culture holds, then understandably a ceremonial is better therapy for that disease than any drug. If a Spanish-American villager languishes because of having been *embrujado*, it is reasonable to consult an *albolario* rather than a physician because it is common knowledge that physicians do not do well with diseases of this nature. And if an Anglo is not very clear about the role of micro-organisms in the etiology of disease, he is not likely to get excited about the possible contamination of his water supply or rush to have his children immunized.

Faced with the threat of disease or the reality of disease, almost anybody will do something. But what anyone does will be influenced by a variety of factors many of which are cultural and social. The social pressures of neighbors, friends, and relatives can be strong forces for moving behavior in one direction or another. A Pueblo or Navajo Indian, for example, is not entirely free to choose between Anglo medicine and tribal medicine for any given case of illness. Whatever choice he may make will be influenced not only by what he thinks is the right course of action, but also by what his associates think. This is not to say that a council is called and a group decision taken. Such an action is not necessary. Indians, like all the rest of us, have pretty good ideas about what their associates think and feel about many things and their behavior is to an extent oriented by these ideas. If any of you are not certain just how such pressures work, just imagine that you woke up one morning with a strong desire to wear a purple uniform to work. There's nothing that I know of that says you can't; and yet anyone who did it would have to be a person of enormous ego strength, and even such a person would, I suspect, be quite uncomfortable. And, if pressures can be so strong for conformity in such an apparently unimportant matter as the color of cloth one wears, how much more powerful they must be where health and well being are at stake.

The way group pressures and cultural patterns can sway an individual's decisions with respect to medical treatment is well illustrated by the findings Earl L. Koos reports in his book, *The Health of Regionville*. A lower class housewife, for example, told the interviewer: "There's a lot of things I know you're supposed to do something about, but there's lots of reasons why you don't . . . I'd look silly, wouldn't I, going to see a doctor for a backache? My mother always had a backache, as long as I can remember, and didn't do anything about it. It didn't kill her either. If I went to the doctor for that, my friends would hoot me out of town. That's just something you have, I guess."6 A quite different point of view was expressed by an upper class man with prostate trouble: "When you get as old as I am, you can begin to have trouble there. Naturally, if you do have trouble, you go to a doctor about it. Maybe it isn't too bad right then, but you do it. You sort of belong to a club—the bladder trouble boys."7 Here, in the same community, in one subcultural pattern, a disease or symptom should be brought to medical attention immediately; in another pattern it was proper to ignore it. In either case, the individual tends to follow the prescriptions of his fellows, to behave as they do, or as he thinks they would.

Preventive measures, like treatment procedures, are also influenced by cultural factors. Our interviews of this past summer indicate that people on the social class level of those we talked to were more swayed by social pressures in accepting immunizations for themselves and their children than they were by any conviction that such immunizations actually prevent disease. Time and again we went through conversations like this:

"Can smallpox (or polio) be prevented?"
"No."
"Have you ever been vaccinated?"
"Yes."
"What for?"
"Smallpox, I guess."
"Well, will that prevent you from getting the disease?"
"No, not really. But I won't have it so bad if I do get it."

The whole concept of preventive activity seemed quite vague to many of our informants, and we were frequently asked the counter-question: "How can you prevent something if you don't know you're going to get it?" And yet most of the people we talked to felt that good health could be promoted by "taking care of yourself," by "living right," and by getting the "right amounts" of exercise, rest, fresh air and sunshine, although few of them expressed any definite thoughts about what the "right amounts" might be or what "living right" consists of.

The influence of socio-economic position on behavior related to prevention is illustrated by a report by Deasy of the differential responses of mothers in a Virginia county to a polio vaccine trial in the spring of 1954.[8] Briefly stated, the findings were that more mothers in the upper and middle socio-economic groups than in the lower gave consent for the participation of their children, and more mothers in these groups were already taking some precautions to protect their children. The important point for us here is that how people behaved in a health matter was directly related to their social class position.

The relation of ethnic group membership to preventive activity is shown in another comment by a physician who works in public health in New Mexico.

There is a very strong belief among many of our isolated rural Spanish-American people that if the fontanelle drops it knocks down the roof of the mouth and kills the child. It just happens that one of the criteria I use for increasing the amount of Vitamin D given a child is the size of the fontanelle. If it is large I increase the dosage. It is very unusual for mothers bringing children to well child conferences not to give the Vitamin D as prescribed. I am quite convinced that it is because they want to get the fontanelle closed as quickly as possible rather than because of anything we may tell them of its need for the building of bones and teeth. On the other hand I know of one mother who refuses to bring her baby to well child conference because I touch the fontanelle and some day she's sure I'll make one fall. Now, we explain, using very simple language, that the fontanelle falls because the baby is dehydrated and that this is the serious situation that causes some babies to die if it is not corrected. But this pattern of fear of the mechanical falling of the fontanelle has been part of their beliefs for generations and so although they understand the words we say the concept we present makes very little impression. It is just as if they did not hear us. This is not a language barrier; it is a concept barrier. However, if I agree that it is serious for a baby's fontanelle to fall, and that as soon as there is any suggestion of its falling they must take the child to a physician immediately, that can be accepted without any difficulty as it is an extension of a concept they already hold.[9]

One final area that can be briefly mentioned is that of the patterns of relationship that develop in illnesses among patients, family, healers, and other persons. Our ideal pattern is that professional people take over full responsibility for the patient and assume direction of the course of events. The patient is to carry out faithfully the orders and suggestions of the professional people; the family has a passive role largely limited to providing some emotional support and paying the bills; the rest of the community does not directly enter into the relationship at all. This is a pattern that Anglos generally understand and accept, although there may be some difference in degree of acceptance among socio-economic sub-groups. This, however, is not necessarily a pattern that is congenial to persons conditioned in another culture. Traditional Indian medicine, for example, requires wide community participation, and although the medicine men and "singers" may possess a specialized kind of knowledge or skill, they operate under much closer survelliance by family and lay community members than is true in our pattern. In Spanish-American villages, the family traditionally has played a very active role. Much of the treatment was decided upon and carried out by family members and when it was thought necessary to call in a *curandera,* a *medica,* a *partera,* or some other lay specialist, the family, knowing almost as much as the expert did, remained very active. The acceptance of the Anglo pattern thus involves for many people a sharp break with traditional roles and traditional conceptions of proper behavior that is not always easy to make. In these circumstances, it is important that the physician or nurse be aware of the cultural influences that are operating and be prepared to give such extra support and assurance as may be required.

Nurses, in their everyday work, whether on hospital wards, in well baby clinics, in schools, or in the homes of people who require their services, are constantly faced with the necessity to recognize and adjust to many aspects of cultural and sub-cultural difference. They must take account, for example, of the food taboos of Jewish people, of the religious beliefs and rites of Catholics, of the special importance of family relationships to many Spanish-speaking patients, of the grossly different medical orientation of Navajos, Pueblos, and Apache Indians, of the problems of language differences, of the loose family relationships and apparent indifference to health matters of some persons of low socio-economic status, and of the relative lack of knowledge about body functions and health matters that nearly all laymen exhibit. Cultural factors, along with physiological and psychological factors, are omnipresent influences in the work of the nurse, and they need to be understood, assessed, and where possible controlled for the mutual advantage of the nurse and the patient, just as the more familiar organic and emotional factors are.

Reference Matter

BIBLIOGRAPHY TO CHAPTER 1

Richard N. Adams, "On the Effective Use of Anthropology in Public Health Programs," *Human Organization*, 13 (Winter, 1955), 5–15.

Odin W. Anderson, "The Sociologist and Medicine," *Social Forces*, 31 (October, 1952), 38–42.

Odin W. Anderson and Milvoy Seacat, "The Behavioral Scientists and Research in the Health Field" (New York: Health Information Foundation, Research Series #1, 1957).

Gordon W. Blackwell, "Behavioral Sciences and Health," *Social Forces*, 32 (December, 1953), 211–215.

Walter E. Boek and Jean K. Boek, *Society and Health* (New York: G. P. Putnam's Sons, 1956).

Walter E. Boek and H. E. Hilleboe, "Role of a Social Scientist in Public Health," *Human Organization*, 14 (Summer, 1955), 25–27.

William Caudill, "Applied Anthropology in Medicine," in A. L. Kroeber (ed.), *Anthropology Today* (Chicago: University of Chicago Press, 1953), 771–806.

Wayne Dennis, et al, *Current Trends in the Relation of Psychology to Medicine* (Pittsburgh: University of Pittsburgh Press, 1950).

Joseph W. Eaton, "The Social Science Content of a Medical Curriculum," *American Sociological Review*, 21 (October, 1956), 614–617.

Howard E. Freeman and Leo G. Reeder, "Medical Sociology: A Review of the Literature," *American Sociological Review*, 22 (February, 1957), 73–81.

Mary E. W. Goss and George G. Reader, "Collaboration Between Sociologist and Physician," *Social Problems*, 4 (July, 1956), 82–89.

Oswald Hall, "Sociological Research in the Field of Medicine: Progress and Prospects," *American Sociological Review*, 16 (October, 1951), 639–644.

E. Gartly Jaco, "Areas for Research in Medical Sociology," *Sociology and Social Research*, 42 (July–August, 1958), 441–445.

Hugh R. Leavell, "Contributions of the Social Sciences to the Solution of Health Problems," *New England Journal of Medicine*, 247 (December 4, 1952), 885–897.

A. R. Mangus, "Medical Sociology: Study of the Social Components of Illness and of Health," *Sociology and Social Research*, 39 (January–February, 1955), 158–164.

Joseph D. Matarazzo, "Comprehensive Medicine: A New Era in Medical Education," *Human Organization*, 14 (Spring, 1955), 4–9.

Joseph D. Matarazzo, "The Role of the Psychologist in Medical Education and Practice," *Human Organization*, 14 (Summer, 1955), 9–14.

Ivan N. Mensh, "Psychology in Medical Education," *The American Psychologist*, 8 (February, 1953), 83–85.

George P. Murdock, "Anthropology and Its Contributions to Public Health," *American Journal of Public Health*, 42 (January, 1952), 7–11.

Benjamin D. Paul, "The Cultural Context of Health Education," from *Symposium Proceedings* (School of Social Work, University of Pittsburgh, 1953), 31–38.

S. B. Sells, "The Purposes of Psychology Curricula in Medical Education," *The American Psychologist*, 11 (December, 1956), 679–683.

Henry E. Sigerist, "The Social Sciences in the Medical School," in Henry E. Sigerist, *The University at the Crossroads* (New York: Henry Schuman, Inc., 1946), 127–142.

Edward Stainbrook and Murray Wexler, "The Place of the Behavioral Sciences in the Medical School," *Psychiatry*, 19 (August, 1956), 263–269.

Robert Straus, "The Nature and Status of Medical Sociology," *American Sociological Review*, 22 (April, 1957), 200–204.

A. Weider (ed.), *Contributions Toward Medical Psychology* (New York: Ronald Press, 1953).

NOTES TO CHAPTER 2

* The paper appeared in a condensed version in *"The Child"* in April, 1953.

1. United Nations: *Demographic Yearbook, 1949–50.* N.Y., United Nations, 1950, pp. 413, 415.

2. Scotland. General Register Office: *Ninety-Third Annual Report, 1947.* Edinburgh, H. M. Stationery Office, 1950, p. 68.

3. United Nations: *op. cit.*, p. 415.

4. United Nations: *op. cit.*

5. Sverige. Statistiska Centralbyrån: *Statistisk Årsbok för Sverige.* Trettiosjunde Årgången. 1950, Stockholm, Statistiska Centralbyrån, 1950, pp. 53–57.

6. Scotland. General Register Office: *op. cit.*, pp. 77–78.

7. Vilmundur Jonsson: *Skipun Heilbrigidismala a Islandi.* Reykjavik, Gutenberg, 1942, p. 150; United Nations: *op. cit.*, p. 414; Great Britain. General Register Office; *Statistical Review of England and Wales for the Year 1945.* (New Annual Series, No. 25). Tables. Part I. Medical. London, H. M. Stationery Office, 1947, p. 2; Denmark. Statistiske Department: *Statistisk Årbog, 1950.* Köbenhavn, Bianco Lugo, 1950, p. 33; Norge. Statistisk Sentralbyrå: *Statistiske Oversikter,* 1948. Oslo, Aschehough, 1949, p. 40.

8. Kingsley Davis: *The Population of India and Pakistan.* Princeton, N.J., Princeton University Press, 1951, p. 34; Cyprus. Colonial Administrative Service: *Census of Population and Agriculture, 1946, Report.* London, Crown Agents for the Colonies, 1949, p. 18; Jamaica. Registrar General's Department: *Annual Report for the Year Ended 31st, December, 1949.* Kingston, Government Printer, 1950, p. 38; Espana. Instituto Nacional de Estadistica: *Anuario Estadistico de Espana, 1950.* Madrid, Instituto Nacional Estadistica, 1950, p. 108.

9. C.-E. A. Winslow and Dorothy F. Holland: The Influence of Certain Public Health Procedures upon Infant Mortality. *Human Biology,* May, 1937, 9, pp. 133–174.

10. Howard W. Green: *Infant Mortality and Economic Status, Cleveland Five-City Area,* 1919–1937. Cleveland, Cleveland Health Council, 1939, p. 10.

11. U.S. Children's Bureau. Statistical Series No. 9, *Charts on Infant, Childhood and Maternal Mortality,* 1949. Washington, The Bureau, 1951, p. 28.

12. Canada. Dominion Bureau of Statistics: *Vital Statistics,* 1946. Ottawa, The Bureau, 1948, pp. 24, 30.

13. Alfred E. Cohn and Claire Lingg: *The Burden of Disease in the United States,* N.Y., Oxford University Press, 1950, p. 32.

14. Charles V. Chapin: Deaths among Taxpayers and non-Taxpayers Income Tax, Providence, 1865. *American Journal of Public Health,* Aug. 1924, 14, p. 648.

15. They are: Class I–Upper professional and managerial strata; Class II–Lesser employers, managers and professions; Class III–Skilled and blackcoated workers; Class IV–Semi-skilled including agricultural workers; Class V–Unskilled workers.

16. Scotland. Registrar-General: *op. cit.*, p. 68.

17. Howard W. Green: *op. cit.*, p. 33.

18. Marion E. Altenderfer and Beatrice Crowther: Relationship Between Infant Mortality and Socio-economic Factors in Urban Areas, *Public Health Reports,* March 18, 1949, p. 333.

19. A. D. H. Kaplan: Significance of Infant Mortality Data in Appraisal of an Urban Community. *American Journal of Public Health, October, 1932,* 22, pp. 1037–49. A range of from 24 to 210 was found. C. A. McMahan: *The People of Atlanta: A Demographic Study of Georgia's Capital City.* Athens, Ga., University of Georgia Press, 1950, pp. 172–173. A range of 14 to 53 was noted.

20. Mary Gover: Negro Mortality. II. The Birth Rate and Infant and Maternal Mortality. *Public Health Reports, Oct. 25, 1946,* 61, pp. 1529–1538; Amanda L. Stoughton: A Study of Negro Infant Mortality. *Public Health Reports, Nov. 8, 1929,* 44, pp. 2705–2731; Howard W. Green: *op. cit.*, 123 pp; Alfred Yankauer: The Relationship of Fetal and Infant Mortality to Residential Segregation; an Inquiry into Social Epidemiology. *American Sociological Review, Oct., 1950,* 15, pp. 644–648; Harry Bakwin: The Negro Infant. *Human Biology, Feb., 1932,* 4, pp. 1–33; Herbert L. Sommers: Infant Mortality in Rural and Urban Areas. *Public Health Reports, Oct. 2, 1942,* 57, pp. 1474–1501. There is evidence that the infant mortality rate in rural areas was lower than in urban areas before the Twenties. The foregoing article by Sommers indicates that as well as British Data in 1915.

Great Britain. Registrar-General: *Seventy-Eighth Annual Report of Births, Deaths and Marriages in England and Wales, 1915.* London, H. M. Stationery Office, 1917, p. xix.

21. Robert M. Woodbury: *Causal Factors in Infant Mortality: A Statistical Study Based on Investigations in Eight Cities.* Washington, Government Printing Office, 1925, 245 pp. (U.S. Children's Bureau. Pub. No. 142); Louis Rosenberg: *Canada's Jews: A Social and Economic Study of the Jews in Canada.* Montreal, Canadian Jewish Congress, 1939, 418 pp.

21a. A gross example: in particular instances the provision of a bottle sterilizer can have greater effect in reducing infant mortality than an increase in wages of $500, providing there is assurance that the sterilizer will be used.

22. C. M. Burns: *Infant and Maternal Mortality in Relation to Size of Family and Rapidity of Breeding: A Study in Human*

Responsibility. Newcastle-upon-Tyne, Department of Physiology, King's College, University of Durham, 1924, p. 4.

23. J. Doughty: Some Observations from a Preliminary Study of Infant Mortality in British Columbia, Based on Birth-Date Linkage. *Canadian Journal of Public Health,* 40: 303, July, 1949.

24. B. Seebohm Rowntree: *Poverty and Progress; A Second Social Survey of York.* London, Longmans, Green, 1941, p. 451.

25. Cogently discussed by Fred Grundy in his forward to: R. M. Dykes: *Illness in Infancy: A Comparative Study of Infant Sickness and Infant Mortality in Luton.* Luton, Leagrave Press, 1950, 46 pp.

26. Fred Grundy and E. Lewis-Faning. *Morbidity and Mortality in First Year of Life: A Field Enquiry in Fifteen Areas of England and Wales.* Cardiff, Wales, The Eugenics Society, 1957, p. 130.

BIBLIOGRAPHY TO CHAPTER 2

1. Altenderfer, Marion E.: Relationship between per Capita Income and Mortality, in the Cities of 100,000 or More Population. *Public Health Reports,* November 28, 1947, 62, pp. 1681–1690.

2. Altenderfer, Marion E. and Crowther, Beatrice: Relationship between Infant Mortality and Socio-economic Factors in Urban Areas. *Public Health Reports,* March 18, 1949, 64, pp. 331–339.

3. Baird, Dugald: Social and Economic Factors Affecting the Mother and Child. *American Journal of Public Health,* May, 1952, 42, pp. 516–520.

4. Bakwin, Harry: The Negro Infant. *Human Biology,* February, 1932, 4, pp. 1–33.

5. Brownlee, John: The Health of London in the Eighteenth Century. *Proceedings of the Royal Society of Medicine,* 1925, 18, part 2, pp. 73–85.

6. Burns, C. M.: *Infant and Maternal Mortality in Relation to Size of Family and Rapidity of Breeding: A Study in Human Responsibility.* Newcastle-upon-Tyne, Dept. of Physiology, King's College, Univ. of Durham, 1942, 247 pp.

7. Chapin, Charles V.: Deaths among Taxpayers and non-Taxpayers Income Tax, Providence, 1865. *American Journal of Public Health,* August, 1924, 14, pp. 647–651.

8. Collins, Selwyn D.: *Economic Status and Health: A Review and Study of the Relevant Morbidity and Mortality Data.* Washington, Government Printing Office, 1927, 74 pp. (U.S. Public Health Service. Public Health Bulletin No. 165.)

9. Doughty, J.: Some Observations from a Preliminary Study of Infant Mortality in British Columbia, Based on Birth-Death Linkage. *Canadian Journal of Public Health,* July, 1949, 40, pp. 302–305.

10. Douglas, J. W. B.: Social Class Differences in Health and Survival during the First Two Years of Life; The Results of a National Survey. *Population Studies,* July, 1951, 5, pp. 35–58.

11. Dykes, R. M.: *Illness in Infancy: A Comparative Study of Infant Sickness and Infant Mortality in Luton.* Luton, England, Leagrave Press, 1950, 46 pp.

12. Findlay, Leonard and Paton, D. Noël: *Poverty, Nutrition, and Growth: Studies of Child Life in Cities and Rural Districts of Scotland.* London. H. M. Stationery Office, 1926, 333 pp. (Medical Research Council. Special Report Series No. 101.)

13. Gover, Mary: Negro Mortality. II. The Birth Rate and Infant and Maternal Mortality. *Public Health Reports, October 25, 1946,* 61, pp. 1529–1538.

14. Great Britain. Medical Research

Committee. Special Report Series No. 10, *The Mortalities of Birth, Infancy, and Childhood.* London, The Committee, 1917, 84 pp.

15. Great Britain. Royal Commission of Population. *Reports of the Biological and Medical Committee.* London, H. M. Stationery Office, 1950, 52 pp.

16. Green, Howard W.: *Infant Mortality and Economic Status: Cleveland Five-City Area, 1919–1937,* Cleveland, Cleveland Health Council, 1939, 123 pp.

17. Grundy, Fred, and Lewis-Faning, E.: *Morbidity and Mortality in the First Year of Life: A Field Enquiry in Fifteen Areas of England and Wales.* Cardiff, Wales, The Eugenics Society, 1957, 145 pp.

18. Haley, Theresa: *Infant Mortality: Results of a Field Study in Akron, Ohio, Based on Births in One Year.* Washington, Government Printing Office, 1920, 118 pp. (U.S. Children's Bureau. Infant Mortality Series No. 11, Bureau Publication No. 72.)

19. Hughes, Elizabeth: *Infant Mortality: Results of a Field Study in Gary, Ind., Based on Births in One Year.* Washington, Government Printing Office, 1923, 122 pp. (U.S. Children's Bureau, Infant Mortality Series No. 11, Bureau Publication No. 112.)

20. Kaplan, A. D. H.: Significance of Infant Mortality Data in Appraisal of an Urban Community. *American Journal of Public Health,* Oct. 1942, 22, pp. 1037–1049.

21. Lathrop, Julia C.: Income and Infant Mortality. *American Journal of Public Health,* April, 1919, 9, pp. 270–274.

22. Morales-Otero, P. & Perez, Manuel A., and others: *Health and Socio-Economic Studies in Puerto Rico.* San Juan, Puerto Rico, 1937–1940. (Collection of articles.)

23. Neff, Joseph S.: Recent Public Health Work in the United States Especially in Relation to Infant Mortality. *American Journal of Public Health,* October, 1915, 5, pp. 965–981.

24. Newman, George: *Infant Mortality: A Social Problem.* London, Methuen, 1906, 356 pp.

25. Oppenheimer, Ella: *Infant Mortality in Memphis.* Washington, Government Printing Office, 1937, 103 pp. (U.S. Children's Bureau. Publication No. 233.)

26. Peller, Sigismund: Studies on Mortality since the Renaissance. *Bulletin of the History of Medicine and Allied Sciences,* 1943, 13, pp. 427–461.

27. Phillips, Harry T.: An Inter-racial Study in Social Conditions and Infant Mor-

tality in Cape Town, *Milbank Memorial Fund Quarterly,* 35:7–28, Jan., 1957.

28. Prinzing, Friedrich. *Handbuch der Medizinischen Statistik.* Jena, Fischer, 1906. Quoted in: Selwyn D. Collins: *Economic Status and Health: A Review and Study of the Relevant Morbidity and Mortality Data.* Washington, Government Printing Office, 1927, 74 pp. (U.S. Public Health Service. Public Health Bulletin No. 165.)

29. Rietz, E.: *Sterblichkeit und Todesursachen in den Kinderjahren.* Stockholm, 1930. Quoted in: Richard M. Titmuss: *Birth, Poverty and Wealth: A Study of Infant Mortality.* London, Hamish Hamilton Medical Books, 1943, 118 pp.

30. Rochester, Anna: *Infant Mortality: Results of a Field Study in Baltimore, Md., Based on Births in One Year.* Washington, Government Printing Office, 1923, 400 pp. (U.S. Children's Bureau. Publication No. 119.)

31. Rosenberg, Rena, and Donahue, A. Madorah: *The Welfare of Infants of Illegitimate Birth in Baltimore.* Washington, Government Printing Office, 1925, 24 pp. (U.S. Children's Bureau. Publication No. 144.)

32. Rowntree, B. Seebohm: *Poverty and Progress: A Second Social Survey of York.* London, Longmans, Green, 1941, 540 pp.

33. Sommers, Herbert J.: Infant Mortality in Rural and Urban Areas. *Public Health Reports,* October 2, 1942, 57, pp. 1494–1501.

34. Stevenson, Alan C.: *Recent Advances in Social Medicine.* London, Churchill, 1950, 241 pp.

35. Stoughton, Amanda L.: A Study of Negro Infant Mortality. *Public Health Reports,* November 8, 1929, 44, pp. 2705–2731.

36. Sutherland, Ian: *Stillbirths: Their Epidemiology and Social Significance.* London, Oxford Univ. Press, 1949, 93 pp. (Oxford Medical Publications.)

37. Tandy, Elizabeth C.: *Infant and Maternal Mortality among Negroes.* Washington, Government Printing Office, 1937, 34 pp. (U.S. Children's Bureau. Publication No. 243.)

38. Titmuss, Richard M.: *Birth, Poverty and Wealth: A Study of Infant Mortality.* London, Hamish Hamilton Medical Books, 1943, 118 pp.

39. Vidakovitch, Slobadan: Influence des Conditions Economiques et Sociales sur la Natalite, la Morbidite et la Mortalite des Enfants dans les Villes de Yougoslavie.

Office International d'Hygiene Publique. Bulletin Mensuel, February, 1938, 30, pp. 339–362.

40. Whitney, Jessamine S.: *Infant Mortality: Results of a Field Study in New Bedford, Mass., Based on Births in One Year.* Washington, Government Printing Office, 1920, 114 pp. (U.S. Children's Bureau. Infant Mortality Series No. 10, Bureau Publication No. 68.)

41. Wiehl, Dorothy G.: Mortality and Socio-Environmental Factors. *Milbank Memorial Fund Quarterly,* October, 1948, 26, pp. 335–365.

42. Winslow, C. E. E. A., and Holland, Dorothy F.: The Influence of Certain Public Health Procedures upon Infant Mortality. *Human Biology,* May, 1937, pp. 133–174.

43. Woodbury, Robert M.: *Causal Factors in Infant Mortality: A Statistical Study Based on Investigations in Eight Cities.* Washington, Government Printing Office, 1925, 245 pp. (U.S. Children's Bureau. Pub. No. 142.)

44. Woolf, Barnet and Waterhouse, John: Studies on Infant Mortality. Part 1. Influences of Social Conditions in County Boroughs of England and Wales. *Journal of Hygiene,* April, 1945, 44, pp. 67–98.

45. Woolf, Barnet: Studies on Infant Mortality. Part II. Social Aetiology of Stillbirths and Infant Deaths in County Boroughs of England and Wales. *British Journal of Social Medicine,* 1947, 1, pp. 73–125.

46. Wright, G. Payling and Wright, Helen P.: Etiological Factors in Broncho-Pneumonia amongst Infants in London. *Journal of Hygiene,* 1945, 44, pp. 15–30.

47. Yankauer, Alfred: The Relationship of Fetal and Infant Mortality to Residential Segregation: An Inquiry Into Social Epidemiology. *American Sociological Review,* October, 1950, 15, pp. 644–648.

NOTES TO CHAPTER 3

1. M. E. Altenderfer: "Relationship Between Per Capita Income and Mortality in Cities of 100,000 or More Population," *Public Health Reports,* 62:1681–1691, 1947.

1a. *National Health Survey, 1935–36.* Disability from Specific Causes in Relation to Economic Status. Preliminary Reports, Sickness and Medical Care Series, Bulletin No. 9, Washington, 1938.

2. J. H. Sheps, Cecil and Watkins: "Mortality in the Socio-Economic Districts of New Haven," *Yale Journal of Biology and Medicine,* 20:51–80, 1947.

3. L. C. Coombs: "Economic Differentials in Causes of Death," *Medical Care,* 1:246–255, 1941.

4. Study of Health Needs—New York City under the Joint Auspices of the Health Council of Greater New York & the New York Academy of Medicine (Manuscript).

5. Hiscock and Hugh R. Leavell: "Survey of the Social and Health Needs and Services of Greater Boston," Boston, 1949, p. 18 (mimeographed).

6. Registrar-General's Decennial Supplement, Part II. Occupational Mortality, Fertility and Infant Mortality England and Wales, London. These reports have been analyzed by Morris, J. N. and Titmuss, R. M., "Epidemiology of Juvenile Rheumatism," *Lancet,* 2:59–63, 1942.

7. Metropolitan Life Insurance Company, *Studies in Heart Disease,* New York, 1946, p. 7.

8. Mary Grover: "Mortality from Heart Disease (all forms) Related to Geographic Section and Size of City," *Public Health Reports,* 64:439–456, 1949.

9. Mary Grover and M. Y. Pennell: "Mortality from Eight Specific Forms of Heart Disease Among White Persons," *Public Health Reports,* 65:824, 1950.

10. Grover and Pennell: *loc. cit.*

11. F. D. Mott and M. I. Roemer: *Rural Health and Medical Care.* New York, 1948, p. 58–60, 72.

12. Grover and Pennell, *ibid.,* p. 822.

13. M. Grover: "Negro Mortality. III. Course of Mortality from Specific Causes," 1920–1944, *Public Health Reports,* 63:201–213, 1948.

14. Metropolitan Life Insurance Company, "Large Decline in Mortality from Degenerative Diseases," *Statistical Bulletin,* March 1946, p. 3.

15. L. G. Rowntree, K. H. McGill, and C. H. Folk: "Health of Selective Service Registrants," *Journal American Medical Association,* 118:1223–1227, 1942.

16. W. S. Hunter, "Coronary Occlusion in Negroes," *Journal of the AMA,* 131: 12–14, 1946.

M. M. Weiss and J. J. Pruskmack: "Essential Hypertension in the Negro," *American Journal Medical Science,* 195:510–516, 1938. L. I. Orenstein: "Hypertension in Young Negroes," *War Medicine,* 4:422–424, 1943.

M. Kesilman: "The Incidence of Essential Hypertension of White and Negro Males," *Medical Record*, 154:16–19, 1941. E. H. Schwab and V. E. Schulze: "Heart Disease in the American Negro in the South," *American Heart Journal*, 7:710–717, 1932.

17. L. J. Usilton and G. C. Ruhland: "Survey of Venereal Diseases in the District of Columbia," *Venereal Disease Information*, 21:224–254, 1940. H. H. Hazen: "Syphilis in the Negro," U.S. Public Health Service, Venereal Disease Information Supplement, No. 15, Washington, 1942, p. 7.

18. William Osler: "Lumleian Lectures on Angina Pectoris," *Lancet I*, 697–702, 839–844, 973–977, 1910.

19. P. D. White: *Heart Disease*, New York, 1931, p. 414.

20. M. G. Wilson: *Rheumatic Fever*, New York, 1940.

21. J. N. Morris, R. M. Titmuss: "Epidemiology of Juvenile Rheumatism," *Lancet*, 2:159–63, 1942.

22. S. D. Collins: The Incidence of Rheumatic Fever as Recorded in General Morbidity Surveys of Families, Supplement No. 198 to the Public Health Reports, Washington, 1947, pp. 39–41.

23. A. G. Wedum and B. G. Wedum: "Rheumatic Fever in Cincinnati in Relation to Rentals, Crowding, Density of Population and Negroes." *American Journal Public Health*, 34:1065–1070, 1944.

24. J. R. Paul, *Rheumatic Fever in New Haven*, Lancaster, Pa. 1941, p. 40.

25. B. G. Wedum, A. G. Wedum and A. L. Beagler, "Prevalence of Rheumatic Heart Disease in Denver School Children," *American Journal of Public Health*, 35:1271–1281, 1945.

26. O. F. Hedley: "Rheumatic Heart Disease in Philadelphia Hospitals," *Public Health Reports*, 55:1599–1619, 1940.

27. M. D. Wilson, M. D. Schweitzer and R. Lubschez: "The Familial Epidemiology of Rheumatic Fever, Genetic and Epidemiologic studies II," *Journal of Pediatrics*, 22:581–611, 1943.

28. J. N. Morris & R. M. Titmuss: "Health and Social Change I. The Recent History of Rheumatic Heart Disease." *The Medical Officer*, 72:69–71, 77–79, 85–87, 1944.

J. A. Glover, "War-Time Decline of Acute Rheumatism." *Lancet*, 2:51–52, 1943.

29. S. D. Collins: The Incidence of Rheumatic Fever as Recorded in General Morbidity Surveys of Families, Supplement No. 198 to the Public Health Reports, Washington, 1947, pp. 36–37.

30. George Wolff: "Childhood Mortality from Rheumatic Fever and Heart Diseases," *Children's Bureau Publication 322*, 1948, pp. 2, 14, 17.

31. They are reviewed by J. R. Paul, *"The Epidemiology of Rheumatic Fever,"* Second Edition, New York, 1943, p. 67–70.

32. J. N. Morris and R. M. Titmuss, "Epidemiology of Juvenile Rheumatism," *Lancet*, 2:59–63, 1942.

NOTES TO CHAPTER 4

* This paper is based on material from the writer's unpublished doctoral dissertation, "Mortality in Houston, Texas, 1949–1951: A Study of Socio-Economic Differentials," Department of Sociology, The University of Texas, 1956. It is a revision of a paper appearing in *Social Problems*, 5 (July, 1957); Copyright 1957 by The Society for the Study of Social Problems.

1. United States National Office of Vital Statistics, *Vital Statistics of The United States, 1950*, I, Washington: Government Printing Office, 1954, Table 8.26, p. 170.

2. Albert J. Mayer and Philip M. Hauser, "Class Differentials in Expectation of Life at Birth," *Revue de l'Institute International de Statistique*, 18 (1950), pp. 197–200. Iwao M. Moriyama, "Recent Mortality Trends and Differentials," *Journal of the American Statistical Association*, 46

(June, 1951), pp. 213–219. Paul H. Price, "Trends in Mortality Differentials in the United States," *The Southwestern Social Science Quarterly*, 35 (December, 1954), pp. 255–263.

3. Floyd P. Allen, *People of the Shadows*, Cincinnati: The Public Health Federation, 1954, pp. 15–21. Floyd P. Allen, *We Pay With Our Lives*, Cincinnati: The Public Health Federation, 1948, pp. 5–7.

4. Lolagene Convis Coombs, "Economic Differences in Causes of Death," *Medical Care*, 1 (July, 1941), pp. 246–255.

5. Constantine A. Yeracaris, "Differential Mortality, General and Cause-Specific in Buffalo, 1939–1941," *Journal of the American Statistical Association*, 50 (December, 1955), pp. 1235–1247.

6. *Ibid.*

7. United States Bureau of the Census, *United States Census of Population: 1950. Census Tract Statistics, Houston, Texas,* 3, Chapter 24, Washington: Government Printing Office, 1952.

8. United States Bureau of the Census, *Sixteenth Census of the United States, Population, Characteristics by Age,* 4, Part I, Washington: Government Printing Office, 1943.

9. Margaret Jarman Hagood, *Statistics*

For Sociologists, New York: Henry Holt and Company, 1941, pp. 843–847.

10. Jack E. Dodson, "Differential Fertility in Houston, Texas, 1940–1950: A Study of Recent Trends," Unpublished doctoral dissertation, Department of Sociology, The University of Texas, 1955.

11. *Ibid.,* p. 67.

12. *Ibid.,* pp. 195–196.

13. Yeracaris, *op. cit.,* pp. 1241–1242.

14. *Op. cit.*

NOTES TO CHAPTER 5

1. The 72 families excluded because of deaths from nonchronic causes differ only slightly from the included families. There were 45.8 percent of the 72 excluded families and 41.6 of the 1,310 included families in the "poor" and "very poor" economic groups in 1923. Similarly, 25 percent of the excluded families and 21.3 percent of the included families were in these two economic groups in 1943. No appreciable differ-

ences in age composition exist. Chronic illness was present in 1923 in 52.8 percent of the excluded families and in 55.0 percent of the included families.

2. Throughout this report the age and family size or age and sex adjustments have been made according to the direct method described by Pearl (4) as "adjusted death-rates (B)."

REFERENCES TO CHAPTER 5

1. Ciocco, A.: Chronic sickness in relation to survivorship twenty years later. *Human Biol. 18:* 33–48 (1946).

2. Sydenstricker, E.: A study of illness in a general population group. Hagerstown Morbidity Studies No. 1. The method of study and general results. *Pub. Health Rep. 41:* 2069–2088 (1926).

3. Lawrence, P. S.: An estimate of the incidence of chronic disease. *Pub. Health Rep. 63:* 69–82 (1948).

4. Pearl, R.: *Introduction to Medical Biometry and Statistics.* W. B. Saunders Company, Philadelphia, 1940.

5. Bigelow, G. H. and Lombard, H. F.: *Cancer and Other Chronic Diseases in Massachusetts.* Houghton Mifflin Co., Boston, 1933.

6. Britten, R. H. and Altman, I.: Ill-

ness and accidents among persons living under different housing conditions. Data based on the National Health Survey. *Pub. Health Rep. 56:* 609–640 (1941).

7. The National Health Survey: Illness and Medical Care in Relation to Economic Status. Preliminary Reports, Sickness and Medical Care Series, *Bull. No. 2,* Public Health Service, 1938.

8. Perrott, G. St. J., and Collins, S. D.: Relation of sickness to income and income change in 10 surveyed communities. Health and Depression Studies No. 1. Method of study and general results for each locality. *Pub. Health Rep. 50:* 595–622 (1935).

9. Boas, E. P.: *The Unseen Plague—Chronic Disease.* J. J. Augustin, New York, 1940.

NOTES TO CHAPTER 6

1. Committee on the Hygiene of Housing, *Basic Principles of Healthful Housing,* New York: American Public Health Association, 1939; Subcommittee on the Hygiene of Housing, *Planning the Neighborhood,* New York: American Public Health Association, 1949; H. D. Kruse, "The Place of Nutrition in the Relationship Between Environment and Health," in *Backgrounds of Social Medicine,* New York: Proceedings

of the Milbank Memorial Fund, 1949, pp. 138–155.

2. J. M. May, "Cultural Aspects of Tropical Disease," *American Journal of Tropical Medicine and Hygiene,* 3 (1954): 422–430; "The Contribution of Medical Geography to the Etiology of Disease," *American Journal of Tropical Medicine and Hygiene,* 4 (1955): 776–780; "The Geography of Pathology," *The Scientific*

Monthly, LXXII (1951): 128–131; "The Geography of Disease: The American Geographical Society's Approach to the Problem," *Meteorological Monographs*, 2 (1954): 104–110; and the maps in the *Atlas of Diseases*, New York: American Geographical Society.

3. M. Mead, "Cultural Contexts of Nutritional Patterns," *Centennial: Collected Papers Presented at the Centennial Celebration*, Washington: American Association for the Advancement of Science, 1950, pp. 85–96.

4. F. Dunbar and L. G. Rowntree, *Psychosomatic Diagnosis*, New York: Hoeber, Inc., 1943; E. Weiss and O. S. English, *Psychosomatic Medicine*, Philadelphia: Saunders, 1949; E. Ziskind, *Psychophysiologic Medicine*, Philadelphia: Lea and Febiger, 1954; L. A. Mirsky, S. Kaplan, and R. H. Broh-Kahn, "Pepsinogen Secretion (Uropepsin) as an Index to the Influence of Various Life Situations on Gastric Secretion," in *Life Stress and Disease*, Baltimore: Williams and Wilkins, 1950.

5. M. Mead, "Some Relationships Between Social Anthropology and Psychiatry," in F. Alexander and H. Ross (eds.), *Dynamic Psychiatry*, Chicago: University of Chicago Press, 1952, pp. 401–448; C. K. Aldrich, *Psychiatry for the Family Physician*, New York: McGraw-Hill, 1955; L. W. Simmons and H. G. Wolff, *Social Science in Medicine*, New York: Russell-Sage, 1954, pp. 170–193; A. B. Hollingshead and F. C. Redlich, "Social Stratification and Psychiatric Disorders," *American Sociological Review*, 18 (1953): 163–169.

6. T. Francis, Jr., "Correlations in Clinical and Epidemiological Investigation," *American Journal of the Medical Sciences*, 226 (1953): 376–382.

7. J. Paul, "The Patient and his Environment," in T. R. Harrison (ed.) *Principles of Internal Medicine*, New York: McGraw-Hill, 1954, pp. 7–9.

8. J. L. Melnick and N. Ledinko, "Social Serology: Antibody Levels in a Normal Young Population During an Epidemic of Poliomyelitis," *The American Journal of Hygiene*, 54 (1951): 354–382; and "Development of Neutralizing Antibodies Against the Three Types of Poliomyelitis Virus During an Epidemic Period —the Ratio of Inapparent Infection to Clinical Poliomyelitis," *The American Journal of Hygiene*, 58 (1955): 207–222.

9. It should also be remembered that the environment contributes to other aspects of microbiology. cf. O. Rahn, *Microbes of Merit*, New York: Ronald Press, 1945.

10. E. G. Erickson, *Urban Behavior*, New York: Macmillan Co., 1954, pp. 446–459. Construction and Civic Development Department, *Zoning and Civic Development*, Washington: Chamber of Commerce of the U.S., 1950.

11. S. Riemer, *The Modern City*, New York: Prentice-Hall, 1952, pp. 411–432; Committee on the Hygiene of Housing, *Planning the Neighborhood*, Chicago: Public Administration Service, 1948, pp. 1–72.

12. Report of the Urbanism Committee to the National Resources Committee, *Our Cities*, Washington: U.S. Government Printing Office, 1937, pp. 1–87. See also E. M. Hoover, *The Location of Economic Activity*, New York: McGraw-Hill, 1948, pp. 15–144.

13. A. H. Hawley, *Human Ecology*, New York: Ronald Press, 1950; J. A. Quinn, *Human Ecology*, New York: Prentice-Hall, 1950.

14. W. Firey, *Land Use in Central Boston*, Cambridge: Harvard University Press, 1946.

15. cf. E. C. Andrus (ed.), *Advances in Military Medicine Made by American Investigators Working Under the Sponsorship of the Committee on Medical Research*, Boston: Little-Brown, 1948.

16. W. D. Forbus, *Reaction to Injury*, Baltimore: Williams & Wilkins, 1943, p. 30.

17. A. E. Feller, "Common Respiratory Disease," in T. R. Harrison (ed.), *op. cit.*, pp. 1062–1079; see also P. H. Long, J. A. Doull, J. M. Bourn, and E. McComb, "The Etiology of Acute Upper Respiratory Infection (Common Cold)," *Journal of Experimental Medicine*, 53 (1931): 447 ff.

18. Bureau of the Census, *Key to Published and Tabulated Data for Small Areas*, Washington: U.S. Government Printing Office, 1951; and U.S. Bureau of the Census, *U.S. Census of the Population: 1950. Vol. III, Census Tract Statistics*, Washington: U.S. Government Printing Office, 1952.

19. J. H. S. Bossard, "A Spatial Index for Family Interaction," in *Parent and Child: Studies in Family Behavior*, Philadelphia: Pennsylvania U. Press, 1953.

20. E. M. Watkins, "The Problem of Space," in *Housing and Health*, New York: Proceedings of the Milbank Memorial Fund,

1951, pp. 47–57; Committee on Hygiene of Housing, *Planning the Home for Occupancy*, Chicago: American Public Health Association, Public Administration Service, 1950.

21. J. H. S. Bossard, *op. cit.*

22. E. M. Watkins, *op. cit.* and Committee on Hygiene of Housing, *op. cit.*

REFERENCES TO CHAPTER 8

1. Bennett, L. A.: The Personality of the Rheumatoid Arthritis Patient, Unpublished master's dissertation, McGill University, 1952.

2. Boland, E. W.: Arthritis and Allied Conditions in an Army General Hospital, *California & West. Med. 60:* 7, 1944.

3. Boland, E. W.: Psychogenic Rheumatism: The Musculoskeletal Expression of Psychoneurosis, *California Med. 68:* 273, 1948.

4. Boland, E. W.: Psychogenic Factors in Rheumatic Disease. In Hollander, J. L. (Ed.): *Arthritis and Allied Conditions*, Philadelphia, 1953, Lea & Febiger.

5. Boland, E. W., and Headley, N. E.: Rheumatoid Arthritis, *Ann. West. Med. & Surg. 2:* 289, 1948.

6. Blom, G. E.: Personal communication.

7. Blom, G. E., and Nicholls, G.: Emotional Factors in Children With Rheumatoid Arthritis, *Am. J. Orthopsychiat. 24:* 588, 1954.

8. Booth, G. C.: Personality and Chronic Arthritis, *J. Nerv. & Ment. Dis. 85:* 637, 1937.

9. Cecil, R. L.: Environmental Factors in the Etiology of Rheumatic Conditions, *Med. Clin. North America 29:* 566, 1945.

10. Cleveland, S. E., and Fisher, S.: Behavior and Unconscious Fantasies of Patients With Rheumatoid Arthritis, *Psychosom. Med. 16:* 327, 1954.

11. Cobb, S.: Personal communication.

12. Cobb, S., Bauer, W., and Whiting, I.: Environmental Factors in Rheumatoid Arthritis, *J. A. M. A. 113:* 668, 1939.

13. Edstrom, G.: Rheumatoid Arthritis and Trauma, *Acta med. scandinav. 142:* 11, 1952.

14. Ellman, P., and Mitchell, S. D.: The Psychological Aspects of Chronic Rheumatic Joint Disease, *Rep. Chron. Rheumat. Dis. 2:* 109, 1936.

15. Funkenstein, D. H., and King, S. H.: Manuscript in preparation.

16. Gordon, R. G.: The Psychological Factor in Chronic Rheumatism, *Brit. M. J. 1:* 1165, 1939.

17. Gottschalk, L. A., Serota, H. M., and Roman, K. G.: Handwriting in Rheumatoid Arthritics, *Psychosom. Med. 11:* 354, 1949.

18. Gottschalk, L. A., Serota, H. M., and Shapiro, L. B.: Psychologic Conflict and Neuromuscular Tension. I. Preliminary Report on a Method, as Applied to Rheumatoid Arthritis, *Psychosom. Med. 12:* 315, 1950.

19. Gregg, D.: The Paucity of Arthritis Among Psychotic Cases, *Am. J. Psychiat. 95:* 853, 1939.

20. Halliday, J. L.: Psychological Factors in Rheumatism, *Brit. M. J. 1:* 213, 264, 1937.

21. Halliday, J. L.: Psychological Aspects of Rheumatoid Arthritis, *Proc. Roy. Soc. Med. 35:* 455, 1942.

22. Halliday, J. L.: Concept of a Psychosomatic Affection, *Lancet 2:* 692, 1943.

23. Halliday, J. L.: Psychosomatic Medicine and the Rheumatism Problem, *Practitioner 152:* 6, 1944.

24. Jelliffe, S. E.: The Neuropathology of Bone Disease, *Tr. Am. Neurol. Assoc.*, 49th Annual Meeting, p. 419, 1923.

25. Jelliffe, S. E., and White, W. A.: *Diseases of the Nervous System*, Philadelphia, 1935, Lea & Febiger.

26. Johnson, A., Shapiro, L. B., and Alexander, F.: Preliminary Report on a Psychosomatic Study of Rheumatoid Arthritis, *Psychosom. Med. 9:* 295, 1947.

27. Kaufman, W.: The Over-All Picture of Rheumatism and Arthritis, *Ann. Allergy 10:* 47, 1952.

28. King, S. H., and Henry, A. F.: Aggression and Cardiovascular Reactions Related to Parental Control Over Behavior, *J. Abnorm. & Soc. Psychol. 50:* 206, 1955.

29. Law, S. G.: Interview Therapy of Psychosomatic Arthritis, *Rheumatism 15:* 38, 1949.

30. Lewis-Faning, E.: Report on an Enquiry Into the Aetological Factors Associated With Rheumatoid Arthritis, *Ann. Rheumat. Dis. 9,* (supplement), 1950.

31. Lowman, E. W., Miller, S., Lee, P. R., Stein, H., King, R., and Heald, L.: Psychosocial Factors in Rehabilitation of the Chronic Rheumatoid Arthritic, *Ann. Rheumat. Dis. 13:* 312, 1954.

32. Ludwig, A. O.: Emotional Factors

in Rheumatoid Arthritis: Their Bearing on the Care and Rehabilitation of the Patient, *Physiotherapy Rev. 29:* 339, 1949.

33. Ludwig, A. O.: Psychiatric Studies of Patients With Rheumatoid Arthritis, *In* Slocum, C. H., (Ed.): *Rheumatic Diseases*, Philadelphia, 1952, W. B. Saunders Co.

34. Ludwig, A. O.: Psychogenic Factors in Rheumatoid Arthritis, *Bull. Rheumat. Dis. 2:* 15, 1952.

35. McGregor, H. G.: The Psychological Factor in Rheumatic Disease, *Practitioner 143:* 627, 1939.

36. McLaughlin, J. T., Zabarenko, R. N., Diana, P. P., and Quinn, B.: Emotional Reactions of Rheumatoid Arthritics to ACTH, *Psychosom. Med. 15:* 187–199, 1953.

37. Newsholme, H. P.: Health Disease and Integration, London, 1929, George Allen & Unwin, Ltd.

38. Nissen, H. A.: Chronic Arthritis and Its Treatment, *New England J. Med. 210:* 1109, 1934.

39. Nissen, H. A., and Spencer, K. A.: The Psychogenic Problem (Endocrinal and Metabolic) in Chronic Arthritis, *New England J. Med. 214:* 576, 1936.

40. Patterson, R. M., Craig, J. B., Waggoner, R. W., and Freyberg, R.: Studies of the Relationship Between Emotional Factors and Rheumatoid Arthritis, *Am. J. Psychiat. 99:* 775, 1943.

41. Plugge, H., Anthropologische Beobachtungen bei primarchronischen Arthritikern, *Ztschr. Rheumaforsch. 12:* 231, 1953.

42. Ray, M. B.: *Rheumatism in General Practice*, London, 1934, H. K. Lewis & Co.

43. Rivers, T. M.: *The Automatic Diseases or the Rheumatic Syndrome*, Philadelphia, 1934, Dorrance & Co.

44. Robinson, W. D., Boland, E. W., Bunim, J. J., Crain, D. C., Engleman, E. P., Graham, W., Lockie, L. M., Montgomery, M. M., Ragan, C., Ropes, M. W., Rosenberg, E. F., and Smyth, C. J.: Rheumatism and Arthritis, *Ann. Int. Med. 39:* 497, 1953.

45. Short, C. L.: Arthritis in the Mediterranean Theater of Operations, *New England J. Med. 236:* 383, 1947.

46. Smith, M.: A Study of 102 Cases of Atrophic Arthritis. III. Etiologic Factors, *New England J. Med. 206:* 211, 1932.

47. Snorrason, E.: Rheumatoid Arthritis and Occupation, *Acta med. scandinav. 140:* 355, 1951.

48. Stein-Lewinson, Thea.: Handwriting in Chronic Arthritis (A Study in Graphology), *Rheumatism 1:* 91, 1938.

49. Swaim, L. T.: The President's Address, Ninth Annual Meeting of the American Rheumatism Association, June 8, 1942, Atlantic City, New Jersey, *Ann. Int. Med. 19:* 118, 1943.

50. Thomas, G. W.: Psychic Factors in Rheumatoid Arthritis, *Am. J. Psychiat. 93:* 693, 1936.

* Publication number 3 of the Pittsburgh Arthritis Study. Grateful acknowledgment is given to the Russell Sage Foundation for support of the work reported here.

REFERENCES TO CHAPTER 10

1. T. W. Adorno, Else Frenkel-Brunswik, Daniel J. Levinson, and R. Nevitt Sanford; *The Authoritarian Personality*, New York, Harper & Bros., 1950.

2. Daniel H. Funkenstein, Stanley H. King, and Margaret Drolette: The experimental evocation of stress, In *Symposium on Stress*. Washington, D.C.: Walter Reed Army Medical Center and Army Medical Service Graduate School, 1953.

3. Daniel H. Funkenstein, Stanley H. King, and Margaret Drolette: The direction of anger during a laboratory stress-inducing situation. *Psychosomatic Med.*, 16:404, 1954.

4. Daniel H. Funkenstein and Lydia Meade. Nor-epinephrine-like and epinephrine-like substance and the elevation of blood pressure during acute stress. *J. Nerv. & Ment. Dis.* 119: 380, 1954.

5. Stanley H. King, *Emotional and cardiovascular responses during stress.* Unpublished doctor's dissertation, Harvard University, 1953.

6. Stanley H. King and Andrew F. Henry: Aggression and cardiovascular reactions related to parental control over behavior. *J. ab. soc. Psychol.*, 50:206, 1955.

7. A full report on all aspects of this study has been prepared and will be published by the Harvard University Press next winter.

8. Daniel J. Levinson, The intergroup relations workshop: Its psychological aims and effects. *J. Psychol.* 38:103, 1954.

NOTES TO CHAPTER 11

1. Cf. W. A. N. Dorland, the *American Illustrated Medical Dictionary*, W. A. Saunders Company, Philadelphia and London, 1955: "Health: a normal condition of body and mind, i.e., with all the parts functioning normally."

2. Dorland, *op. cit.*, "In general, any departure from a state of health; an illness or sickness. More specifically a definite morbid process having a characteristic train of symptoms. . . ."

3. American Psychiatric Association, *Diagnostic and Statistical Manual*, American Psychiatric Association, Washington, D.C., 1952.

4. Charles Wardell Stiles, *The Rockefeller Sanitary Commission for the Eradication of Hookworm Disease*, Judd and Deteiler, Washington, D.C., 1911.

5. George Peter Murdock, *Social Structure*, Macmillan Company, New York, 1949.

6. E. S. Maclachlan, *Dietary Patterns of the South*, unpublished M. A. thesis, University of North Carolina, 1932, *passim*.

7. Benedict, Ruth F., *Patterns of Culture*, Houghton Mifflin Co., Boston & New York, 1934.

8. The division of MCLXXXXIIIII by VII presents tedious difficulties, the extraction of the tenth root of −25 (X/−XXV) even more.

9. Robert L. Sutherland and Julian L. Woodward, *Introductory Sociology*, J. B. Lippincott Company, Philadelphia, 1940, p. 722.

10. Among some tribal peoples the weaning process is not complete for several years after the birth of the child, so that no clearcut break is observed dividing 'infancy' from 'childhood.'

11. Margaret Mead, *Male and Female*, William Morrow & Co., New York, 1930.

12. The total population of 1940 is the base for standardization. Data are from Vital Statistics—Special Reports, Volume 43, No. 17, National Office of Vital Statistics, Public Health Service, U.S. Department of Health Welfare, August 3, 1956. Since computations were made on a 10 percent sample of reported deaths, the rates should be considered as indicative rather than definitive.

13. August B. Hollingshead and Frederick C. Redlich, "Social Stratification and Psychiatric Disorders," *American Sociological Review*, 18 (April, 1953), pp. 163–169.

14. Alfred C. Kinsey, Wardell B. Pomeroy, and Clyde E. Martin, *Sexual Behavior in the Human Male*, W. B. Saunders Co., Philadelphia, 1948.

15. J. M. Maclachlan, *Alcoholism in Florida*, (unpublished manuscript), Florida Alcoholic Rehabilitation Program, Avon Park, Florida, 1957.

16. J. J. Honigmann, *Culture and Personality*, Harper and Brothers, New York, 1954, p. 382.

17. Dorland, *op. cit.*

18. Cf. W. L. Warner, "The Society, the Individual, and His Mental Disorders," *American Journal of Psychiatry*, 94:275–284: and Hutton Webster, *Magic; A Sociological Study*. Stanford, Stanford University Press, 1948, 486.

19. See W. B. Cannon, "Voodoo Death," *American Anthropologist*, 44:169–180.

20. L. W. Simmons and H. G. Wolff, *Social Science in Medicine*, Russell Sage Foundation, New York, 1954, pp. 94–95.

21. *Ibid*, p. 94.

22. W. Lloyd Warner, *A Black Civilization: A Social Study of An Australian Tribe*, Harper and Brothers, New York, 1937.

23. Abram Kardiner, *The Individual and His Society*, Columbia Univ. Press, New York, 1939.

24. Herman Melville, *Typee*, Dodd, Mead & Co., New York, 1923.

25. John J. Honigmann, *op. cit.*, pp. 381–382.

26. John J. Honigmann, *ibid*, p. 380.

27. A myth may be defined anthropologically as a dramatic tale relating man to the supernatural, and having a definite power to influence social behavior. This distinguishes it from the legend, which is a tale told for its own sake.

28. Honigmann, *op. cit.*, 378–379.

29. Donald Horton, "The Functions of Alcohol in Primitive Societies: A Cross-Cultural Study," *Quarterly Journal of Studies on Alcohol*, IV (September 1943), pp. 199–320.

30. John J. Honigmann, *op. cit.*, p. 397 ff.

31. Ruth Benedict, *op. cit.*, pp. 85–89.

32. Most recently in *The Sane Society*, Rinehart and Co., Inc., New York and Toronto, 1955.

33. *Ibid*, p. viii.
34. Rutgers Press, New Brunswick, N.J., 1950.
35. Gordon Macgregor, *Warriors With-* *out Weapons; A Study of the Society and* *Personality Development of the Pine Ridge* *Sioux*, Univ. of Chicago Press, Chicago, 1946.

BIBLIOGRAPHY TO CHAPTER 11

Alexander, Franz, *Our Age of Unreason*, J. B. Lippincott Co., New York and Philadelphia, 1951, Revised Edition.

Alexander, Franz, *Psychosomatic Medicine*, W. W. Norton and Company, Inc., New York, 1950.

Altschule, Mark D., *Bodily Physiology in Mental and Emotional Disorders*, Grune & Stratton, New York, 1953.

Bachman, George W. and associates, *Health Resources in the United States*, Brookings Institution, Washington, D.C., 1952.

Bonner, John Tyler, *Cells and Societies*, Princeton Univ. Press, Princeton, N.J., 1955.

Cooley, Carol H., *Social Aspects of Illness*, W. B. Saunders Co., Philadelphia, 1951.

Derner, Gordon F., *Aspects of the Psychology of the Tuberculous*, Paul B. Hoeber, Inc., New York, 1953.

Dunbar, Flanders, *Emotions and Bodily Changes*, Columbia Univ. Press, New York, Fourth Edition, 1954.

Eaton, J. W. and R. J. Weil, *Culture and Mental Disorders*, The Free Press, Glencoe, Ill., 1955.

Frank, Lawrence K., *Society as the Patient*, Rutgers Univ. Press, New Brunswick, N.J., 1948.

Fromm, Erich, *The Sane Society*, Rinehart and Company, New York, 1955.

Galdston, Iago, *Social Medicine: Its Derivations and Objections*, The Commonwealth Fund, New York, 1949.

Halliday, James L., *Psychosocial Medicine*, W. W. Norton and Co., Inc. New York, 1948.

Honigmann, John J., *Culture and Personality*, Harper & Brothers, New York, 1954.

Kardiner, Abram and Herbert Spiegle, *War Stress and Neurotic Illness*, Paul B. Hoeber, Inc., New York, Second Edition, 1947.

Kluckhohn, Clyde and Henry A. Murray, *Personality in Nature, Society, and Culture*, Alfred A. Knopf, New York, 1948.

Koos, Earl Lomon, *The Sociology of the Patient*, McGraw-Hill Book Company, New York, Second Edition, 1954.

Linton, Ralph, *The Cultural Background of Personality*, Appleton-Century-Crofts, Inc., New York, 1945.

Linton, Ralph, *Culture and Mental Disorders*, Charles C. Thomas, Springfield, Illinois, 1956.

Saunders, Lyle, *Cultural Difference and Medical Care*, Russell Sage Foundation, New York, 1954.

Simmons, Leo W. and Harold G. Wolff, *Social Science in Medicine*, Russell Sage Foundation, New York, 1954.

Sparer, Phineas J., *Personality, Stress and Tuberculosis*, International Universities Press, Inc., New York, 1956.

Weiss, Edward and O. Spurgeon English, *Psychosomatic Medicine*, W. B. Saunders Company, Philadelphia, Third Edition, 1957.

Wittkower, Eric and Brian Russell, *Emotional Factors in Skin Disease*, Paul B. Hoeber, Inc., New York, 1953.

Wolf, Stewart; Philippe V. Cardon, Jr.; Edward M. Shepard; and Harold G. Wolff, *Life Stress and Essential Hypertension*, The William Wilkins Company, Baltimore, 1955.

Wolff, Harold G., *Stress and Disease*, Charles C. Thomas, Springfield, Ill., 1953.

NOTES TO CHAPTER 12

1. Revised version of a paper read at the 1955 annual meetings of the American Anthropological Association, Boston, Mass.

2. R. H. Shryock, *The Development of Modern Medicine:* An Interpretation of the Social and Scientific Factors Involved, New York, 1947.

3. The writer is indebted to Dr. Edward Wellin for suggesting this instance of class differentials in disease, and in particular for bringing out the significance of the contrast between tuberculosis and polio.

4. National figures for three sample years are as follows (from the Massachusetts Bureau of Health Information):

Year	POLIOMYELITIS		TUBERCULOSIS	
	Cases	Deaths	Cases	Deaths
1940	9,804	1,026	102,984	60,428
1945	13,624	1,186	114,931	52,916
1950	33,330	1,686	121,742	33,633

5. The role of class factors in these contrasting public reactions seems clear, but obviously there are always other variables associated with specific diseases that play some part as well. In the case of tuberculosis and polio, there may be, e.g., differences in dramatic impact and publicity. Polio has physically visible after-effects, although this must be compared with the social visibility associated with tuberculosis. Also, any disease, like polio, that tends to victimize children in disproportionately large numbers, seems to excite more public reaction. However, in view of the great overlap in age between those who contract the two diseases, it is difficult to say what part this factor may actually play in determining public attitudes. Although comparable information for tuberculosis is lacking, the importance of class factors in evaluating polio is borne out by Deasy's findings regarding participation in the 1954 polio vaccine field trials, namely that upper status mothers were much more likely to have taken previous precautions against the disease, knew more about the trials, and demonstrated a higher awareness of the disease entity itself. See Deasy, Leila C., "Socio-Economic Status and Participation in the Poliomyelitis Vaccine Trial." *American Sociological Review,* 21: 185–191, 1956.

6. Paffenbarger and Watt, in their epidemiological study of polio in South Texas, report that "groups of individuals living under better economic circumstances with the many associated 'advantages' of greater personal cleanliness, less crowding, better food, and less association with verminous insects may suffer a significantly higher attack rate to the paralytic disease and suggests that . . . for the United States (this) is somehow related to an improved standard of living." Ralph S. Paffenbarger, Jr., and James Watt, "Poliomyelitis in Hidalgo County, Texas, 1948; Epidemiological Observations." *The American Journal of Hygiene,* 58:269–287, 1953.

7. Lyle Saunders, *Cultural Difference and Medical Care.* New York, 1954.

8. Cf. McKim Marriott, "Western Medicine in a Village of Northern India," *in*

Benjamin D. Paul (ed.), *Health, Culture and Community:* Case Studies of Public Reactions to Health Programs. New York, 1955, pp. 239–268.

9. Cf. Alan Grey, "Relationships between Social Status and Psychological Characteristics of Psychiatric Patients." Unpublished Ph.D. thesis. University of Chicago, 1949. See also F. C. Redlich, A. B. Hollingshead, and Elizabeth Bellis, "Social Class Differences in Attitudes toward Psychiatry." *American Journal of Orthopsychiatry,* 25: 60–70, 1955.

10. Edward Wellin, "Water Boiling in a Peruvian Town." *in* Benjamin D. Paul (ed.), *op. cit.,* pp. 71–103.

11. Ozzie G. Simmons, *The Health Center of San Miguel:* An Analysis of a Public Health Program in Chile. Institute of Inter-American Affairs, Santiago, 1953.

12. See Ozzie G. Simmons, "The Clinical Team in a Chilean Health Center." *in* Benjamin D. Paul (ed.), *op. cit.,* pp. 325–348.

13. Earl L. Koos, *The Health of Regionville.* New York, 1954.

14. Charles J. Erasmus, "Changing Folk Beliefs and the Relativity of Empirical Knowledge." *Southwestern Journal of Anthropology,* 8:411–428, 1952.

15. This refers to public health not only in the United States but in all areas that have been importantly influenced by the British and American varieties of public health.

16. In the preparation of this section, the writer is indebted for suggestions to an address by Dr. Walter B. Miller entitled "Social Class: Its Influence on Health Behavior," delivered at the October, 1955, meeting of the Massachusetts Public Health Association.

17. This and the following formulation of middle-class norms were suggested by a summary description of middle-class standards in Albert Cohen, *Delinquent Boys: The Culture of the Gang.* Glencoe, Illinois, 1955, pp. 87–90.

18. See Erasmus, *op. cit.;* George M. Foster, "Relationships between Theoretical

and Applied Anthropology: A Public-Health Program Analysis." *Human Organization*, 11:5–16, 1952; and Ozzie G. Simmons, "Popular and Modern Medicine in Mestizo Communities of Coastal Peru and Chile." *Journal of American Folklore*, 68: 57–71, 1955.

19. Cf. Arnold W. Green, "The Middle-Class Male Child and Neurosis." *American Sociological Review*, 11:31–41, 1946.

NOTES TO CHAPTER 13

* This paper was presented before the Medical Care Section of the American Public Health Association at the Eighty-Third Annual Meeting in Kansas City, Missouri, November 16, 1955.

This is a first reporting of one portion of a study of urban health attitudes and behavior conducted under grants G-3221 and G-3221c (National Institutes of Health). Other portions of the study dealt with morbidity experience and the use of resources for medical care; all are to be reported as a unit in book form at a later date.

1. Cf. the rural counterpart of this study, i.e., the writer's Health of Regionville. New York: Columbia University Press, 1954.

2. *Ibid.*, pp. 93–111.

3. Paul, John R. Clinical Epidemiology. J. Clin. Investigation 17:593–641, (Sept.), 1938.

NOTES TO CHAPTER 14

* In addition to the authors, the following members of the staff of the Laboratory of Socio-environmental Studies participated in the project formulation and field operations, or both: Rosalie Kasaba, Gladys Morris, Frances Polen, Charlotte G. Schwartz, Marian Radke-Yarrow, and E. Grant Youmans.

The research here reported was designed and carried out by the Laboratory of Socio-environmental Studies in collaboration with the National Foundation for Infantile Paralysis. Field interviewing was conducted by the Bureau of Social Science Research, American University, under a grant from NFIP. Local arrangements were facilitated by Harold Kennedy, M.D., health officer of Fairfax County, Va., without whose interest and very full cooperation this study would not have been possible.

1. As carried out in this country, all second-grade children were eligible to receive the vaccine. First- and third-grade children were designated as controls. Therefore, no question of the child's receiving a placebo was entailed.

2. Two of the schools represented primarily rural areas, and three, suburban. One of the suburban schools was for Negro children, the other schools were for white children. The consent rate for other public schools in the county ranged from 21 percent in a rural school to 85 percent in a large suburban school.

3. The decision process, of course, frequently involved the child and the father. The mother was, however, our source of data, and our purpose was to discover what factors influenced her in the decision that was reached.

NOTES TO CHAPTER 15

* Paper presented at the Medical Sociology section, meetings of the American Sociological Society, Detroit, Michigan, September 7, 1956.

1. Sampling procedures were established by Donovan J. Thompson, Ph.D., Department of Biostatistics, Graduate School of Public Health, University of Pittsburgh. The advice and encouragement of Antonio Ciocco, Sc.D., Head of that Department, throughout the course of planning and execution of the project and in the analysis of data were invaluable, and grateful thanks are hereby tendered. Discussions with Professor A. B. Hollingshead, Ph.D., Department of Sociology, Yale University, have also been of material aid.

2. The diseases were classified after examination of the categories into which they fell in the *Manual of the International Statistical Classification of Disease, Injuries, and Causes of Death*, World Health Organization, 1948. The diseases were classified as follows:

Acute:
Infective and Parasitic: 002–019, 48–102.
Diseases of the Nervous System and Sense Organs: 331–332, 370–379, 388–394.
Diseases of the Circulatory System: 400–401, 434, 456, 463–468.
Diseases of the Respiratory System: 463–501, 511, 517–519.
Diseases of the Digestive System: 533–539, 543–544, 550–551, 570–571, 575–576, 578–580, 583, 586–587.
Diseases of the Genito-Urinary System: 590–593, 600, 605, 606, 610, 621, 624, 630.
Deliveries and Complications of Pregnancy, Childbirth and the Puerperium: 650–689.
Diseases of the Skin and Cellular Tissues: 690–695, 698, 703, 714, 716.
Diseases of the Bones and Organs of Movement: 722, 727, 730, 735, 738–741.
Diseases of Early Infancy: 761.
Symptoms, Senility and Ill-Defined Conditions: 780, 783–789.

All Accidents, Poisonings, Violence.
Chronic:
Infective and Parasitic: 130–138.
Neo-plasms: 130–239.
Allergic, Endocrine System, Metabolic, and Nutritional Diseases: 240–296.
Diseases of the Nervous System and Sense Organs: 334, 350–369, 385, 396–398.
Diseases of the Circulatory System: 416–420, 443–455, 460–462.
Diseases of the Respiratory System: 502–510, 512–516, 522–526.
Diseases of the Digestive System: 540–541, 545, 552–560, 572–573, 581, 584.
Diseases of the Genito-Urinary System: 594, 602–603, 612, 620, 633–637.
Diseases of the Skin and Cellular Tissue: 696, 701–702, 708–713.
Diseases of the Bones and Organs of Movement: 725–726, 732, 734, 737, 744–749.
Congenital Malformations: 750–757.
Symptoms, Senility and Ill-Defined Conditions: 782, 790–791, 794.

REFERENCES TO CHAPTER 15

1. Sydenstricker, Edgar: Economic Status and the Incidence of Illness, Hagerstown Morbidity Studies No. x. *Public Health Reports,* July 26, 1929, 44, pp. 1821–1833; Lawrence, P. S.: Chronic Illness and Socio-Economic Status. *Public Health Reports,* November 19, 1948, 63, No. 47, Tables I and II, pp. 1510–1511; Britten, Rollo H.; Collins, Selwyn D.; and Fitzgerald, James S.: The National Health Survey: Some General Findings. *Public Health Reports,* March 15, 1940, 55, No. 11, Table V, pp. 444, 470; Britten, Rollo H.: Blindness, as Recorded in the National Health Survey. *Public Health Reports,* November 14, 1941, 56, No. 46, Table II, pp. 2191–2215; Hoffer, Charles R.: Medical Needs of the Rural Population of Michigan. *Rural Sociology,* June, 1947, 12, No. 2, pp. 162–168; Hailman, David E.: The Prevalence of Disabling Illness Among Male and Female Workers and Housewives. *Public Health Service Bulletin No. 260,* 1941, Table 8, p. 29; Moore, Fredrika and Hemblen, Angeline: Physical Defects of School Children. *American Journal of Public Health,* October, 1928, 18, No. 10, pp. 1268–1272.

2. Britten, Rollo H.: The National Health Survey: Receipt of Medical Services in Different Urban Population Groups. *Public Health Reports,* November 29, 1940, 55, No. 48, Table 8 and Table 10, pp. 2199–2224; Falk, I. S.; Klem, Margaret S.; and Sinai, Nathan: The Incidence of Illness and the Receipt and Costs of Medical Care Among Representative Families. Chicago, University of Chicago Press, 1933, Table 20, p. 92.

3. Falk, Klem, and Sinai: *Idem,* Table 11, p. 48, and Table 13, p. 54; Lombard, Herbert L.: A Sickness Survey of Winchester, Massachusetts. *American Journal of Public Health,* September, 1928, 18, No. 9, pp. 1089–1097.

4. Britten, Rollo H.; Collins, Selwyn D.; and Fitzgerald, James S.: The National Health Survey: Some General Findings. *Public Health Reports,* March 15, 1940, 55, No. 11, Table V, pp. 444, 470.

5. Ciocco, Antonio; Graham, Saxon; and Thompson, Donovan J.: Illness and Receipt of Medical Services in Pittsburgh (Arsenal) and Butler County, Pennsylvania. *Pennsylvania's Health,* in press.

NOTES TO CHAPTER 16

° This study was first published in *Health, Culture, and Community*, pp. 15–41. Benjamin Paul, ed. Russell Sage Foundation, 1955, under the title of "A Comprehensive Health Program Among South African Zulus."

°° For a more detailed description of the technics and programs of the South African health centers see:

Kark, Sidney L, and Cassel, John. The Pholela Health Centre—A Progress Report. *South African M. J.* 26:101–104 (Feb. 9); 132-136 (Feb. 16), 1952.

Kark, Sidney L. "Health Centre Service —A South African Experiment in Family Health and Medical Care." *Social Medicine*, Chap. 26. E. H. Cluver, ed. Central News Agency, Johannesburg, South Africa, 1951.

REFERENCES TO CHAPTER 16

1. Simmons, Leo W., and Wolff, Harold G.: *Social Science in Medicine*. New York: Russell Sage Foundation, 1954.

2. Slotkin, J. S.: Culture and Psychopathology. *J. Abnorm. & Social Psychol.* 51: 269 (Sept.), 1953.

3. Holmes, T. H., et al.: Psychosocial and Psychophysiologic Studies of Tuberculosis. *J. Am. Psychosomat. Soc.* XVII (Nov., Dec.), 1955.

4. Paul, Benjamin D.: *Health, Culture and Community*. New York: Russell Sage Foundation, 1955.

5. Saunders, Lyle: *Cultural Difference and Medical Care: The Case of the Spanish Speaking People of the Southwest*. N.Y.: Russell Sage Foundation, 1954.

6. Du Bois, Cora.: Attitudes Toward Food and Hunger in Alor *in Language*, *Culture and Personality*. Eds. Leslie Spier, et al. Menasha, Wis.: Sapir Memorial Publication Fund, 1941.

7. Wellin, Edward: Maternal and Infant Feeding Practices in a Peruvian Village. *J. Am. Dietet. A.* 31:889 (Sept.), 1955.

8. Cussler, Margaret and de Give, Mary L.: *'Twixt the Cup and the Lip*. New York: Twayne Publishers, 1952.

9. Bennet, John W.; Smith, Harvey L.; and Passin, Herbert. Food and Culture in Southern Illinois—A Preliminary Report. *Am. Soc. Rev.* 7:645 (Oct.), 1942.

10. Lewin, Kurt. Group Decision and Social Change *in Readings in Social Psychology*, pp. 459–473. Eds. Swanson, Newcomb, Hartley, et al. New York: Henry Holt, 1952.

NOTES TO CHAPTER 18

1. Robert Bierstedt, "An Analysis of Social Power"—*American Sociological Review*, XV (December, 1950), 733. The author states that "power is always successful; when it is not successful it is not, or ceases to be power." While the voluntary system of the community has power, its projects are not *always* successful. In instances of failure, the voluntary system is without power.

2. Floyd Hunter, *Community Power Structure*—Chapel Hill: The University of North Carolina Press, 1953.

3. Walter B. Cannon, "Relation of Biological and Social Homeostasis," *The Wisdom of the Body*. New York: W. W. Norton and Company, 1939, pp. 305–324.

4. Christopher Sower and Walter Freeman, "III—Role of Social Relationships in Achieving Community Health Goals," in Odin W. Anderson, "Symposium on Community Self-surveys in Health," *American Journal of Public Health* XLV (March, 1955), 283. The authors state that in a community organizational involvement process . . . there must be a set of relationships "to decide whether the action is right or wrong." This aspect of the process is called legitimation. Actually, there are three stages that must be fulfilled—initiation, legitimation, and execution. Different sets of relationships are required for each stage.

5. Talcott Parsons, "The Structure of the Social System, I: The Organization of the Components Into Sub-systems," *The Social System*—Glencoe: The Free Press, 1951, pp. 68–112.

6. Roland L. Warren, "Toward A Typology of Extra-Community Control Limiting Local Community Autonomy," *Social Forces*, XXXIV (May, 1956), 338.

7. Talcott Parsons, *op. cit.*, p. 538.

8. Robert Bierstedt, *op. cit.*, p. 738.

9. *Ibid.*, p. 737.
10. *Ibid.*
11. *Ibid.*
12. *Ibid.*
13. *Ibid.*
14. Paul A. Miller et al., *Community Health Action*. East Lansing: Michigan State University Press, 1953, O. 20.
15. *Ibid.*, p. 21.
16. *Loc. cit.*
17. *Ibid.*, p. 30.
18. *Ibid.*, p. 23.

19. *Ibid.*, p. 26.
20. *Ibid.*, p. 29.
21. Floyd Hunter, "I—Social Aspects of Health Action: Salem, Mass.," in Odin W. Anderson, *op. cit.*, 275–276. The author indicates that had this community secured outside help, "they might have received more for their money" in surveying the community as a basis for policy considerations in health practices.
22. Paul A. Miller, *op. cit.*, p. 25.
23. *Ibid.*, p. 26.

NOTES TO CHAPTER 20

1. Both health and illness, in general, I would like to treat as states of the individual person; the "pathology" of social systems, real and important as it is, should not be called "illness" nor the absence of it, "health." Cf. Talcott Parsons, "The Mental Hospital as a Type of Organization," in *The Patient and the Mental Hospital*, edited by Milton Greenblatt, Daniel J. Levinson, and Richard H. Williams. The Free Press, 1957.
2. I have put forward this general type of view on two previous occasions. For the general conception of the relation of personality to the internalization of social and cultural objects, see Parsons and Bales, *Family, Socialization and Interaction Process*, Free Press, 1955. A more extended discussion of the relation of personality and organism will be found in Parsons, "An Approach to Psychological Theory in Terms of the Theory of Action," American Psychological Association, *Studies in General Theory*, ed. Sigmund Koch, McGraw-Hill, 1958.
3. This definition clearly matches that put forward by Merton as the "role-set." See R. K. Merton "The Role-Set," *British Journal of Sociology*, June 1957.
4. Thus I am at present engaged in the task of "writing" a paper on the institutionalization of the patterns of health and illness in American society. The "technique" I have chosen for this task is manipulating the keyboard and other parts of a typewriter. This process clearly engages the hands and fingers, eyes, and other parts of the physical organism; internally above all, the brain. The physical result is the arrangement on a number of sheets of paper, previously blank, of a very large number of what we call linguistic symbols; letters arranged in words, sentences and paragraphs. I could have chosen alternative techniques, such as writing longhand with a pen, or possibly dictat-

ing to a machine. In these cases the physical result might well have been different. But in any case the "significance" of the task is only partly "physical," it lies more in the "meanings" of what has been physically "written." Finally, the task of writing this paper is only one rather clearly defined subsystem of my *role* as sociologist.
5. Referring to the writing task, a paralysis of both arms would obviously incapacitate me for writing this and other papers on the typewriter, and for all other manual tasks, but not necessarily for dictating them to a secretary.
6. This view of the relation of mind and body and in turn, their relations to the two great categories of health and disease with which we are here concerned, does not imply that all "somatic" phenomena can be analyzed as standing on one level. For various reasons it seems to me that at least one comparably basic distinction needs to be made within the organism, as defined above, namely, between the "behavioral" system and what might be called the "homeostatic" system (what Franz Alexander calls the "vegetative" system—cf. his *Psychosomatic Medicine: Its Principles and Applications*, W. W. Norton and Co., Inc., 1950). For present purposes, however, it is not necessary to go into these further refinements.
7. Cf. M. Zelditch, Jr., "Role Differentiation in the Nuclear Family," Chapter VI of Parsons and Bales, *Family, Socialization and Interaction Process*, Free Press, 1955.
8. For a general discussion of the significance of the incest taboo, cf. Talcott Parsons, "The Incest Taboo in Relation to Social Structure and the Socialization of the Child," *British Journal of Sociology*, Vol. V, (June 1954), pp. 101–117.
9. Cf. Talcott Parsons, "A Sociologist Looks at the Legal Profession," in *Essays in*

Sociological Theory, Revised Edition, Free Press, 1954.

10. C. I. Barnard, *The Functions of the Executive*, Harvard University Press, 1938.

11. An interesting case of difficulty with respect to the line of discrimination discussed above is presented by Mark Field in his study of Soviet medical practice, where pressure has been put on physicians, more than in our own system, to provide excuses for avoiding extremely onerous and rigorously enforced role-obligations. Cf. his *Doctor and Patient in Soviet Russia*, Harvard University Press, 1957.

12. This is a major thesis of Durkheim in *The Elementary Forms of the Religious Life*, Free Press, 1947.

13. Cf. Alex Inkeles, *Public Opinion in Soviet Russia*, Harvard University Press, 1950.

14. I have dealt with them primarily in the following places: *The Social System*, Chapter X, Free Press, 1951; the paper "Illness and the Role of the Physician," *American Journal of Orthopsychiatry*, July 1951, pp. 452–460, also printed in Kluckhohn, Murray and Schneider, *Personality, in Nature, Society and Culture*, 2nd Edition, Alfred A. Knopf, 1953, and in somewhat more specialized context in Parsons and Fox, "Illness, Therapy and the Modern Urban American Family," *Journal of Social Issues*, Vol. 8, pp. 31–44 (chapter 25 in this volume).

15. The latter does of course happen in hospital situations. It has been clearly shown (Cf. Ivan Belknap, *Human Problems of a State Mental Hospital*, McGraw-Hill Book Co., 1956, and Barbara Burt Arnason, unpublished Ph.D. Dissertation, Radcliffe College, 1958) that in mental hospital settings the social group of chronic patients, particularly in a kind of symbiosis with attendants, can, under certain circumstances, come to constitute a seriously *anti*-therapeutic social community.

16. In my own technical terms, it is a "pattern-maintenance" function.

17. Dr. R. N. Bellah, in an unpublished paper, has suggested the great importance of revivalist religion in the former of these contests.

18. Cf. Parsons and Fox, *op. cit.* for a further analysis of this problem.

19. Cf. *The Social System*, Free Press, 1951, Chapter VII, and R. K. Merton, *Social Theory and Social Structure*, Free Press, 1957, rev. ed., Chapter IV.

20. By the three criteria, then, of aliena-tion, passivity, and object-orientation, the pattern of illness should be considered a case of "compulsive independence" (*Social System, op. cit.*, p. 259). Compulsive independence in this case may be interpreted to involve reaction-formation against underlying dependency needs, as I shall note.

21. A fuller discussion of the nature of the "regression scale" will be found in *Family, Socialization and Interaction Process, op. cit.*, especially Chapter II.

22. In this light the motivation to illness may, with only apparent paradox, be characterized as a case of "compulsive independence from the requirement to be independent." It is a kind of "to hell with it all" pattern of withdrawal.

23. Unfortunately, there will be no opportunity in this paper to take up the empirical problem of how far the available data on illness bear out this interpretation of the central importance of the dependency-independency axis. Not only do I suggest that this is more important in the American case than in others but also that it applies to somatic as well as mental illness. The ulcer complex is widely believed to relate especially to this problem. It may also be suggested that the special concern with polio in America relates to our horror of the dependency which the permanent cripple must bear. Almost better death than not to be able to do one's part, but remain dependent on others.

24. Cf. *The Social System, op. cit.*, Chapter VII and Parsons, Bales and Shils, *Working Papers in the Theory of Action*, Chapter V. In earlier versions, what I am now calling selective rewarding was called "denial of reciprocity" (this term emphasized only the negative aspect) and what I now call reinforcement was called "manipulation of rewards." The new term for the latter emphasizes the continuity of a *pattern* of rewards over time.

25. In Parsons and Fox, *op. cit.*, it was suggested that the trend toward hospitalization, again in cases of both mental and somatic illness, was related to these factors. On the one hand, it is related to technological exigencies of modern medicine. Also it is a way of relieving the family of burdens of "care." But at the same time it is both a way of protecting the family from the patient, that is above all the impact of his dependency needs on other members, and the point of primary present importance, of protecting the patient from his family. The

family, that is to say, is very likely to be "over-protective" and over supportive. Because of the temptations of "seduction" of the patient into more or less permanent dependency, it lacks the basis of effective leverage which a more "impersonal" agency may be in a position to exert. Also, it was noted above, there is reason to believe that the acuteness of the dependency problem has been increasing with recent developments in family structure.

26. My most important sources on Soviet medicine are Field, *op. cit.*, and

R. A. Bauer, *The New Man in Soviet Psychology.* I am also indebted to Dr. Field for suggestions made in personal discussion which go beyond his book.

27. Cf. Bauer, *op. cit.*

28. The extent to which the ego as distinct from the id has come to be emphasized in American versions of psychoanalysis seems to fit with this interpretation.

29. Cf. *Social System, op. cit.* This is Merton's "ritualism."

30. On this point I am directly indebted to Dr. Field (personal discussion).

NOTES TO CHAPTER 21

1. Ackerknecht cites the case of a South American tribe in which *pinto* (dyschromic spirochetosis) is so common that those who have it are regarded as healthy, those who do not as ill. Ackerknecht, Erwin H., "The Role of Medical History in Medical Education," *Bulletin of the History of Medicine,* vol. 21, March–April, 1947, pp. 135–145.

For a discussion of illness as a social role see: Henderson, L. J., "The Physician and Patient as a Social System," *New England Journal of Medicine,* vol. 212, May 2, 1953, pp. 819–823; Parsons, Talcott, "Illness and the Role of the Physician," *American Journal of Orthopsychiatry,* vol. 21, July, 1951, pp. 452–460; Parsons, Talcott, "Social Structure and Dynamic Process: The Case of Modern Medical Practice" in *The Social System,* The Free Press, Glencoe, Ill., 1951, chap. 10; Parsons, Talcott, and Renée Fox, "Illness, Therapy and the Modern Urban American Family," *Journal of Social Issues,* vol. 8, no. 4, 1952, pp. 31–44 (chapter 25 in this volume.)

2. The distinction between these various types of lay practitioners is not always clear and the terms are sometimes used interchangeably. In general *parteras* are concerned with childbirth and associated illness conditions; *curanderas* and *médicas* devote themselves to what in Anglo culture is called internal medicine; *albolarias* and *brujas* represent, respectively, the benevolent and malevolent aspects of witchcraft.

3. Folk medicine, as the term is used here, is not identical with primitive medicine. Folk medicine, in any culture, consists of the beliefs, practices, and collective attitudes which are the common possession of all the people of that culture. See Saunders, Lyle, and Gordon Hewes, "Folk Medicine and Medical Practice," *Journal*

of Medical Education, vol. 28, September, 1953, pp. 43–46.

4. The differences between folk and "scientific" medicine are sharply illuminated in a discussion of "Medicine and Faith in Rural Rajasthan," by G. Morris Carstairs, in Paul, Benjamin, (Ed.). *Health, Culture, and Community,* Russell Sage Foundation, New York, 1955, Chapter 4.

5. The principal source of information on Mexican folk medicine has been the studies of George Foster and his associates in the Smithsonian Institute of Social Anthropology, particularly their mimeographed report, *A Cross-Cultural Analysis of a Technical Aid Program,* Smithsonian Institution, Washington, July 25, 1951. Other helpful studies dealing in whole or part with the folk medicine of Latin America are: Adams, Richard N., *Un analisis de las enfermendades y sus curaciones en una poblacion indigena de Guatemala,* Instituto de Nutricion de Centro America y Panama, Guatemala, October, 1951; Foster, George, "Relationship Between Spanish and Spanish-American Folk Medicine," *Journal of American Folklore,* vol. 66, July–September, 1953, pp. 201–217; Gillin, John, "Magical Fright," *Psychiatry,* vol. 2, no. 4, 1948, pp. 387–400; Idem. *The Culture of Security in San Carlos,* Middle American Research Institute, Publication 16, Tulane University, New Orleans, 1951; Redfield, Robert, *The Folk Culture of Yucatan,* University of Chicago Press, 1941; Simpson, Eyler N., *The Ejido: Mexico's Way Out,* University of North Carolina Press, Chapel Hill, 1937; Whetten, Nathan L., *Rural Mexico,* University of Chicago Press, 1948.

6. Redfield, Robert, *The Folk Culture of Yucatan,* University of Chicago Press, 1941, pp. 128–129. The concepts of 'hot' and 'cold' are not nearly so prevalent in the

Southwest as in Mexico and other Latin American countries.

7. The vast sums spent on laxatives and the ubiquity of advertising references to the desirability of achieving "regularity" are evidence that the concept of a "clean" interior is also an important component in Anglo folk medicine.

8. Notions about the importance of blood for health and the dangers of losing any considerable amounts of it may be important factors in the reluctance of Spanish-speaking people in parts of the Southwest to contribute to blood banks.

9. Injections of various kinds may be obtained from druggists or other sellers of medicines or from an *inyeccionista,* a person, usually female and with some minimal training in a health field such as nursing, who specializes in the giving of this type of service.

10. Simmons, Ozzie, *Anglo Americans and Mexican Americans in South Texas,* Ph.D. dissertation, Harvard University, 1951, p. 98.

11. Mead, Margaret, editor, *Cultural Patterns and Technical Change,* United Nations Educational, Scientific, and Cultural Organization, Paris, 1953, p. 247.

12. Extensive accounts of folk medical beliefs and practices of Mexican-Americans will be found in Dodson, Ruth, "Folk Curing Among the Mexicans," in *Tone the Bell Easy,* Texas Folklore Society, Publication 10, Southern Methodist University Press, Dallas, 1932, pp. 82–98; and Hudson, William M., editor, *The Healer of Los Olmos and Other Mexican Lore,* Texas Folklore Society, Publication 24, Southern Methodist University Press, Dallas, 1951.

13. Curtin, L. S. M., *Healing Herbs of the Upper Rio Grande,* Laboratory of Anthropology, Sante Fe, 1947. This fascinating book has been drawn upon as the source of much of the information presented herein on Spanish-American herbal lore. Other sources are Campa, Arthur L., "Some Herbs and Plants of Early California," *Western Folklore,* vol. 9, October, 1950, pp. 338–347; Hurt, Wesley, *Manzano: A Study of Community Disorganization,* Master's thesis, University of New Mexico, 1941; Bourke, John G., "Notes on the Language and Folk-Usage of the Rio Grande Valley," *Journal of American Folklore,* vol. 9, April-June, 1896, pp. 81–115; Moya, Benjamin S., *Superstitions and Beliefs Among the Spanish-Speaking People of New Mexico,* Master's thesis, University of New Mexico, 1940.

14. Curtin, L. S. M., *op. cit.,* p. 11.

15. van der Eerden, Sister Mary Lucia, *Maternity Care in a Spanish-American Community of New Mexico,* Catholic University of America, Anthropological Series 13, Catholic University of America Press, Washington, 1948.

16. When told that an eclipse was about to occur, a young Spanish-American married woman who was confined in a Denver hospital during 1953 requested a "pass key" to wear during the danger period.

17. It is easy to understand why the services of a *partera* might be preferred to those of more highly trained physicians and nurses. *Parteras* are known to be *simpatico,* or sympathetic, since they are themselves Spanish-speaking and understand the point of view and ways of thinking and feeling of the mother and her family. They are relatively inexpensive as compared with the costs of Anglo medical and hospital care. And they do not require that the patient leave familiar surroundings and go among strangers in what might become a period of crisis.

At the time of her study, Sister Mary Lucia found more than 50 *parteras* practicing in Taos County. None lived at Ranchos, but five were available in a nearby village and one, who owned an automobile, was able to come from Taos. No special qualifications were required for becoming a *partera,* but the job was regarded as highly responsible one requiring considerable knowledge and a willingness to work hard, long hours, and at inconvenient times. Most *parteras* began their profession at a fairly advanced age, after having had much experience in bearing children of their own.

The information available to *parteras* came mainly from three sources: other *parteras* who were the repository of village knowledge about childbirth; Anglo physicians, with some of whom a number of the *parteras* had a good working relationship; and the New Mexico State Department of Public Health, which has been seeking in a systematic and organized way to make the midwives more proficient. The process of acquiring information about their work is difficult for most of the *parteras* can read only Spanish or cannot read at all, and have reached the age where it is not easy to acquire new knowledge. Techniques must be memorized and retained in memory for use when needed.

For a number of years the State Department of Public Health has conducted a program for the training and supervision of midwives. The result has been a reduction in the number of practicing midwives, an increase in the competence of those who remain in the field, and the development of relations between physicians and midwives to the point where the latter feel free to refer cases in which labor is especially difficult or complications arise.

18. This is a highly generalized account, following the description as given by Sister Mary Lucia. Certainly today, and undoubtedly during the time about which she was writing, many local variations of each of these details exist and are followed by many families. In childbirth, as in the treatment of many diseases, the folk medicine of the Spanish-Americans was rich in alternative procedures.

19. Anglo physicians advise first of all that women be delivered in hospitals rather than homes. However, in northern New Mexico there are frequently many reasons why hospital delivery is either not possible or not preferred by the expectant mother and her family.

20. The catalogue of the Trinidad "laboratory" gives a long list of "yerbas and medicinales," priced at from 25 cents to $3.00, including (using the catalogue spelling) Raiz de Immortal, Yerba De El Manzo

Raiz, Chuchupaste, Gobernadora, Alusema, Flor de Mansanilla, Polello, Yerba Buena, Oregano, Valeriana, Alumbre, Romero, Gardenias, Yerba Mora, Culiantrillo, and Flor de Asufre Mexicano, as well as syrup of onions, green oil liniment, an eye wash made of "el manzo herb," and a preparation advertised as a cockroach chaser.

21. Samora, Julian, *The Acculturation of the Spanish-Speaking People of Fort Collins, Colorado, in Selected Culture Areas*, Master's thesis, Colorado Agricultural and Mechanical College, 1947, pp. 120–125. It should perhaps be pointed out that there is no problem of availability of Anglo medical care in Fort Collins.

22. Thomas, Howard E., and Florence Taylor, "Medical and Health Care," in *Migrant Farm Labor in Colorado: A Study of Migratory Families*, National Child Labor Committee, New York, 1951, chap. 4. Inasmuch as these were low-income families living in rural areas, both the availability and cost of Anglo medicine would be limiting factors.

23. *Ibid.*, p. 55.

24. *New Mexico Health Council News-Letter*, November, 1946.

25. Foster, George M., editor, *A Cross-Cultural Analysis of a Technical Aid Program*, p. 85.

NOTES TO CHAPTER 22

* This paper is based on a field study, supported by grant MH 255 of the National Institute of Mental Health: "Cultural and Psychiatric Factors in the Mental Health of the Hutterites." The writer is indebted to Robert J. Weil, M.D. of the Department of Psychiatry at Dalhousie University who interviewed and examined many Hutterite mothers and children. Drs. Bert Kaplan and Thomas F. A. Plaut were the psychological collaborators of the field study. Other members of staff were: Evelyn McPuroff Plaut, Helen Fay Eaton, William F. Pratt, Marvin Margolis and Miriam Straussburger Moss. Mrs. May Oyakawa prepared the manuscript for publication.

1. Bakwin, Harry, "Pure Maternal Overprotection," *Journal of Pediatrics*, Vol. XXXIII, No. 6, December 1938: 788–794.

2. Benedict, Ruth, "Child Rearing in Certain European Countries," *American Journal of Orthopsychiatry*, Vol. XIX, No. 2, 1949: 343–350.

3. Bossard, James H., *The Large Family*

System (Philadelphia, University of Pennsylvania Press) 1956.

4. Eaton, Joseph W., "Controlled Acculturation," *American Sociological Review*, Vol. 17, No. 3: 331–340.

5. Eaton, Joseph W. and Mayer, Albert J., *Man's Capacity to Reproduce*, (Glencoe, Illinois, The Free Press) 1954.

6. Eaton, Joseph W. in collaboration with Weil, Robert J., *Culture and Mental Disorders* (Glencoe, Illinois, The Free Press,) 1955.

7. Escalona, Sibylle, "A Commentary upon Some Recent Changes in Child Rearing Practices," *Child Development*, Vol. XX, No. 3, September 1949: 157–162.

8. *Genesis*, Chapter XI, Verse 1.

9. *Genesis*, Chapter III, Verse 15.

10. Gesell, A. and Ilg, Frances L., *Infant and Child Care in the Culture of Today* (New York, Harper and Brothers) 1943.

11. Holway, Amy R., "Early Self-Regulation of Infants and Later Behavior in

Play Interviews," *American Journal of Orthopsychiatry*, Vol. XIX, 1949: 612–623.

12. Jackson, Edith B., Olmsted, Richard W., Ford, Alan, Thomas, Herbert, and Hyder, Kate, "A Hospital Rooming-In Unit for Four Newborn Infants and their Mothers," *Pediatrics*, Vol. 1, No. 1, January 1948: 28–43.

13. D. B. Jelliffe, "Cultural Variations and the Practical Pediatrician," *The Journal of Pediatrics*, Vol. 49, No. 6, December 1956: 661–671; (Chapter 39 in this volume).

14. Kaplan, Bert and Plaut, Thomas F. A., *Personality in a Communal Society* (Lawrence, Kansas, The University of Kansas Publications) 1956.

15. Kluckhohn, Clyde, "Some Aspects of Navaho Infancy and Early Childhood," Editor, Roheim, G., *Psychoanalysis and the Social Sciences* (New York, International Universities Press, Vol. I, 1947) 85–86.

16. Leighton, Dorothea and Kluckhohn, Clyde, *Children of the People* (Cambridge, Harvard University Press, 1948): 24–26.

17. Mead, Margaret, Discussion of Ruth Benedict's article, "Child Rearing Practices in Certain European Countries," *American Journal of Orthopsychiatry*, Vol. XIX, No. 2, 1949: 349.

18. Moore, Wilbert E. and Tumin, Melvin M., "Some Social Functions of Ignorance," *American Sociological Review*, Vol. 14, No. 6, 1949: 787–795.

19. This useful concept was first brought to the writer's attention by John C. Montgomery, M.D., a pediatrician who helped to found the *Cornelian Corner* at Detroit. He used it to describe certain patients who are emotionally and culturally unable to accept some of the permissive infant care practices which he generally advocates. Some mothers are so compulsive in carrying out his advice and ignore their own personal and social needs to such an extreme extent, that their efforts to be permissive make them anxious, nervous and sub-consciously resentful. These attitudes, when transmitted to the infant, upset him. Such mothers have to be advised to become more permissive towards their own needs.

20. Orlansky, Harold, "Infant Care and Personality," *Psychological Bulletin*, Vol. 46, No. 1, January 1949: 1–48.

21. Rideman, Peter, *Rechenschaft Unserer Religion Lehr und Glaubens, von don Bruedern, So Man die Hutterischen Nennt*. Issued in 1565, newly printed in 1938, Publishing House of the Hutterite Brethren in U.S.A., Canada and England. Cotswold Bruderhoff, Ashton, Keynes, Wiltshire, England: 103. Translation by the writer.

22. Romine, Elizabeth, Montgomery, John C., Walser, Howard, "Adapting Rooming-In Maternity Plan to Physical Plant of Hospital," *Hospital Management*, Vol. 64, No. 3, September 1947: 36–39.

23. Sperling, Melitta, "The Role of Mothers in Psychosomatic Disorders in Children," *Psychosomatic Medicine*, December 1949, Vol. 11, No. 6: 377.

24. Spock, Benjamin, *Baby and Child Care* (New York, Pocket Books, Inc., Rockefeller Center, 1946): 32.

25. Standler, Celia B., "Sixty Years of Child Training Practices," *Journal of Pediatrics*, Vol. 36, No. 1, January 1950: 122–134.

26. Whiting, John W. M. and Child, Irvin L., *Child Training and Personality: A Cross-Cultural Study* (New Haven, Yale University Press, 1953): 330–337, include a list of ethnographic studies of 75 nonliterate cultures in America and in other continents used in their comparative survey of child-rearing.

27. U.S. Children's Bureau, *Infant Care*, Washington, U.S. Government Printing Office, 1956: 11.

28. Zieglschmid, A. J. F., *Das Kleingeschichtsbuch der Hutterischen Brueder*, Philadelphia, The Carl Schurz Memorial Foundation, 1947: 404–405. Translation by the writer.

NOTES TO CHAPTER 23

1. These findings are reported in more detail in a paper in preparation titled "Level of Medical Information among Clinic Patients" by Arthur Seligmann, Neva McGrath and Lois Pratt.

2. An average of 1.4 requests for information per visit, 0.5 requests for action, and 2.7 statements to direct the physician's attention or to volunteer information.

3. Our findings on this problem are discussed in more detail in a paper by George Reader, Lois Pratt and Margaret Mudd, titled "Patients' Expectations of Medical Care," read at the American Public Health

Association Meetings on November 14, 1956, in the Section on The Role of the Out Patient Department.

4. Harry F. Dowling, M.D. and David Shakow, Ph.D., "Time Spent by Internists on Adult Health Education and Preventive Medicine," *Journal of the A.M.A.*, June 14, 1952, Vol. 149, pp. 628–631.

5. From a study now in progress at the Bureau of Applied Social Research of Columbia University, by David Caplowitz.

6. The first measure is based on the questionnaire study of 89 physicians, and the second on observation of 50 patient-physician relationships.

7. Too few physicians overestimated patients' knowledge to analyze this group separately.

8. Both junior physicians and attending physicians were observed. While certain differences were found in the explanations given by these two groups of physicians, the patterns to be reported below apply to both groups.

9. "Patients' Medical Care Expectations as Influenced by Patient-Physician Interaction," by Lois Pratt & Margaret Mudd, Cornell Medical College. Paper read at American Sociological Society Meetings, September 7, 1956.

NOTES TO CHAPTER 24

1. There has been very little careful bacteriological investigation of possible transmission of TB in such "life situations." What has been done suggests that the tubercle bacilli are unlikely to be transmitted under the circumstances described.

2. In Illinois, where there is no such law, public libraries freely lend books to TB hospital patients.

3. Professor Everett C. Hughes pointed out to me the implications of the use of the same word "law" for both the regularities of nature and the rules of conduct made by man.

NOTES TO CHAPTER 25

1. This general approach to the sociology of the two types of roles and the therapeutic process as a process of social interaction will be found most fully set forth in T. Parsons' *The Social System* (Glencoe, Illinois: The Free Press, 1951), Chaps. VII & X, and in his article "Illness and the Role of the Physician," *The American Journal of Orthopsychiatry*, July, 1951. Certain further developments are analyzed in T. Parsons, F. Bales, & E. Shils, *Working Papers in the Theory of Action* (Glencoe, Illinois: The Free Press, 1953), Chap, V. Sec. VII.

2. In our submitted draft of this paper, we placed considerably more emphasis upon psychological mechanisms than this final version incorporates. All of our major social structural arguments were complemented by their psychologically-phrased equivalents. Space was limited, however, and so it became necessary to omit some of our more "psychologistic" points. We hope that such deletions in no way impair our foremost intent, which is to show how the simultaneous use of psychological and sociological theory can serve to illuminate a given problem area.

3. For a grounding of this classification of types of deviant orientation see T. Parsons, *The Social System*, Chap. VII, and R. K. Merton, "Social Structure and Ano-

mie," Chap. III of *Social Theory and Social Structure* (Glencoe, Ill.: The Free Press, 1949).

4. Cf. "Sources and Patterns of Aggression in the Social Structure of the Western World," in Parsons, *Essays in Sociological Theory*, (Glencoe, Ill.: The Free Press, 1949), Chap. XII.

5. As we will point out in a later section of this article, despite the paring down process which our family system has undergone, its residual functions as primary socializer, social control agent, and emotional bulwark, are so crucial that the over-all importance of kinship in our society has not diminished. Indeed, as Robin Williams phrases it in his study of *American Society*, though "the scope of family activities has narrowed, the emotional significance of the surviving relationships has, in one sense, increased" (p. 77).

A brief analysis of these features of the American family will be found in Parsons, Bales, and Shils, *Working Papers in the Theory of Action*, Chap. V, Sec. viii.

6. We know how important (particularly at the Oedipal period) the significance of the parental marriage solidarity is to children, and how sensitive they are to a feeling of being excluded.

7. It must not be forgotten that the sick

role has a *positive* function in American society. There is much reason to believe that illness is less harmful to the society than other forms of deviant behavior—for example, crime and some types of political involvement. For, sickness not only exposes the actor to the counteractive therapy of the doctor and his adjuncts, but (with the important exception of "magic-mountain-like" communities of the chronically ill) illness usually prevents the individual from attaching himself to a solidary subculture of similarly-oriented deviants. Thus, the inability of the family to tolerate the illness of its members runs counter to a social need to increase, rather than decrease, the relative amount of illness. This is not to say that illness is positively valued in our culture. It is merely to point out that there is pressure to divert unavoidable deviant motivation from other channels into this one—with a net functional gain for the society. (The situation is analogous to the positive function of the national debt. From the point of view of private finance, debt is undesirable; but from the point of view of economy as a whole, it has certain positive function.) On this aspect of illness, cf. Parsons, *The Social System*, Chaps. VII and X.

8. The discomforts of the double-dependency characteristic of the patient role, would undoubtedly be experienced more acutely by an activistically-oriented personality type, for example, than by a more compliantly-organized individual. We are assuming, however, that even in the case of motivated illness, wherein the acquiescence is "chosen" by the actor, this choice is always an ambivalent one; and thus, the difficulties experienced by the patient-initiate though perhaps milder in degree, will be qualitatively the same.

9. In outlining the components of therapy, we are assuming that not only the psychiatrist's role, but the role of the physician in the more general sense, is psychotherapeutic. Indeed, it is clear that "the basic structuring of the physician's role in our society did not come about through the application of theories of the ideal situation

for psychotherapy. It was a sponstaneous, unplanned development of social structure which psychiatry was able to utilize and develop . . ." (Parsons, *Social System*, p. 462.)

10. In the latter type of case, an as yet unpublished field study by the junior author of this paper of a hospital ward comprised of patients ill with chronic, progressively debilitating diseases, demonstrates this phenomenon clearly.

11. To reiterate an earlier point: the fact that the patient is a partially socialized adult, whose tolerance of dependence has upper limits is relevant here, too. What is more, the sick actor's difficulties in accepting the passive-dependent obligations of the patient role is one of the best pieces of evidence we know for correcting the common tendency to regard the child and sick person as psychologically identical.

12. Cf. Levy, D. M., *Maternal Over-Protection* (New York: Columbia University Press, 1943).

13. The role of the physician, however, is more closely analogous to the father role than to that of the mother. In this special sense, mother, father, and therapist may be said to vary over a continuous range: with the mother giving the highest level of permissiveness and support; the physician, the greatest incentive to acceptance of discipline.

14. It is not easy, of course, for the hospital staff—with its bureaucratic structuring and its multiple technical responsibilities to large groups of patients—to provide such personalized care. In this respect it resembles the school more than the family.

15. Even so, the restoration of the actor to his kinship unit, to his job, and to his other non-sick orbits, is usually problem-laden. For one thing, we have already shown that at this juncture we encounter the well-known phenomenon of secondary gain; a possible consequence if the transference relationship of patient and physician, and the supportive-exemptive features of illness are not adequately controlled.

NOTES TO CHAPTER 26

1. Barker, R. G., *et al.*, "Social psychology of acute illness," in *Adjustment to Physical Handicap and Illness* (rev. ed.). New York: Social Science Research Council, 1953.

2. Binger, C. *The Doctor's Job*. New York: Norton, 1945.

3. Upham, Frances. *A Dynamic Approach to Illness*. New York: Family Service Association of America, 1949.

4. Mann, Thomas, *The Magic Mountain*. New York: Knopf, 1945.
5. Barker, *et. al., op. cit.*
6. Upham, *op. cit.*
7. Barker, *et. al., op. cit.*
8. Levine, M., *Psychotherapy in Medical Practice*. N.Y.: Macmillan, 1942.
9. *Ibid.*
10. Conference on Convalescent Care, New York Academy of Medicine, 1940.
11. Barker, *et. al., op. cit.*
12. Lamb, Charles, *Essays*. New York: Viking, 1949.
13. Barracough, W., "Mental reactions of normal children to physical illness," *American Journal of Psychiatry*, 1937, 93.
14. Ferenezi, S., "Disease or Pathoneurosis," in *Further Contributions to the* *Theory and Technique of Psychoanalysis*. London: Hogarth, 1926.
15. Romano, J., "Emotional components of illness," *Connecticut State Medical Journal*, 1943, 7.
16. Barker, *et. al., op. cit.*
17. Lamb, *op. cit.*
18. Unpublished data from studies in progress, Department of Psychiatry, College of Medicine, University of Cincinnati.
19. Watson-Jones, R. "Rehabilitation in the Royal Air Force," *British Medical Journal*, 1942, 1, 403–407; Wilson, E. H., "Rehabilitation in war-time Britain," *Archives of Surgery*, 1943, 46; and Thorndike, A., "Convalescent reconditioning," *American Medical Association Journal*, 1944, 126.

NOTES TO CHAPTER 27

1. This paper is based upon material collected as part of the study "Cultural Components in Attitudes toward Pain," under a grant of the U.S. Public Health Service.
2. James D. Hardy, Harold G. Wolff, and Helen Goodell, *Pain Sensations and Reactions*. Baltimore: Williams and Wilkins Company, 1952, p. 23.
3. *Ibid.*, p. 204.
4. *Ibid.*, p. 262.
5. I should like to take the opportunity to express my appreciation to Dr. Harold G. Wolff, Professor of Neurology, Cornell University Medical College, Dr. Hinland

Flowers, Chief of Neuropsychiatric Service, Dr. Robert Morrow, Chief of Clinical Psychology Section, Dr. Louis Berlin, Chief of Neurology Section, and the Management of the hospital for their cooperation in the setting up of the research at the Kingsbridge Veterans Hospital.
6. Italian respondents are mainly of South Italian origin; the Jewish respondents, with one exception, are all of East European origin. Whenever the Jews are mentioned they are spoken of in terms of the culture they represent and not in terms of their religion.

NOTES TO CHAPTER 28

* Coordinator of an interdisciplinary project entitled "Psychological and Sociological Aspects of Facial Deformities and Plastic Surgery" which is being carried on under the Departments of Psychiatry and Surgery at New York University College of Medicine. This study is supported by a grant from the National Institute of Mental Health, U.S. Public Health Service.
1. For extensive bibliography of studies on these subjects see R. G. Baker, B. A. Wright, and M. R. Gonick, *Adjustment to Physical Handicap and Illness: A Survey of the Social Psychology of Physique and Disability*, Social Science Research Council, Bulletin 55, New York, 1946.
2. Gustav Ichheiser, "Misunderstandings in Human Relationships," *American Journal of Sociology*, 55 (September, 1949), 19.

3. For example, Otto Klineberg, *Social Psychology*, New York: Henry Holt & Co., 1940, pp. 374–399; Gustav Ichheiser, "Sociopsychological and Cultural Factors in Race Relations," *American Journal of Sociology*, 54 (March 1949), 395.
4. Even those with scientific training are sometimes influenced by a deeply entrenched emotional quality which obscures their intellectual objectivity. For example, an anthropologist told of interviewing an American Indian who had a facial paralysis; and while he recognized the affliction for what it was, he couldn't overcome his feeling that she was not "quite on the square" because of her distorted mouth. A social worker attached to a child adoption center was heard to ask, "Harelips are really due to congenital syphilis, aren't they?"
5. Hadley Cantril, "The Nature of So-

cial Perception," *Transactions of the New York Academy of Sciences*, Ser. II, Vol. 10, February, 1948, p. 148.

6. Study of clinic patients was made possible from 1947–48 by a research fellowship from the Manhattan Eye, Ear and Throat Hospital, New York City. The opportunity to interview private patients was made possible through the generous cooperation of Dr. John Marquis Converse.

An exploratory study prior to the above was made in 1946–47, the results of which are incorporated in "The Sociological Aspects of Facial Deformities," Master's Thesis (unpublished), University of Missouri, 1947.

7. The classification "cultural" has been employed by the author to define those cases in which plastic surgery is requested for the purpose of changing an inherited physical trait, usually the nose, which identifies the individual as a member of a particular ethnic or cultural group. When the

deviation is due to a congenital malformation or familial trait, but plastic surgery is requested because the possessor feels the feature identifies him with a group to which he does not belong, the cases are also classified under the heading of "cultural."

8. George H. Mead, *Mind, Self, and Society*, Part III, Chicago: University of Chicago Press, 1934.

9. Another patient, a girl of 21 with a similar deformity, said she noticed that people looked over her shoulder when they talked to her. "This makes me self-conscious. It's as though they didn't want to look directly at me. They think if they do that I'll be embarrassed so they think they're doing me a favor by looking over my shoulder. I'd rather have them look at me—my eyes—back and forth, yet not stare." She complained that children mimicked her expressions and made funny faces—especially when she was in school and attempting to recite.

NOTES TO CHAPTER 31

1. Oswald Hall, "The Informal Organization of Medical Practice in an American City" (unpublished Ph.D. thesis, University of Chicago, 1944).

2. M. Leven, *The Incomes of Physicians* ("Publications of the Committee on

the Costs of Medical Care," No. 24, Chicago: University of Chicago Press, 1932).

3. Oswald Hall, "The Informal Organization of the Medical Profession," *Canadian Journal of Economics and Political Science*, XII (February, 1946), 30–44.

NOTES TO CHAPTER 32

1. Leonard D. Eron, "Effect of Medical Education on Medical Students," *Journal of Medical Education*, 10 (October, 1955), 559–566.

2. This study is sponsored by Community Studies, Inc., of Kansas City, Missouri, and is being carried on at the University of Kansas Medical School, to whose dean, staff, and students we are indebted for their wholehearted cooperation. Professor Everett C. Hughes of the University of Chicago is director of the project.

3. The technique of participant observation has not been fully systematized, but some approaches to this have been made. See, for example, Florence R. Kluckhohn, "The Participant Observer Technique in Small Communities," *American Journal of Sociology*, 45 (November, 1940), 331–343; Arthur Vidich, "Participant Observation and the Collection and Interpretation of Data," *ibid.*, 60 (January, 1955), 354–360; William Foote Whyte, "Observational Field-Work Methods," in Maria Jahoda,

Morton Deutsch, and Stuart W. Cook (eds.), *Research Methods in the Social Sciences* (New York: Dryden Press, 1951), II, 393–514, and *Street Corner Society* (Enlarged Edition) (Chicago: University of Chicago Press, 1955), 279–358; Rosalie Hankey Wax, "Twelve Years Later: An Analysis of Field Experience," *American Journal of Sociology*, 63 (Sept. 1957), 133–42; Morris S. Schwartz and Charlotte Green Schwartz, "Problems in Participant Observation," *ibid.*, 60 (January, 1955), 343–353; and Howard S. Becker and Blanche Geer, "Participant Observation and Interviewing: A Comparison," *Human Organization* (forthcoming). The last item represents the first of a projected series of papers attempting to make explicit the operations involved in this method. For a short description of some techniques used in this study, see Howard S. Becker, "Interviewing Medical Students," *American Journal of Sociology*, 62 (September, 1956), 199–201.

4. A fuller analysis and presentation of evidence will be contained in a volume on this study now being prepared by the authors in collaboration with Everett C. Hughes and Anselm L. Strauss.

5. Renée Fox has shown how complex one aspect of this whole subject is in her analysis of the way medical students at Cornell become aware of and adjust to both their own failure to master all available knowledge and the gaps in current knowledge in many fields. See her "Training for Uncertainty," in Robert K. Merton, George G. Reader, M.D., and Patricia L. Kendall, *The Student Physician: Introductory Studies in the Sociology of Medical Education* (Cambridge: Harvard University Press, 1957), 207–241.

6. Compare Fox' description of student reaction to this problem at Cornell, (*op. cit.*, 209–221).

7. The concept of student culture is analyzed in some detail in Howard S. Becker and Blanche Geer, "Student Culture in Medical School," *Harvard Educational Review*, Winter, 1957.

8. Dana L. Farnsworth, "Some Observations on The Attitudes and Motivations of the Harvard Medical Student," *Harvard Medical Alumni Bulletin*, January, 1956, p. 34.

9. See the discussion in Howard S. Becker, "Interviewing Medical Students," *op. cit.*

10. See Philip Selznick's related discussion of fanaticism in *TVA and the Grass Roots* (Berkeley: University of California Press, 1953), pp. 205–213.

11. George Orwell gives the layman's side in his essay, "How the Poor Die," in *Shooting an Elephant and Other Essays* (London: Secker and Warburg, 1950), 18–32.

NOTES TO CHAPTER 33

1. Roberts, David: "Psychotherapy and a Christian View of Man," p. 110.

2. Based on the conclusions of Cole, Wm.: "Sex in Christianity and Psychoanalysis" and Hiltner, Seward: "Sex Ethics and the Kinsey Reports."

NOTES TO CHAPTER 34

1. A statement written by a second year medical student in an Eastern medical college, based upon a continuing study of the Sociology of medical education conducted by the Bureau of Applied Social Research of Columbia University under a grant from the Commonwealth Fund.

2. Robert K. Merton, "Some Preliminaries to a Sociology of Medical Education," in Robert K. Merton, George Reader, and Patricia L. Kendall (eds.) *The Student-Physician*; Harvard University Press (for the Commonwealth Fund) Cambridge, Mass., 1957, pp. 40–42, 287–293.

3. Arthur K. Davis, "Bureaucratic Patterns in the Navy Officer Corps," *Social Forces*, 27:143–153 (Dec. 1948).

4. George Packer Berry, "Medical Education in Transition," *J. of Med Education*, Vol. 28, 17–42 (March, 1953).

5. *Ibid.*, p. 17.

6. Robert K. Merton, et al.. "Studies in the Sociology of Medical Education," *J. of Med. Ed.*, 31:552–565, Aug., 1956.

7. See Merton, *op. cit.*, 125–126.

8. Abraham Flexner, *Medical Education in the United States and Canada: A Report to the Carnegie Foundation for the*

Advancement of Teaching, Bulletin No. 4, New York, 1910, p. 20.

9. *Ibid.*, pp. 21–22.

10. Dr. John Rose, Child Psychiatrist at The University of Pennsylvania Childrens Hospital, in an unpublished address to first year medical students, 1954.

11. Dr. Isaac Starr, Professor of Therapeutics, University of Pennsylvania School of Medicine, in an unpublished address to first year students, 1954.

12. *Op. cit.*, p. 20.

13. L. J. Henderson, "The Patient and Physician as a Social System," *New England Journal of Medicine*, 212:819–823, 1935.

14. Kenneth E. Appel, John McK. Mitchell, and William T. Lhamon, "Psychiatric Values in a New Method of Medical Education," *Am. J. of Psychiatry*, 109 (2):102–107, August, 1952.

15. Edward O'Neill Harper, "An Experiment in Medical Education," *Medical Social Work*, Vol. 2, No. 4, (Oct., 1953), pp. 125–126.

16. See Edward Stainbrook and Murray Wexler, "The Place of the Behavioral Sciences in the Medical School," *Psychiatry*,

Vol. 19, No. 3, 263–269, August, 1956.

17. Based upon a continuing study by the Bureau of Applied Social Research, *op. cit.*

18. See *A Proposal for Continuation of a Sociological Study of Medical Schools,* addressed to The Commonwealth Fund, by the Bureau of Applied Social Research,

Columbia University, June, 1954, pp. 36–39.

19. Howard S. Becker, in his study of a Midwestern school of medicine, has reported that students call such information "pearls", and keep score cards which rate the "pearl-value" of lectures.

20. Cited in Flexner, *op. cit.*, p. 4.

NOTES TO CHAPTER 35

1. The extended papers reported here in condensed form appear in *The Student Physician* edited by Robert K. Merton, George G. Reader, M.D. and Patricia L. Kendall (Cambridge: Harvard University Press, 1957); copyright 1957 by Harvard University Press. We are indebted to the Syndics of the Harvard University Press and to the Commonwealth Fund for permission to publish extracts from that volume; the authors of the papers are indicated at the beginning of each extract.

2. For a recent short overview, see Ernest O. Smigel, "Trends in Occupational Sociology in the United States: A Survey of Postwar Research." *American Sociological Review,* 19:398–404, August, 1954; see also Theodore Caplow, *The Sociology of Work* (Minneapolis: University of Minnesota Press, 1954).

3. Robert E. Park did much to initiate the sociological study of occupations at the University of Chicago in the 1920's. This was developed further by his colleague, Everett C. Hughes, who turned his attention in part to studies of professions. At Harvard University, Talcott Parsons contributed theoretical formulations which did much to enlarge interest in the sociological study of the professions. And during the past decade, studies in this field have been carried forward at Columbia University.

4. The work of the Seminar was greatly facilitated by a grant from the Russell Sage Foundation. A volume based on the proceedings of the Seminar is nearing completion: William J. Goode, Robert K. Merton, and Mary Jean Huntington, *The Professions in American Society.*

5. For a recent account of this convergence of interest, see Leo W. Simmons and Harold G. Wolff, *Social Science in Medicine* (New York: Russell Sage Foundation, 1954). The Health Information Foundation has been issuing an inventory of *Social and Economic Research in Health* which bears witness to a growing volume of sociological research in this field, year by year.

6. This census was carried out by Robert Straus.

7. This new phase in the empirical study of organization was largely generated by the work of Elton Mayo and his associates of the Harvard Business School. See, for example, Elton Mayo, *The Human Problems of an Industrial Civilization* (New York: The Macmillan Company, 1933), and for the major report on these studies, Fritz J. Roethlisberger and William Dickson, *Management and the Worker* (Cambridge, Mass.: Harvard University Press, 1939). The accumulation of subsequent studies is by now considerable; for critical reviews of these, see George C. Homans, *The Human Group* (New York: Harcourt, Brace and Company, 1950); William Foote Whyte, "Small Groups and Large Organizations," and Conrad M. Arensberg, "Behavior and Organization: Industrial Studies," in: John H. Rohrer and Muzafer Sherif, eds., *Social Psychology at the Crossroads* (New York: Harper and Brothers, 1951). For theoretical statements, see Talcott Parsons, "Sociological Approach to the Theory of Organization," *Administrative Science Quarterly,* June and September, 1956; Herbert A. Simon, *Administrative Behavior* (New York: The Macmillan Company, 1947).

8. Again, only a few among these many studies can be cited here: Philip Selznick, *TVA and the Grass Roots* (Berkeley: University of California Press, 1949); Alvin W. Gouldner, *Patterns of Industrial Bureaucracy* (Glencoe, Ill.: The Free Press, 1954); Peter M. Blau, *The Dynamics of Bureaucracy* (Glencoe, Ill.: The Free Press, 1955); S. M. Lipset, M. Trow, and J. Coleman, *Union Democracy* (Glencoe, Ill.: The Free Press, 1956); R. G. Francis and R. C. Stone, *Service and Procedure in Bureaucracy* (Minneapolis: University of Minnesota Press, 1956); A. H. Stanton and M. S. Schwartz, *The Mental Hospital: A Study of Institutional Participation in Psychiatric Illness and Treatment* (New York: Basic

Books, Inc., 1954). (In view of the greatly differing connotations of "bureaucracy" apparently current in medical and in sociological circles, it should be remarked that for the social scientist, "bureaucracy" is a technical term designating a formal, hierarchic organization of statuses, each with its sphere of competence and responsibility. In the social science vocabulary of organization, "bureaucracy" is not pejorative.)

9. It is advisable to acknowledge the historical fact that the word "socialization" has quite a different and longstanding connotation in medical circles. This fact cannot be exorcized; it must, instead, be taken into account if we are not to become needlessly involved in semantic confusions and controversies. With this in mind, Appendix A of *The Student-Physician* contains a detailed terminological note on the concept of socialization.

10. Talcott Parsons, *The Social System* (Glencoe, Ill.: The Free Press, 1951), Chapter VI and, in particular, the remarks on adult socialization on pp. 207–208; John Dollard, "Culture, Society, Impulse, and Socialization," *Am. J. of Sociol.*, 45:50–63, 1939; Irwin L. Child, "Socialization," in: Gardner Lindzey, ed., *Handbook of Social Psychology* (Cambridge, Mass.: Addison-Wesley Publishing Company, 1954) which includes an extensive bibliography.

11. Among these, see William J. Goode and Paul K. Hatt, *Methods in Social Research* (New York: McGraw-Hill Book Company, 1952); Paul F. Lazarsfeld and Morris Rosenberg, eds., *The Language of Social Research: A Reader in the Methodology of Social Research* (Glencoe, Ill.: The Free Press, 1955); Leon Festinger and Daniel Katz, eds., *Research Methods in the Behavioral Sciences* (New York: The Dryden Press, 1953); Marie Jahoda, Morton Deutsch, and Stuart W. Cook, *Research Methods in Social Relations* (New York: The Dryden Press, 1951), 2 volumes; John Madge, *The Tools of Social Science* (London: Longmans, Green and Company, 1953). For comparison with how matters stood a generation ago see Sidney and Beatrice Webb, *Methods of Social Study* (London: Longmans, Green and Company, 1932).

12. The data reported here were obtained from questionnaires administered to three succesive classes of students just prior to their entrance into the School of Medicine of the University of Pennsylvania.

13. Thereby setting distinct limits to the generalizability of these results; we know nothing about "those who got away," who, at one age or another, had considerd a career in medicine but ultimately took up some other occupation. A more comprehensive study of the matter would require cohort- or panel-analysis in which a representative sample of young people would be studied through successive years to learn how they made occupational decisions, abandoned them or put them into effect. Only so can we have a thoroughly-grounded basis for conclusions about the process of decision. The data for medical students do, however, allow us to formulate some problems and hypotheses concerning the choice of medicine as a professional career.

14. The evidence for these conclusions is found in Figures 5 and 6 in *The Student-Physician*.

15. The information about medical students reported here was obtained from questionnaires administered to the entire student body enrolled at the University of Pennsylvania School of Medicine in the fall of 1953. The information about law students was obtained from a comparable questionnaire administered to the class entering an Eastern law school at the same time.

16. It should be noted that more law entrants than medical entrants (19 percent compared with 4 percent) were professional option students, entering professional school after completing three years of undergraduate study. However, this factor does not affect the time of decision: among the law entrants, 64 percent of those on professional option had decided within the last 2 years, compared with 65 percent of the remainder.

17. Included as relatives: father, mother, step-parent, brother, sister, grandparent, uncle, aunt, cousin, spouse, and father-, mother-, brother-, and sister-in-law.

18. In discussing the differences found between the law and medical groups, this paper offers explanations which are in the main only indirectly supported by statistical evidence. Without further study, for instance, no data are available to provide a table showing the extent to which greater contact of medical students with their profession accounts for their generally earlier decision.

19. Cecil C. North and Paul K. Hatt, "Jobs and Occupations: A Popular Evaluation." Reprinted, in part, in: Logan Wilson and William L. Kolb, *Sociological Analysis*

(New York: Harcourt, Brace and Company, 1949), pp. 464–473.

20. This section is based on materials collected at Cornell University Medical College. It employs several different kinds of data. The basic findings are panel results obtained from questionnaires administered to all Cornell students in the spring of 1952 and a year later, in 1953. In addition, however, we have drawn on the observations of our field workers, on journals kept by a small number of students at different stages of training, and on documentary records of the internship assignments received by two classes of graduating students.

21. This pattern turns up repeatedly in our own data. Furthermore, it is found in the data collected by the Association of American Medical Colleges from a representative sample of medical students in 81 medical schools in the United States and Canada. (This study, carried out in the spring of 1957 under the direction of Dr. Helen Gee, provided background information for the 1957 Institute on the Ecology of the Medical Student. The proceedings of the Institute will be published in the fall of 1958).

22. John E. Deitrick and Robert C. Berson, *Medical Schools in the United States at Mid-Century* (New York: McGraw-Hill Book Company, 1953), pp. 276–277 and passim.

23. The question on internship choices was not asked of the graduating students, for they had already received their internship assignments.

24. As a matter of fact, of the factors which we have investigated, stage of training stands almost alone as an important determinant of internship plans. As we shall see later, for example, the students' cumulative grades have no discernible influence on the preferences which they express: good students are no more likely than less capable ones to say that they hope to obtain specialized internships.

25. The same result is found when we examine the first- and second-year classes. Among those students too there is no consistent relationship between the internship preferences which they express and the grades which they have received in medical school.

26. One important question is the extent to which the findings reported in this paper would be duplicated in another kind of medical school, one for example, which considers its primary objective to be to turn out well-trained general practitioners.

27. The findings reported here are based on information obtained from two successive classes of first-year students at Western Reserve School of Medicine, just before they began their studies and again at the end of their first year.

28. These self-images were reported in response to the question, "In the most recent dealings you have had with patients, how have you tended to think of yourself, primarily as a doctor rather than as a student, or primarily as a student rather than as a doctor?

29. The term, "definition of the situation," first introduced by William I. Thomas and Florian Znaniecki in *The Polish Peasant in Europe and America* (Boston: Richard G. Badger, 1918), Vol. 1, pp. 68–69, refers to the individual's prior conception of, and attitudes toward, a given situation that influence his behavior when he meets that situation.

30. The statistical findings reported here are based on the questionnaire responses of several classes of fourth-year students: two successive classes in the School of Medicine at the University of Pennsylvania; two at Cornell Medical College; and one in the Western Reserve School of Medicine. In addition, the analysis draws on the diary of a fourth-year student at Cornell.

31. Doris Schwartz, "The Use of Nursing Care Plans with a Group of Fifty Non-Conformist Clinic Patients," Cornell University Medical College, Comprehensive Care and Teaching Program Research Memorandum No. 2, Series B, December 1955. The definitions of uncooperative behavior given above are responses by medical personnel to the questions, "If the term 'uncooperative patient' is used in this clinic, of whom do you think? Why do you consider them uncooperative?"

32. Students were asked whether they agreed or disagreed with the following statement: "I sometimes became very irritated with patients who were uncooperative."

33. This study is based on qualitative data: unless otherwise indicated, all quoted phrases and passages draw upon the diaries kept by 11 Cornell students at various stages of training, interviews conducted with these student-diarists and some of their classmates, and observations of selected situations in the school.

34. Limitations of space restrict this account to the preclinical phases of the process of learning to recognize and to cope with uncertainty.

35. Cf. "The Autopsy: Its Place in the Attitude-Learning of Second-Year Medical Students," by Renée C. Fox, to be published in a forthcoming volume containing further studies in the sociology of medical education.

NOTES TO CHAPTER 36

1. Quoted by William Osler in *An Alabama Student* (New York, Oxford University Press, 1908), p. 29.

2. Quoted by Wyndham B. Blanton in *Medicine in Virginia in the Eighteenth Century* (Richmond, Garrett and Massie, 1931), p. 13.

3. James E. Lebensohn, "Ophthalmology in Illinois, 1840–1940," *Illinois Medical Journal* (May, 1940), vol. 77, pp. 481–482.

4. Quoted by Lebensohn, *ibid.,* p. 482.

5. S. Weir Mitchell, "The History of Instrumental Precision in Medicine," *University Medical Magazine* (Philadelphia, October, 1891), vol. 4, p. 1.

6. Quoted by Lebensohn, *op. cit.,* p. 495.

7. American Medical Association, "Report of the Committee on Specialties, and on the Propriety of Specialist Advertising," *Transactions of the American Medical Association* (1869), vol. 20, pp. 111–113.

8. Frank Billings, "The Future of Private Medical Practice," *Journal of the American Medical Association* (February 5, 1921), vol. 77, pp. 349–354; *idem.,* "The Resourceful General Practitioner of Modern Practice" (February 24, 1923), vol. 80, pp. 519–524; Frank B. Wynn, "The Triumphs and Dangers of Specialism," *Journal of the Indiana State Medical Association* (October, 1920), vol. 13, pp. 338–343; *idem,* "The General Practitioner" (November, 1920), vol. 13, pp. 365–371; Robert T. Noble, "Address of the President, Academy of Medicine, Toronto," *Canadian Journal of Medicine and Surgery* (1921), vol. 50, pp. 113–118; George Rosen, "Changing Attitudes of the Medical Profession to Specialization," *Bulletin of the History of Medicine* (July 1942), vol. 12, No. 2, pp. 343–354.

9. For an analysis of the roots of similar opposition to innovations in other fields see Bernhard J. Stern, "Resistances to the Adoption of Technological Innovations," National Resources Committee, *Technological Trends and National Policy* (Washington, Government Printing Office, 1937), pp. 39–66.

10. Michael M. Davis, "The Supply of Doctors," *Medical Care* (November, 1942), vol. 2, p. 316.

11. *American Medical Directory* (Chicago, American Medical Association, 1942.)

12. *Directory of Medical Specialties Certified by American Boards* (New York, Columbia University Press 1942), pp. 1969–1970, 1850–1852, 1818–1820, 1831, 1895.

13. Antonio Ciocco and Isidore Altman, "The Patient Load of Physicians in Private Practice," *Public Health Reports* (September 3, 1943), vol. 58, no. 36, pp. 1335–1336.

14. Michael M. Davis, *America Organizes Medicine* (New York, Harper, 1941), p. 58.

15. Maurice Leven, *The Incomes of Physicians,* The Committee on Costs of Medical Care, Publication No. 24 (Chicago: University of Chicago Press, 1932), p. 55.

16. H. G. Weiskotten, "Trends in Medical Practice," *Journal of the Association of American Medical Colleges* (September, 1937), vol. 12, no. 5, p. 344.

17. Iago Galdston, *Progress and Medicine* (New York: Knopf, 1940), pp. 286–289.

18. Linsly R. Williams, "The Present Status of the Practice of Medicine," *New York State Journal of Medicine* (September 1, 1928), vol. 28, p. 1028.

19. Lewellys F. Barker, "The Specialist and the General Practitioner in Relation to Team Work in Medical Practice," *Journal of the American Medical Association* (March 18, 1922), vol. 78, p. 776.

20. G. Canby Robinson, *The Patient as a Person* (N.Y.: The Commonwealth Fund, 1939).

21. Walter C. Alvarez, "The Handling of the Nervous Patient," *Collected Papers of the Mayo Clinic and the Mayo Foundation* (1941), vol. 33, p. 994; *idem, Nervousness, Indigestion and Pain* (New York, Hoeber, 1943).

22. Charles L. Dana, "The Doctor's Future," *New York Medical Journal,* (January 4, 1913), vol. 97, p. 3.

23. Gladys V. Swackhamer, *Choice and*

Change of Doctors (New York, Committee on Research in Medical Economics, 1939), pp. 38–44.

24. State of New York, New York State Commission to Formulate a Long Range Health Program, *Interim Report*, Legislative Document 1941, No. 83, (Albany, 1941), p. 114.

REFERENCES TO CHAPTER 37

1. Mountin, J. W.; Pennell, E. H., and Brockett, G. S.: Location and Movement of Physicians, 1923 and 1938—Changes in Urban and Rural Totals for Established Physicians, *Pub. Health Rep. 60:* 173–185, (Feb. 16), 1945.

2. Weiskotten, H. G., and Altenderfer, M. E.: Trends in Medical Practice: Analysis of Distribution and Characteristics of Medical College Graduates, 1915–40, *J. M. Educ. 72:* 3–41 (Sept., pt. 2), 1952.

3. Merrell, M., and Shulman, L. E.: Determination of Prognosis in Chronic Disease, Illustrated by Systemic Lupus Erythematosus, *J. Chron. Dis. 1:* 12–32 (Jan.), 1955.

FOOTNOTES TO CHAPTER 40

1. We wish to acknowledge a debt of gratitude to Doctors Leo M. Davidoff and Herbert Volk, Professor and Chairman and Assistant Professor of Surgery, Department of Surgery, Albert Einstein College of Medicine, and to Doctor Charles S. Brant, Assistant Professor of Anthropology, Portland State College, for many suggestions and ideas contained in this paper. Of course, the author assumes full responsibility for its substance.

2. Medical indigency should be distinguished from financial indigency. In the former case, the person cannot sustain payments for private medical care. In the latter case, the person has no financial resources and is usually receiving aid from the local welfare organization.

3. Only one patient in 650 succumbs to surgery in the United States.

REFERENCES TO CHAPTER 40

1. Bard, Morton and Dyk, Ruth B., "The Psychodynamic Significance of Beliefs Regarding the Cause of Serious Illness," *The Psychoanalytic Review*, 43, No. 2, April 1956, 146–162.

2. Bard, Morton and Sutherland, Arthur N., "Psychological Impact of Cancer and Its Treatment," IV: Adaptation to Radical Mastectomy, *Cancer*, 8, No. 4, July–August 1955, 656–672.

3. Bartemeier, Leo H., "Interpersonal Relations in the Practice of Medicine," *The Journal of the Michigan State Medical Society*, 55, September, 1956, 1106–1108.

4. Bartlett, F. C., *Remembering*, Cambridge, England, Cambridge University Press, 1932.

5. Blanton, Meiling and Kirk, Virginia, "A Psychiatric Study of 61 Appendectomy Cases," *Annals of Surgery*, 126, September 1947, 305–314.

6. Burling, Temple; Lentz, Edith M. and Wilson, Robert N., *The Give and Take in Hospitals.* New York, G. P. Putnam's Sons, 1956, pp. 355.

7. Brant, Charles S. and Kutner, Bernard, "Interpersonal Relationships and Comprehensive Surgical Care in a Municipal Teaching Hospital," *The New Physician*, In Press.

8. Brant, Charles S. and Kutner, Bernard, "Physician-Patient Relations in a Teaching Hospital," *Journal of Medical Education*, 32, No. 10, October 1957, 703–707.

9. Brant, Charles S.; Volk, Herbert and Kutner, Bernard, "A Plan for 'Total Care' of Surgical Patients in a Municipal Teaching Hospital," 12 p. (Mimeo).

10. Caplovitz, David, "Value-Orientations of Medical Students and Faculty Members," Paper delivered at the American Sociological Society Convention, Washington, D.C., August 1957, 12 p. (Dittoed).

11. Cockerill, Elena E., "Psychiatric Understanding in Social Case Work with Surgical Patients," *The Family Journal of Social Case Work*, 23, No. 10, 1943, 369–374.

12. Coser, Rose Laub, "A Home Away From Home," *Social Problems*, 4, No. 1, July 1956, 3–17.

13. Craig, James B., "Psychological Implications of Surgery," *Journal of the Medi-*

cal Association of Georgia, August 1956, 358–361.

14. Davis, Loyal, Presidential Address "A Letter to Alastair Crovenay, M.D.," *Annals of Surgery*, 146, No. 3, September 1957, 305–313.

15. Dunbar, Flanders, Discussion of Zwerling, Israel, et. al., "Personality Disorder and the Relationships of Patients," *American Journal of Psychiatry*, 112, No. 4, October 1955, 276–277.

16. Dyk, Ruth B. and Sutherland, Arthur M., "Adaptation of the Spouse and Other Family Members to the Colostomy Patient," *Cancer*, 8, No. 1, January–February 1956, 123–138.

17. Ernstene, A. Carlton, "Explaining to the Patient: A Therapeutic Tool and a Professional Obligation," *The Journal of the American Medical Association*, 165, November 2, 1957, 1110–1113.

18. Kaufman, William, Presidential Address: "The Physician's Role in the Preparation of a Patient for Surgery" in Cantor, Alfred J. and Foxe, Arthur N. (Editors), *Psychosomatic Aspects of Surgery*, New York, Grune and Stratton, 1956.

19. Kroger, William S. and Freed, S. Charles, *Psychosomatic Gynecology; Including Problems of Obstetrical Care*, Philadelphia, W. B. Saunders Company, 1951.

20. Kutner, Bernard and Brant, Charles S., "Communication Deficiency and Role Conflict in a Surgical Service," Paper read at the 65th Annual Convention of the American Psychological Association, New York City, August 31, 1957, 4 p. (Mimeo).

21. Kutner, Bernard and Brant, Charles S., "Role Perceptions of Surgeons and Surgical Patients in a Resident-Centered Teaching Hospital," Paper read at the 52nd Annual Meeting of the American Sociological Society, Washington, D.C., August 29, 1957, 6 p. (Mimeo).

22. Levine, Gene Norman and Fox, Renée C., "Observing Norms in Action: The Doctor and His Patients," Paper read at the 52nd Annual Meeting of the American Sociological Society, Washington, D.C., August 27, 1957, 11 p., (Dittoed).

23. Macgregor, Frances Cooke and Schaffner, Bertram, "Screening Patients for Nasal Plastic Operations: Some Sociologic

and Psychiatric Considerations," *Psychosomatic Medicine*, XII, No. 5, September–October 1950, 277–291.

24. Michaels, Joseph J., "Psychiatric Implications of Surgery," *The Family Journal of Social Case Work*, 23, February 1943, 363–369.

25. Moore, Wilbert E. and Tumin, Melvin M., "Some Social Functions of Ignorance," *American Sociological Review*, XIV, No. 6, December 1949, 787–795.

26. Nathan, Helmuth and Standard, Samuel (Editors), *Should the Patient Know the Truth?*, New York, Springer Publishing Company, 1955, pp. 159.

27. Pratt, Lois, Seligmann, Arthur, and Reader, George, "Physicians' Views on the Level of Medical Information Among Patients," *American Journal of Public Health*, 47 (October, 1957), 1277–1283.

28. Priest, Walter S., Zaks, Misha S., Yacorzynski, George K. and Boshes, Benjamin, "The Neurologic, Psychiatric and Psychologic Aspects of Cardiac Surgery," *The Medical Clinics of North America*, January 1957, 155–169.

29. Rothenberg, Robert E. (Editor) Author's Preface of *Understanding Surgery*, New York, Pocketbooks, Inc., October 1955, XVII–XVIII.

30. Sherif, Muzafer, *The Psychology of Ego-Involvements, Social Attitudes and Identifications*, New York, J. Wiley and Sons, Inc. London, Chapman and Hall, Ltd., 1947, 525 p.

31. Sutherland, Arthur M.; Orbach, Charles E.; Dyk, Ruth B. and Bard, Morton, "Psychologic Impact of Cancer Surgery, I: Adaptation to the Dry Colostomy. Preliminary Report and Summary of Findings," *Cancer*, 5, 1952, 857–872.

32. Szasz, Thomas S. and Hollender, Marc H., "A Contribution to the Philosophy of Medicine," *American Medical Association Archives of Internal Medicine*, 97, May 1956, 585–592.

33. Zwerling, Israel; Titchener, James; Gottschalk, Louis; Levine, Maurice; Culbertson, William; Cohen, Senta Feibleman and Silver, Hyman, "Personality Disorder and the Relationships of Patients," *The American Journal of Psychiatry*, 112, No. 4, October, 1955, 270–277.

REFERENCES TO CHAPTER 41

1. Mead, M., ed: Cultural Patterns and Technical Change, UNESCO Publications, Holland, 1953, Ijsel Press.

2. Foster, G. M.: Guidelines to Community Development Programs, Pub. Health Rep. 70:19, 1955.

3. Foster, G. M.: A Cross-Cultural Anthropological Analysis of a Technical Aid Program (mimeographed), Washington, 1951, Smithsonian Institution, Institute of Anthropology.

4. Foster, G. M.: Relationships Between Theoretical and Applied Anthropology: A Public Health Program Analysis, Human Organization II:5, 1952.

5. Whiting, J. W. M., and Child, I. L.:

Child Training and Personality—A Cross-Cultural Study, New Haven, 1953, Yale University Press.

6. Jelliffe, D. B.: Infant Nutrition in the Subtropics and Tropics, Geneva, 1955, World Health Organization Monograph No. 29.

7. Kelly, I.: An Anthropological Approach to Midwifery Training in Mexico, J. Trop. Pediat. 1:200, 1956.

NOTES TO CHAPTER 42

1. *Dictionary of Occupational Titles*, United States Employment Service. United States Government Printing Office, 1939.

2. The writer conducted a study of anesthesiology in 1948 and 1949 and the current article is based in large part upon that work, plus some more recent inquiries to bring the general materials up-to-date. See Lortie, Dan C. "Doctors Without Patients: The Anesthesiologist—A New Medical Specialist." Unpublished Master's Thesis, Department of Sociology. University of Chicago, 1949. See also Lortie, Dan C. "The Sociologist Looks at the Profession of Anesthesiology," *Current Researches in Anesthesia and Analgesia*, July–August, 1950, pp. 181–188.

3. See *From Max Weber: Essays in Sociology*. Edited by H. H. Gerth and C. Wright Mills. London: Routledge and Kegan Paul Ltd., 1952.

4. No supposition is made that the five sub-systems listed are complete, as they omit, for example, the various components dealing with medical training. They seem adequate, however, to our purpose in this article.

5. For detailed consideration of the problems involved in the operating room, see Lortie, "Doctors Without Patients: The Anesthesiologist—A New Medical Specialist," *op. cit.*, pp. 30–57.

6. The concept of the referral system is developed originally in the work of Oswald Hall, and further work has been done by David N. Solomon. See Hall, Oswald, "The Informal Organization of Medical Practice in an American City." Unpublished Ph.D. dissertation, Department of Sociology, University of Chicago, 1944. See also by the

same author, "The Informal Organization of the Medical Profession," *Canadian Journal of Economics and Political Science*, February, 1946, pp. 30–44; and "The Stages of a Medical Career," *The American Journal of Sociology*, March, 1948, pp. 327–336. See also Solomon, David N. "Career Contingencies of Chicago Physicians." Unpublished Ph.D. dissertation, Department of Sociology, University of Chicago, 1952.

7. Smith, Harvey. "The Sociological Study of Hospitals." Unpublished Ph.D. dissertation, Department of Sociology, University of Chicago, 1949.

8. Garceau, Oliver. *The Political Life of the American Medical Association*. Cambridge: Harvard University Press, 1941.

9. One of the principal complaints of the anesthesiologists was, of course, that surgeons and other doctors were ill-disposed toward their efforts to visit patients and explain the role of the anesthesiologist in their operation. Where such contact was obtained, it was highly valued. The part to be played by anesthesiologists in carrying their story into the community was the principal theme of a Presidential Address by Dr. Boyd Stewart at the Annual Meeting of the American Society of Anesthesiologists, in St. Louis in 1948.

10. Smith, in his study of hospitals, found that in the bifurcated structure of medical and administrative authority, ill-feeling could often arise toward those on the administrative side. Physicians taking on administrative posts, for example, soon found themselves isolated from their former colleagues, and even came to be known as "hotel men."

NOTES TO CHAPTER 43

1. The material reported in this paper is made possible by a Research Training Fellowship from the Social Science Re-

search Council which the writer held during the academic year 1955–1956. This is part of Ph.D dissertation now in progress,

"The Osteopathic Students: A Study in Role Conflict," University of Missouri.

2. For an excellent discussion on medical students, see Robert K. Merton, George Reader, and Patricia L. Kendall, *The Student-Physician* (Cambridge, Mass.: Harvard University Press, 1957). Also, Howard S. Becker and Blanche Geer, "The Fate of Idealism in Medical Schools," *American Sociological Review*, 23 (February, 1958) 50–56, and "Student Culture in Medical Schools," *Harvard Educational Review*, Winter, 1957.

3. For a detailed description of this concept, see Irwin Deutscher, *Public Images of the Nurse* (Kansas City, Mo.: Community Studies, Inc., 1955), p. 41.

4. The method and problems of interviewing these students have been discussed by the writer, "The Personal Identification of the Interviewer," *American Journal of Sociology*, 62 (September, 1956), pp. 213–214.

5. The terms "orthodox medicine" and "allopaths" are used frequently by members of the osteopathic profession to refer to the M.D. profession and its members.

6. Proceedings of the New York Meeting, "Report of the Committee for the Study of Relations Between Osteopathy and Medicine," *Journal of the American Medical Association*, 152 (June 20, 1953), pp. 734–739; Proceedings of the Atlantic City Meeting, "Report of the Committee for the Study of Relations Between Osteopathy and Medicine," *Journal of the American Medical Association*, 158 (July 2, 1955), pp. 736–741.

It may be interesting to note that along with A.M.A.'s apparent change of policy toward the American Osteopathic Association, there has been a renewal of interest in manipulation. For a field which began with manipulation, this completion of the full circle is indeed significant.

7. Arthur G. Hildreth, *The Lengthening Shadows of A. T. Still* (Kirksville, Mo.: published by the author, 1904).

8. Peter K. New and Mary L. New, "Life Style of Chinatowners in San Francisco and Oakland," *Midwest Sociologist*, Spring (1956), p. 31.

9. Paul Williamson, M.D., *Office Procedures* (New York: W. B. Saunders, 1955).

10. Marginal professions have been discussed in several papers; for example, Howard S. Becker and James W. Carper, "The Development of Identification with an Occupation," *American Journal of Sociology*, 61 (January, 1956), pp. 289–298; Thelma H. McCormack, "The Druggists' Dilemma: Problems of a Marginal Occupation," *American Journal of Sociology*, 61 (January, 1956), pp. 308–315; Walter I. Wardwell, "A Marginal Professional Role: The Chiropractor," *Social Forces*, 30 (May, 1952), pp. 339–348.

11. Ralph H. Turner, "Role-Taking, Role Stand-Point, and Reference-Group Behavior," *American Journal of Sociology*, 61 (January, 1956), pp. 316–318.

12. Robert K. Merton and Alice S. Rossi, "Contributions to the Theory of Reference Groups and Social Structure," both in Robert K. Merton, *Social Theory and Social Structure* (Glencoe, Ill.: The Free Press, 1957).

13. For more details, see Peter Kongming New and Irwin Deutscher, "An Application of Reference Group Theory: The Case of the Osteopathic Student," a paper read at the American Sociological Society meetings, Washington, D.C., August 29, 1957.

NOTES TO CHAPTER 44

1. "Human Migration and the Marginal Man," *American Journal of Sociology*, 33 (1928), pp. 881–893.

2. *The Marginal Man: A Study in Personality and Culture Conflict* (New York: Scribners, 1937).

3. Park, *op. cit.*, p. 892.

4. Stonequist, "The Problem of the Marginal Man," *American Journal of Sociology*, 41:1 (1935), p. 6.

5. "A Re-examination of the Marginal Man Concept," *Social Forces*, 26:2 (1947).

6. "A Qualification of the Marginal Man Theory," *American Sociological Review*, 6:1 (1941), p. 58.

7. This paper is based on the writer's doctoral dissertation, Social Strain and Social Adjustment in the Marginal Role of the Chiropractor, Department of Social Relations, Harvard University, February, 1951.

8. The second problem area—that of adjustment in a marginal social role—will be reserved for a subsequent paper.

9. Massachusetts is not typical of the country as a whole since, being one of four states that do not license chiropractors, they

are subject there to arrest at any time for "practicing medicine without registration" and have occasionally been confined to jail. Nevertheless it is believed that the analysis presented holds, in general, for the rest of the country, for the following reasons: (a) The laws are seldom enforced against chiropractors in the states which do not license them; (b) In licensed states the laws often narrowly restrict the scope of their practice, with the result that some chiropractors practice without licenses or beyond their authorized scope of practice; (c) Chiropractors are everywhere denounced by medical spokesmen as imposters in the doctor's role; and (d) Practically all Massachusetts chiropractors hold licenses to practice in other states, indicating that they are not located in Massachusetts because of inability to practice elsewhere.

10. G. K. Abbot, "The Smoke Screen of Quackery," Hygeia, 2:9 (1924), p. 583. See also Morris Fishbein, The Medical Follies (New York: Boni & Liveright, 1925).

11. Robert B. Osgood, Body Mechanics: Education and Practice (Report of the Subcommittee on Orthopedics and Body Mechanics, White House Conference on Child Health and Protection) (New York: The Century Company, 1932), p. 49.

12. Lee A. Hadley, "Constriction of the Intervertebral Foramen," Journal of the American Medical Association, 140:5 (1949), p. 474. See also H. Dinken, "War Injuries of the Vertebral Column and Spinal Cord, with Special Reference to physical treatment," Medical Clinics of North America, 27 (1943), p. 1077, and additional references in the writer's doctoral dissertation, pp. 120–5.

13. This term is equivalent to the term actor as it has been used by Talcott Parsons and others in the so-called "voluntaristic theory of action." See Parsons, The Structure of Social Action (New York: McGraw-Hill, 1937), esp. pp. 44–46.

14. Cf. "Incomes of Chiropractors and Chiropodists in the U.S." Monthly Labor Review, L (1940), 453; Louis Reed, The Healing Cults (Chicago: Publications of the Committee on the Costs of Medical Care, No. 16, University of Chicago Press, 1932), p. 36; and "Occupational Outlook Handbook: Employment Information on Major Occupations for Use in Guidance," Bulletin No. 940, Bureau of Labor Statistics, U.S. Dept. of Labor, 1948.

15. A few small chiropractic schools

continue to grant the Doctor of Chiropractic (D.C.) degree for less than this standard course of training.

16. Figures, as of September, 1950, obtained from Dr. John J. Nugent, Director of Education of the National Chiropractic Association.

17. Membership figures are taken from the World Almanac, published by the New York World Telegram, 1951, p. 594.

18. This hypothetical situation of course presumes that the chiropractor is not himself responsible for the death.

19. G. W. Hartmann, "The Relative Social Prestige of Representative Medical Specialties," Journal of Applied Psychology, 20 (1936), pp. 659–663.

20. New York State Chiropractic Journal, 17:4 (1948), pp. 17–18.

21. C. R. Hoffer, et. al., Health Needs and Health Care in Michigan (East Lansing, Michigan State College Agricultural Experiment Station, 1950), pp. 49–50.

22. However, a survey conducted at one of the larger accredited chiropractic colleges disclosed that roughly 38 percent of the 160 members of the senior class had completed two or more years of academic college and that another 38 percent had had some academic college training.

23. Reed, op. cit., p. 41.

24. Ibid., p. 55.

25. A term suggested by Dr. Harry B. Solomon of Harvard Univ. Medical School.

26. Compare the following statement of Wilhelm Reich, the unorthodox psychoanalyst: "Every muscular rigidity contains the history and the meaning of its origin. . . . A certain psychic structure is at the same time a certain biophysical structure. . . . In a great many cases inhibitions give way only to a direct loosening of the muscular tensions." The Function of the Orgasm, trans. by T. P. Wolfe (New York: Orgone Institute Press, 1948), pp. 235–236. Italics his. Cf. also Georg Groddeck, "Massage and Psychotherapy," in his Exploring the Unconscious, trans. by M. Collins (London: C. W. Daniel Co., 1933), pp. 46–53.

27. H. S. Schwartz, "What is the Connection between Nerves and 'Nervousness?' " Journal of the National Chiropractic Association, 19:5 (1949), p. 21.

28. See, for example, F. J. Kottke, "Physical Treatment of Backache," Journal of the American Medical Association, 139: 16 (1949), pp. 1956–7.

29. "The Informal Organization of the Medical Profession," *Canadian Journal of Economics and Political Science*, 12:1 (1946).

30. *The Political Life of the American Medical Association* (Cambridge, Massachusetts: Harvard University Press, 1941), p. 171.

31. This finding is not surprising in view of the well known relationship between personal insecurity and prejudice; cf. Robin M. Williams, Jr., *The Reduction of Intergroup Tensions* (New York: Social Science Research Council, 1947), pp. 53 ff.

32. "Basic Science a Recurring Problem," pamphlet published by the International Chiropractors Association, no date, p. 34; italics supplied.

33. "Profession," *Dictionary of Sociology* (New York: Philosophical Library, 1944), p. 235.

34. Alternatively, the chiropractic role could become institutionalized independent of, but on a par with, that of the physician, or simply disappear.

35. Cf. Harold D. McDowell, Osteopathy: A Study of a Semi-Orthodox Healing Agency and the Recruitment of Its Clientele, unpublished Master's Thesis, Department of Sociology, University of Chicago, 1950.

36. *The Chirogram* (Published by the Los Angeles College of Chiropractic), 20:2 (1951), p. 19.

37. There is already an organization called "The National Medical Society" which is working for the integration of practitioners of medicine, osteopathy, chiropractic, and naturopathy into one national association. It plans to establish a "National Medical University" in the vicinity of Washington, D.C., which will synthesize all branches of the healing art. It publishes the *Journal of the National Medical Society*.

REFERENCES TO CHAPTER 45

Balint, M. (1954): *Brit. med. J.*, i, 115.

Batchelor, I. R. C. (1953): *Ibid.*, i, 1041.

Bennet, E. A. (1953): *Ibid, ii*, 554.

Frankl, V. E. (1954): *Proc. Roy. Soc. Med.*, 47, 975.

Central Council for Health Education (1954): "Group Discussion in Educational, Social and Working Life," London. *Lancet* (1955): i, 188.

Lewis, R., and Maude, A. (1952): "Professional People," London.

Ling, T. M. (1954): "Mental Health and Human Relations in Industry," London.

M'Lennan, J., and Small, M., (1955): *Lancet, i*, 142.

Needles, R. J. (1954): *J. Amer. Med. Assn., 186*, 6, 585.

Ozani, L. D. (1954): *Amer. J. Psychiat.*, 111, 5.

Pinsent, R. J. F. H., (1951): *Brit. Med. J., ii*, 1335.

Roth, M. (1956): *Proc. Roy. Soc. Med.* (in the press).

Wittkower, E. D., and White, K. L., (1954): *Brit. med. J.*, i, 1432.

NOTES TO CHAPTER 46

1. Howard W. Haggard, M.D., "The Physician and the Alcoholic," *Quarterly Journal of Studies on Alcohol*, 6: September 1945, p. 220.

2. Florence Powdermaker, M.D., "The Relation Between the Alcoholic and the Physician," *Quarterly Journal of Studies on Alcohol*, 5: September 1944, p. 249.

3. Haggard. *op. cit.*, p. 213.

4. John W. Riley, Jr. & C. F. Marden, "The Medical Profession and the Problem of Alcoholism," *Quarterly Journal of Studies on Alcohol*, 7: Sept. 1946, pp. 240–270.

5. The Committee on Public Health Relations of the New York Academy of Medicine, "A Survey of Facilities for the Care and Treatment of Alcoholism in New York City," *Quarterly Journal of Studies on Alcohol*, 7: December 1946, pp. 405–438.

6. Robert Straus, "Community Surveys: Their Aims and Techniques," *Quarterly Journal of Studies on Alcohol*, 13: June 1952, pp. 254–270.

7. August B. Hollingshead, "Views on the Etiology of Alcoholism" in H. D. Kruse, M.D. Editor, *Alcoholism As A Medical Problem*, New York, 1956, p. 59.

NOTES TO CHAPTER 47

1. The fullest sociological analysis of the general hospital is Temple Burling, Edith Lentz and Robert N. Wilson, *The Give and Take in Hospitals.* (New York; 1956). A very full description of the hospital from the administrative point of view is Malcolm T. MacEachern, *Hospital Organization and Management,* (2nd Edition, Chicago; 1947). For a sociologist's views on hospital administration, see Edith Lentz, "Hospital Administration—One of a Species," *Administrative Science Quarterly,* 1, 1957, 444–463. And for a concise exposition of the historical development of the modern hospital, see Edward D. Churchill, "The Development of the Hospital," in Nathaniel Faxon (Ed.), *The Hospital in Contemporary Life.* (Cambridge, 1949), pp. 1–69.

2. Some of the sources of this formulation include Chester I. Barnard, *The Functions of the Executive.* (Cambridge, 1938), Bronislaw Malinowski, *A Scientific Theory of Culture and Other Essays.* (Chapel Hill, 1944), and E. Wight Bakke, *Bonds of Organization.* (New York, 1950).

3. This material is drawn from the author's dissertation, *The Social Structure of a Modern Hospital.* (Unpublished MS, Yale University Library).

4. Medical and surgical wards, as well as those assigned to other specialty services, have of course quite different characteristics. Likewise, private, semi-private, and charity ward units have their typical peculiarities. In the final analysis, each ward unit has an individual identity all its own. Here, however, we wish to discuss certain features which all ward units have in common.

5. This generalization obviously does not apply to all patients. In particular, it does not apply to those who remain in the hospital for more than a fortnight and who during a substantial share of this time are able to observe and participate in events other than those having to do with their own care.

6. The order of listing these occupations within the subgroups is not necessarily according to rank. Moreover, in various hospitals the terminology for some of these jobs is variable. We utilize those in force at Yankee Hospital.

7. This form of status distinction is more marked at Yankee Hospital than in many other institutions of its kind. It should also be stated that what is here described is not prescribed by formal rules but is habitual practice.

8. Along with separate dining rooms, there are special locker rooms and washrooms for doctors as distinguished from all other men, and for nurses as distinguished from all other women.

9. See also Rose Coser, "Authority and Decision Making in a Hospital," *American Sociological Review,* 23, February, 1958, 56–63.

10. Exceptions include dietary department employees, who are responsible directly to the floor dietitians, and paramedical professionals such as social workers who operate on a "referral" basis. There exists a continuum along which the relative power of ward authorities varies as contrasted to that of the administrative supervisors. Thus, the relations of the trained attendants and the nurses' aides to their supervisors approaches the minimum; nursing supervisors and the male aids' supervisor exert somewhat more direct authority and the housekeeping department supervisors exert much more authority over their employees than does the head nurse. This establishment of a dual hierarchy of authority is, of course, a product of the trend toward rationalization and business management in hospital administration.

11. Mention should also be made of a rather evanescent group of volunteers who come to the ward on a part-time basis, usually to perform such specifically defined tasks as offering library books to patients or serving them mid-afternoon "nourishment."

12. This concept is especially in evidence among nursing administrators.

13. George C. Homans, *The Human Group.* (New York, 1950), p. 145.

14. This enforced deference to the status of the physician continues to be observed—and expected—despite a marked decrease in the formality of the doctor-nurse relationship during the past few years.

15. This need of the surgeon for assistance from the nurse carries over into the surgical ward, where it is very common for a doctor to ask for a nurse's help in technical procedures, in removing and replacing dressings, etc. These collaborations occur somewhat less frequently on medical wards. The result is that there tends to be *more*

interaction between surgeons and nurses than between internists and nurses.

16. Talcott Parsons, *The Social System.* (Glencoe, Illinois, 1951), Chapter X.

17. On the sociological use of the concept "ideology," see for example, Karl Mannheim, *Ideology and Utopia.* (1936), p. 63 *et passim*, and Richard T. LaPiere, *Sociology.* (1946), pp. 285 ff. Compare the concept of "charter" in Malinowski, *op. cit.*

18. Homans, *op. cit.*, p. 120.

19. In this and the following analyses, our purpose is to present the majority point-of-view. Not all interviewees agreed with these formulations, and they do not necessarily represent the feelings of doctors, nurses, and other hospital workers at institutions other than Yankee Hospital.

20. George Devereux and Florence R. Wiener, "The Occupational Status of Nurses," *American Sociological Review*, 15, October 1950, 628–634.

NOTES TO CHAPTER 48

1. An eminent German social scientist who died in 1920.

2. A nursing Sister to whom this term was explained said, "Oh yes, I know what you mean. We call it the Jehovah complex!"

3. Barnard has combined a successful career as an industrial executive with insightful analyses of industrial organization.

NOTES TO CHAPTER 49

1. See, for example, S. Kirson Weinberg, "Aspects of the Prison's Social Structure," *American Journal of Sociology* (March, 1942) 47, pp. 717–26; F. J. Roethligsberger and W. J. Dickson, *Management and the Worker*, (Cambridge, Mass.: Harvard University Press, 1939); J. Fremont Bateman and H. Warren Dunham, "The State Mental Hospital as a Specialized Community Experience," *American Journal of Psychiatry*, 1948, 105, pp. 445–48; In addition to the references to be cited, data for this inquiry are derived from interviews with patients and staff members from state and private hospitals.

2. S. Kirson Weinberg, *Society and Personality Disorders* (New York: Prentice-Hall, Inc., 1952) Chapters 15–17; Ivan Belknap, *Human Problems of a State Mental Hospital*, (New York: McGraw-Hill Book Co., 1956); Alfred H. Stanton and Morris S. Schwartz, *The Mental Hospital*, (New York: Basic Books, Inc., 1954).

3. S. Kirson Weinberg and H. Warren Dunham, *The Structure and Functions of a State Mental Hospital*, (unpublished manuscript.)

4. *Ibid.*

5. Figures computed from data on resident patients at the end of the year in the state and private hospitals. *Patients in Mental Institutions: 1953. Part II: Public Hospitals for the Mentally Ill*, (U.S. Department of Health, Education, and Welfare, 1953). (Washington, D.C.: U.S. Government Printing Office, 1953); Part II, Table I; Part III, Table I.

6. *Ibid*, Part II, Table 4;–Part III, Table 2.

7. *Ibid*, Part II, Table 17;–Part III, Table 3.

8. *Ibid.*

9. S. Kirson Weinberg, "The Sociological Analysis of a Schizophrenic Type," *American Sociological Review*, (October, 1950) 15, pp. 600–10.

10. *Ibid.*, pp. 600–610.

11. Alfred H. Stanton and Morris S. Schwartz, *The Mental Hospital*, (New York: Basic Books, Inc., 1954).

12. *Ibid.*; S. Kirson Weinberg, *Society and Personality Disorders*, Chapter 16; Ivan Belknap, *Human Problems of a State Mental Hospital*, (New York: McGraw-Hill Book Co., Inc., 1956); George Devereaux, "The Social Structure of the Hospital as a Factor in Total Therapy," *American Journal of Orthopsychiatry*, (1949), 19, pp. 492–500.

13. Weinberg, *op. cit.*, pp. 378–381.

14. *Fact Sheet No. 1* (Washington, D.C.: Joint Information Service, March, 1957) p. 5.

15. See Ivan Belknap, *op cit.*, pp. 106–122.

16. *Fact Sheet No. 1*, (March, 1957), p. 5.

17. Stanton and Schwartz, *op. cit.*, pp. 100, 101.

18. Personal Document; See also Milton Greenblatt, et al., editors, *The Patient and the Mental Hospital*, (Glencoe, Ill., The Free Press, 1957).

19. See Greenblatt, Milton; York, Rich-

ard; Brown, Esther L., with Hyde, Robert W.: *From Custodial to Therapeutic Care in Mental Hospitals* (New York: Russell Sage Foundation, 1955); Weinberg, *op. cit.*; Belknap, *op. cit.*

20. See William Menninger, "Psychoanalytic Principles in Psychiatric Hospital Therapy," *Southern Medical Journal* (1939) 32, pp. 348–54; Paul S. Barrabee, "A Study of the Mental Hospital: The Effect of its Social Structure on its Functions," Unpublished doctoral dissertation (Cambridge: Harvard University, March, 1951).

21. Stanton and Schwartz, *op. cit.*, pp. 103–04.

22. Weinberg, *Society and Personality Disorders*, pp. 382–386

23. Stanton and Schwartz, *op. cit.*, pp. 106–07.

24. Weinberg, *op. cit.*; See W. Caudill, F. C. Redlich; H. R. Gilmore, and E. B. Brody: "Social Structure and Interaction Processes in a Psychiatric Ward," *American Journal of Orthopsychiatry* (1952) 22, pp. 314–34.

25. *Patients in Mental Institutions: 1950 and 1951*. Public Health Service Publication No. 356 (Washington: United States Government Printing Office, 1954, Table 79) pp. 218–19.

26. Personal Document; See also Stanton & Schwartz, *op. cit.*, pp. 92, 93.

27. Albert Deutch, *Shame of the States* (New York: Harcourt, Brace and Co., Inc.,

1948); and *The Mentally Ill in America* (New York: Doubleday and Co., Inc., 1937) pp. 449–450. Before 1947, 95 percent of 45 state hospitals surveyed were over-crowded. See Frank L. Wright, *Out of Sight, Out of Mind*, (Philadelphia: National Mental Health Foundation, Inc., 1947).

28. Weinberg, *op. cit.*, pp. 380–381.

29. Personal Document of a former patient discharged from a private hospital. See also Maurice Grimes, *When Minds Go Wrong* (Chicago: Maurice Grimes, 1951)

30. Personal document. See also J. F. Bateman and H. W. Dunham, "The State Mental Hospital as a Specialized Community Experience," *American Journal of Psychiatry*, (1948) 105, 445–48.

31. Belknap, *op. cit.*, pp. 79–80.

32. *Loc. cit.*

33. See Weinberg, *op. cit.*, Chapters 16, 17.

34. See Frieda Fromm-Reichman, "Problems of Therapeutic Management in a Psychoanalytic Hospital," *Psychoanalytic Quarterly* (1947) 16, pp. 325–56; Dexter M. Bullard, "The Organization of Psychoanalytic Procedure in the Hospital," *Journal of Nervous and Mental Disease* (1940) 91, pp. 697–703.

35. Edward C. Adams, "Problems of Attitude Therapy in a Mental Hospital," *The American Journal of Psychiatry* (December, 1948) 105: 6, pp. 456–57.

NOTES TO CHAPTER 50

1. It has been remarked by many observers that in some sense the body on the table is no longer a human being in his fullest significance. The "person" becomes an "object" so that a complete emotional response to him (it) is no longer necessary or possible. As the chief surgeon once remarked to an observer seated in the gallery of the operating room: "This is a man; just wait, we'll put him back together and you'll see." T. S. Eliot, in *The Cocktail Party*, has also commented on the patient as object:

"Or take a surgical operation
In consultation with the doctor and the
    surgeon
In going to bed in the nursing home,
In talking to the matron, you are still the
    subject.
The centre of reality. But stretched on the
    table,
You are a piece of furniture in a repair shop

For those who surround you, the masked
    actors;
All there is of you is your body
And the 'you' is withdrawn."

2. It should be noted that this comment, while perhaps not "typical," illustrates more than a simple stress on intimacy and experience. It expresses also the prestige difference between the two main hospital roles, with the surgeon implicitly derogating the nurse role by comparing her with an "instrument" or tool of the doctor.

3. The separate, confined spatial arrangement of the surgery may, in some cases, contribute to the surgeon's feeling of tension. He, the captain, is alone with the heavy responsibility of a difficult job. In one hospital, perhaps inadvertently, the physical arrangement was such that fellow surgeons might drop by the open door to the scrub room for a casual chat and for consultation. The door leading to the hos-

pital corridor remained closed, but the scrub room entrance, always open, provided easy access for interested colleagues. Numerous observations demonstrated convincingly that certain elements of support were derived from this "open-door" situation.

* The study was part of a larger project

sponsored by the American Hospital Association. The research was under the general direction of Temple Burling, M.D. Miss Edith M. Lentz was the field work supervisor and senior research associate. The Carnegie Corporation of New York has provided the major support for this study.

NOTES TO CHAPTER 51

* Paper read at the annual meeting of the American Sociological Society, August, 1953.

1. A. B. Hollingshead and F. C. Redlich, "The Relationship of Social Structure to Psychiatric Disorders" aided by U.S.P.H.S. Mental Health Act Grant MH 263 (R).

2. F. C. Redlich, A. B. Hollingshead, et al., "Social Structure and Psychiatric Disorders," American Journal of Psychiatry, 109 (April, 1953), pp. 729–34; A. B. Hollingshead and F. C. Redlich, "Social Stratification and Psychiatric Disorders," American Sociological Review, 18 (April, 1953), pp. 163–69; H. A. Robinson, F. C. Redlich, and J. K. Myers, "Social Structure and Psychiatric Treatment," in press for American Journal of Orthopsychiatry; B. H. Roberts and J. K. Myers, "Religion, National Origin, Immigration, and Mental Illness," American Journal of Psychiatry, 110 (April, 1954), pp. 759–64.

3. Twelve cases which could not be

class-typed because of paucity of data were omitted from the following analysis.

4. Redlich, Hollingshead, et al., op. cit.

5. A brief description of each class is as follows: Class I comprises families of wealth, education, and top social prestige; Class II consists of families in which the adults for the most part hold college degrees and in which the husbands have executive, high-level managerial or professional occupations; Class III includes proprietors, white-collar workers and some skilled workers; they are mostly high school graduates; Class IV consists largely of semi-skilled workers with less than a high school education; Class V includes unskilled and semiskilled workers, who have a grade-school education or less, and who live in the poorest areas of the community.

6. The social class distribution of the New Haven population is as follows: class I—3 percent, class II—8 percent, class III—21 percent, class IV—50 percent, and class V—18 percent.

NOTES TO CHAPTER 53

* This paper may be identified as Publication No. A 190 of the Bureau of Applied Social Research, Columbia University. The study was supported by a grant from Chas. Pfizer & Co., Inc., manufacturers of chemicals and pharmaceuticals. The authors acknowledge the contribution of Dr. Joseph A. Precker, then Director of Market Research, Chas. Pfizer & Co., Inc., in initiating the study and in participating in its design. Contributions to various phases of the planning of the study were made by James Coleman, Philip Ennis, Marjorie Fiske, and Rolf Myersohn, all then of the Bureau of Applied Social Research. An earlier version of this article was presented at the 1955 meetings of the American Association for Public Opinion Research.

1. See, e.g., Lazarsfeld, Berelson, and Gaudet, The People's Choice (New York: Columbia University Press, 1948), Chap. XVI; R. K. Merton, "Patterns of Influence,"

in Lazarsfeld and Stanton, eds., Communication Research 1948–49 (New York: Harper, 1949); and Katz and Lazarsfeld, Personal Influence, (Glencoe: Free Press, 1955); and especially Elihu Katz's review article, "The Two-Step Flow of Communication—An Up-to-Date Report on an Hypothesis," Public Opinion Quarterly, Vol. 21, 1957, pp. 61–78.

2. See Berelson, Bernard, Paul F. Lazarsfeld and William McPhee, Voting, (Chicago: University of Chicago Press, 1954).

3. Riley, M. W. and J. W. Riley, "A Sociological Approach to Communications Research," Public Opinion Quarterly, Vol. 15, pp. 445–60.

4. Shils, E. A. and M. Janowitz, "Cohesion and Disintegration in the Wehrmacht," Public Opinion Quarterly, Vol. 12, pp. 280–315.

5. This is the thinking implicit, for ex-

ample, in Kurt Lewin's approach to "Group Decision and Social Change," in Swanson, Newcomb and Hartley, eds., *Readings in Social Psychology*, (New York: Henry Holt, 1952), and in subsequent studies in this tradition. An important illustration is H. H. Kelley and E. H. Volkart, "The Resistance to Change of Group-Anchored Attitudes," *American Sociological Review*, Vol. 17, pp. 453–465. Of obvious relevance, too, is the tradition of research and theory concerning "reference groups" synthesized in R. K. Merton and A. Kitt, "Contributions to the Theory of Reference Group Behavior," in Merton and Lazarsfeld, eds., *Continuities in Social Research: Studies in the Scope and Method of the American Soldier*, (Glencoe: Free Press, 1950).

6. This is not, of course, to say that such communication is "unscientific"; direct communication among colleagues is vital to all sciences. This paper attempts to show how influential such communication is, even on the local level, and in spite of the existence of multitudes of professional journals—which—potentially—bring relevant articles by the top authorities in each field directly to the desk of each practicing physician.

6a. This work has been completed since publication of the original article. See Coleman, James, Elihu Katz, and Herbert Menzel, "The Diffusion of an Innovation among Physicians," *Sociometry*, vol. 20, December, 1957, pp. 253–270; Menzel, Herbert, "Public and Private Conformity under Different Conditions of Acceptance in the Group," *Journal of Abnormal and Social Psychology*, vol. 55, November, 1957, pp. 398–402; and Coleman, James, Elihu Katz, and Herbert Menzel, *Doctors and New Drugs: A Case Study in the Diffusion of an Innovation*, (Glencoe: Free Press, forthcoming).

7. The Sociogram was constructed by a trial-and-error method. Clusters of mutually choosing stars were first identified, and others then grouped around them, so that individuals were nearest that cluster to which they seemed most closely tied, and so that cross-overs were minimized. For the larger study, more standardized techniques have been devised. See Coleman, James, Elihu Katz, and Herbert Menzel, "The Diffusion of an Innovation among Physicians," *op. cit.*

8. Regarding the relatively low overall frequency of mentions of "colleagues" in Table 1, see note 12 below.

9. Our findings fit very well with Os-

wald Hall's much more extensive study of interpersonal relations in a New England medical community considerably larger than the one under discussion here. See "The Informal Organization of the Medical Profession," *Canadian Journal of Economics and Political Science*, vol. 12, no. 1.

10. Data collected elsewhere subsequent to the termination of this survey make it likely that most of these "diehards" did at least try out the new drug some time during 1954.

11. In the case of Propositions 1 and 2 (Table 4), we have not, so far, been able to determine the chance-expected values for the case of "complete independence." Reflection on what would constitute a "chance" model from which empirical deviations in the direction of satisfying our hypotheses could be measured suggests that these hypotheses imply deviation from "independence" in some or all of at least three different ways: (1) That the community-wide distribution of adoptions over time deviates from the chance-expected distribution over time. (It is an open question what the proper model for the chance-expected distribution should be.) (2) That the clique specific-distribution curves of adoptions over time have their peaks and other characteristic features at different points along the time-continuum. (3) That all the clique-specific curves of adoptions over time have a similar shape, which approximates some one hypothesized characteristic shape (e.g., that corresponding to a "spurt").

12. Only the first of these four mechanisms by which groups may reach simultaneous decisions requires "personal influence" in the strict sense of the term. In the doctors' own accounts of the channels of information and influence which went into the making of a drug decision, it may be recalled (Table 1), colleagues constitute only 16% of the channels mentioned. (They are mentioned in 30% of the accounts, but most accounts contain more than one channel). This is much less often than personal influence is usually mentioned in interviews on marketing or similar decisions, and also much less than would seem to correspond to the indications just reported, that the spread of this innovation flows through social channels. Two explanations of the low frequency of mentions of colleagues in the doctors' own accounts are possible: (1) that the doctors' own reports understate the extent to which their colleagues actually have a part in their decisions; (2) that personal influ-

ence actually is lower in these drug decisions, and that the congruence of social relations and drug adoptions reported in this section is not achieved by direct personal influence, but through one of the other three mechanisms suggested above.

13. See E. A. Wilkening, "Informal Leaders and Innovators in Farm Practices," *Rural Sociology*, Vol. 17, pp. 272–275; H. F. Lionberger, "Some Characteristics of Farm

Operators Sought as Sources of Farm Information in a Missouri Community," *Rural Sociology*, Vol. 18, pp. 327–338; C. P. Marsh and A. L. Coleman, "Farmers' Practice Adoption Rates in Relation to Adoption Rates of Leaders," *Rural Sociology*, Vol. 19, pp. 180–181. These three studies are excellent representatives of a research tradition of the greatest importance for students of communication.

NOTES TO CHAPTER 54

1. For a more thorough analysis of the patient role see Talcott Parsons, *The Social System* (Glencoe, Ill.: The Free Press, 1951), pp. 430–447.

2. *Ibid.*, pp. 25, 38–39.

3. George Devereux, "Normal and Abnormal: The Key Problem of Psychiatric Anthropology," in *Some Uses of Anthropology: Theoretical and Applied* (Washington, D.C.: The Anthropological Society of Washington, 1956), p. 23.

4. Helene Deutsch, *The Psychology of Women* (New York: Grune and Stratton, 1945), Vol. II, pp. 294–298.

5. Willystine Goodsell, *A History of Marriage and the Family* (New York: The Macmillan Company, 1934), pp. 39–41.

6. It is interesting to note that Gerald Caplan assigns to the maternal-pediatric nurse a "sibling role" in her relationships with patients. The qualities of this role closely resemble those which the writer has assigned to the mother surrogate role. Both labels are indicative of familial closeness. See Caplan's "The Mental Hygiene Role of the Nurse in Maternal and Child Care," *Nursing Outlook*, 2: 17, January, 1954. [After completion of this paper the writer had the opportunity of reading Hildegard Peplau's *Interpersonal Relations in Nursing* (New York: G. P. Putnam's Sons, 1952) which he had not seen previously. The parallel development in part of the concept of the role of the mother surrogate here and in Miss Peplau's book, pp. 51–61, is most evident. It is sincerely hoped that this effort will complement Miss Peplau's provocative presentation.]

7. Frances R. Kreuter, "What is Good Nursing Care?" *Nursing Outlook*, 5: 302, May, 1957. See also Margaret Mead, "Nursing—Primitive and Civilized," *American Journal of Nursing*, 56: 1002, August, 1956.

8. The information on *tsukisoi* has been gathered from a personal interview with Dr. Tsuneo Nakamura, Fulbright Postdoc-

toral Fellow at the Medical Branch of the University of Texas, and from notes on a lecture delivered by Dr. William Caudill in the Seminar on Health and Illness in Cross-Cultural Perspective, Harvard School of Public Health, February 20, 1957.

9. From informant, Dr. Tsuneo Nakamura.

10. Saint Vincent de Paul, "The Rule of the Confraternity," in Anne L. Austin, *History of Nursing Source Book* (New York: G. P. Putnam's Sons, 1957), p. 139.

11. Lyle Saunders, "The Changing Role of Nurses," *American Journal of Nursing*, Vol. 54, September, 1954, p. 3.

12. *Ibid.*

13. W. H. R. Rivers, *Medicine, Magic, and Religion* (London: Kegan Paul, Trench, Trubner and Co., Ltd., 1924), p. 5.

14. Parsons, *op. cit.*, pp. 434–435. See also his "Propaganda and Social Control," in *Essays in Sociological Theory* (Glencoe, Ill.: The Free Press, 1954), pp. 154–155.

15. Parsons, *Social System*, pp. 451–452.

16. Kreuter, *ibid.*

17. Parsons, *op. cit.*, 280.

18. Kenneth Benne, "Problems of Role Confusion and Conflict in Nursing," Transcript of a Talk and Discussion Period at Meeting at Hillel House, (Boston, Mass.), February 13, 1957 (Processed); Edith M. Lentz, "A Study of Changing Relationships in Hospitals," *American Journal of Nursing*, 56: 187–189, February, 1956; Otto Pollak, Charles Westoff, and Martin Bressler, "Pennsylvania Pilot Study of Nursing Functions," *Nursing Research*, 2: 15–22, June, 1953.

19. From a student theme, School of Nursing, Medical Branch, University of Texas.

20. See Robert P. Bullock, "Position, Function, and Job Satisfaction of Nurses in the Social System of a Modern Hospital," *Nursing Research*, 2: 7–10; Mel J. Ravitz,

"Occupational Values and Occupational Selection," *Nursing Research,* 6: 35–40, June, 1957.

21. From a private interview with informant.

22. Benne, *op. cit.,* pp. 3–4. In a conference held by Dr. Benne's research group of the Boston University Human Relations Center, headed by Dr. Warren Bennis, in May, 1957, some preliminary observations on this matter were presented in the course of discussions on the role of the nurse in out-patient departments. Publications coming out of this research should be very revealing. See also: Marvin Bressler and William Kephart, *Career Dynamics: A Survey of Selected Aspects of the Nursing Profession* (Harrisburg, Pa.: Pennsylvania Nurses Association, 1955), pp. 16–18.

23. *The Evaluation of Nurses by Male Physicians* (Part I of A Study of the Registered Nurse in a Metropolitan Community; Kansas City, Mo.: Community Studies, Inc., March, 1955), pp. 9–12.

24. *Public Images of the Nurse* (Part II of A Study of the Registered Nurse in a Metropolitan Community; Kansas City, Mo.: Community Studies, Inc., August, 1955), pp. 59–61.

25. Marion Pearsall, "Nursing Supervisors: A Social Profile," June, 1957 (Processed), pp. 24–25.

26. Dorothy I. Roth, "Roll Call—A Study of Roles in Nurse-Patient Relations," *Nursing Research,* I: 42, October, 1952.

27. Isidor Thorner, "Nursing: The Functional Significance of an Institutional Pattern," *American Sociological Review,* 20: 532, October, 1955.

28. Esther L. Brown, *Nursing For the Future,* (New York: Russell Sage Foundation, 1948), pp. 76 *ff.*

29. George Devereux and Florence R. Weiner, "The Occupational Status of Nurses," *American Sociological Review,* 15: 633.

30. Dorothy Smith, "Let's Help Students Learn and Grow," *Nursing Outlook,* 5: 16, January, 1957.

31. Each of the conferences was based upon the reading of a very provocative scenario by Dr. Marguerite Kakosh, illustrating the admission and discharge of a patient by two nurses who represented a hospital-oriented non-affective person on the one hand, and an affective patient-oriented person on the other.

32. Temple Burling, Edith Lentz, and Robert Wilson, *The Give and Take in Hospitals* (New York: G. P. Putnam's Sons, 1956), pp. 146–160; Milton Greenblatt, Richard York, and Esther L. Brown, *From Custodial to Therapeutic Care in Mental Hospitals* (New York: Russell Sage Foundation, 1955), pp. 149–152.

NOTES TO CHAPTER 55

1. Zborowski, Mark: "Cultural Components in Response to Pain." *Journal of Social Issues,* 8(4): 16–31, 1952, pp. 18–19.

2. Wellin, Edward: "Water Boiling in Peru." In Benjamin D. Paul, editor, *Health, Culture, and Community,* New York: Russell Sage Foundation, 1955, pp. 100–101.

3. Brown, Esther Lucile: "Contributions of the Behavior Sciences to Understanding in Public Health Nursing." Paper read at the Public Health Nursing Section, American Public Health Association, November 16, 1955.

4. Paul, Benjamin D., *op. cit.,* pp. 459–460.

5. Unpublished correspondence.

6. Koos, Earl L: *The Health of Regionville.* New York: Columbia University Press, 1954, p. 36.

7. *Ibid.,* p. 36.

8. Deasy, L. C.: "Socio-economic Status and the Poliomyelitis Vaccine Trial." *American Sociological Review,* 21: 185–190, April 1956.

9. Unpublished correspondence.

Glossary of Selected

Behavioral Science Terms

Accommodation—A state of equilibrium between groups achieved by mutual agreement, such as an armed truce, tolerance; also the social adjustment between persons or groups designed to reduce conflict.

Acculturation—the merging of two or more cultures or subcultures, ranging from accommodation to full assimilation.

Action—human behavior that has been assessed or evaluated, and assigned meaning or significance by others.

Actor—another term for the person as a role-performer, group member, or participator in some form of social interaction.

Aggregate—a bunching together or grouping of individuals; not to be confused with "group"; has no social traits.

"Anomie"—state of social normlessness; devoid of sociocultural meaning and value.

Asceticism—willingness to postpone immediate goals or gratification with the belief that it will bring about greater rewards later on; "postponed gratification," voluntarily imposed.

Assimilation—fusion of heterogeneous aspects of two or more groups or societies into a common social system or structure.

Attitude—tendency to act or react typically towards an object, situation, or value.

Caste—a closed group or social stratum resulting from stratification in which status is defined and fixed by kinship, by ascription.

Class, social—a group or stratum resulting from stratification in which status may be achieved as well as ascribed.

Collectivity—an abtraction denoting the formation of an aggregate of individuals possessing something in common.

Community—a unit of territory within which is distributed a population which possesses the basic social institutions by means of which a common way of life is made possible.

Competition—the process of striving for something that is being sought for simultaneously by others, often without being aware of the other's efforts.

Conduct—"moral behavior," "normative behavior," or "faith-behavior"; action whose meaning is defined by the social norms or values of a particular society.

Culture—the accumulated products of human association; the functional whole which provides the form and content or significance of human behavior and ideas and values common to a group, community, or society. It consists of both material and non-material components. It is held that only man has culture.

Culture-complex—a combination of cultural traits into a functional whole; a controversial term now held to be obsolete by many anthropologists (see culture-pattern.)

Culture-pattern—two or more traits of culture organized into some form or configuration.

Culture-trait—the single unit or feature of a culture-pattern.

Culture-lag—a condition of imbalance emerging from an uneven rate of change in two or more cultural elements which are functionally interrelated.

"Definition of the Situation"—an individual's perception of a given object or feature of the environment which influences his attitudes, ideas, emotions, and actions; an interpretation, point of view, frame of reference, evaluation, which eventually may become a policy, principle or a behavior pattern whereby quick judgments and decisions are made at every point in everyday life. Approaches much of what psychologists term a "Gestalt," although its origins may differ.

Deprivation, relative—the feeling-state that one is being prevented from attaining objects, ends, goals or rewards that are at the same time being permitted to others.

Diffusion—the spread in space of culture patterns from one society to another.

Enculturation—the process of inducting the individual into the culture of his group.

Endogamy—a practice of restricting marriage to a member of one's extended kinship system, but outside of the immediate family.

Esteem—a component of social status based upon an invidious evaluation of the qualities assessed to the personality of an individual based upon how well he meets the expectations and demands of his social roles.

Ethnocentrism—belief that one's group, society, or culture is superior to all others.

Family—a group associated with the marriage institution having these characteristics: (1) ties of marriage, blood, adoption; (2) members living together in a common household; (3) members interacting in social roles implied in family status, such as father-mother; son-daughter roles; (4) maintaining a common culture.

Family, extended—a family composed of two or more generations residing in the same household, or mutually interacting.

Family, nuclear—The immediate family, composed of parents and their offspring only.

Family of Orientation—the family in which one is reared.

Family of Procreation—the family produced by one after entering the adult stage of his life-cycle.

Family of Gerontation—the family remaining to one after his offspring acquire their own families of procreation; usually associated with the terminal segment of the life-cycle.

Folk Society—an "ideal-type" construct depicting a simple, homogeneous, unchanging, nonliterate society isolated from contact with other societies; in polar contrast to modern industrial society.

Folkways—group habits or norms common to a society, community, or group that are unconsciously performed and whose violation arouses only a mild reaction from others.

Functional—pertaining to a condition indicating that the "needs" of a group and its members are being fulfilled by their collective actions.

"Generalized Other"—a generalization whereby all others significant in one's social environment are summarized into a meaningful whole or totality, in terms of their reactions to one's own actions; crucial to the development of the "self" in George Mead's theory: "the organized community or social group which gives the person his unity of self."

Group—a type of collectivity having norms or means, and "social ideals" or ends to the actions of its members that may not be possessed by non-members.

Group, Ethnic—a type of group whose norms and "ideals" are based upon belonging to a particular subculture.

Group, In—a group toward which a person has a strong sense of belonging or identification.

Group, Out—a group toward which a person feels a strong sense of rejection, or devaluation.

Group, Peer—a type of group whose members have equal status, such as children's play-groups, or cliques.

Group, Primary—basic group whose relationships are intimate, informal, and usually face-to-face.

Group, Reference—an abstract, psychological group to which a person refers or with which he identifies himself, but often he may not be a participant or actual member.

Group, Secondary—a type of group whose relationships are formal and impersonal; usually "special-interest" groups and voluntary associations; most prevalent in urban communities.

Grouping—an aggregate or simple gathering together of individuals; has no social characteristics.

"Ideal-Type"—an analytical construct whereby the most extreme case known is used to depict that particular phenomenon, assuming that it embodies the totality of qualities or characteristics of that phenomenon.

Incumbent, role—one who occupies a social role and who attempts to carry out the pattern of action defined as that role; also a "role-object," or "role-player."

Institution—a system or structure of actions, oriented around certain values, which are expected to be followed and which one feels he "ought" to perform.

Interaction—activity between persons involving reciprocal communication; relationship involving two or more people in terms of each other or in regard to some common object or situation.

Life-cycle—the sequence of roles and statuses established in the culture which a person prepares for, acquires, and relinquishes as he grows, matures, and decays during his maturation as a human organism; the two systems are not universally correlated in the world of cultures.

Marginality—the state or condition of interacting between two or more distinct social spheres or systems without being fully accepted by either; also identifying and attempting to participate in two incompatible or "foreign" groups simultaneously.

Marriage—a social affair giving status of husband and wife, after a union of male and female, so sanctioned by society. Not to be confused with "mating."

Mass, social—an anonymous aggregate, loosely organized, with members from all levels pursuing individual goals.

Mass society—modern populations which are chiefly characterized by secondary-group relations, by high specialization of role and status, by anonymity, high mobility and impersonal relationships in general.

Matriarchal—pertaining to a family-type where authority is vested in the mother.

Matricentric—specifying a family structure oriented and centered around the mother.

Matrilineal—pertaining to a family system whose ancestry and lineage is transferred through the mother with each generation.

"Meanings"—an analytic construct to include all of the "pure concepts" of a culture, such as ideas, ideologies, theories, dogma, principles, values, ideals, norms, in their pure conceptual state (Sorokin).

Migration—the change in place of residence by movement of people in space (spatial mobility. Not to be confused with mobility or fluidity).

Mobility, social—the process whereby a person or group moves from one social class or status to another class or status.

Mobility, horizontal—change in social relationships brought about by a change or shift in group affiliation, without changing one's social station.

Mobility, vertical—change in status, by either "going up" or "going down" the social ladder or scale; movement up or down the class scale.

Mores—folkways or action-patterns of a group or society which have a moral value or connotation, arousing "righteous wrath" or "moral indignation" when violated. (Singular form—"mos.")

Norm—a rule which defines how one is to act in a particular social situation; the means to socially prescribed ends or goals.

Patriarchal—pertaining to a family system whose authority is invested in the father, or eldest male member.

Patricentric—indicating a family structure oriented and centered around the father.

Patrilineal—specifying a family system whose ancestry or lineage is transferred through the father with each generation.

"Person"—an "individual" possessed with status; the socialized organism; role-player.

Power, social—ability to subordinate the interest or actions of others to one's own ends.

Prestige—a component of status based upon the social role or roles one assumes.

Race—a dubious division of the human species whose members are supposed to possess certain common, non-modifiable biological traits.

Racialism—social interaction based upon racial distinctions of an invidious character.

Role, social—pattern of action normatively organized; totality of duties and set of expectations assuming an action-pattern usually associated with a certain status.

Role-taking—the process of assuming or learning a social role.

Role-playing—the actual performance of the duties and expectations constituting a social role.

Sacred—pertaining to the absolute, unquestioned, perfect, and universal qualities from apparent superhuman or non-human origins.

Secular—a term stressing objects and events of this world in contrast to "other-worldly" values; sensate, of the everyday man-made world of the present.

Self—the sense of personal identity, of individuality or uniqueness emerging from role-taking and role-playing, from obtaining status, and with learning to view one's habits, attitudes, and ideas as other people do; the social part of personality.

Social—pertaining to the relationship existing when two or more persons interact or sociate; interpersonal relation.

"Social Distance"—label often given to measure or indicate the amount of differentiation assessed between persons and groups.

Social Structure—set or system of action-patterns or roles, acquiring an identity of its own when viewed in its total functioning.

Socialization—the interactional process by which the organism becomes a "person" by learning the socio-cultural qualities that make him a member of human society and hence a "human being."

Society—general term for men living in social relations; more specifically, the largest form of collectivity which encompasses groups, institutions, and their value-systems, and having the traits of omnipotence, autonomy, and cultural self-sufficiency.

Solidarity, social—high degree of group-identification, "we-feeling," consensus, and cohesiveness, with a consequent strong distinction made between members and non-members.

Station, social—social position assumed as a sum total of all of one's statuses.

Status, social—social position or rank based upon prestige and esteem; the rights and privileges associated with if not derived from, a social role.

Status, achieved—rank or position acquired by one's own efforts.

Status, ascribed—status fixed at birth.

Stratification—process whereby a system of statuses or ranking becomes established or recognized and accepted by the members of society.

Sub-culture—a part or division of a culture, having an identity of its own apart from the total culture, although related to the total culture in many aspects.

Symbiosis—the possession of a community by different groups and social strata whereby the functioning or survival of each group or stratum is facilitated by the presence and functioning of the other.

Value—the quality of appreciation, believed intrinsic in an idea, object, or action, assessing and giving significance to ways of acting or believing that are important to a society's sense of identity.

THE CONTRIBUTORS

Robert H. Albright is co-owner and operator of a medical and dental bureau.

Odin W. Anderson, Ph.D., is Research Director, Health Information Foundation, New York City, and Adjunct Associate Professor of Administrative Medicine, School of Public Health, Columbia University.

Howard S. Becker, Ph.D., is Field Director, Medical School Study, Community Studies, Inc., of Kansas City, and Research Associate (Assistant Professor). Department of Sociology, University of Chicago.

Samuel W. Bloom, Ph.D., is Assistant Professor of Sociology, Department of Psychiatry, Baylor University College of Medicine.

Walter E. Boek, Ph.D., is Research Anthropologist, New York State Department of Health, and Research Associate, Department of Sociology and Anthropology, Cornell University.

John Charles Cassel, M.B.B.Ch., M.P.H., is Associate Professor of Epidemiology, School of Public Health, University of North Carolina.

John A. Clausen, Ph.D., is Chief, Laboratory of Socio-environmental Studies, National Institute of Mental Health.

Beatrix Cobb, Ph.D., is Head, Medical Psychology, University of Texas, M.D. Anderson Hospital and Tumor Institute.

Marjorie Browne Davis, R.N., Ph.D., is currently Associate Professor, Pratt Institute; at the time of writing, was a research assistant, Graduate School of Arts and Science, New York University.

Leila Calhoun Deasy, Ph.D., is Research Sociologist, National Institute of Mental Health.

Joseph W. Eaton, Ph.D., is Lecturer, School of Social Welfare, University of California at Los Angeles.

John M. Ellis, Ph.D., is Instructor in Social Science, Lee College.

Robert S. Ferguson, M.D., is Consultant Psychiatrist and Deputy Medical Superintendent, Lancaster Moor Hospital, and formerly Assistant Psychiatrist, St. Nicholas Hospital, Gosforth, Newcastle-upon-Tyne, England (at the time of writing.)

Renée C. Fox, Ph.D., is currently Research Associate, Bureau of Applied Social Research, Columbia University, and Assistant Professor of Sociology, Barnard College; at the time of writing, was a graduate student in sociology in the Department of Social Relations, Harvard University.

Howard E. Freeman, Ph.D., is Research Associate in Sociology, School of Public Health, Harvard University; at the time of writing, was research assistant, Graduate School of Sociology, New York University.

Daniel H. Funkenstein, M.D., is Clinical Associate in Psychiatry, Harvard Medical School, and Director of Research, Harvard University Health Services.

Blanche Geer is Research Associate, Community Studies, Inc.

Saxon Graham, Ph.D., is Director, Community Epidemiological Surveys, Roswell Park Memorial Institute, and Assistant Professor of Medical Sociology, University of Buffalo Medical School and College of Arts and Sciences; formerly Assistant Professor of Medical Sociology, Graduate School of Public Health, University of Pittsburgh.

Oswald Hall, Ph.D., is Professor, Department of Political Economy, University of Toronto; formerly Associate Professor of Sociology, McGill University, at the time of writing.

Lois Hoffman is Associate Editor of *Medical Economics.*

E. Gartly Jaco, Ph.D., is Associate Professor of Sociology in the Departments of Preventive Medicine & Public Health, and Neuropsychiatry, and Director, Division of Medical Sociology, University of Texas Medical Branch in Galveston.

Derrick Brian Jelliffe, M.D., is Visiting Professor of Tropical Medicine, Tulane University, and Editor, *Journal of Tropical Pediatrics;* formerly W.H.O. Visiting Professor of Pediatrics, All-India Institute of Hygiene and Public Health in Calcutta.

Elihu Katz, Ph.D., is Visiting Lecturer in Sociology, The Hebrew University in Jerusalem, and currently on leave as Assistant Professor of Sociology, University of Chicago.

Patricia L. Kendall, Ph.D., is Research Associate, Bureau of Applied Social Research, Columbia University.

Stanley H. King, Ph.D., is Assistant Professor in the Graduate School of Public Health, University of Pittsburgh.

Earl Lomon Koos, Ph.D., is Professor of Social Welfare, Florida State University, and Consulting Social Scientist, Florida State Board of Health.

Bernard Kutner, Ph.D., is Assistant Professor, Department of Preventive and Environmental Medicine, Albert Einstein College of Medicine.

Philip S. Lawrence, Sc. D., is Chief, Survey Analysis, National Health Survey ,U.S. Public Health Service; formerly (at the time of writing) Chief, Family Studies, Division of Public Health Methods, U.S. Public Health Service.

Henry D. Lederer, M.D., is Associate Professor of Psychiatry, University of Cincinnati, College of Medicine.

Dan C. Lortie, Ph.D., was formerly Associate Director, Kansas City Study of Adult Life, and Field Director at the National Opinion Research Center of the University of Chicago.

John H. Mabry, Ph.D., is Assistant Professor of Preventive Medicine (Sociology), State University of New York, Upstate Medical Center, and Attending Sociologist, V.A. Hospital in Syracuse.

Frances Cooke Macgregor, Ph.D., is Associate Professor of Social Science, New York Hospital, School of Nursing, Cornell University.

John M. Maclachlan, Ph.D., is Head, Department of Sociology and Anthropology, and Consultant, Health Center Study, J. Hillis Miller Health Center, University of Florida.

Herbert Menzel, Ph.D., is Research Associate, Bureau of Applied Social Research, Columbia University.

Robert K. Merton, Ph.D., is Professor of Sociology and Associate Director, Bureau of Applied Social Research, Columbia University.

Mary A. Monk, Ph.D., is Research Associate in Postgraduate Education, and Associate in Preventive Medicine and Public Health, University of Buffalo School of Medicine.

Jerome K. Myers, Ph.D., is Associate Professor of Sociology, Yale University.

Peter Kong-ming New, Ph.D., is Project Director of the Nurse-Patient Relationship Study of Community Studies, Inc.

Herbert Notkin, M.D., is Medical Director, Onondaga County Welfare Department and Van Duyn Memorial Hospital, and Clinical Associate Professor of Preventive Medicine, New York State University College of Medicine.

Talcott Parsons, Ph.D., is Professor of Sociology in the Department of Social Relations, Harvard University.

Lois Pratt, Ph.D., is Assistant Professor, Fairleigh Dickinson University; at the time of writing was Director of Studies, Comprehensive Care and Teaching Program, Cornell University College of Medicine.

George G. Reader, M.D., is Professor of Medicine, and Director, Comprehensive Care and Teaching Program, Cornell University Medical College.

Julius A. Roth, Ph.D., is Research Associate, Committee on Human Development, University of Chicago.

Lyle Saunders is Associate Professor, Department of Preventive Medicine and Public Health, University of Colorado School of Medicine.

Leslie Schaffer, M.D., is Psychiatrist, Clinical Investigations, National Institute of Mental Health and member of the faculty of the Washington School of Psychiatry; at the time of writing was a Research Fellow, Department of Psychiatry, Yale University.

Sam Schulman, Ph.D., is Assistant Professor of Medical Sociology, University of Texas Medical Branch.

Morton A. Seidenfeld, Ph.D., is Director, Division of Psychological Services and Public Education, National Foundation for Infantile Paralysis.

Arthur Seligmann, M.D., is Instructor of Clinical Medicine, New York Hospital, Cornell Medical Center.

Ozzie G. Simmons, Ph.D., is Lecturer on Social Anthropology, School of Public Health, Harvard University.

Harvey L. Smith, Ph.D., is Professor of Sociology, Department of Sociology and Anthropology, and Director, Social Research Section, Division of Health Affairs, and Research Professor, Institute for Research in Social Science, University of North Carolina.

Bernhard J. Stern, Ph.D., (1894–1956) was Lecturer in Sociology, Columbia University and Lecturer in Anthropology, New School for Social Research, at the time of his death.

Robert Straus, Ph.D., is Professor of Medical Sociology, Medical Center, University of Kentucky.

Milton Terris, M.D., is Assistant Dean for Postgraduate Education, and Associate Professor of Preventive Medicine and Public Health, University of Buffalo School of Medicine.

John Useem, Ph.D., is Head and Professor, Department of Sociology and Anthropology, Michigan State University.

Ruth Hill Useem, Ph.D., is Research Consultant in Sociology and Anthropology, Michigan State University.

Walter Irving Wardwell, Ph.D., is Assistant Professor of Sociology, University of Connecticut.

H. Ashley Weeks, Ph.D., is Research Associate, Program in Hospital Administration, School of Business Administration, University of Michigan; formerly (at the time of writing) Associate Professor and Director, Research Division, Graduate Department of Sociology, New York University.

S. Kirson Weinberg, Ph.D., is Professor of Sociology, Roosevelt University.

Albert F. Wessen, Ph.D., is Assistant Professor of Medical Sociology, Department of Preventive Medicine, University of Vermont College of Medicine.

Granger E. Westberg is Associate Professor of Religion and Health, University of Chicago.

Charles V. Willie, Ph.D., is Instructor of Preventive Medicine (Sociology), State University of New York College of Medicine, and coordinator of the Community Health Seminar in Syracuse. He has also served on the research staff of the New York State Mental Health Commission.

Robert N. Wilson, Ph.D., is Lecturer in Sociology, Division of Psychiatry, Harvard Medical School and a director of the Harvard University Training Program for Social Scientists in Medicine. At the time of writing was Research Associate, Cornell University.

Harold G. Wolff, M.D., is Professor of Medicine (Neurology), Cornell University Medical College, and Attending Physician, New York Hospital, in addition to many other consultant and research positions.

Mark Zborowski, Ph.D., is Research Associate, School of Public Health, Harvard University; at the time of writing was Fellow of Cornell University Medical College. He is presently assistant director, Community Health Project, Harvard School of Public Health.